ASTRONOMICAL DATA ANALYSIS SOFTWARE AND SYSTEMS XII

COVER ILLUSTRATION:

For spacecraft observations of variable targets, monitoring programs, and targets of opportunity, there is a need for flexible scheduling to obtain scientifically interesting exposures. Anuradha Koratkar, Sandy Grosvenor, Jeremy Jones, and Karl Wolf (see their paper on p.152) argue that re-prioritizing and rescheduling must be done automatically by the spacecraft, in accordance with the goals of the observer. The components of a science goal monitoring (SGM) system is shown in this figure: *(left)* a tool for capturing science goals, *(center)* an analyzer that monitors the science data stream and decides whether or not science goals are being met, and *(right)* an interface for interacting with the science goal analyzer.

A SERIES OF BOOKS ON RECENT DEVELOPMENTS IN ASTRONOMY AND ASTROPHYSICS

Publisher

THE ASTRONOMICAL SOCIETY OF THE PACIFIC

390 Ashton Avenue, San Francisco, California, USA 94112-1722
Phone: (415) 337-1100   **E-Mail: orders@astrosociety.org**
Fax: (415) 337-5205   **Web Site: www.astrosociety.org**

ASP CONFERENCE SERIES - EDITORIAL STAFF
Managing Editor: D. H. McNamara
Production Manager: Enid L. Livingston
Production Assistant: Andrea Weaver

PO Box 24453, Room 211 - KMB, Brigham Young University, Provo, Utah, 84602-4463
Phone: (801) 422-2111   Fax: (801) 422-0624   E-Mail: pasp@byu.edu

LaTeX-Computer Consultant: T. J. Mahoney (Spain) – tjm@ll.iac.es

A listing of all of the ASP Conference Series Volumes and IAU Volumes
published by The ASP may be found at the back of this volume

THE ASTRONOMICAL SOCIETY
OF THE PACIFIC – CONFERENCE SERIES

Volume 295

ASTRONOMICAL DATA ANALYSIS
SOFTWARE AND SYSTEMS XII

Proceedings of a meeting held at
Baltimore, Maryland, USA
13-16- October 2002

Edited by

Harry E. Payne
Space Telescope Science Institute, Baltimore, Maryland, USA

Robert I. Jedrzejewski
Space Telescope Science Institute, Baltimore, Maryland, USA

and

Richard N. Hook
Space Telescope European Coordinating Facility, Garching, Germany

Library of Congress Cataloging in Publication Data
Main entry under title

ISSN: 1080-7926
ISBN: 1-58381-142-7

ASP Conference Series - First Edition

Printed in United States of America by Sheridan Books, Ann Arbor, Michigan

Contents

Part 1. Virtual Observatory Technologies

Part 2. Virtual Observatory Interoperability

Part 5. Telescopes and Observatory Operations

Part 6. Calibration

Part 7. Data Management and Pipelines

Part 13. Algorithms

Part 14. Data Analysis Software and Systems

Preface

This volume contains papers presented at the twelfth annual conference for Astronomical Data Analysis Software and Systems (ADASS XII). It was held October 13–16, 2002 at the Marriott Waterfront Hotel on Baltimore's Inner Harbor, and hosted by the Space Telescope Science Institute.

1. Conference Overview

The meeting took place under fine autumn weather. The meeting location was actually nestled between the Inner Harbor (National Aquarium, many places to eat, several pubs, and a large chain book store) and Little Italy (more places to eat, including the banquet location, one of our favorite pubs, and Baltimore's most famous spot for coffee and dessert). The hotel itself sported a number of inviting locations, provided a lot of great food (the opening reception being especially memorable), and unobtrusively kept things running smoothly.

ADASS XII was attended by 291 registered participants, including 85 people representing 16 countries outside the United States and Canada. The program included 12 invited speakers and 25 contributed oral presentations. In addition, there were 95 poster presentations, 11 computer demonstrations, and 6 Birds of a Feather (BoF) sessions. This volume consists of 109 contributions: 27 papers presented orally (including 8 of the invited papers), 75 poster papers, 5 demonstration summaries, and 2 BoF summaries.

Oral presentations were solicited by the Program Organizing Committee (POC) around "Key Topics," reflected in session titles. We are past the point of discussing "Virtual Observatories" (VO) as a concept, and got down to business with sessions on VO "Technologies" and "Interoperability." A VO orientation was also present in many other presentations, as well as demonstrations and posters. "Next-Generation Telescopes and Control Systems" was an interesting new area, while other key topics were familiar from recent conferences: "Sky Surveys," "Enabling Technologies," "Calibration," and "Data Management." The science topic was given a slight spin to emerge as "Optimizing Science."

The BoF sessions took place on Monday afternoon and evening. The topics and organizers were: FITS (Don Wells, NRAO), Reuseable Software Components (Frank Tanner, STScI), Education and Public Outreach (Steve McDonald, UMASS Boston and Silicon Spaceships), Python in Astronomy (Perry Greenfield, STScI), Astronomical Websites (Tony Ferro), and Teaching Scientific Computing with N-body Simulations (Vicki Johnson, Interconnect; Peter Teuben, UMd). The BoF sessions are a volunteer effort by the organizers, and we thank them.

Sunday's program was devoted to a very well attended tutorial on XML and Web Services for Astronomers, presented by Roy Williams and Robert Brunner. XML is now a mainstream topic, but the emergence of Web services was supported by a number of poster presentations, as well.

2.   The People Behind the Conference

The ADASS Program Organizing Committee was Todd Boroson (NOAO), Dick Crutcher (UIUC/NCSA), Daniel Durand (CADC), Daniel Egret (CDS), Brian Glendenning (NRAO), Tom Handley (IPAC/Caltech/JPL), Richard Hook (ST-ECF), Gareth Hunt (NRAO), Glenn Miller (STScI), Koh-Ichiro Morita (NAOJ), Jan Noordam (NFRA), Michele Peron (ESO), Arnold Rots (SAO), Dick Shaw (chair, NOAO), Betty Stobie (Univ. of Arizona), Christian Veillet (CFHT), and Patrick Wallace (RAL).

The Local Organizing Committee was chaired by Perry Greenfield. Other members were David Adler, Paul Barrett, Howard Bushouse, Brian McLean, Lauretta Nagel, and Steve Hulbert, all of Space Telescope Science Institute. We thank them for a very well organized meeting. We also thank these other STScI staff: John Bedke for taking the conference photo, Mike Venturella for his help in producing the printed program, Christine Klicka for the ADASS XII graphics, and Carolyn Liou for the web site (and see Liou & Hulbert, p. 332).

Finally, we gratefully acknowledge the support of the conference sponsors: the National Aeronautics and Space Administration, the National Science Foundation, the European Southern Observatory, the National Radio Astronomy Observatory, the Smithsonian Astrophysical Observatory, the National Optical Astronomy Observatory, the Canada-France-Hawaii Telescope, the Infrared Processing and Analysis Center, the Centre de Données Astronomiques de Strasbourg, the University of Arizona, the National Center for Supercomputing Applications, and the Space Telescope Science Institute. Their support was critical to the success of ADASS XII.

3.   ADASS Information

ADASS XIII will be held at the Palais des Congrès in Strasbourg, France, October 12–15, 2003, and will be hosted by the Centre de Données Astronomiques de Strasbourg.

Details about ADASS XII, including the final program, are available from the conference web site.[1] Links to all of the ADASS web sites, and electronic versions of the proceedings, can be found on the ADASS web site.[2]

The ADASS XII Editors

Harry E. Payne and Robert I. Jedrzejewski
Space Telescope Science Institute

Richard N. Hook
Space Telescope European Coordinating Facility

February 2003

---

[1]http://adass2002.stsci.edu/

[2]http://www.adass.org/

Participant List

Katsumi Abe, Fujitsu, Inc., Nakase 1-9-3, Mihama-Ku, 261-8588 Chiba, Japan
   (katsumi@ssd.ssg.fujitsu.com)
Mark Abernathy, Space Telescope Science Institute, 3700 San Martin Dr.,
   Baltimore, MD 21218, USA (abernathy@stsci.edu)
Faith Abney, Space Telescope Science Institute, 3700 San Martin Dr.,
   Baltimore, MD 21218, USA (abney@stsci.edu)
Alberto Accomazzi, Harvard-Smithsonian CfA, 60 Garden St. MS 83,
   Cambridge, MA 02138, USA (aaccomazzi@cfa.harvard.edu)
Mark Ackerman, University of Michigan/EECS, 1506 Morton Ave., Ann
   Arbor, MI 48104, USA (ackerm@umich.edu)
Nancy Adams-Wolk, Harvard-Smithsonian CfA, 60 Garden St. MS 81,
   Cambridge, MA 02138, USA (nadams@cfa.harvard.edu)
David Adler, Space Telescope Science Institute/Computer Sciences
   Corporation, 3700 San Martin Dr., Baltimore, MD 21218, USA
   (adler@stsci.edu)
Anastasia Alexov, ST-ECF, C/o ESO, Karl-Schwarzschild-Str. 2 D-85748,
   Garching, Germany (aalexov@eso.org)
Alasdair Allan, University of Exeter, School of Physics, Stocker Rd., EX4 4QL
   Exeter, UK (aa@astro.ex.ac.uk)
Mark Allen, CDS, 11 rue de l'Université 67000, Strasbourg, France
   (allen@astro.u-strasbg.fr)
Steven Allen, UCO/Lick Observatory, University of California, Santa Cruz,
   CA 95064, USA (sla@ucolick.org)
Roberta Allsman, National Optical Astronomy Observatory, 950 N. Cherry
   Ave., Tucson, AZ 85726-6732, USA (robyn@noao.edu)
Amar Amarnath, University of Maryland, Department of Astronomy,
   Computer & Space Science Bldg, College Park, MD 20742-2421, USA
   (amar@astro.umd.edu)
Kenneth Anderson, Johns Hopkins University, Department of Physics &
   Astronomy, 3701 San Martin Dr., Baltimore, MD 21218, USA
   (anderson@pha.jhu.edu)
Alex Antunes, School of Computational Sciences, George Mason University,
   Fairfax, VA 22030, USA, (aantunes@science.gmu.edu)
Richard Arendt, SSAI/GSFC, Code 685, NASA/GSFC, Greenbelt, MD 20771,
   USA
Christophe Arviset, ESA, PO Box 50727, Villafranca del Castillo 28080,
   Madrid, Spain (christophe.arviset@esa.int)
Charles Backus, Jet Propulsion Labororatory, M/S 169-506, 4800 Oak Grove
   Dr, Pasadena, CA 91109-8099, USA (backus@beta.jpl.nasa.gov)
Carlo Baffa, INAF-Osservatorio Di Arcetri, Largo E.. Fermi 5 I-50125,
   Firenze, Italy (baffa@arcetri.astro.it)
Klaus Banse, European Southern Observatory, Karl-Schwarzschild-Str. 2
   D-85748, Garching, Germany (kbanse@eso.org)
Paul Barrett, Space Telescope Science Institute, 3700 San Martin Dr.,
   Baltimore, MD 21218, USA (barrett@stsci.edu)

John Baum, Space Telescope Science Institute, 3700 San Martin Dr.,
     Baltimore, MD 21218, USA (baum@stsci.edu)
David Bazell, Eureka Scientific, Inc., 6509 Evensong Mews, Columbia, MD
     21044, USA (bazell@comcast.net)
Ugo Becciani, INAF-Astrophysical Observatory of Catania, Via S. Sofia 78,
     CT 1-95123 Catania, Italy (ube@sunct.ct.astro.it)
Stephane Beland, University of Colorado, 1255 38th St., Campus Box 593,
     Boulder, CO 80303, USA (sbeland@colorado.edu)
Bruce Berriman, IPAC, California Institute of Technology, Caltech MS 100-22,
     Pasadena, CA 91125, USA (gbb@ipac.caltech.edu)
Sanjay Bhatnager, National Radio Astronomy Observatory, PO Box O,
     Socorro, NM 87801, USA (sbhatnag@aoc.nrao.edu)
Scott Binegar, Space Telescope Science Institute, 3700 San Martin Dr.,
     Baltimore, MD 21218, USA (binegar@stsci.edu)
James Blackburn, California Institute of Technology, LIGO Laboratory,
     Caltech MS 18-34, Pasadena, CA 91125, USA (kent@ligo.caltech.edu)
Emily Blecksmith, Smithsonian Astrophysical Observatory, 60 Garden St. MS
     81, Cambridge, MA 02138, USA (emily@head-cfa.harvard.edu)
Martin Bly, Starlink, Ral, Rutherford Appleton Lab, Chilton OX11 OQX,
     Didcot, UK (bly@star.rl.ac.uk)
John Boia, Space Telescope Science Institute, 3700 San Martin Dr., Baltimore,
     MD 21218, USA (jboia@stsci.edu)
Kirk Borne, NASA Goddard Space Flight Center Code 630, Greenbelt, MD
     20771, USA, (kirk.borne@gsfc.nasa.gov)
Todd Boroson, National Optical Astronomy Observatory, PO Box 26732,
     Tucson, AZ 85726-6732, USA (tyb@noao.edu)
Bob Boyer, Space Telescope Science Institute, 3700 San Martin Dr., Baltimore,
     MD 21218, USA (rmboyer@stsci.edu)
James Braatz, National Radio Astronomy Observatory, PO Box 2, Green
     Bank, WV 24944, USA (jbraatz@nrao.edu)
Arthur Bradley, Spacecraft System Engineering Serv., PO Box 91, Annapolis
     Junction, MD 20701, USA (artbradley@comcast.net)
Molly Brandt, Space Telescope Science Institute, 3700 San Martin Dr.,
     Baltimore, MD 21218, USA (brandt@stsci.edu)
Alan Bridger, UK Astronomy Technology Centre, Royal Observatory,
     Blackford Hill EH9 EHJ, Edinburgh, Scotland, UK (ab@roe.ac.uk)
William Bridgman, Scientific Visualization Studio, Code 935, GSFC,
     Greenbelt, MD 20771, USA, (bridgman@wyeth.gsfc.nasa.gov)
Paul Bristow, ST-ECF, Karl-Schwarzschild-Str. 2 D-85748, Garching,
     Germany (bristowp@eso.org)
Robert Brunner, NCSA/University of Illinois, Department of Astronomy, 1002
     W. Green St., Urbana, IL 61801, USA (rb@ncsa.uiuc.edu)
Tamas Budavari, The Johns Hopkins University, 3400 N. Charles St.,
     Baltimore, MD 21218, USA (budavari@pha.jhu.edu)
Andrea Bulgarelli, CNR/IASF Bologna, Via Gobetti 101, 40129 Bologna, Italy
     (bulgarelli@bo.iasf.cnr.it)
Peter Bunclark, Cambridge University, Institute of Astronomy, Madingley Rd
     CB3 0HA, Cambridge, UK (psb@ast.cam.ac.uk)

Howard Bushouse, Space Telescope Science Institute, 3700 San Martin Dr., Baltimore, MD 21218, USA (bushouse@stsci.edu)

Ivo Busko, Space Telescope Science Institute, 3700 San Martin Dr., Baltimore, MD 21218, USA (busko@stsci.edu)

Nicola Caon, Instituto De Astrofisica de Canarias C/Vía Láctea s/n 38200, La Laguna, Spain (ncaon@ll.iac.es)

William Carithers, LBNL, LBNL MS 50b-5039, Berkeley, CA 94720, USA (wccarithers@lbl.gov)

Clayton Carter, Harvard-Smithsonian CfA, 60 Garden St. MS 81, Cambridge, MA 02138, USA (crcarter@cfa.harvard.edu)

Brad Cavanagh, Joint Astronomy Centre, 660 N. A'ohoku Pl, Hilo, HI 96720, USA (b.cavanagh@jach.hawaii.edu)

Maurizio Chavan, European Southern Observatory, Karl-Schwarzschild-Str. 2 D-85748, Garching, Germany (amchavan@eso.org)

Greg Chisholm, National Optical Astronomy Observatory, 950 N. Cherry Ave., Tucson, AZ 85719, USA (chisholm@noao.edu)

Tom Comeau, Space Telescope Science Institute, 3700 San Martin Dr., Baltimore, MD 21218, USA (tcomeau@stsci.edu)

Andrew Connolly, University of Pittsburgh, Department of Physics & Astronomy, Pittsburgh, PA 15260, USA (ajc@phyast.pitt.edu)

Kem Cook, Lawrence Livermore National Laboratory, PO Box 808, MS L-413, Livermore, CA 94550, USA (kcook@llnl.gov)

Tim Cornwell, National Radio Astronomy Observatory, PO Box O, Socorro, NM 87801, USA (tcornwell@nrao.edu)

Mark Cresitello-Dittmar, Smithsonian Astrophysical Observatory, 60 Garden St., Cambridge, MA 02138, USA (mdittmar@cfa.harvard.edu)

Richard Crutcher, University of Illinois, 1002 W. Green St., Urbana, IL 61801, USA (crutcher@uiuc.edu)

Malcolm Currie, Starlink, R 68 Rutherford Appleton Laboratory, Chilton OX11 OQX, Didcot, UK (mjc@star.rl.ac.uk)

Jean-Pierre De Cuyper, Royal Observatory of Belgium, Ringlaan 3 B1180, Ukkel, Belgium (jean-pierre.decuyper@oma.be)

Michele De la Peña, Steward Observatory, University of Arizona, 933 N. Cherry Ave., Tucson, AZ 85721-0065, USA (mdelapena@as.arizona.edu)

Bernard Debray, Observatoire de Besançon, 41 Bis Ave. de l'Observatoire, BP 1615, 25010 Besançon Cedex, France (debray@obs-besancon.fr)

Nadezhda Dencheva, Space Telescope Science Institute, 3700 San Martin Dr., Baltimore, MD 21218, USA (dencheva@stsci.edu)

Janet Deponte Evans, SAO/CXC, 60 Garden St., Cambridge, MA 02138, USA (janet@cfa.harvard.edu)

Sebastien Derriere, CDS, 11 rue de l'Université, 67000 Strasbourg, France (derriere@astro.u-strasbg.fr)

Erik Deul, Leiden Observatory, Niels Bohrweg 2 2333 CA, Leiden, Netherlands (deul@strw.leidenuniv.nl)

Paola Di Matteo, Universitay Di Roma La Sapienza, Physics Department, P.le Aldo Moro 2 00185, Rome, Italy (p.dimatteo@uniroma1.it)

Mark Dickinson, Space Telescope Science Institute, 3700 San Martin Dr., Baltimore, MD 21218, USA (med@stsci.edu)

William Dixon, The Johns Hopkins University, Department of Physics &
   Astronomy, 3400 N. Charles St., Baltimore, MD 21218-2686, USA
   (wvd@pha.jhu.edu)
Jesse Doggett, Space Telescope Science Institute, 3700 San Martin Dr.,
   Baltimore, MD 21218, USA (doggett@stsci.edu)
Markus Dolensky, European Southern Observatory, Karl-Schwarzschild-Str. 2
   D-85748, Garching, Germany (mdolensk@eso.org)
Thomas Donaldson, Space Telescope Science Institute, 3700 San Martin Dr.,
   Baltimore, MD 21218, USA (tdonaldson@stsci.edu)
Robert Douglas, Space Telescope Science Institute, 3700 San Martin Dr.,
   Baltimore, MD 21218, USA (rdouglas@stsci.edu)
Patrick Dowler, Canadian Astronomy Data Centre, 5071 W. Saanich Rd. V9E
   2E7, Victoria, BC, Canada (patrick.dowler@nrc.ca)
Marie-Lise Dubernet-Tuckey, Lerma, Observatoire De Paris, Section Meudon 5
   Place Janssen 92195 Meudon Cedex, France
   (marie-lise.dubernet@obspm.fr)
Daniel Durand, National Research Council Canada, 5071 W. Saanich Rd. V9E
   2E7, Victoria, BC, Canada (daniel.durand@nrc.ca)
Frossie Economou, Joint Astronomical Ccenter, 660 N. A'ohoku Pl, Hilo, HI
   96720, USA (frossie@jach.hawaii.edu)
Daniel Egret, CDS, 11 rue de l'Université 67000, Strasbourg, France
   (egret@astro.u-strasbg.fr)
Ron Ekers, CSIRO, Australia Telescope National Facility, Sydney, NSW 2121,
   Australia, (rekers@atnf.csiro.au)
Lori Enright, NASA Goddard Space Flight Center, Code 588, Greenbelt Rd.,
   Greenbelt, MD 20771, USA (lori.maks@gsfc.nasa.gov)
Ian Evans, SAO/CXC, 60 Garden St. MS 29, Cambridge, MA 02138, USA
   (ievans@cfa.harvard.edu)
Pepi Fabbiano, SAO, 60 Garden St., Cambridge, MA 02138, USA,
   (pepi@cfa.harvard.edu)
Nazma Ferdous, Space Telescope Science Institute, 3700 San Martin Dr.,
   Baltimore, MD 21218, USA (nframan@stsci.edu)
Pierre Fernique, Centre de Donnees Astro. de Strasbourg, 11 rue de
   l'Université 67000, Strasbourg, France (fernique@astro.u-strasbg.fr)
Anthony Ferro, University of Arizona, Steward Observatory, 933 N. Cherry
   Ave., Tucson, AZ 85721-0065, USA (tferro@as.arizona.edu)
Luca Fini, Osservatorio Di Arcetri, Largo E.. Fermi, 5 I-50125, Firenze, Italy
   (lfini@arcetri.astro.it)
Michael Fitzpatrick, National Optical Astronomy Observatory, 950 N. Cherry
   Ave., Tucson, AZ 85719, USA (fitz@noao.edu)
Juan Gabriel, ESA, Villafranca del Castillo, Satellite Tracking Station, 28016,
   Madrid, Spain (cgabriel@xmm.vilspa.esa.es)
Niall Gaffney, Space Telescope Science Institute, 3700 San Martin Dr.,
   Baltimore, MD 21218, USA (gaffney@stsci.edu)
Mark Galassi, Los Alamos National Laboratory, MS-D436, Los Alamos, NM
   87501, USA (rosalia@galassi.org)
Xiaofeng Gao, UK Astronomy Technology Centre, Blackford Hill EH9 EHJ,
   Edinburgh, Scotland, UK (xg@roe.ac.uk)

David Gasson, National Optical Astronomy Observatory, 950 N. Cherry Ave., Tucson, AZ 85719, USA (dgasson@noao.edu)

Severin Gaudet, CADC/HIA/NRC, 5071 W. Saanich Rd. V9E 2E7, Victoria, BC, Canada (severin.gaudet@nrc.ca)

Francoise Genova, CDS, Observatoire de Strasbourg, 11 rue de l'Université 67000, Strasbourg, France (genova@astro.u-strasbg.fr)

Claudio Gheller, CINECA, via Magnanelli 6/3, 40033 Casalecchio di Reno, Italy (c.gheller@cineca.it)

David Giaretta, Starlink, CLRC, Rutherford Appleton Laboratory, Chilton OX11 0QX, Didcot, UK (d.l.giaretta@rl.ac.uk)

Mark Giuliano, Space Telescope Science Institute, 3700 San Martin Dr., Baltimore, MD 21218, USA (giuliano@stsci.edu)

Brian Glendenning, National Radio Astronomy Observatory, PO Box O, Socorro, NM 87801, USA (bglenden@nrao.edu)

Claus Goessl, Universitaets-Sternwarte Muenchen, Scheienrstrasse 1, 81679, Munich, Germany (cag@usm.uni-muenchen.de)

Daniel Goscha, National Center For Supercomputing Apps., 1002 W. Green, Urbana, IL 61801, USA (dgoscha@uiuc.edu)

Gretchen Greene, Space Telescope Science Institute, 3700 San Martin Dr., Baltimore, MD 21218, USA (greene@stsci.edu)

Perry Greenfield, Space Telescope Science Institute, 3700 San Martin Dr., Baltimore, MD 21218, USA (greenfield@stsci.edu)

Eric Greisen, National Radio Astronomy Observatory, PO Box O, Socorro, NM 87801, USA (egreisen@nrao.edu)

Gerry Grieve, University of British Columbia, 6224 Agricultural Rd. V6T 1Z1, Vancouver, BC, Canada (grieve@astro.ubc.ca)

David Grumm, Space Telescope Science Institute, 3700 San Martin Dr., Baltimore, MD 21218, USA (grumm@stsci.edu)

Jonas Haase, ST-ECF, Karl-Schwarzschild-Str. 2 D-85748, Garching, Germany (jhaase@eso.org)

Warren Hack, Space Telescope Science Institute, 3700 San Martin Dr., Baltimore, MD 21218, USA (hack@stsci.edu)

Roger Hain, Harvard-Smithsonian CfA, 60 Garden St., Cambridge, MA 02138, USA (rhain@head-cfa.harvard.edu)

Robert Hanisch, Space Telescope Science Institute, 3700 San Martin Dr., Baltimore, MD 21218, USA (hanisch@stsci.edu)

Christopher Hanley, Space Telescope Science Institute, 3700 San Martin Dr., Baltimore, MD 21218, USA (chanley@stsci.edu)

Michael Harris, Smithsonian Astrophysical Observatory, 60 Garden St. MS 81, Cambridge, MA 02138, USA (meharris@cfa.head.edu)

Robert Hawkins, Space Telescope Science Institute, 3700 San Martin Dr., Baltimore, MD 21218, USA (rhawkins@stsci.edu)

Jeffrey Hayes, NASA Hq, 300 E. St. NW, Washington, DC 20546, USA (jhayes@hq.nasa.gov)

Martin Heemskerk, Astronomical Institute Amsterdam, Kruislaan 403 1098 SJ, Amsterdam, Netherlands (martin@science.uva.nl)

Marci Hendrickson, Johns Hopkins University, Department of Physics & Astronomy, 3400 N. Charles St., Baltimore, MD 21218-2686, USA (marcih@pha.jhu.edu)

Jose Hernandez, European Space Agency, Villafranca del Castillo, Satellite
   Tracking Station, 28016, Madrid, Spain (jose.hernandez@esa.int)
Norman Hill, CADC/HIA/NRC, 5071 W. Saanich Rd. V9E 2E7, Victoria, BC,
   Canada (norman.hill@nrc.ca)
Peter Reinhard Hiltner, Sonneberg Observatory, Sternwartestr. 32 D-96515,
   Sonneberg, Germany (prh@stw.tu-ilmenau.de)
Rafael Hiriart, National Optical Astronomy Observatory/CTIO, 950 N. Cherry
   Ave., Tucson, AZ 82719, USA (rhiriart@ctio.noao.edu)
Christian Hirt, University of Hanover, Institut Far Erdmessung, Schneiderberg
   50 30167, Hanover, Germany (hirt@mbox.ife.uni-hanover.de)
Tin Kam Ho, Bell Laboratories, Lucent Technologies, 700 Mountain Ave
   2c425, Murray Hill, NJ 07974, USA (tkh@research.bell-labs.com)
Rick Hobbs, OVRO, 1200 E. California Blvd MS 105-24, Pasadena, CA 91125,
   USA (rick@ovro.caltech.edu)
Philip Hodge, Space Telescope Science Institute, 3700 San Martin Dr.,
   Baltimore, MD 21218, USA (hodge@stsci.edu)
Andras Holl, Konkoly Observatory, PO Box 67 H-1525, Budapest, Hungary
   (holl@konkoly.hu)
Richard Hook, ST-ECF, Karl-Schwarzschild-Str. 2, D-85748, Garching,
   Germany (rhook@eso.org)
Toshihiro Horaguchi, National Science Museum, Tokyo, 3-23-1 Hyakunin-cho,
   Shinjuku 169-0073, Tokyo, Japan (horaguti@kahaku.go.jp)
Allan Hornstrup, Danish Space Research Institute, Juliane Maries Vej 30 2100,
   Copenhagen, Denmark (allan@dsri.dk)
Wolfgang Hovest, Max-Planck-Institut für Astrophysik,
   Karl-Schwarzschild-Str.1 D-85741, Garching, Germany
   (hovest@mpa-garching.mpg.de)
Jin-chung Hsu, Space Telescope Science Institute, 3700 San Martin Dr.,
   Baltimore, MD 21218, USA (hsu@stsci.edu)
Edwin Huizinga, Space Telescope Science Institute, 3700 San Martin Dr.,
   Baltimore, MD 21218, USA, (huizinga@stsci.edu)
Stephen Hulbert, Space Telescope Science Institute, 3700 San Martin Dr.,
   Baltimore, MD 21218, USA, (hulbert@stsci.edu)
Gareth Hunt, National Radio Astronomy Observatory, 520 Edgemont Rd.,
   Charlottesville, VA 22903, USA (ghunt@nrao.edu)
Joseph Jacob, Jet Propulsion Laboratory, 4800 Oak Grove Dr. MS 126-104,
   Pasadena, CA 91109-8099, USA (joseph.jacob@jpl.nasa.gov)
Robert Jedrzejewski, Space Telescope Science Institute, 3700 San Martin Dr.,
   Baltimore, MD 21218, USA (rij@stsci.edu)
Vicki Johnson, Interconnect Technologies Corp., PO Box 788, Claremont, CA
   91711-0788, USA (vlj@interconnect.com)
Jeffrey Jones, California Institute of Technology, 770 S. Wilson Ave.,
   Pasadena, CA 91125, USA (jjones@ipac.caltech.edu)
Jeremy Jones, NASA Goddard Space Flight Center, Code 588, Greenbelt Rd.,
   Greenbelt, MD 20771, USA (jeremy.e.jones@gsfc.nasa.gov)
William Joye, Smithsonian Astrophysical Observatory, 60 Garden St. MS 81,
   Cambridge, MA 02138, USA (wjoye@cfa.harvard.edu)
Athol Kemball, National Radio Astronomy Observatory, PO Box O, Socorro,
   NM 87801, USA (akemball@nrao.edu)

Farshid Khoui, Space Telescope Science Institute, 3700 San Martin Dr., Baltimore, MD 21218, USA (khoui@stsci.edu)

Alexander Kilpio, Institute of Astronomy, Ras, Pyatnitskaya St. 48, Moscow, 119017 Russia (skilpio@inasan.ru)

David King, National Radio Astronomy Observatory, PO Box O, Socorro, NM 87801, USA (dking@nrao.edu)

Anuradha Koratkar, Space Telescope Science Institute, 3700 San Martin Dr., Baltimore, MD 21218, USA (koratkar@stsci.edu)

James Kraybill, UC Berkeley Raido Astronomy Lab, 601 Campbell Hall, Berkeley, CA 94720, USA (colby@astro.berkeley.edu)

Vicki Laidler, Space Telescope Science Institute, 3700 San Martin Dr., Baltimore, MD 21218, USA (laidler@stsci.edu)

Uwe Lammers, European Space Agency, PO Box 299, ESA/ESTEC/SCI-SD 2200 AG, Noordwijk, Netherlands (ulammers@rssd.esa.int)

Karen Levay, Space Telescope Science Institute/Computer Sciences Corporation, 3700 San Martin Dr., Baltimore, MD 21218, USA (klevay@stsci.edu)

James Lewis, Institute of Astronomy, Madingley Rd. CB3 7XT, Cambridge, UK (jrl@ast.cam.ac.uk)

Chris Lidman, European Southern Obser. (Paranal), Alonso De Cordova 3107, Vitacura, Chile (clidman@eso.org)

Sergey Likhachev, Astro Space Center, Profsojuznaya St. 84/32 GSP-7, Moscow, 117997 Russia (slikhach@asc.rssi.ru)

Romain Linsolas, Institut d'Astrophysique Spatiale/CNRS, Université Paris XI, batiment 121, F-91405 Orsay, France (romain.linsolas@medoc-ias.u-psud.fr)

Carolyn Liou, Space Telescope Science Institute, 3700 San Martin Dr., Baltimore, MD 21218, USA, (liou@stsci.edu)

Miron Livny, University of Wisconsin - Madison, 1210 W. Dayton St., Madison, WI 53706, USA (miron@cs.wisc.edu)

Stephen Lowe, Smithsonian Astrophysical Observatory, 60 Garden St., Cambridge, MA 02138, USA (slowe@head-cfa.harvard.edu)

Stephen Lubow, Space Telescope Science Institute, 3700 San Martin Dr., Baltimore, MD 21218, USA (lubow@stsci.edu)

Daniel Magee, UCO/Lick Observatory, 1156 High St., Santa Cruz, CA 95064, USA (magee@ucolick.org)

David Makovoz, California Institute of Technology, 1300 California Blvd. MC 220-6, Pasadena, CA 91125-0600, USA (davidm@ipac.caltech.edu)

Robert Mann, University of Edinburgh, Royal Observatory, Blackford Hill EH9 3HJ, Edinburgh, Scotland, UK (rgm@roe.ac.uk)

Frank Masci, SIRTF Science Center/California Institute of Technology, 12 E. California Blvd, MC 314-6, Pasadena, CA 91125, USA (fmasci@ipac.caltech.edu)

Sabine McConnell, Queen's University, 17 Van Order Dr 7-104, U7M 1B5, Kingston, ON, Canada (mcconnell@cs.queensu.ca)

Peter McCullough, Space Telescope Science Institute, 3700 San Martin Dr., Baltimore, MD 21218, USA (pmcc@stsci.edu)

Robert McCutcheon, Space Telescope Science Institute/Computer Sciences Corp., 1054 West St., Laurel, MD 20910, USA (rmccutch@csc.com)

Steve McDonald, University of Massachusetts Boston & Silicon Spaceships, 74
Bay State Ave., Somerville, MA 02144, USA
(steve@siliconspaceships.com)

Jonathan McDowell, Harvard-Smithsonian CfA, 60 Garden St., Cambridge,
MA 02138, USA (jcm@cfa.harvard.edu)

Thomas McGlynn, Heasarc NASA Goddard Space Flight Center (USRA),
Code 660.2, Greenbelt, MD 20771, USA (tam@lheapop.gsfc.nasa.gov)

Vincent McIntyre, Australia Telescope National Facility, PO Box 76, Epping
NSW 1710, Australia (vmcintyr@atnf.csiro.au)

Brian McLean, Space Telescope Science Institute, 3700 San Martin Dr.,
Baltimore, MD 21218, USA (mclean@stsci.edu)

David Mehringer, National Center For Supercomputing App, Department of
Astronomy, 1002 W. Green St., Urbana, IL 61801, USA
(dmehring@astro.uiuc.edu)

Laurent Michel, Observatoire Astronomique De Strasbourg, 11 rue de
l'Université 67000, Strasbourg, France (laurent.michel@astro.u-strasbg.)

Alberto Micol, ST-ECF, Karl-Schwarzschild-Str. 2, D-85748, Garching,
Germany (alberto.micol@eso.org)

Kenneth Mighell, National Optical Astronomy Observatory, 950 N. Cherry
Ave., Tucson, AZ 85719, USA (mighell@noao.edu)

Glenn Miller, Space Telescope Science Institute, 3700 San Martin Dr.,
Baltimore, MD 21218, USA (miller@stsci.edu)

Todd Miller, Space Telescope Science Institute, 3700 San Martin Dr.,
Baltimore, MD 21218, USA (jmiller@stsci.edu)

Warren Miller, Space Telescope Science Institute, 3700 San Martin Dr.,
Baltimore, MD 21218, USA (wmiller@stsci.edu)

Doug Mink, Smithsonian Astrophysical Observatory, 60 Garden St.,
Cambridge, MA 02138, USA (dmink@cfa.harvard.edu)

Yoshihiko Mizumoto, Natl. Astron. Observatory of Japan, Osawa, Mitaka,
181-8588 Tokyo, Japan (mizumoto.y@nao.ac.jp)

Dave Monet, US Naval Observatory, PO Box 1149, Flagstaff, AZ 86001, USA,
(dgm@nofs.navy.mil)

Koh-ichiro Morita, Nobeyama Radio Observatory, National Astronomical
Observatory, Nobeyama, Minamimaki, Minamisaku, Nagano 384-1305,
Japan (morita@nro.nao.ac.jp)

Mehrdad Moshir, SIRTF Science Center/Caltech/JPL, Caltech MC 314-6,
Pasadena, CA 91125, USA (mmm@ipac.caltech.edu)

Christian Motch, Observatoire Astronomique de Strasbourg, 11 rue de
l'Université, 67000 Strasbourg, France (motch@astro.u-strasbg.fr)

Pat Murphy, National Radio Astronomy Observatory, 520 Edgemont Rd.,
Charlottesville, VA 22903-3475, USA (pmurphy@nrao.edu)

Lauretta Nagel, Space Telescope Science Institute, 3700 San Martin Dr.,
Baltimore, MD 21218, USA (nagel@stsci.edu)

Jon Nielsen, Australian National University, Mount Stromlo Observatory,
Cotter Rd., Weston ACT 2611, Australia (jon@mso.anu.edu.au)

Maria Nieto-Santisteban, Johns Hopkins University, Physics Department, 3701
San Martin Dr., Baltimore, MD 21218, USA (nieto@stsci.edu)

Michael Noble, Smithsonian Astrophysical Observatory, 60 Garden St. MS 81,
Cambridge, MA 02138, USA (mnoble@cfa.harvard.edu)

Jan Noordam, Astron, PO Box 2, 7933 RA, Dwingeloo, Netherlands (noordam@astron.nl)

Francois Ochsenbein, CDS, 11 rue de l'Université, 67000 Strasbourg, France (francois@astro.u-strasbg.fr)

Ryusuke Ogasawara, Subaru Telescope, 650 N. Aohoku Pl, Hilo, HI 96720, USA (ryusuke.ogasawara@naoj.org)

Nikita Ogievetsky, Cogitech, Inc., PO Box 72, Hewlett, NY 11557-0072, USA (nogievet@hotmail.com)

Masatoshi Ohishi, National Astronomical Observatory of Japan, 2-21-1 Osawa, 181-8588 Mitaka, Japan (masatoshi.ohishi@nao.ac.jp)

William O'Mullane, Space Telescope Science Institute, 211 Ocean Heights, Gibraltar, UK, (womullan@yahoo.co.uk)

Patricio Ortiz, Astrogrid, University of Leicester, Department of Physics and Astronomy, LE1 7RH, Leicester, UK (pfo@star.le.ac.uk)

Stephan Ott, ESA/ESTEC, PO Box 299, ESA/ESTEC/SCI-SD 2200 AG, Noordwijk, Netherlands (scott@rssd.esa.int)

Clive Page, University of Leicester, Department of Physics & Astronomy, University Rd., LE1 7RH, Leicester, UK (cgp@star.le.ac.uk)

Susan Parker, Institute For Astronomy, 640 N. A'ohoku Pl., Hilo, HI 96720, USA (parker@ifa.hawaii.edu)

Alexandra Patz, Smithsonian Astrophysical Observatory, 60 Garden St. MS 81, Cambridge, MA 02138, USA (apatz@head-cfa.harvard.edu)

Harry Payne, Space Telescope Science Institute, 3700 San Martin Dr., Baltimore, MD 21218, USA (payne@stsci.edu)

William Pence, HEASAC, NASA/GSFC, Code 662, Greenbelt, MD 20771, USA (pence@tetra.gsfc.nasa.gov)

Steven Penton, CASA/University of Colorado-Boulder, 1255 38th St., Boulder, CO 80303, USA (spenton@casa.colorado.edu)

Eric Perlman, Univerity of Maryland Baltimore Co., 1000 Hilltop Circle, Physics Bldg. Room 211, Baltimore, MD 21250, USA, (rray@umbc.edu)

Michele Peron, European Southern Observatory, Karl-Schwarzschild-Str. 2, D-85748, Garching, Germany (mperon@eso.org)

Karla Peterson, Space Telescope Science Institute, 3700 San Martin Dr., Baltimore, MD 21218, USA (peterson@stsci.edu)

Olga Pevunova, NED/IPAC/Caltech, 770 S. Wilson, Pasadena, CA 91125, USA (olga@ipac.caltech.edu)

Matthew Phelps, Harvard-Smithsonian CfA, 60 Garden St. MS 39, Cambridge, MA 02138, USA (mphelps@cfa.harvard.edu)

Francesco Pierfederici, ST-ECF, Karl-Schwarzschild-Str. 2, D-85748, Garching, Germany (fpierfed@eso.org)

Benoit Pirenne, European Southern Observatory, Karl-Schwarzschild-Str. 2, D-85748, Garching, Germany (bpirenne@eso.org)

Norbert Pirzkal, ST-ECF, Karl-Schwarzschild-Str. 2, D-85748, Garching, Germany (bsjoeber@eso.org)

Raymond Plante, National Center For Supercomputing Apps., 1002 W. Green St., Urbana, IL 61801, USA (rplante@ncsa.uiuc.edu)

Joe Pollizzi, Space Telescope Science Institute, 3700 San Martin Dr., Baltimore, MD 21218, USA, (pollizzi@stsci.edu)

Marc Pound, University of Maryland, Astronomy Department, College Park, MD 20742, USA (mpound@astro.umd.edu)

Alexei Pozanenko, Space Research Institute (IKI), Profsoyuznaja, 84/32, Moscow, 117997 Russia (apozanen@iki.rssi.ru)

Andrew Ptak, Johns Hopkins University, Department of Physics & Astronomy, 3400 N. Charles St., Baltimore, MD 21218, USA (ptak@pha.jhu.edu)

Andreas Quirrenbach, University of California, San Diego, Center For Astrophysics and Space, MC 0424, La Jolla, CA 92093-0424, USA (aquirrenbach@ucsd.edu)

Reiko Rager, Space Telescope Science Institute, 3700 San Martin Dr., Baltimore, MD 21218, USA (tsuneto@stsci.edu)

Padmanabhan Ramadurai, Smithsonian Astrophysical Observatory, 60 Garden St. MS 70, Cambridge, MA 02138, USA (durai@cfa.harvard.edu)

Kevin Rauch, University of Maryland, Department of Astronomy, College Park, MD 20742-2421, USA (rauch@astro.umd.edu)

Arno Riffeser, Universitaets-Sternwarte Muenchen, Scheienrstrasse 1, 81679, Munich, Germany (arri@usm.uni-muenchen.de)

Guy Rixon, University of Cambridge, Institute of Astronomy, Madingley Rd., CB3 0HA, Cambridge, UK (gtr@ast.cam.ac.uk)

Anthony Roman, Space Telescope Science Institute, 3700 San Martin Dr., Baltimore, MD 21218, USA (aroman@stsci.edu)

Jim Rose, Space Telescope Science Institute, 3700 San Martin Dr., Baltimore, MD 21218, USA (rose@stsci.edu)

Arnold Rots, SAO/CXC, 60 Garden St. MS 81, Cambridge, MA 02138, USA (arots@head-cfa.harvard.edu)

Philip Sadler, Harvard-Smithsonian CfA, 60 Garden St. MS 71, Cambridge, MA 02138, USA (psadler@cfa.harvard.edu)

David Sahnow, The Johns Hopkins University, Department of Physics & Astronomy, 3400 N. Charles St., Baltimore, MD 21218, USA (sahnow@pha.jhu.edu)

Ga Ran Sandell, USRA, NASA Ames Research Center, MS 144-2, Mountain View, CA 94035, USA (gsandell@mail.arc.nasa.gov)

Andre Schaaff, CDS, Observatoire de Strasbourg, 11 rue de l'Université, 67000, Strasbourg, France (schaaff@astro.u-strasbg.fr)

Skip Schaller, Las Campanas Observatory, Casilla 601, La Serena, Chile (skip@lco.cl)

Darrell Schiebel, National Radio Astronomy Observatory, 520 Edgemont Rd., Charlottesville, VA 22903, USA (drs@nrao.edu)

Dennis Schmidt, SAO, 60 Garden St., Cambridge, MA 02138, USA (dennis@head-cfa.harvard.edu)

Glenn Schneider, Steward Observatory Univ. Arizona, 933 N. Cherry Ave., Tucson, AZ 85721, USA (gschneider@as.arizona.edu)

Isabelle Scholl, Institut d'Astrophysique Spatiale/CNRS, Université Paris XI, batiment 121, F-91405 Orsay, France (isabelle.scholl@medoc-ias.u-psu)

Stephen Scott, California Institute of Technology/OVRO, PO Box 968, Big Pine, CA 93513, USA (scott@ovro.caltech.edu)

Rob Seaman, National Optical Astronomy Observatory, 950 N. Cherry Ave., Tucson, AZ 85719, USA (seaman@noao.edu)

Brian Seitz, Space Telescope Science Institute, 3700 San Martin Dr.,
    Baltimore, MD 21218, USA (bseitz@stsci.edu)
Eric Sessoms, National Radio Astronomy Observatory, 2515 Efland-cedar
    Grove Rd., Efland, NC 27243, USA (esessoms@nrao.edu)
Julie Shaw, SAO, 60 Garden St. MS 39, Cambridge, MA 02138, USA
    (jshaw@cfa.harvard.edu)
Richard Shaw, National Optical Astronomy Observatory, 950 N. Cherry Ave.,
    Tucson, AZ 85719, USA (shaw@noao.edu)
Lisa Sherbert, Space Telescope Science Institute, 3700 San Martin Dr.,
    Baltimore, MD 21218, USA (lisa@stsci.edu)
Bernie Shiao, Space Telescope Science Institute, 3700 San Martin Dr.,
    Baltimore, MD 21218, USA (shiao@stsci.edu)
Patrick Shopbell, California Institute of Technology, Department of Astronomy,
    MC 105-24, Pasadena, CA 91125, USA (pls@astro.caltech.edu)
Rick Singer, Space Telescope Science Institute, 3700 San Martin Dr.,
    Baltimore, MD 21218, USA (singer@stsci.edu)
Petr Skoda, Astron. Institute Academey of Sciences, Fricova 298 25165,
    Ondrejov, Czech Republic (skoda@sunstel.asu.cas.cz)
Riccardo Smareglia, INAF-Astronomical Observatory of Trieste, Via GB
    Tiepolo 11, I-34131 Trieste, Italy (smareglia@ts.astro.it)
Oleg Smirnov, Astron, PO Box 2, Oude Hoogeveensedijk 4, Dwingeloo, 7990
    AA, Netherlands (smirnov@astron.nl)
William Smith, AURA, 1200 New York Ave., Suite 350, Washington, DC
    20005, USA (wsmith@aura-astronomy.org)
R. Chris Smith, National Optical Astronomy Observatory/CTIO, 950 N.
    Cherry Ave., Tucson, AZ 82719, USA (csmith@noao.edu)
Scott Speck, Space Telescope Science Institute, 3700 San Martin Dr.,
    Baltimore, MD 21218, USA (speck@stsci.edu)
Bradley Spitzbart, Smithsonian Astrophysical Observatory, 60 Garden St.,
    Cambridge, MA 02138, USA (bspitzbart@cfa.harvard.edu)
Scott Stallcup, Space Telescope Science Institute, 3700 San Martin Dr.,
    Baltimore, MD 21218, USA (stallcup@stsci.edu)
Dan Starr, Los Alamos National Laboratory, MS-D436, Los Alamos, NM
    87545, USA (dstarr@nis.lanl.gov)
Elizabeth Stobie, University of Arizona, Steward Observatory, 933 N. Cherry
    Ave., Tucson, AZ 85721, USA (bstobie@as.arizona.edu)
Anatoly Suchkov, Space Telescope Science Institute, 3700 San Martin Dr.,
    Baltimore, MD 21218, USA (suchkov@stsci.edu)
Quentin Sun, California Institute of Technology, 770 S. Wilson Ave., Pasadena,
    CA 91125, USA (qsun@ipac.caltech.edu)
Daryl Swade, Space Telescope Science Institute, 3700 San Martin Dr.,
    Baltimore, MD 21218, USA (swade@stsci.edu)
Mike Swam, Space Telescope Science Institute, 3700 San Martin Dr.,
    Baltimore, MD 21218, USA (mswam@stsci.edu)
Alexander Szalay, The Johns Hopkins University, Dept. of Physics &
    Astronomy, 3400 N. Charles St., Baltimore, MD 21218, USA
    (szalay@jhu.edu)
Frank Tanner, Space Telescope Science Institute, 3700 San Martin Dr.,
    Baltimore, MD 21218, USA (tanner@stsci.edu)

Mark Taylor, Bristol Unversity, H H Wills Physics Laboratory, Tyndall Ave.,
      BS8 1TL, Bristol, UK (m.b.taylor@bristol.ac.uk)
Peter Teuben, University of Maryland, Astronomy Department, College Park,
      MD 20742, USA (teuben@astro.umd.edu)
Aniruddha Thakar, The Johns Hopkins University, Center For Astrophysical
      Sciences, 3701 San Martin Dr., Baltimore, MD 21218-2695, USA
      (thakar@pha.jhu.edu)
Brian Thomas, RITSS/NASA GSFC, Code 630.1, Goddard Space Flight
      Center, Greenbelt, MD 20771, USA (thomas@mail630.gsfc.nasa.gov)
Doug Tody, National Radio Astronomy Observatory, 1003 Lopezville Rd., PO
      Box O, Socorro, NM 87801, USA
Ralph Tremmel, Max-Planck-Institut, Koenigstuhl 17 69126, Heidelberg,
      Germany (tremmel@mpia-hd.mpg.de)
Euan Troup, CSIRO, Locked Bag 194, 2390 Narrabri, Australia
      (crystal.gay@csiro.au)
Alan Uomoto, The Johns Hopkins University, Dept. of Physics & Astronomy,
      3400 N. Charles St., Baltimore, MD 21218, USA (au@jhu.edu)
Frank Valdes, National Optical Astronomy Observatory, 950 N. Cherry Ave.,
      Tucson, AZ 85719, USA (fvaldes@noao.edu)
Robert Vallance, The University of Birmingham, School of Physics and
      Astronomy, Edgbaston Park Rd., B 15 2TT, Birmingham, UK
      (rjv@star.sr.bham.ac.uk)
Gustaaf Van Moorsel, National Radio Astronomy Observatory, 1003 Lopezville
      Rd., PO Box O, Socorro, NM 87801, USA (gvanmoor@nrao.edu)
Cosimo Antonio Volpicelli, Space Telescope Science Insitute, 3700 San Martin
      Dr., Baltimore, MD 21218, USA (volpicelli@stsci.edu)
Patrick Wallace, Rutherford Appleton Laboratory, Chilton, OX11 0QX,
      Didcot, UK (ptw@star.rl.ac.uk)
Nicholas Walton, University of Cambridge, Institute of Astronomy, Madingley
      Rd., CB3 OHA, Cambridge, UK (naw@ast.cam.ac.uk)
Zhong Wang, SAO, 60 Garden St. MS 66, Cambridge, MA 02138, USA,
      (zwang@cfs.harvard.edu)
Rein Warmels, European Southern Observatory, Karl-Schwarzschild-Str. 2,
      Garching, D-85748, Germany (rwarmels@eso.org)
Phillip Warner, National Optical Astronomy Observatory, 950 N. Cherry Ave.,
      Tucson, AZ 85719, USA (pwarner@noao.edu)
Boyd Waters, National Radio Astronomy Observatory, 1003 Lopezville Rd.,
      PO Box O, Socorro, NM 87801, USA (bwaters@aoc.nrao.edu)
Michael Watson, University of Leicester, Department of Physics & Astronomy,
      LE14 2HB, Leicester, UK (mgw@star.le.ac.uk)
Donald Wells, National Radio Astronomy Observatory, 520 Edgemont Rd.,
      Charlottesville, VA 22903, USA (dwells@nrao.edu)
Roy Williams, California Institute of Technology, MS 158-79, Pasadena, CA
      91125, USA (roy@cacr.caltech.edu)
Eric Winter, NASA GCFC, MS 662.0, Greenbelt, MD 20771, USA
      (elwinter@milkyway.gsfc.nasa.gov)
Karl Wolf, Aquilent, Inc., 1100 West St., Laurel, MD 20707, USA
      (karl.wolf@aquilent.com)

Lisa Wolff, Space Telescope Science Institute, 3700 San Martin Dr., Baltimore, MD 21218, USA (wolffl@stsci.edu)

Mark Wolfire, University of Maryland, Astronomy Department, College Park, MD 20742, USA (mwolfire@astro.umd.edu)

Scott Wolk, Harvard-Smithsonian CfA, 60 Garden St. MS 70, Cambridge, MA 02138, USA (swolk@cfa.harvard.edu)

Naoki Yasuda, National Astronomical Observatory of Japan, 2-21-1 Osawa, 181-8588 Mitaka, Japan (naoki.yasuda@nao.ac.jp)

Honglin Ye, National Radio Astronomy Observatory, PO Box O, Socorro, NM 87801, USA (hye@aoc.nrao.edu)

Nelson Zarate, National Optical Astronomy Observatory, 950 N. Cherry Ave., Tucson, AZ 85719, USA (zarate@noao.edu)

Anzhen Zhang, California Institute of Technology, 1200 E. California, Pasadena, CA 91125, USA (azhang@ipac.caltech.edu)

Leslie Zimmerman Foor, Space Telescope Science Institute, 3700 San Martin Dr., Baltimore, MD 21218, USA (foor@stsci.edu)

David Zurek, American Museum of Natural History, Dept of Astrophysics, Central Park W. at 79th St., New York, NY 10024, USA (dzurek@amnh.org)

Astronomical Data Analysis Software and Systems
Twelfth Annual Conference
October 13–16, 2002, Baltimore, MD

Part 1. Virtual Observatory Technologies

Astronomical Data Analysis Software and Systems XII
ASP Conference Series, Vol. 295, 2003
H. E. Payne, R. I. Jedrzejewski, and R. N. Hook, eds.

Rapid Development for Distributed Computing, with Implications for the Virtual Observatory

Michael S. Noble

Center for Space Research, Massachusetts Institute of Technology

Abstract. There remains a significant gap in grid and distributed computing between what *can be achieved* by advanced research groups and what *is realized* by typical scientists on the desktop. We argue that Java-based tuplespaces (JTS) can shrink this gap by lessening the impediments of complexity and institutional buy-in which traditionally accompany the development and use of distributed systems. Drawing from our benchmarking experience, we analyze the strengths of JTS for node configuration, scalability, and failure recovery. We then illustrate how JTS were leveraged to rapidly prototype a powerful end-to-end Virtual Observatory analysis thread within the Chandra Data Analysis System.

1. Introduction

As has been charted by Top500.org for the past decade, peak computer performance continues to grow at an impressive clip. However, these advances in parallel and distributed computing tend to be accessible to only a small portion of researchers, mainly those within focused research projects at national, university, and corporate laboratories. These groups characteristically benefit from generous funding and can afford to purchase (or build) the best equipment and hire whatever staff is necessary to program and maintain it.

At the other end of the performance spectrum are individual researchers and small collaborative groups. These are by far the more common organizational units in which science is daily practiced, and cumulatively represent a much larger fraction of the total researcher population. Yet the scale of computing power available to many of these researchers, or perhaps more accurately that which is *actually used by them on a regular basis*, remains merely the desktop workstation.

A variety of issues inhibit the adoption of high performance computing (HPC) by the individual, many of which can be grouped under the rubric of *the buy-in problem*. After several decades of research it is generally accepted that parallel and distributed programming has not kept pace with improvements in hardware (Hwang & Xu 1998). Despite the breadth of programming models available, HPC has not evolved into the mainstream, and skilled programmers are still hard to find. The complexity of industrial-strength HPC toolkits typically requires a significant investment of time and learning, not only for application or algorithm development, but also for installation and maintenance, especially on today's heterogeneous networks. Our experience is that few practicing scientists have the time or inclination to cultivate these skills (nor, as can be the case, do their technical support staff), with the net effect being that much of the computing potential available to them, at least in principle, goes unused.

This trend manifests itself at several levels. The clearest indication is at the granularity of the network, where the desire to harness the CPU cycles of idle machines has motivated an entire subdiscipline of computer science. The second indication stems from the cycles of hardware upgrades which play out at every computing center. In step with Moore's Law, our older machines are replaced with newer ones, with few second thoughts as to their ultimate destination; as often as not these otherwise functional systems wind up collecting dust in a dark closet. Lastly, observe that while we are at the cusp of another evolutionary step in desktop computing, namely the emergence of the personal multiprocessor system, the extra CPUs in such machines are as yet rarely employed in general scientific development, particularly within the analysis packages used most frequently by astronomers. The wasted CPU cycles in each of these cases would in principle be straightforward to reclaim if parallel and distributed computing skills were more commonplace.

Together these factors create a formidable entry barrier for HPC newcomers, a class into which—drawing from our collaborations at several international research centers—a majority of astronomers still fall, and strongly motivate our investigation of tuplespaces (TS) for rapid distributed computing development.

2.   Tuplespaces Primer

Introduced in the 1980's, the Linda model has been thoroughly described in the literature and exists in a variety of implementations. The central idea is that of *generative communication* (Gelernter 1985), whereby processes do not communicate directly, but rather by adding and removing tuples (ordered collections of data and/or code) to and from a *space* (a process-independent storage abstraction with shared-memory-like characteristics, accessed by associative lookup). This provides an object-like form of distributed shared memory whose semantics can be expressed by adding only a handful of tuple operators [essentially write(), read(), take(), and eval()] to a base language. This approach gives rise to distinctive properties such as time-uncoupled anonymous communication (sender and receiver need not know each other's identity, nor need they exist simultaneously), networked variable sharing (tuples may be viewed as distributed semaphores), and spontaneous multiparty communication patterns that are not feasible in point-to-point models. The simplicity and clean semantics of TS present an attractive alternative to other parallel programming models (e.g., message-passing, shared-variable, remote-procedure call) and foster natural expressions of problems otherwise awkward or difficult to parallelize (Carriero & Gelernter 1988).

2.1.   Commoditized by Java

Linda tuplespaces have been offered as custom C, C++, and Fortran compilers, with a commercial license that can be a barrier to adoption for smaller research groups. Furthermore, as is the case with other parallelizing compilers, and with message passing libraries, such Linda programs are architecture-specific binary code, meaning one cannot compile a *single* Linda application for use on highly heterogeneous networks.

The marriage of the TS model with the popular Java platform addresses these concerns, and extends Linda with transactions, tuple leasing, and event notification. The arrival of two free, commercial-grade Java tuplespace (JTS) platforms—Sun's JavaSpaces (Freeman et al. 1999) and IBM's TSpaces (Wyckoff et al. 1998)—opens an entirely new avenue of exploration in distributed computing with commodity technology.

2.2. JTS for Science: The Perfect versus The Good

The notion of using Java for computational science is not new, and significant advances have been reported in numerous areas (JavaGrande Forum[1]). Given the tight deadlines under which research is conducted, the value of using commodity mechanisms is clear. Observational astronomers, for example, who cannot analyze data with the software at their disposal typically have little choice but to write their own if they wish to publish during their proprietary period. Theorists may be impacted, too, considering e.g., the role high-performance simulations play in development and confirmation.

It is our contention that, if asked to choose between achieving *theoretically maximum* performance some unspecified N months into the future or achieving *suboptimal but good* performance in a fraction of that time, many researchers would gladly select the latter. In Noble & Zlateva (2001) we discuss JTS in this context and present benchmark results which exhibit good speedups for several parametric master/worker algorithms, relative to both sequential Java and native compiled C (Figure 1). Other researchers have also reported substantial

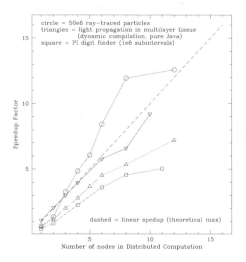

Figure 1.   Peak JTS speedups vs. sequential GCC -O3

---

[1]http://www.javagrande.org

speedups using JTS (Batheja & Parashar 2001, Teo et al. 2002). While several weaknesses of JTS were noted in our work (notably communication latency and a lack of collective broadcast/gather/reduce communication operations), they nonetheless remain enticing as a poor man's HPC platform by addressing off-the-shelf numerous issues with distributed systems.

2.3. Generality

The programmatic simplicity of tuple retrieval in Java masks a powerful network-enabled runtime code loader. This mechanism fosters an uncoupling of generic "dumb workers" (which loop endlessly, waiting to pull tasks from the space to blindly execute their *run()* methods) from task execution code, and provides several clear advantages over traditional message-passing or shared-memory HPC implementations.

First, by remaining wholly ignorant of the details of the computations they perform, generic JTS workers may be written just once for a variety of computations, and breezily deployed on any Java-capable platform. While it is true that similar levels of runtime generality and portability are attainable by other means, e.g., Java RMI, most fall short of the ease of use and semantic clarity that is *built in* to JTS in that the programmer can be required e.g., to abstract the network interactions themselves (or use a package which does so), use RPC compilers to explicitly generate client stubs, and so forth.

Second, such workers need be started only once *per compute node*, after which they idle as low-consumption daemons until tasks appear in the space. With native-compiled PVM, MPI, or OpenMP implementations, however, master and worker tend to be far more tightly coupled. This approach is typically characterized by workers being coded with explicit algorithmic knowledge and masters being directly responsible for the spawning of workers. Together these make the typical worker unsuitable for use in a wide variety of computations, and present additional difficulties on heterogeneous networks as one body of compiled code cannot be used on multiple architectures.

2.4. Dynamic Scaling

Likewise, when masters are responsible for spawning workers en masse the size of the worker pool is usually fixed in advance, effectively prohibiting the addition of workers after the computation has initiated. With static scaling, long-running calculations, for example, cannot be sped up after launching, and instead need to be restarted to add more horsepower. In a JTS solution the master—whose chief responsibilities are to parcel a job into subtasks, funnel them to the space, and collect results—directly interacts with only the space, which allows the computation to be *dynamically scaled*, either up or down, simply by adding or removing workers. Moreover, given the simplicity of threading in Java relative e.g., to POSIX, it was straightforward to have workers in our benchmark framework adapt to multiprocessor hosts by spawning multiple lightweight-process copies of themselves.

It is worthwhile to note that using $N=1$ worker is effectively a sequential invocation, while parallelism is achieved by using $N=k>1$ workers. This semantic clarity can be very beneficial to the application developer, since one of the more difficult aspects of programming for concurrency is that sequential algorithms frequently do not map cleanly to parallel implementations. In such cases it is difficult or impossible to utilize one body of sourcecode for both sequential and parallel execution.

2.5. Factoring Administrators Out Of The HPC Equation

As is the case with large-scale databases, many traditional approaches to HPC require direct involvement of a system administrator, and can eventually mandate hiring additional, even dedicated, staff. Whether to research and purchase exotic massively-parallel hardware, install enabling software on multiple nodes, activate low-level daemons with root privileges, create special user accounts, or manage pooled disk space, the need to involve yet another outside party diminishes individual autonomy and introduces a recurring usage bottleneck.

Recent work, though, shows that combining network class loaders with JTS can eliminate many of these difficulties (Noble 2000,[2] Lehman et al. 2001, Hawick & James 2001). In fact, in the 47-node MAN testbed used to derive the results of Figure 1: the JTS system software was installed on non-privileged diskspace, and was booted from an ordinary user account, master and workers were run from ordinary user accounts, and 6 of the 14 machines used did not even have a local JTS installation.

Remote Node Configuration In fairness we should note that some of these benefits were derived as much from our lack of security concerns as from any specific technology choice, but our contention, again, is that to promote rapid development and results "faster and looser" is the prevailing mindset in smaller research groups (especially those whose goal is *not* publication of research papers in computer science). However, the fact that a JTS installation was *not required at all* on participant nodes is considerable step forward in the configuration and management of distributed systems on heterogenous networks. To achieve this we merged the client portion of JavaSpaces[3] and our worker code into a single bootstrap jar file, and made it available on a well-known compute portal.

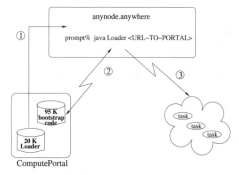

Figure 2.   Simplified remote node configuration with JTS.

---

[2]http://hea-www.harvard.edu/~mnoble/tonic/doc

[3]We have not tried this yet with TSpaces, but (Lehman et al. 2001) suggests it will work.

Users electing to participate in the distributed computation framework need only install a network launcher onto the prospective node(s), the cost of which can be as small as a 20K download.[4] At runtime the loader is pointed at the established portal to retrieve the bootstrap jar and invoke the worker class within, after which the worker contacts the space and idles for compute tasks. Whatever class loader is used, it need be downloaded just once per node, after which it can be reused regardless of how many revisions are made to the bootstrap code or computation framework.

With this approach it is no longer necessary to consume administrator time to configure or employ distributed systems—a JTS solution may be installed and activated without knowledge of the system password *on any machine*; nor is it necessary to maintain multiple native binary builds—of either the HPC toolkit or your computational codes—to utilize multiple CPU architectures in a single distributed computation. The significance of this technique increases in direct proportion to both the number and architectural diversity of nodes within the computation environment, as well as the workload of your system administrators.

2.6.   Fault Tolerance and Checkpointing

In sharp contrast with other parallel and distributed programming mechanisms, failure recovery is an intrinsic feature of available JTS implementations. First note that any space—a persistent external store into which tasks are doled out and intermediate results accumulate—is itself a checkpointing mechanism. Checkpointing, where partial results are incrementally saved, is used in long-running calculations to avoid restarting from scratch after failures. It contributes nothing to computed solutions, per se, but typically requires explicit coding within the algorithm for message-passing and shared-memory implementations. Second, while in our benchmarking efforts we found the JTS implementations very robust (capable of running unhindered for weeks and months on end), it is a fact of life that node failures will occur. With JTS transactions, though, the demise of participants *during* a computation is in principle fully recoverable. Wrapping worker interactions with the space within a transaction, for example, ensures that if a worker dies the transaction cannot commit; this in turn will cause the subtask being computed by the worker to be automatically returned to the space (in virgin form) as the transaction is unrolled. Similar benefits may be gained by wrapping the results collection phase (in the master) within a transaction.

3.   Prototyping the Virtual Observatory

A number of the benefits discussed above map well to the Virtual Observatory problem space. The loosely coupled master/worker pattern, for example, generalizes to the use of TS for coordinating ensembles of anonymous processes (Gelernter & Carriero 1992). A fully-realized VO should in principle permit the

---

[4]Our experiments were conducted in 2000, prior to the wide availability of JNLP and Java WebStart. Instead, we implemented a custom loader based upon WebRun from Michael Sinz.

spontaneous formation of any number of such ensembles. The degree to which this becomes accessible to the typical astronomer, unencumbered by system administrator or programmer hand-holding, will be a key metric of success. Other crucial factors include the flexibility with which back-end services can be glued together, how rapidly they may be deployed, and how well VO mechanisms integrate with existing astronomy software. To explore these concepts further we have constructed a testbed (Cresitello-Dittmar et al. 2003) which uses JTS to define and coordinate a number of services (name resolution, multi-archive lookup and retrieval) which automate the generation of composite images and multi-waveband flux plots. Several distinguishing features of the prototype are that it is accessible from a publicly-available analysis toolset (CIAO), that the VO capability is *anonymously* invoked, and that it was deployable after a very short coding period by two new hires. User interactions are managed by a scriptable Gtk GUI coded in S-Lang and loaded at runtime into the *chips* visualization tool. The name and identity of each VO service was discovered at runtime by the GUI client, which needed knowledge only of how to contact the space.

3.1. Testbed Architecture

Workflow is modeled in our testbed by Service Providers, Requestors, and Portals, which interact by exchanging Advertisement and Job tuples. An Advertisement describes *what* work the provider is willing to perform, while a Job—a quanta of work—indicates *how much*. In the following illustration two providers have written two advertisements and three jobs in an INITIAL state. By writing

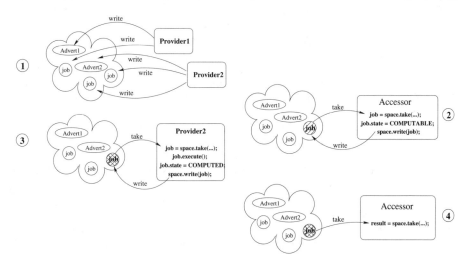

two job tuples to the portal Provider2 indicates that it is willing to service two requests for Advertisement2 simultaneously, perhaps because it is a multiprocessor (the owner of, say, a 16-cpu machine might choose to make any number of its processors available in like fashion). The accessor, having scanned the portal for advertisements, requests that a service be computed on its behalf by retrieving a job from the space, marking its state as COMPUTABLE, and writing it back to the space. Provider2, who is woken by the presence of a computable service request, executes the job, marks its state as COMPUTED, and writes it back to the space. Finally, the accessor notices the arrival of its completed request and retrieves the result.

3.2.   Analysis

This architecture is heavily influenced by the decoupled nature of TS communication, and manifests a number of useful properties beyond mere clarity of object flow. For example, advertisements gracefully expire from the portal if not refreshed by the provider within a lease period, which serves as an implicit heartbeat mechanism. With such *dynamic service lifetime management*, partial state—which can accumulate in an explicit deregistration model when a provider joins the portal and then suffers a catastrophic failure—is automatically flushed. Assuming zero transmission errors, a requestor is guaranteed—within the granularity of the lease—that its service request will at least initiate, rather than merely spilling into the ether of an offline provider.

Likewise, the separation of advertisement from job execution yields an implicit mechanism for detecting a saturated provider *without further contributing to that saturation*: if an advertisement exists in the portal with no corresponding job tuples then the provider must be busy servicing other requests. A client can detect this state without issuing an ill-fated request (yet more work for the overloaded provider) doomed to merely timeout. This fosters smoother client operation, especially important when human interaction is involved, and promotes deterministic behavior of the system as a whole. The use of jobs as quanta of work lets providers retain full control over how much community service they will perform, and when, and makes it *virtually impossible* for them to saturate from requests. While the space itself is a potential saturation point, the tasks it handles (mostly funneling small-ish tuples back and forth) are not computationally expensive, and its function can be replicated for scalability as needs arise (although more investigation is needed in this area).

Another form of load balancing is manifest in the ability of the space to store partial results. Imagine for instance a provider who offers a computationally expensive service that takes N input parameters. Since the result of that computation can be stored in the space (or a reference to it if the result, e.g., a file, is too large), new requests with matching inputs need not result in entirely new service invocations at the provider.

Finally, note that while service discovery and requests are coordinated by the space, its use is not mandatory. A provider is free to negotiate more effective means of interaction with the requestor, and in fact archive retrievals in our testbed are carried out by direct download between the hosting site and client.

What About Web Services?   Web Services advocates in the VO community may contend that a Java-centric approach such as we have employed here lacks neutrality by binding one too closely to a specific language or object model. While this position is not without merit, its wholesale acceptance would seem to require overlooking several issues of significance.

For one, many of the features described here—simple service coordination, accumulation and persistence of partial results, asynchrony, transactional support, fault tolerance, and dynamic lifetime management—are not well-supported in other service hosting implementations, such as those providing Web Services through a UDDI registry. These factors—plus the heavy bias of UDDI towards commerce, and the performance of SOAP (Davis & Parashar 2002, Govindaraju et al. 2000[5])—should concern those considering adopting Web Services for scientific use. In response the grid community is developing more robust alternatives, such as the Open Grid Services Architecture (forming the core of the next generation Globus 3.0 Toolkit, which incidentally also requires Java for service management, though wider language support is planned) and the Web Services Discovery Architecture (WSDA). Until these mature, however, the scientific community is left with few off-the-shelf options for service management. Our JTS-based scheme productively fills this interim niche.

Next, a commitment to use Java *somewhere* within a project does not mandate its use *everywhere*, given the availability of the Java native interface (JNI) and fork()/exec(). Our testbed amply demonstrates this by seamlessly binding libraries, applications, and HTTP services—legacy and new—written in a variety of compiled and interpreted languages. In principle "using Java to talk to the network" is not dissimilar from "using XML to talk to the network": either would represent just another layer within a codebase, each with its own advantages and disadvantages.

Finally, note that our aim in comparing JTS with Web Services is didactic, rather than to suggest that our approach to service management should, or even can, supplant the use of Web Services in the VO arena. Our hope is that the more intriguing features of our portal find their way into evolving registry schemes, and that we can find a way to embrace emerging grid and VO standards while not sacrificing the clear gains JTS have delivered in our work. We anticipate that the latter will not be difficult, since the Java platform is by a large margin the dominant vehicle for Web Services deployment (SoapWare.org, [6] InfoWorld survey[7]).

4. Conclusion

Most astronomers remain newcomers to high-performance and grid computing, in part because the barrier to entry remains high: significant cognitive and administrative commitments can be required—at both the institutional and individual scope—to utilize the industrial-strength packages typically employed within these milieux. We have argued that JTS compellingly resolves several aspects of the buy-in problem, and that what one *may* sacrifice by adopting a lighter-weight JTS solution (e.g., peak performance) is adequately compensated for by their ease and autonomy of use, wealth of built-in features, and flexibility. As a partial validation of this assertion we have deployed a space-based VO testbed which augments an existing astronomical toolset, CIAO, with

---

[5]http://www.sc2000.org/techpapr/papers/pap.pap261.pdf

[6]Note the extent (and sometimes exclusivity) of Java support in the listed SOAP implementations.

[7]http://www.infoworld.com/articles/hn/xml/01/12/21/011221hnjavasurvey.xml

anonymous discovery of multi-waveband search, retrieval, and analysis capability. Our service coordination infrastructure was implemented in less than 700 lines of Java code, and required virtually zero modification of legacy archive interfaces. The testbed pushes the VO envelope beyond the use of static, faulty, and uncoordinated browser-based services into the realm of fault-tolerant ensembles of dynamically coordinated agents, and to our knowledge represents the first demonstration of an end-to-end analysis thread capable of generating publication-quality results with the ease of use portended for the Virtual Observatory.

While in its present form the testbed should adequately fulfill its purpose as a local proving ground for VO datamodel development, plenty of room for improvement remains, notably in the areas of replication and scalability, interoperability with web-services, adoption of emerging VO standards, streamlining agent interactions with event notification and broader use of JNI, and more graceful co-existence with firewalls.

Acknowledgments. The author would like to thank the entire NVO team at the Harvard-Smithsonian Center for Astrophysics, particularly Stephen Lowe and Michael Harris, for enthusiastic use of, and constructive feedback on, the Tonic and SLgtk packages. This work was supported in part by the Chandra X-Ray Center, under NASA contract NAS8-39073.

References

Batheja, J. & Parashar, M. 2001, Proc. IEEE Cluster Computing, 323

Carriero, N. & Gelernter, D. 1988, ACM SIGPLAN Notices, 23(9), 173

Cresitello-Dittmar, M. et al. 2003, this volume, 65

Davis, D. & Parashar, M. 2002, IEEE Clust. Comp. and the GRID

Freeman, E., Hupfer, S. & Arnold, K. 1999, JavaSpaces: Principles Patterns, and Practice (Reading, MA: Addison-Wesley)

Gelernter, D. 1985, ACM Trans. on Prog. Lang. and Sys. 7(1), 80

Gelernter, D. & Carriero, N. 1992, Comm. of the ACM 35(2), 97

Hawick, K. & James, H. 2001, Proc. IEEE Cluster Computing, 145

Hwang, K. & Xu, Z. 1998, Scalable Parallel Computing (Boston: McGraw-Hill)

Lehman, T. et al. 2001, Computer Networks, 35, 457

Noble, M. & Zlateva, S. 2001, Lecture Notes in Computer Science (Berlin: Springer-Verlag), 2110, 657

Teo, Y. M., Ng, Y. K., & Onggo, B. S. S. 2002, Proc. 16th IEEE Work. on Parallel and Distrib. Simulation, 3

Wyckoff, P. et al. 1998, IBM Systems Journal, 37(3), 454

Astronomical Data Analysis Software and Systems XII
ASP Conference Series, Vol. 295, 2003
H. E. Payne, R. I. Jedrzejewski, and R. N. Hook, eds.

eSTAR: Building an Observational GRID

Alasdair Allan, Tim Naylor

School of Physics, University of Exeter, Stocker Road, Exeter, EX4 4QL, U.K.

Iain Steele, Dave Carter, Jason Etherton, Chris Motteram

Astrophysics Research Institute, Liverpool John Moores University, Twelve Quays House, Egerton Wharf, Birkenhead CH41 1LD, U.K.

Abstract. The eSTAR Project[1] is a programme to build a prototype robotic telescope network to design and test the infrastructure and software which could be used in larger scale projects. The network consists of a number of autonomous telescopes, and associated rapid data reduction pipelines, connected together using Globus middleware. Intelligent agents carry out resource discovery, submit observing requests, and analyse the reduced data returned by the telescope nodes. The agents are capable of carrying out data mining and cross-correlation tasks using online catalogues and databases and, if necessary, requesting follow-up observations from the telescope nodes. We discuss the design and implications of the eSTAR software and its implications with respect to the GRID.

1. Just Imagine...

Imagine a system which has unified access to archived data, to telescopes and to bibliographic data. In addition the system has intelligent agents (IAs) which can interpret the results.

In this paper I hope to persuade you that such a system, with a seamless interface between telescopes and databases, indeed making telescopes look like databases and visa versa, will bring enormous benefits.

2. The Observational Grid

There are two fundamental ideas behind eSTAR which make it a unique project. The first is to treat both telescopes and databases in as similar a fashion as possible, both being made available as a resource on the 'Observational Grid'. The second is that the main user of that grid should not be humans making observing requests, but should be intelligent agents.

---

[1] http://www.estar.org.uk/

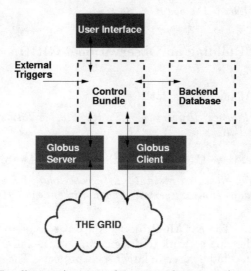

Figure 1.   Intelligent Agent architecture diagram. A central control bundle handles both user input and input from external triggers, such as γ-ray burst alerts. The Globus middleware layer is separated from the control bundle to allow easy substitution, e.g., with SOAP.

The design is analogous to computational grids, with no overall supervisor, giving the system scalability with multiple agents talking to multiple nodes.

Intelligent agents submit requests to nodes on the network rather than commands. Each telescope has its own scheduler, which can talk to the agents using the Robotic Telescope Markup Language[2] (RTML) transported over Globus[3] middleware.

A typical sequence begins with the IA carrying out resource discovery, using LDAP to characterise each telescope node and associated instrument suite. Next each telescope is asked by the agent whether it could carry out a particular observation, each node returning a weighted score which encodes the predicted quality of the observation.

The IA will then select the node it wishes to carry out the observation, which will usually be the highest scoring node, and requests that the observation be put in the nodes observing queue by its scheduler.

Once the observation is complete the raw and reduced data are made available to the IA via the grid.

3.   Intelligent Agents

One can view the eSTAR network as a unified information grid, within which intelligent agents live.

---

[2]http://alpha.uni-sw.gwdg.de/~hessman/RTML/

[3]http://www.Globus.org/

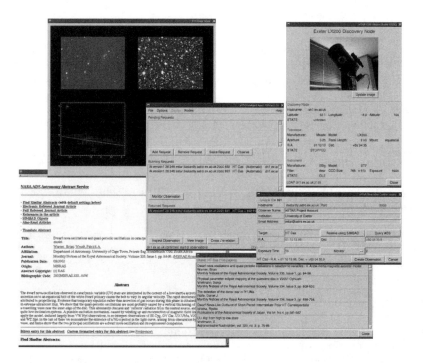

Figure 2. Intelligent Agent prototype developed to monitor Dwarf Novae. The main observation tracker window is shown centre field, with the node window in the upper right. The results of a real time cross correlation of a returned field with the USNO-A2 catalogue are shown in the upper left, while results from datamining SIMBAD and ADS for information about the possible variable the agent has discovered are displayed in the lower part of the figure.

The current prototype agent, see Figure 1, cross correlates the point source catalogue returned by the telescope node with USNO-A2 (in real time) in an attempt to find candidate variable stars, datamining SIMBAD for possible known variables to match the candidate stars.

If the candidate turns out to be a dwarf nova of interest, then the IA will request further followup observations from the network of telescope nodes.

We have been pleasantly surprised by the speed of the cross-correlation stage, which normally completes in 4–10 seconds, including recovering data from three different web sites, indicating that the IA would not be the limiting factor in a system which would be expected to react rapidly to external triggers.

While the prototype agent does lack complexity, it was deliberately developed in a modular fashion to maximise code reuse, and could be trivially re-engineered to handle a very different science goal. For instance, to listen for and response to external triggers such as γ-ray burst alerts.

Indeed, our vision is that agents should be developed by astronomers to address their own science problems, perhaps using some 'agent builder toolkit.'

4. Discovery Nodes

For the prototype we have made use of off the shelf hardware, Meade LX200 and ETX telescopes with SBIG and Apogee CCD cameras, as telescope nodes.

However in general a node is any telescope, or archive, which delivers astronomical data or other resources using a uniform interface. From the point of view of an intelligent agent (or indeed a astronomer) there is little difference between a telescope and a database except the timestamps on the data.

5. Middleware

Currently the project makes use of Globus IO to transport RTML documents between the agents and the discovery nodes, with SSL encryption providing a secure data stream.

Additionally, a new version of RTML (Pennypacker et al. 2002) has been developed by the project, with our improvements being rolled back into the ongoing development of the protocol.

6. Where Now?

We are currently developing the software to make use of emerging web services, and re-engineering the agent to support the next generation Globus Toolkit using Open Grid Service Architecture (OGSA), within which SOAP and WSDL will provide natural language neutral interoperability between the components of the system.

Additionally we are looking to deploy the system on research class telescopes such as the Liverpool Telescope and the United Kingdom Infra-Red Telescope (UKIRT).

7. Summary

We view it as vitally important that federated databases and automated telescopes should share a common interface, as there is little, if any, fundamental differences between them other than the time it takes to return the data and the date stamp.

However if a system similar to this is to become widespread, the idea of requesting observations is equally important. This allows telescopes to join the network and retain their independence, with the intelligent agent contributing, perhaps, only a small fraction of the observations to the telescope scheduler.

Furthermore, telescopes can and must be able to reject requests from an IA if, for example, the astronomer to whom the IA belongs has no time allocated on the telescope.

References

Pennypacker C. et al. 2002, A&A, in press

Astronomical Data Analysis Software and Systems XII
ASP Conference Series, Vol. 295, 2003
H. E. Payne, R. I. Jedrzejewski, and R. N. Hook, eds.

Astrocomp: A Web Portal for High Performance Computing on a Grid of Supercomputers

P. Di Matteo, R. Capuzzo Dolcetta, P. Miocchi

Dipartimento di Fisica, Universitá di Roma "La Sapienza," P.le Aldo Moro 2, 00185 Roma, Italy

V. Antonuccio-Delogu, U. Becciani, A. Costa

Osservatorio Astrofisico di Catania, Cittá Universitaria, Via Santa Sofia 78, 95123 Catania, Italy

V. Rosato[1]

ENEA, Casaccia Research Center, Computing and Modelling Unit (CAMO), P.O. Box 2400 Roma, Italy

Abstract. Astrocomp is a project based on a collaboration among the University of Roma La Sapienza, the Astrophysical Observatory of Catania and ENEA. The main motivation of the AstroComp project is to construct a portal, which allows to set up a repository of computational codes and common databases, making them available and enjoyable, with a user-friendly graphical web interface, to the international community. AstroComp will allow the scientific community to benefit by the use of many different numerical tools implemented on high performance computing (HPC) resources, both for theoretical astrophysics and cosmology and for the storage and analysis of astronomical data, without the need of specific training, know-how and experience either in computational techniques or in database construction and management methods. An essential feature of Astrocomp is that it makes available to subscribers some CPU time on large parallel platforms, via specific grants. Astrocomp is partly financed by a grant of the Italian national research Council (CNR).

1. Present Project Status and Description

The main aim of the AstroComp project is to create a portal that provides both astrophysical numerical codes and platforms to run them, with no need by the user to get grants or to pay expensive computational resources. A prototype of the AstroComp portal is already working and can be visited at http://www.astrocomp.it (see Figure 1), where it is possible to find a description of the main features of the project. Clicking on the *Software* session, it is

---

[1]INFM Unitá di Ricerca Roma I

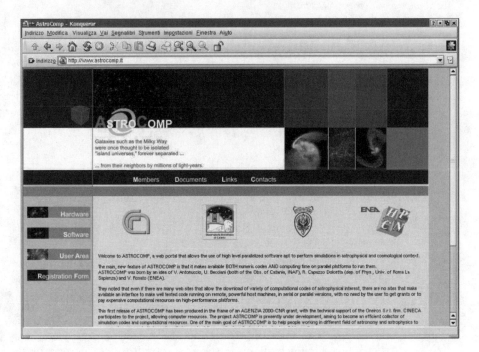

Figure 1.   Home page of the present version of the AstroComp web
portal.

possible to find a description of the codes that are presently available through
the portal. At the present stage, AstroComp hosts three N-body codes:

1. the *ATD* treecode, a parallel tree-code for the simulation of the dynamics
   of self-gravitating systems (Miocchi & Capuzzo Dolcetta 2002);
2. the *FLY* code, a cosmological code for studying three-dimensional collisionless self-gravitating systems with periodic boundary conditions (Becciani & Antonuccio-Delogu 2001); and
3. the *HSN*body, a direct-summation code which is presently under implementation into the portal (Di Matteo, 2001).

ATD and *FLY* have been already tested and are fully working on the server.
The main features of the platforms now available to run these codes can be found
clicking on the *Hardware* session, from the AstroComp home page. At the moment, the portal can provide four machines: an IBM SP4 and a SGI Origin 3800
(both located at CINECA), a Linux Alpha Cluster (located at ENEA Casaccia Research Center) and an IBM SP3 (located at the Catania Astrophysical
Observatory).

Anyone who wants to use the provided facilities has to register first, doing
the following steps:

1. click on the *Registration Form*, available from the AstroComp home page
   and fill the form, entering personal data and e-mail address; and

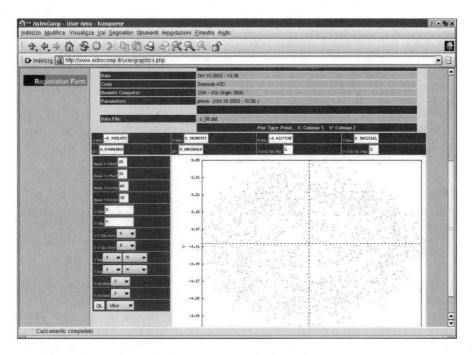

Figure 2.   The 2-D plot page available from the AstroComp portal.

2. wait for a confirmation e-mail sent quickly by the portal administrator as soon as the account is added for the new user, with the username and password he will have to use to enter in the *User Area*.

Clicking on the *User Area* button, after a usual login procedure, any registered user can have the access to the computational facilities of the AstroComp portal.

At present, an AstroComp user is able to:

- start a new simulation by choosing which code to run and by determining the simulation parameters via the *Parameters* on line form; and
- choose among different platforms from the pool of the available resources;

or

- browse the status of a previously launched job, possibly checking the intermediate results with a preliminary "on-the-fly" visualization tool available in the portal itself (see Figure 2); then
- download the final and/or intermediate results.

In the first case, if the user wants to start a new simulation, after the code he wants to run has been chosen, he has to assign the parameters of his own simulation. Two possibilities are available: the user can choose either to use the AstroComp default values (described in the *New Job* session) or to give his own parameters. After having entered all these parameters, a name can be given to the job. The last step to do, before submitting the job, is to give the initial configuration files. Also in this case it is possible to choose either to use the AstroComp default files or to assign others.

If the user wants to check the status of a previously launched job, he has to click on the *Job Status* button (in the *User Area* page). Here he will find the list of the submitted jobs, the dates of the submissions, the job status (pending, not in queue or running) and the platform used to run it. Clicking on the *Results* button from this list, it is possible to see the list of the files produced by the simulation.

The user can choose either to delete files (in this case he will lose them definitely) or to plot them, using a visualization tool available on the portal itself. Plotting the files could be useful to check the simulation results.

2. Near Future Perspectives

Many improvement are planned to be carried out in the short-term activity. They include:

- implementation of on-line tools for the automatic generation of the most used and relevant initial conditions for astrophysical/cosmological simulations;
- implementation of scheduling methods for the management of very-long term simulations by subdividing them in shorter "sub-simulations" that could satisfy the CPU times restrictions of the various queue job systems; and
- inclusion of advanced data analysis and storage tools (for example, AstroMD, Becciani et al. 2000).

To conclude, note that the AstroComp server is based on a PHP/MYSQL environment and that the databases structure has been designed with the capability of an easy interface with the middleware and the Resource Broker for a future grid-based computational environment.

Anyone who is interested on this project and wants to add astrophysical codes to the portal can contact us, sending an e-mail to one of the AstroComp members (e-mail addresses are available in the *AstroComp Members*[1] page).

References

Becciani, U. & Antonuccio-Delogu, V. 2001, Comp. Phys. Comm., in press (astroph/0101148)

Becciani, U., Antonuccio-Delogu, V., Gheller, C., Calori, L., Buonomo, F. & Imboden, S. 2000, IEEE CG&A, submitted (astroph/0006402)

Di Matteo, P. 2001, Graduation Thesis, Univ. of Rome "La Sapienza," Italy

Miocchi, P. & Capuzzo Dolcetta, R. 2002, A&A, 382, 758

---

[1]http://www.astrocomp.it/members.it

Astronomical Data Analysis Software and Systems XII
ASP Conference Series, Vol. 295, 2003
H. E. Payne, R. I. Jedrzejewski, and R. N. Hook, eds.

Architecture for All-Sky Browsing of Astronomical Datasets

Joseph C. Jacob, Gary Block, and David W. Curkendall

Jet Propulsion Laboratory, California Institute of Technology, 4800 Oak Grove Drive, Pasadena, CA 91109-8099

Abstract. A new architecture for all-sky browsing of astronomical datasets has been designed and implemented in the form of a graphical front-end to the yourSky custom mosaicking engine. With yourSky, any part of the sky can be retrieved as a single FITS image with user-specified parameters such as coordinate system, projection, resolution and data type. The simple HTML form interface to yourSky has been supplemented with a graphical interface that allows: (i) All-sky, web-based pan and zoom; (ii) Interactive, multi-spectral viewing; (iii) Vector graphic overlays from object catalogs; and (iv) Invocation of the yourSky mosaicking engine once a desired view has been selected in the browser.

1. Introduction

A number of "Virtual Observatory (VO)" efforts exist around the world, including the National Virtual Observatory (NVO 2002) in the United States, with the objective of applying modern information technology to facilitate all aspects of the access, processing, analysis, and visualization of massive astronomical datasets. As a community effort, the VO will consist of many widely distributed components developed and deployed by domain experts in different areas. Many of these components will need to exploit state of the art high performance computing and communications assets due to the sheer size of the datasets or the complexity of the algorithms. However, much of astronomical research is being conducted by students or researchers without direct access to these expensive computing assets. Therefore, the VO will need to deploy portals that provide access to these assets, supercomputers, massive data archives, and the high bandwidth networks that interconnect them, but these portals will also need to be able to cope with meager computing resources and low bandwidth network connections on the client side.

In this paper we present a working implementation of an image mosaicking and all-sky browsing service that fits the distributed architecture of the VO, described above. This computational architecture is used in two complimentary ways. First, a "Browse Mode" provides a web-based, interactive, all-sky pan and zoom capability for astronomical images and catalogs. In this mode a very rapid, interactive response is required, with a delay of no more than a few seconds from the time a user requests an image of some part of the sky to the time when that image is delivered. To achieve the necessary interactive response, it is expected that the astronomical data in remote archives would have to be preprocessed into an online data store from which a cutout image of any part of the sky can be rapidly extracted. The second mode of operation is a "Batch Mode," which provides a science quality image mosaicking service that can retrieve the highest science quality data available from remote, possibly off-line, archives, and deliver custom image mosaics based on this data to the scientist's desktop. The yourSky web portal at http://yourSky.jpl.nasa.gov provides both all sky browsing and a highly customizable parallel image mosaicking capability that together provide a very powerful tool for accessing modern terabyte-level astronomical datasets.

This synergy between all sky image browsing and more focused science quality custom image mosaicking enables a number of important science activities in astronomy: (i) the overall region of coverage of any included dataset can be determined at a glance by browsing the all-sky, coarse-resolution representation of the dataset, (ii) any region of the sky can be retrieved from any included dataset in a specific coordinate system and projection as a single, high science quality image regardless of how that data is stored in the native archive, (iii) mosaicking multiple wavelengths to the same grid enables novel, multi-spectral analysis of astronomical data.

The remainder of this paper describes in more detail the yourSky custom mosaicking engine (Section 2) and all-sky browsing capabilities (Section 3).

2.   yourSky Custom Mosaicking Engine

The yourSky custom mosaicking engine (Jacob et al. 2002) includes subsystems for: (i) construction of the image mosaics on multiprocessor systems, (ii) managing simultaneous user requests, (iii) determining which image plates from member surveys are required to fulfill a given request, (iv) caching input image plates and the output mosaics between requests, and (v) retrieving input image plates from remote archives. The only client software required to access yourSky is the ubiquitous web browser.

The parallel image mosaicking software emphasizes custom access to mosaics, allowing the user to specify parameters that describe the mosaic to be built, including the datasets to be used, location on the sky, size of the mosaic, resolution, coordinate system, projection, data type, and image format. Values for these parameters are specified using a simple form interface found on the yourSky web page (http://yourSky.jpl.nasa.gov). The galactic, ecliptic, J2000 equatorial and B1950 equatorial coordinate systems are supported, as are all of the sphere to image plane projections specified by the World Coordinate System (WCS) (Greisen & Calabretta 1995). Pixel data types may be 8-, 16-, or 32-bit signed or unsigned integer, or single or double precision floating point. The mosaic may be output in the FITS data format, well known in the astronomy community, or in another common image format such as JPEG, PGM, PNG, or TIFF.

The yourSky portal may be used to access any region of the sky as a single image, regardless of the size of the region or how the image data is partitioned and stored in the native archives. The image mosaics are constructed from the highest science quality data product in the remote archives. Currently all of the publicly released data from the Two Micron All Sky Survey (2MASS) and the Digitized Palomar Observatory Sky Survey (DPOSS) are accessible with yourSky. The only requirements on the input images to yourSky are that they be FITS format images with valid WCS information stored in the FITS header. The mosaicking software developed for yourSky is designed to support input images and output mosaics of any size, including all-sky images at sub-arc-second resolution.

3. yourSky Interactive All Sky Browser

The simple yourSky form interface described in Section 2 has been supplemented with a graphical front end that permits interactive, web-based pan and zoom over an all-sky representation of each yourSky dataset. This image browser features efficient navigation by either mouse point-and-click or by directly inputting a right ascension, declination, and zoom level to jump to the desired view. Multi-spectral viewing is supported by allowing the user to map any wavelength from the included datasets to each of the red, green, and blue video channels to produce a pseudocolor image. Catalogs of tabular data may be visualized as vector graphic overlays that pan and zoom in concert with the image. Finally, this interactive, graphical front-end is interoperable with the yourSky batch mosaic engine described in Section 2. Once a desired view of the sky is centered in the interactive display, a simple click of a button brings up the yourSky custom mosaic form with dataset and location fields filled in to match the browser view. This enables the user to easily order a higher science quality version of the image being viewed with the desired coordinate system, projection, data type, and resolution.

The images delivered to the interactive browser are cropped from a set of image plates that were constructed a priori and stored on-line for rapid inter-active response. The yourSky all-sky browser is intended to permit effective interactive viewing of any part of the sky. This would not be possible if we simply enabled pan and zoom over a single all-sky image mosaic, due to the severe distortion that would be apparent in regions far from the projection center. Therefore, instead of using a single all-sky image, the browser images are served from multiple, overlapping image plates. The image plate sizes are small enough to limit the image distortion due to projecting pixels from the sphere to the image plane. The plate sizes are also large enough to ensure full coverage of the sphere and to allow for sufficient overlap between plates that a typical display image can be computed by simply cropping from a single image plate.

Each image plate is in a tangent plane projection, with tangent points located at various locations around the sphere. The tangent point positions are based on a sphere subdivision scheme called the Hierarchical Triangular Mesh (HTM), which was first adopted by the Sloan Digital Sky Survey as a means of organizing astronomical data into bins based on spherical triangles on the sphere (Kunszt et al. 1999). Each yourSky browse image plate is tangent to the sphere at an HTM vertex as illustrated in Figure 1. A set of plates is provided at resolution steps from 8 arc seconds per pixel (258 plates covering the sphere) to 2,048 arc seconds per pixel (1 plate covering the entire sphere).

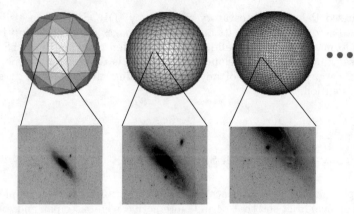

Figure 1.   The yourSky browse image plates are positioned based on
Hierarchical Triangular Mesh vertices.

4. Summary

The yourSky architecture supports two modes of operation: (i) batch mode,
science quality, potentially compute intensive custom mosaic processing, and
(ii) browse mode, interactive, web-based, all-sky pan and zoom. This synergy
between interactive browse capability with science quality custom mosaic processing makes yourSky a flexible portal for astronomical data access, analysis,
and visualization. The yourSky portal is at `http://yourSky.jpl.nasa.gov`.

Acknowledgments.   The authors would like to acknowledge the DPOSS
and 2MASS surveys for making their data available to us. We would like to
thank our colleagues in the astronomy and information technology communities
for their advice: S. G. Djorgovski, A. Mahabal, R. Brunner, J. Good, G. B.
Berriman, G. Kremenek, R. Williams. This research was carried out at the Jet
Propulsion Laboratory, California Institute of Technology, under a contract with
the National Aeronautics and Space Administration.

References

National Virtual Observatory Science Definition Team Report 2002,
    `http://nvosdt.org`

Jacob, J. C., Brunner, R., Curkendall, D. W., Djorgovski, S. G., Good, J. C.,
    Husman, L., Kremenek, G., & Mahabal, A. 2002, SPIE Astronomical
    Telescopes and Instrumentation: Virtual Observatories

Greisen, E. W. & Calabretta, M. 1995, in ASP Conf. Ser., Vol. 77, Astronomical
    Data Analysis Software and Systems IV, ed. R. A. Shaw, H. E. Payne, &
    J. J. E. Hayes (San Francisco: ASP), 233

Kunszt, P. Z., Szalay, A. S., Csabai, I., & Thakar, A. R. 1999, in ASP Conf. Ser.,
    Vol. 216, Astronomical Data Analysis Software and Systems IX, ed. N.
    Manset, C. Veillet, & D. Crabtree (San Francisco: ASP), 141

Astronomical Data Analysis Software and Systems XII
ASP Conference Series, Vol. 295, 2003
H. E. Payne, R. I. Jedrzejewski, and R. N. Hook, eds.

Scoping the UK's Virtual Observatory: AstroGrid's Key Science Drivers

Nicholas A. Walton

Institute of Astronomy, University of Cambridge, Madingley Road, Cambridge, CB3 0HA, UK

Andrew Lawrence

Institute for Astronomy, University of Edinburgh, Royal Observatory, Blackford Hill, Edinburgh, EH9 3HJ, UK

Tony Linde

Department of Physics & Astronomy, University of Leicester, University Road, Leicester, LE1 7RH, UK

Abstract. AstroGrid, a UK e-Science astro-informatics project, with collaborating groups drawn from the major UK data archive centres, is creating the UK's first virtual observatory. AstroGrid is aiming to support a broad spectrum of astronomical activity, with an initial emphasis on meeting the needs expressed by the UK community. This paper discusses how AstroGrid is balancing the scientific requirements of the community (which includes the Solar and STP communities). Note is made of the use of interactive mechanisms provided by the project, especially those linked through the AstroGrid portal, in capturing user requirements.

1. The AstroGrid Project

AstroGrid[1] is one of three major funded world-wide projects (along with the European Astrophysical Virtual Observatory[2] (AVO, Quinn 2002) and US National Virtual Observatory[3] (NVO, Hanisch 2002) which are aiming to create an astronomical Virtual Observatory.

AstroGrid will develop a working implementation of immediate use to astronomers. As a consortium of UK data centres and software providers, AstroGrid aims to pool common resources, including key UK databases, storage, and compute facilities. As a UK e-Science project, its architecture is firmly based on a service/data-grid approach: making use of grid components produced by other

---

[1]http://www.astrogrid.org

[2]http://www.euro-vo.org

[3]http://www.us-vo.org

projects, with AstroGrid developed components being made freely available to the community. The scientific aims of AstroGrid are:

- to improve the quality, efficiency, ease, speed, and cost-effectiveness of on-line astronomical research,
- to make comparison and integration of data from diverse sources seamless and transparent,
- to remove data analysis barriers to interdisciplinary research, and
- to make science involving manipulation of large datasets as easy and as powerful as possible.

The Virtual Observatory (VO) will be a set of co-operating and interoperable software systems that will allow users to interrogate multiple data centres in a seamless and transparent way. The VO will provide powerful new analysis and visualisation tools and give data centres and data producers (e.g., projects, observatories, individuals, etc.) a standard framework for publishing and delivering services using their data.

2.   AstroGrid Development Activities

In its first year AstroGrid has been undertaking activities in a number of areas, with the primary emphasis being to capture the science requirements required to scope the project, together with the development of a project architecture within which the required capabilities (such as authorisation, see Rixon & Walton 2002) can be developed. Subsidiary activities have included engagement with the other international VO projects, closely with the AVO where AstroGrid is a formal partner, and informally with projects such as the NVO. Important activities such as agreeing low level interoperability standards have been undertaken within the context of the International Virtual Observatory Alliance.[4]

3.   The AstroGrid On-line Collaboration Tools

AstroGrid has deployed a set of ground-breaking collaboration tools which have enabled team members to share experiences, seek opinions and expert advice, and create an extensive library of documents pertaining to all aspects of the project. These tools, linked from http://www.astrogrid.org, are

- **News:** [http://news.astrogrid.org]— The news site is to announce issues of interest, including details of AstroGrid product releases.
- **Forum:** [http://forum.astrogrid.org] — The forum is an area where discussions related to the development of the project can be initiated.
- **Wiki:** [http://wiki.astrogrid.org] — The wiki is where all AstroGrid project documentation is not only stored but also developed. The wiki is an area where documents can be edited by public users, with version control enabling differences between versions to be tracked. The wiki has proved itself to be extremely useful in the development of the science and user requirements.

---

[4]http://www.ivoa.net

These collaborative and open sites have proved to be essential for enabling the operation of the distributed development teams that make up the personnel of the project.

4.   Capturing the Science Requirements

AstroGrid has generated and gathered key science cases. Because the consortium contains representatives involved in a wide range of UK astronomy, solar and STP research activity, a broad range of science cases stressing areas such as radio astronomy, solar physics and solar/terrestrial physics has resulted.

In the first instance a number of specific use cases were formulated. These were often concerned with how a part of science problem might be approached, for instance, running a query on a database to locate and show the positions of known QSO's. Other cases are aimed at easing the process of acquiring sufficient data to address a particular problem, e.g., returning the colours of galaxies and their bulges as a function of redshift to study alternative theories of galaxy evolution. The distinction between 'science cases' and more generic 'use cases' rapidly became apparent. Emphasis was placed on capturing and formalising the science cases.

4.1.   Scoping the AstroGrid Science Drivers

An extensive list of requirements, documented as science problems,[5] were gathered. This selection of science drivers will be continually expanded upon throughout the project lifetime. A formal and rigorous process was undertaken in order to select a well defined subset of science drivers, the AstroGrid 'Ten,' which would be used to shape the AstroGrid deliverables.

4.2.   The AstroGrid 'Top Ten' Science Drivers

The AstroGrid 'Ten' science cases have been selected as they demand the delivery of a set of capabilities that will be relevant to aiding scientific output in these topical science areas.

- Discovery of High Redshift Quasars (Astronomy: involves optical and near-IR data sets)
- Locating galaxy clusters at a range of redshifts. This will be linked to predictions from model data. (Astronomy: Models)
- Brown Dwarf selections (Astronomy: involves optical and near-IR data sets)
- Deep Field Surveys (Astronomy: involves linking radio with other data on deep fields such as the Hubble Deep Fields).
- Low Surface Brightness galaxy discovery (Astronomy: optical, near-IR, radio, X-ray)
- Supernova galaxy environments (Astronomy: Optical)
- Solar Stellar Flare Comparison (Astronomy, Solar: linking understanding of solar flares with those seen in stellar events)

---

[5]http://wiki.astrogrid.org/bin/view/VO/ScienceProblemList

- Solar Coronal Waves (Solar: unraveling this phenomenon)
- STP Solar Event Coincidence (STP and Solar: links solar data with STP data in understanding space weather)
- Magnetic storm onsets (STP: federation of in-situ and remote sensing data)

These science topics encompass a wide cross section of areas, and include drivers aiming to bridge subject area gaps. The capabilities demanded by these drivers are seen as being of use more generally in the support of other areas of astronomy. The ten key science problems have been selected to enable the project to be scoped to ensure that a Virtual Observatory capability is generated by the end of the AstroGrid Phase-B period (i.e., end 2004).

5. Architecture Development

For each science driver a typical flow of events was constructed, decomposing the tasks required to complete that process. Sequence Diagrams were thus generated for each of the science cases, and for the generic technical use cases (these covering activities such as negotiating access to jobs, login to the system, etc.). The sum of these tasks represents the components of the system that are required to form the AstroGrid Phase-B product, to be developed within the framework laid down by the project architecture. A complete review of the AstroGrid project is to be found in its Year 1 report.[6]

6. Concluding Remarks

AstroGrid will provide tools and capabilities to help the researcher in producing solutions to these science topics. AstroGrid will not in itself provide the answers, the astronomer will be presented with new capabilities to aid their research. This will be especially so in the areas of data discovery, transformation of data into information via access to processing facilities, and management of the processing flow of events. The researcher will be able to devote more time to the understanding of the astrophysics revealed by their results, more time can be given to the important step of transforming information into knowledge.

References

Hanisch, R. 2002, in Proc. 'Toward An International Virtual Observatory,' ESO Astrophysics Symposia, in press

Lawrence, A. 2002, in Proc. 'Toward An International Virtual Observatory,' ESO Astrophysics Symposia, in press

Quinn, P. J. 2002, in Proc. 'Toward An International Virtual Observatory,' ESO Astrophysics Symposia, in press

Rixon, G. T. & Walton, N. A. 2002, Proc SPIE 4846, in press

---

[6]http://wiki.astrogrid.org/bin/view/Astrogrid/PhaseAReport

Part 2. Virtual Observatory Interoperability

Astronomical Data Analysis Software and Systems XII
ASP Conference Series, Vol. 295, 2003
H. E. Payne, R. I. Jedrzejewski, and R. N. Hook, eds.

SkyQuery – A Prototype Distributed Query Web Service for the Virtual Observatory

Tamás Budavári, Tanu Malik, Alex Szalay, Ani Thakar

Dept. of Physics and Astronomy, The Johns Hopkins University, Baltimore, MD 21218

Jim Gray

Microsoft Bay Area Research Center, San Francisco, CA 94105

Abstract. We present SkyQuery[1], a distributed query system for astronomical catalogs. Using XML Web Services, SkyQuery federates databases at different locations and provides a programming and user interface to access catalog data as easily as if they were in a single database server. The data nodes, called SkyNodes, make their catalogs available by implementing a Web services interface. They may be written in any programming language and hosted on any platform, since the underlying technology is inherently interoperable. SkyQuery recursively performs an implicit probabilistic spatial join of the catalogs on the fly and returns the selected properties from the chosen surveys along with a best guess spatial position and the probability of the match being correct.

1. Introduction

One of the fundamental goals of the Virtual Observatory is to enable astronomical services to be used cooperatively to answer potentially very complex scientific questions. The idea is that these services would build on top of each other, similar to the packages in IRAF. The *core* services provide access to astronomical data and publish certain basic tools, while the *higher level* services would perform more sophisticated scientific analyzes relying on results from the core services. The hierarchy of services would provide a standard interface to all public astronomical resources.

XML Web Services is an industry standard (W3C) that perfectly suits the needs of the astronomical community. It is built on other standards such as XML, XSD, SOAP and WSDL, which guarantees interoperability between platforms and makes it independent from programming languages. Anyone can implement and consume Web Services using practically any computer and language. Currently there exist two fully functional development environments for Java and the .NET Framework that make programming Web Services very easy.

---

[1]http://www.SkyQuery.net/

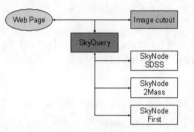

Figure 1.   The relation of the different web services in the SkyQuery application. The SkyQuery web service calls the SkyNode web services on the participating archives. The Image Cutout service provides an image display of the search area.

Here we describe a prototype distributed query system for the VO, a hierarchy of Web Services that federates astronomical databases possibly located all over the World.

2.   SkyQuery Architecture

SkyQuery is a network of Web Services. The Portal provides an entry point into the distributed query system relying on the metadata and query services of the database SkyNodes. The SkyNodes are the individual databases located at different sites along with their WS wrappers. At present, there are 3 SkyNodes linked into SkyQuery: (1) SDSS, (2) 2MASS and (3) FIRST. Having the SkyNodes registered in the Portal, the complexity of the network can be completely hidden from the user, see Figure 1. A sample user interface is implemented as a Web application on the project site that can submit queries, search the metadata and render the XML DataSet into an HTML table. The client web applications also uses the Sloan Digital Sky Survey's Image Cutout web service to display the composite color image of the sky specified in the query.

The primary entry point to SkyQuery is a Web method that accepts a request in an extended SQL format. The slightly modified syntax was required to specify the target archives and area on the sky and to parameterize the probabilistic cross-matching algorithm. Figure 2 shows a sample query.

3.   The SkyNode

The data nodes publish functionalities that are consumed programmatically by the portal. These methods provide access to the data and metadata of the archive. Anyone can publish her data through SkyQuery by implementing a few SOAP methods regardless of how the data are stored. In fact, the 3 methods below are currently the only requirements to register a SkyNode:

- Info(keyword) – Return basic facts, e.g., survey name, area coverage or astrometric precision in arcsecs
- Query(sqlcmd) – Search the catalog by executing the SQL command and return the results in an XML DataSet

```
SELECT o.objId, o.type, o.i, t.objId, t.j_m
  FROM SDSS:PhotoPrimary o, TWOMASS:PhotoPrimary t
  WHERE XMATCH(o,t)<3.5 AND AREA(181.3,-0.76,6.5)
      AND o.type=3 AND t.j_m>14 AND (o.i-t.j_m)<1
```

Figure 2. The query syntax for SkyQuery is similar to SQL. There are special target designators to specify the archive, and there are two special operators, **AREA** and **XMATCH**, used to constrain the search area and the search accuracy.

- **XMatch(xplan)** – Complex task to retrieve data from another SkyNode and cross-match with own data according to the execution plan

The first three SkyNodes were implemented in C#. The .NET Framework Class Library provides a great set of tools not just for developing Web Services but also to access the SQL Server 2000 database that we used at the back end. The cross-matching algorithm was developed entirely inside SQL server with user defined stored procedures. An HTM based spatial indexing supports the fast matching algorithm.

4. Data Flow

How does it really work? The Portal receives a request and parses the query. After locating the referenced SkyNodes, it submits a simple SQL query in parallel to every SkyNode using the **Query()** method to get an estimate for the number density of the objects satisfying the selection criteria. For example, the sample query in Figure 2 is looking for galaxies in the SDSS survey (o.type=3) matched with objects in the 2MASS that are fainter than 14th magnitude in the J band (t.j_m>14). Based on the results, the portal arranges the SkyNode into an execution plan so that running the distributed query would minimize the network traffic. The portal then just executes the plan by calling the **XMatch()** method of the first SkyNode in the "stack" and waits for the results to come back from the SkyNodes that can be just relayed back to the user.

The first SkyNode (**SkyNode 1** in Figure 3) looks at the plan and decides if it has the information to satisfy the request. If not, it then recursively calls the next SkyNode with a simpler execution plan and so on until the last node in the plan (**SkyNode 3**) will see a simple SQL query that it can run against the local database. These requests are done by passing only very light-weight objects on the wire but now real data start streaming from one SkyNode to another. Having received the data from the bottom data node, **SkyNode 2** can do its job: first it matches the catalogs using the astrometric precisions and probabilistic thresholds, then applies the selection criteria and returns the data back to one level up. All that is carried out within the database. Only the necessary parameters are propagated that were selected by the user or that are needed to perform the cross identification of the catalogs. The mixed constraints, e.g., (o.i-t.j_m)<1, are applied as soon as they can be evaluated. The result from the top level SkyNode is sent to the user.

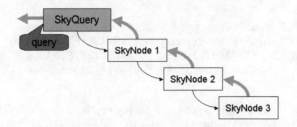

Figure 3.   SkyQuery runs the distribution query by creating an execution plan for the SkyNodes that call each other recursively to satisfy the selection criteria. The narrow lines represent the query requests and the wide lines represent the actual data flow.

For extra credit, the system can calculate the best positions of objects based on the positions measured by the individual surveys and it can also quote a probability on the match-up. The web application at the project site automatically adds the columns of these parameters to the result table.

5.   Summary and Future Works

The observations of large all-sky surveys are stored in separate databases and due to the rapidly changing technology these data sets cannot be built into a centralized system. SkyQuery can federate databases using XML Web Services. It can cross-match many catalogs on the fly using a probabilistic fuzzy join or it can look for drop-outs in certain catalogs. SkyQuery has proven that astronomical services may be adequately implemented as Web Services.

SkyQuery is a work in progress. The planned enhancements to the prototype demonstrated here include support for complex area specification and an advanced query language that is more flexible, e.g., allows local table joins. Next, survey footprint services will be added to the SkyNodes and the dynamical SkyNode registration to the Portal.

Additional SkyNodes will be added soon. A new SkyNode is on its way at the Institute of Astronomy in Cambridge, UK, to publish the Wide Field Survey catalog of the Isaac Newton Telescope.

Acknowledgments.   This work is supported partly by a NASA AISRP 2001 grant NRA-00-01-AISR-035.

References

Szalay, A. S., & Gray, J. 2001, Science, 293, 2037

Szalay, A. S. et al. 2002, Proc. of SPIE, 4846, in press

Kunszt, P. Z., Szalay, A. S., & Thakar, A. 2001, 'The Hierarchical Triangular Mesh' in Mining the Sky: Proc. of the MPA/ESO/MPE workshop, Garching, A. J. Banday, S. Zaroubi, M. Bartelmann (eds.), (Springer-Verlag Berlin Heidelberg), 631

Astronomical Data Analysis Software and Systems XII
ASP Conference Series, Vol. 295, 2003
H. E. Payne, R. I. Jedrzejewski, and R. N. Hook, eds.

Why Indexing the Sky is Desirable

Patricio F. Ortiz

AstroGrid, Department of Physics and Astronomy, University of Leicester, Leicester, LE1 7RH, UK

Abstract.
Indexing the sky is a database-oriented term to indicate a partitioning scheme of the celestial sphere in order to achieve better performance in queries involving finding close neighbours. Several schemes have been proposed: HTM, HEALPix, "IDT: iso-declination tiles", Quadrilateralized Spherical Cube, etc., but their use has not become widespread. The scientific value of the internal indexation files is much higher though, as they keep track of the source density of catalogues and hence allow us to answer a family of questions not easily handled by a standard DB system and providing an unusual visual aid: a snapshot of the location of sources listed in any catalog. The pros and cons of adopting an VO-oriented indexation scheme are analyzed.

1. Introduction

Dividing up the sky is an old practice useful for both locating and identifying objects. The problem imposed today by the large data volume is to have the capacity to quickly locate and compare objects found in the same region of the sky from two (or more) catalogues. Multi-wavelength and time series analysis need these features. Another important issue of today's data is to describe the sky coverage of a catalogue and use that information to speed up the cross correlation process.

From the database point of view, several schemes have been adopted to optimize cross-correlation, among them: Quadrilateralized Spherical Cube (White et al. 1992), Hierarchical Triangular Mesh (HTM) (Kunszt, P et al. 2001) and iso-declination tiles (IDT) (Ortiz & Ochsenbein 2001). Others such as HEALPix (Górski et al. 1998) were created to handle data covering the whole sky, e.g., the COBE mission. These methods split the sky in zones. At a database level, either a particular index may be associated to each object, or the sky zones are used to delimit internal database boundaries which are later used to speed up cross correlation (IDT). Description of the sky coverage, at a meta-data level, helps to speed up queries involving a large number of catalogues.

2. Reasons to use a Sky Indexation Scheme (SIS)

The main reasons presented in this paper are purely based on the handling of catalogues containing positional information. Regardless of the shape and size

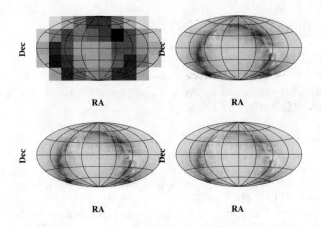

Figure 1.   Star distribution in the Tycho catalogue. Clockwise from top left: 10×5 "zones", 100×50 "zones", 200×100 "zones", and 600×300 "zones"

of the zones in which the sky is partitioned, it is always possible to determine the number of elements which belong to each "tile" (**sky density**), all the above mentioned methods try to split the sky uniformly. How this information is used is the key issue. Figure 1 illustrates the point using different resolutions for the source distribution of the Tycho catalogue.

2.1.   Meta-data

A direct application would be to use the sky density as a method of determining whether, within a list of catalogues, certain areas of the sky contain sources or not, that is, a sort of meta-data which would not require the examination of whole catalogues. Its main application would be to quickly rule out catalogues which have no common areas with a list of targets either taken from an existing catalogue or user generated. At $30'$ resolution ~ 160000 tiles are needed, but it would be enough to have a 1 or 0 in each tile to accomplish the task, reducing the size of the mask to ~ 20Kb which could be compared in $< 0.1s$ without having to "activate" databases unnecessarily. This application of an SIS may be extremely useful in the VO era, as there is no simple way to represent the sky coverage of any catalogue and this method could contribute a uniform representation of the sky and a way to optimize the usage of resources. An interesting application is to query sites with pointed observation data (observing logs) to discover if any of the targets in a list has been observed. Regardless of the size of the list a sky-mask comparison can be faster and preselect the catalogues to be cross correlated.

2.2. Visualisation

A by-product of an SIS is to offer human users a snapshot of the sky coverage of a catalogue by providing a simple image such as the ones shown in Figure 1). Blind usage of VO facilities is a real risk, particularly when statistical algorithms will be implemented in the future; if any assumption of uniform coverage, unbiased observations, or homogeneity is not fulfilled by the catalogues used, the results of applying those methods will be meaningless.

2.3. Database Performance

An SIS should improve the performance of a cross correlation as one is assured that the search for matches is only carried out over the appropriate areas of the sky. If the DBMS allows it, the data could be arranged according to the indexation, which would also improve the I/O performance. For example, using IDT in datoz2k (Ortiz 2002) a cross correlation of Tycho-2 (2.53 million objects) within a radius of 35″ takes 5.5 seconds on a 1.7GHz PC running Linux. Another approach is to add an extra column with a tile-ID: *PCODE* (Page 2002), index the DB on this number, and then perform a match on PCODE, which translates into a great gain over using indexation on declination only. Although they are used internally, SISs are also used across all data centres to improve their response.

2.4. Scientific Usage

There are a number of scientific questions which are very difficult to address if sky-density tools are not operational. All of them deal with the fact it is possible to select areas of the sky where the density satisfies certain criteria. The following list is by no means complete:

At a one catalogue level:

(**1**) Select zones and/or objects located in areas where the density satisfies certain conditions. An example would be areas where the QSO density is high enough for them to be used as astrometric calibrators.

(**2**) Locate areas which represent a local enhancement or depletion of objects. An example might be the location of very frequently observed zones of the sky in an observing log suitable for use in variability studies. We could impose absolute density criteria, but enhancements are often adequate.

(**3**) Compute the sky density for a given type of object in a catalogue and select the areas according to this newly computed density. Example 1: from a wide field image catalogue, select all the galaxies with B−V > 1.5 and look for density enhancements. Example 2: Locate the areas most frequently observed with an instrument in which the seeing is < 1″ and the moon is below the horizon during the observation to produce very long exposures or perform time variation studies.

When two or more catalogues are involved:

(**4**) Determine the intersecting areas between two catalogues. Example: determine which areas observed with HST have objective-prism data (images from the HST observing log vs the observing log of one or more objective-prism surveys).

(5) Find the sky areas with highest density from the combination of data in several catalogues. Example: find the most observed areas in Radio, Optical and X-ray located within 20° of the galactic plane; several catalogues from optical, radio and X-ray could be needed and finding local maxima in the resulting combination does the trick.

Due to intrinsic physical properties and the nature of our accumulated observations the tasks described above are nearly all means to discover areas of interest, either to start collecting data from an archive or to decide where to point the telescope next. However, not having this information nor the tools to explore the data space in this way would prevent astronomers from finding rich areas in which to dig.

3. Conclusions

A sky-indexation scheme provides one of the simplest ways to represent the sky coverage of a catalogue. Using an SIS will give users the chance to select areas of the sky according to their own criteria, a functionality of high scientific interest not provided by today's commercial DBMS, enriching the services provided by any data centre.

The existence of sky coverage masks for each catalogue in a data centre can make answering data-mining questions much faster by reducing the number of catalogues against which to cross correlate; a minimal time is required to know if a catalogue has any chance to have matches with a target list.

The adoption of one or more standard SISs (resolution, method, etc.) by the community, in particular in the context of VO, would provide a means of exchanging information about the properties of a catalogue at a much faster pace, particularly in the case of very large catalogues. This would be a way to include the sky coverage as part of the meta-data.

References

Górski, K. M., Hivon, E., Wandelt, B. D. 1998, in Proceedings of the MPA/ESO Cosmology Conference Evolution of Large-Scale Structure, eds. A.J. Banday, R.S. Sheth and L. Da Costa.

Kunszt, P., Szalay, A. S., Thakar, A. R. 2000, in Mining the Sky, Proceedings of the MPA/ESO/MPE Workshop, edited by A. J. Banday, S. Zaroubi, and M. Bartelmann, Heidelberg: Springer-Verlag, 631

Ortiz, P. F., Ochsenbein, F. 2001, in Mining the Sky, Proceedings of the MPA/ESO/MPE Workshop, edited by A. J. Banday, S. Zaroubi, and M. Bartelmann, Heidelberg: Springer-Verlag, 677

Ortiz, P. F. 2003, in Proceedings of "Toward an International Virtual Observatory", (http://www.eso.org/gen-fac/meetings/vo2002/), in press

Page, C. 2003, this volume, 39

White, R. A., Stemwedel, S. W. 1992, in ASP Conf. Ser., Vol. 25, Astronomical Data Analysis Software and Systems I, ed. D. M. Worrall, C. Biemesderfer, & J. Barnes (San Francisco: ASP), 379

Astronomical Data Analysis Software and Systems XII
ASP Conference Series, Vol. 295, 2003
H. E. Payne, R. I. Jedrzejewski, and R. N. Hook, eds.

A New Way of Joining Source Catalogs using a Relational Database Management System

Clive G. Page

*AstroGrid Project, Department of Physics & Astronomy,
University of Leicester, U.K.*

Abstract. New science often arises from joining source catalogs obtained from different wavebands, but efficient methods for performing such joins depend on multi-dimensional indexing and are poorly handled by most DBMS. A new algorithm, the PCODE, is proposed which allows any relational DBMS to carry out this operation efficiently.

1. The Fuzzy Join Problem

New science often arises from investigations based on the cross-identification of sources in different wavebands. Since source catalogs are often stored as tables in a relational database management system (DBMS), in theory this just requires a suitable JOIN between tables, based on source position. Even if positions alone do not produce unique associations, so that additional criteria are needed, positional coincidence is still the primary key for such joins. In many cases the absence of a counterpart in another band will be scientifically interesting: any unmatched sources can be found using an OUTER JOIN. So much for theory: the practice is more complicated.

- A two-dimensional index is needed to handle the (RA, Dec) coordinate pair, but only a few DBMS support multi-dimensional indexing, and for some of these it is an expensive add-on.
- The join also needs a range search rather than an exact match, since positions always have errors. Typically the errors in RA and Dec are similar, so that the error region is a small circle on the sky.
- This type of positional match has come to be called a *fuzzy join*, since the matching criterion is the overlap of the two error-circles, and the distances need to use a great-circle distance function.
- Indices developed for a Cartesian grid need to be modified when applied to a spherical-polar coordinate frame as the scales are distorted, with singularities at the poles (and wrap-around on the RA axis).

Because of these difficulties, many existing data archives index their catalogs on only one spatial coordinate (usually declination); this is adequate for single object searches, but is neither efficient nor scalable for large-scale joins, because the one-dimensional index is selecting a slice all around the celestial sphere, much larger than the region actually required. And every year catalogs get bigger: the recently announced USNO-B1.0 (Monet & Levine, this conference) has over 10^9 rows and several others are nearly as large.

2.   Multi-dimension Indexing

Multi-dimensional indexing has been a hot topic of computer science research for many years, and many different algorithms have been proposed. The names include: BANG file, BV-tree, Buddy tree, Cell tree, G-tree, GBD-tree, Gridfile, hB-tree, kd-tree, LSD-tree, P-tree, PK-tree, PLOP hashing, Pyramid tree, Q-tree, Quadtree, R-tree, SKD-tree, SR-tree, SS-tree, TV-tree, UB-tree, and Z-order index.

Whereas the B-tree has become the standard one-dimensional indexing method used in every DBMS, none of the multi-dimensional indices has comparable properties such as fast insertion and retrieval, and a worst-case fill-factor of 50%. The problem is, of course, fundamentally intractable, since one cannot serialise the points on a two-dimensional surface. One of the earliest algorithms, the R-tree (Guttman 1984), has been implemented in a few DBMS, including one of the Open Source products: PostgreSQL. But the R-tree has some limitations for source catalogs:

- R-trees index rectangular areas: since some sources within the rectangle will be outside the enclosed error-circle, these have to be removed in a subsequent filtering stage.
- The width of the boxes gets large close to the poles, eventually spanning the whole range of RA.
- The R-tree stores four coordinates per point so it uses much more disc space than a B-tree.
- The wrap-around of RA at zero hours needs special tests in the code.

Kalpakis et al (2001) used Informix, which also supports R-trees, to index large catalogs, but found that the data loading and index creation times were substantial: they estimated it would take 25 days to create an index for the whole USNO-A1.0 catalog.

3.   PCODE Method

An alternative algorithm, proposed here, is based on covering the sky with pixels of approximately equal area, and assigning a unique integer to each pixel. A number of suitable pixelisation schemes have been proposed, the best known being: HTM, the Hierarchical Triangular Mesh, (Kunszt et al. 2000), and HEALPix, the Hierarchical Equal Area iso-Latitude Pixelisation, (Górski et al. 1998). Both pixelisations are suitable for generating PCODE values, and both have selectable resolution.

For each table, the pixel code value corresponding to the central position (RA, Dec) of each source is computed and inserted into a new column called PCODE. A B-tree index is then created on the PCODE column. This cannot be the primary index of a table since PCODE values are not necessarily unique: one pixel may contain more than one source. The two tables can then be joined on their PCODE columns: this is simply an equi-join between integers, which all DBMS handle efficiently. Note that HTM, and one of the two numbering schemes for HEALPix, are designed to assign nearby numbers to adjacent pixels as far as possible, but this property is not used here; indeed indexing schemes based on this, such as the Z-order index, have serious failings.

There are a number of obvious problems with the simple method outlined above, but they can be solved:

1. Two objects may be in the same pixel but do not have overlapping error-circles.
   Solution: filter the results with an additional pass using a great-circle distance function (just as when an R-tree is used).
2. Two sources may have overlapping error circles but centers in different pixels.
   Solution: insert an additional row in the table whenever an error-circle overlaps an additional pixel (this extra row has all the attributes of the original, except for the PCODE value).
3. If two sources both extend into the same two pixels then the product of the join will itself contain this match in duplicate.
   Solution: in the post-filtration stage weed out these duplicates using a DISTINCT clause in the SQL. In many cases the tables will already contain a unique identifier, otherwise an addition column with a unique integer sequence number needs to be added.

A single SQL statement can be devised to do all these filtering stages, but the margin is too small to contain it.

4. R-tree versus PCODE

In theory a B-tree index built on PCODEs should be more efficient than an R-tree, and this was confirmed in practice. We took subsets of the HST Guide Star Catalog and the USNO-A1 Catalog corresponding to an area of around 400 square degrees. This produced tables of 275,154 rows and 3,476,948 rows respectively. The HEALPix pixelisation scheme was used, with $N_{side} = 8192$ giving 805,306,368 pixels, each $\sim$26 arc-seconds across, and required only 32-bit PCODE values. The tests used PostgreSQL v7.2.1, since it supports R-trees, and were run on a 450 MHz PC running Linux.

Algorithm	Table size (MB)	Index size (MB)	Index Creation (secs)	Fuzzy Join (secs)
Native R-tree	496	248	6408	347
PCODE and B-tree	293	64	233	143

Not only is the PCODE method faster and smaller, it can also be used with *any* relational database management system, not just the few which support a spatial index.

5. Scalability of PCODE

In order to ensure that only a small proportion of additional rows are needed, one must choose a pixel size larger than the typical error-circle radius. Actually it is a rule of thumb in sky surveys that detections should be limited to the level at which there is no more than one source per 40 beam-areas, otherwise confusion effects dominate. It should, therefore, always be possible to find a pixel resolution which is fine enough to leave fewer than one object per pixel on average, while coarse enough to have relatively few error-circles crossing a pixel boundary. Of course there will always be a few source postions which lie close to the point at which 4 HEALPix pixels (or 6 HTM pixels) touch. Efficiency may be lower when dealing with surveys where the density of sources is very uneven, with many pixels empty, but some holding large numbers of sources (e.g., in the Galactic Plane). The PCODE method is also less suitable if a wide-area of the sky is of interest, e.g., when making a finding-chart.

A difficulty may still arise when joining two tables with very different resolutions, such as an X-ray catalog from the era preceding XMM-Newton and Chandra, and a modern optical catalog. In practice the problem is less serious, as a catalog with large error regions is, intrinsically, one with fewer sources in it, so the absolute number of extra rows needed is tolerable. In fact the 26 arcsecond pixels we used in our tests turn out to be a good match to most current catalogs.

There is also a potential scalability limitation from the need to use SELECT DISTINCT on the output of the join, since this implies that the results of the join are sorted. This takes a time proportional to $n.log(n)$, where n is the number of rows in the *output* table.

The HTM pixelisation has a useful property which promises additional scalability: the algorithm is recursive so that four pixels at each resolution stage fit exactly in one pixel from the next coarser resolution, and the pixel codes just add extra bits. Hence if a fine mesh is established using a PCODE-equipped table based on the HTM pixelisaton, it can be converted to any required coarser resolution, e.g., for joining with a low-resolution source catalog, just by ignoring pairs of bits at the least-significant end of the integer.

This suggests that all source catalogs could have PCODE values attached, based on HTM at some a suitably high resolution, in order to make a wide range of joins (and cone-searches) efficient. At lower resolution many of the added rows become superfluous but a SELECT DISTINCT will remove them too.

References

Górski, K. M., Hivon, E., & Wandelt, B. D. 1998, in Proc MPA/ESO Cosmology Conference on Evolution of Large-scale Structure

Guttman, A. 1984, in Proc. ACM SIGMOD Int. Conf. on Management of Data, 47

Kalpakis, K., Riggs, M., Pasad, M., Puttagunta, V., & Behnke, J. 2001, in ASP Conf. Ser., Vol. 238, Astronomical Data Analysis Software and Systems X, ed. F. R. Harnden, Jr., F. A. Primini, & H. E. Payne (San Francisco: ASP), 133

Kunszt, P. Z., Szalay, A. S., Csabai, I., & Thakar, A. R. 2000, in ASP Conf. Ser., Vol. 216, Astronomical Data Analysis Software and Systems IX, ed. N. Manset, C. Veillet, & D. Crabtree (San Francisco: ASP), 141

Astronomical Data Analysis Software and Systems XII
ASP Conference Series, Vol. 295, 2003
H. E. Payne, R. I. Jedrzejewski, and R. N. Hook, eds.

A Bit of GLUe for the VO: Aladin Experience

Pierre Fernique, André Schaaff, François Bonnarel, Thomas Boch

Centre de Données astronomiques de Strasbourg, Observatoire de Strasbourg, UMR 7550, 11 rue de l'Université, 67000 Strasbourg, France

Abstract. In this article we describe how the GLU system (Uniform Link Generator) allows the Aladin browsing tool to integrate several image and data servers through a single interface. We describe how it works, how it is updated and how it is implemented in a Java context. We also present the future evolution we foresee for the GLU system in order to allow interaction with the emerging Web Services.

1. Interoperability Needs

Aladin is now widely known as a tool to display and cross-match heterogeneous data and images anticipating future VO portals. It offers transparent access to Simbad, VizieR, CDS image servers (DSS, MAMA, 2MASS), NED, SkyView and SuperCosmos databases, NVSS and FIRST archives, as well as mission logs such as CFHT, Chandra, HST, HUT, ISO, IUE and Merlin.

Like any interoperability tool, Aladin needs to answer the following questions:

1. How to access the data servers? What is the syntax of the query?
2. How to dynamically build interfaces to the data servers?
3. How to manipulate the server results? Which syntax/standard is used?
4. How to update the information required by the previous questions? Who has to do that?

Aladin makes use of the GLU system to answer these questions.

2. GLU Functionalities

The GLU system is a distributed repository of Web server descriptions. It was designed and written in 1996 by the Centre de Données astronomiques de Strasbourg (CDS). Presently, the GLU manages thirty replicated sites all over the world and about five hundred Web resource descriptions.

A GLU resource description, also called a GLU record, typically contains a unique identifier for the resource, a short description, a URL template to query the resource, and additional information describing the data type of the query parameters. The latter may include celestial coordinates, astronomical objects designations, bibliographic codes and so forth. The format of the results, VOTable, FITS image, HTML pages etc must also be included.

```
<RESOURCE ID="CDS/aladin/SSS.img">
   <DESCRIPTION>SuperCOSMOS image server- Edinburgh (UK)</DESCRIPTION>
   <QUERY>
      <URL>http://www-wfau.roe.ac.uk/~sss/cgi-bin/sss_aladin_pix.cgi?
      ra=$1&dec=$2&mime-type=image/x-gfits&
      x=$3&y=$4&waveband=$5</URL>
      <VAR NAME="1">
         <DESCRIPTION>Right Ascension (J2000)</DESCRIPTION>
         <TYPE REF="Coo(J2000,RA)"/>
      </VAR>
      <VAR NAME="2">
         <DESCRIPTION>Declination (J2000)</DESCRIPTION>
         <TYPE REF="Coo(J2000,DE)"/>
      </VAR>
      <VAR NAME="3">
         <DESCRIPTION>Width (arcmin)</DESCRIPTION>
         <TYPE REF="Field(RAm)"/>
         <VALUE DEFAULT="true">10</VALUE>
      </VAR>
      <VAR NAME="4">
         <DESCRIPTION>Height (arcmin)</DESCRIPTION>
         <TYPE REF="Field(DEm)"/>
         <VALUE DEFAULT="true">10</VALUE>
      </VAR>
      <VAR NAME="5">
         <DESCRIPTION>Waveband</DESCRIPTION>
         <VALUE DEFAULT="true">1 - UKST Blue (Bj)</VALUE>
         <VALUE>2 - UKST Red (R)</VALUE>
         <VALUE>3 - UKST Infrared (I)</VALUE>
         <VALUE>4 - ESO red (R)</VALUE>
         <VALUE>5 - POSS-I red (R)</VALUE>
      </VAR>
   </QUERY>
   <RESULT><CONTENT-TYPE>image/gfits</CONTENT-TYPE></RESULT>
   <DOC ROLE="user" HREF="http://www-wfau.roe.ac.uk/sss/"/>
</RESOURCE>
```

Figure 1.   Example GLU record for the SuperCosmos resource.

The GLU is distributed with a library toolkit in C and Perl to access the repository *(gludic tool)* and to generate the URL corresponding to a Web resource *(glufilter tool)*. In this latter task, the GLU not only maps the query parameters passed by the user into the correct fields of the query URL template, but the GLU is also able to make the appropriate transformations to adapt the query parameters to the format and parameter types required by the remote server. For example, astronomical object identifiers are converted into their celestial coordinates, or the coordinates can be precessed and/or edited according to the server's requirements.

Furthermore the GLU has advanced functionalities such as:

- Mirror site management;
- Control of the GLU record distribution to any subset of the existing GLU domains (partial distributions);
- Remote access to the GLU functions via HTTP on each GLU site.

3.　Aladin/GLU Algorithm

To understand how Aladin and GLU interact, we describe step by step the Aladin/GLU algorithm:

1. When it is launched, Aladin looks for the nearest GLU sites, either a local implementation (access by local GLU toolkit) or a remote implementation (access by CGI) depending on the user configuration and on the Java mode — Aladin may run as a Java standalone application, or as a Java applet;
2. Once the GLU site is located, Aladin asks for all the GLU records published in a particular GLU domain named ALADIN;
3. With these GLU records, Aladin dynamically builds the server access forms, using the description of each required parameter, their default values, the data type assigned to each of them and so on;
4. All server accesses are subsequently done by a GLU call (locally or remotely) which generates the appropriate URL which implies: locate the nearest mirror site, map the parameters according to the URL template, convert the parameters if necessary, generate proxy queries if Aladin is run in applet mode.

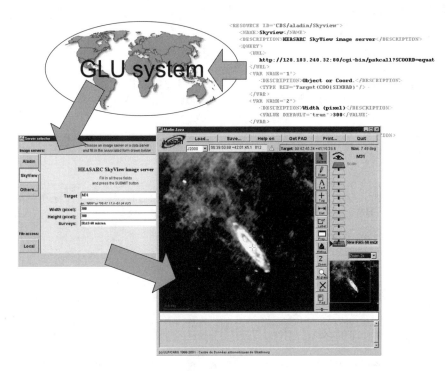

Figure 2.　　GLU/Aladin interactions

4.   GLU and Web Services

With SOAP, WSDL and UDDI, the new Web Services will offer an alternative
to describe and access Web resources. With these new standards we anticipate
that servers will provide one or more SOAP options within the next two years
in addition to the classical HTTP access.

In this context, we have planned to extend the next GLU release in three
directions:

- The GLU will be able to distribute WSDL descriptions in order to offer an
  alternative to the UDDI mechanism for which the future seems uncertain;
- Each GLU site will install SOAP server methods in parallel to the classical
  CGI access, allowing GLU users to consult and use the GLU repository
  via SOAP Web services;
- Each GLU site will be able to query the Web server via SOAP and then
  translate the result into a classical plain ascii text stream — in other
  words, each GLU site would play the role of a gateway between the SOAP
  world and the basic HTTP world. This new functionality will allow VO
  clients such as Aladin to access SOAP servers right away without having
  to modify their code [1].

References

Bonnarel, B. et al. 2001, in ASP Conf. Ser., Vol. 238, Astronomical Data Analysis
     Software and Systems X, ed. F. R. Harnden, Jr., F. A. Primini, & H. E.
     Payne (San Francisco: ASP), 74

Ochsenbein, F. et al. 2000, in ASP Conf. Ser., Vol. 216, Astronomical Data Anal-
     ysis Software and Systems IX, ed. N. Manset, C. Veillet, & D. Crabtree
     (San Francisco: ASP), 830

Wenger, W. et al. 2000, A&AS, 143, 9

Bonnarel, B. et al. 2000, A&AS, 143, 33

Ochsenbein, F. et al. 2000, A&AS, 143, 230

Fernique, P. Ochsenbein, F. Wenger, M. 1998, in ASP Conf. Ser., Vol. 145,
     Astronomical Data Analysis Software and Systems VII, ed. R. Albrecht,
     R. N. Hook, & H. A. Bushouse (San Francisco: ASP), 466

---

[1] In order to create a new client to a SOAP service three steps are required: 1) retrieve the
associated WSDL description; 2) generate the corresponding source code; 3) compile and plug
it. These tasks can easily be done using a development environment such as AXIS or Visual
Studio; in the context of a generic interoperability tool such Aladin, it is difficult to do it
dynamically, especially in applet mode.

Astronomical Data Analysis Software and Systems XII
ASP Conference Series, Vol. 295, 2003
H. E. Payne, R. I. Jedrzejewski, and R. N. Hook, eds.

Interoperability of ESA Science Archives

Christophe Arviset, John Dowson, José Hernández, Pedro Osuna and
Aurèle Venet

*ESA, Research and Scientific Support Department, Science Operations
and Data Systems Division, Villafranca del Castillo, P.O. Box 50727,
28080 Madrid, Spain*

Abstract. The ISO Data Archive (IDA) and the XMM-Newton Science
Archive (XSA) have been developed by the Science Operations and Data
Systems Division of ESA in Villafranca, Spain. They are both built
using the same flexible and modular 3-tier architecture: Data Products
and Database, Business Logic, User Interface. This open architecture,
together with Java and XML technology have helped in making the IDA
and XSA inter-operable with other archives and applications. The various
accesses from the IDA and the XSA to remote archives are described as
well as the mechanism to directly access these ESA archives from remote
archives

1. Open and Flexible 3-Tier Architecture

The IDA and the XSA were both built—by a common team—using the open
3-tier architecture described in Figure 1. The main goal of this architecture is
to separate the data from the presentation, which allows a more modular and
flexible development.

As the data volume is not that big, data are saved on magnetic disks for
fast access as a normal UNIX file system. From the data products, metadata is
extracted and put in a Relational Data Base, SYBASE. Note that the data ingestion from the data producer and the metadata extraction are separate processes
to allow new metadata data extraction when user requirements evolve.

The middle tier, also called the Business Logic, provides transparent access
to the data products and to the metadata. This key layer has been developed
in Java and XML and resides on the archive server.

On the client side, several types of applications can be found. The standard
IDA and XSA User Interface is a Java applet downloaded by the end user to
access the archive content.

Remote applications and other archives can also have access to the data
and the metadata, bypassing the standard User Interface, by speaking to the
Business Logic that will provide them with the required services via Java Server
Pages.

This architecture is especially powerful in the context of the worldwide
Virtual Observatory initiatives where archives will all have to interoperate in a
manner transparent to the end user.

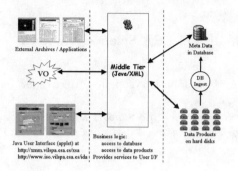

Figure 1.   Open 3-tier Architecture

2.   From ESA Archives to External Archives

2.1.   Name Resolution with NED or SIMBAD

On the IDA or XSA Query Panel, one can query against a target name (see Figure 2). By entering a target name and choosing the name resolver (NED or SIMBAD), the IDA or XSA will make contact with the IPAC or CDS server to resolve the target name into coordinates and then search the ISO observations catalog against these coordinates. This is done completely transparently to the user.

For SIMBAD and NED, the target name is resolved into coordinates, calling the CDS server at Strasbourg, France or the NED one at IPAC, USA respectively via a specific TCP/IP socket.

2.2.   Access to Electronic Articles

From the IDA or XSA Latest Results Panel, the button "Articles" indicates if there are known publications linked to the observation (see Figure 2). By clicking on the button, one gets an extra window showing the Title, Authors, Journal, etc. By clicking the "Abstract" button, the applet will launch a browser window with the ADS WWW mirror at Strasbourg, France with the abstract of the article associated with the selected observation. The call is made through a standard URL/cgi-bin script as defined by the ADS interface.

2.3.   Access to IRAS Data

From the IDA Latest Results Panel, one can see the small icons giving a quick overview of what the observations are about. By clicking on one of them, a bigger window is launched with the postcard giving more information on the ISO observation (see Figure 2). By clicking the button "Access to IRAS", a browser window will open, from the InfraRed Science Archive (IRSA) webpage located at IPAC, USA. The window will contain the data covering the region of the sky of the selected ISO observation. The call is made through a standard URL/cgi-bin script as defined by the IRSA interface.

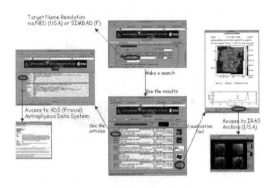

Figure 2.   Access from IDA to External Archives.

3.   From External Archives to ESA Archives

3.1.   General Concepts

ISO and XMM-Newton products can also be obtained directly from external archives or applications, bypassing the standard user interface. That allows such data to be available from other well established archives where multi-missions data can be found.

Such access can be achieved in 3 steps:

- delivery of the archive observation/exposure log to the remote archive;
- integration of this log into the remote archive;
- linking from the remote archive to the *Postcard Server* and/or to the *Product Server*.

3.2.   The Observation/Exposure Log

The Observation log consists of a file (generally ASCII) containing the list of ISO or XMM-Newton observations with associated parameters (observation id, PI name, coordinates, time, quality flag, release date...). In the case of XMM-Newton, each observation contains several instrument exposures with relevant specific parameters.

According to the requirements of the remote archive, the log can contain more or fewer parameters depending on the intended use.

The standard format is ASCII (fixed width, tab or character separated). This log is just a view of the content of the IDA or XSA database and can be easily exported into other formats such as XML, HTML, VOTable, etc... that will make it easier to ingest in remote archive databases.

The delivery can be via FTP, http or electronic mail.

3.3.   ISO and XMM-Newton Postcard Server

Through calling a URL/Java Server Page (JSP) containing the ISO or XMM-Newton observation identifier, the Postcard Server (see Figure 3) returns the ISO

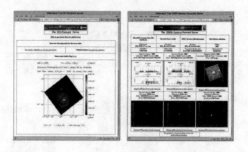

Figure 3.   ISO and XMM-Newton Postcard Servers.

or XMM-Newton postcard (GIF or PNG image) of this observation and ancillary quality information embedded into an HTML page. Within this HTML page, links to relevant documentation as well as the data quality flag can be found.

This service is available for ISO in CDS, IRSA, ADS and HEASARC and should soon be available for XMM-Newton from in CDS, ADS and HEASARC.

3.4.   ISO and XMM-Newton Product Server

The Product Server uses similar concepts to the Postcard Server. The URL/JSP returns an HTML page which automatically initiates an FTP session for downloading the data products.

Both ISO and XMM-Newton Product Servers are now available and can be accessed directly or from the corresponding Postcard Server.

4.   Conclusions

The ESA science archives, in particular the ISO Data Archive and the XMM-Newton Science Archive are based on an open 3-tier architecture which allows easy interoperability with other archives or applications. This will ensure their easy and fast integration in the VO architecture.

The inter-operable mechanisms already in place are flexible, fast, direct and secure both from the ESA archives to external archives and in the other direction.

Currently, dedicated interfaces have been defined with the remote archives inter-operating with the IDA and the XSA. But having common standards, such as XML and VOTables, would help integration of services in the context of the VO.

References

Hernandez, J. 2003, this volume, 275

Astronomical Data Analysis Software and Systems XII
ASP Conference Series, Vol. 295, 2003
H. E. Payne, R. I. Jedrzejewski, and R. N. Hook, eds.

Federating Catalogs and Interfacing Them with Archives: A VO Prototype

Douglas J. Mink, Michael J. Kurtz

Smithsonian Astrophysical Observatory

Abstract. A common scientific requirement is to perform a joint query on two or more remote catalogs, then use the resulting combined catalog as input to query an archive or catalog. We have developed techniques which enable the routine federation of several of the largest astrometric and photometric catalogs from either in-house or remote copies, and use this federated output to query the several archives of spectral and imaging data which we either manage or maintain local copies of.

Allowing the federation of arbitrary sections of large catalogs, with user defined match criteria; and then allowing this result to be used to query several large archives of spectral and imaging data (also subject to user constraints) is a key goal of all VO projects. The problems we have solved in developing our methods will also have to be addressed by any VO project which delivers similar capabilities.

1. Federating Astronomical Catalogs

Catalogs are flat databases keyed on object positions, including other information such as magnitude or flux, spectral type, epoch, redshift, etc. Combining information from different catalogs requires knowledge about the parameters of each catalog. The VOTable standard will eventually be able to describe the contents of a catalog, but for now, since astronomers actually use relatively few large catalogs, this information can be built into software.

Iterated searching can be done through a command line catalog portal, WCSTools' **scat** (Mink 2002), which was written to access the largest astrometric and photometric catalogs, such as the HST Guide Star Catalog and the USNO-A2.0 Catalog. Originally it worked only from in-house copies of catalogs, but over the past two years, the ability to use remote copies accessed over the Internet using the HTTP protocol has been added. **scat** can be used on either end of such a connection as it understands HTTP queries and can return search results as the same tab-separates files it expects to receive over the net.

Input search lists can also be submitted as tab-separated tables, so queries can be chained. **scat** output can be formatted so that the output "catalog" includes information from both the search list and the searched catalog in each entry.

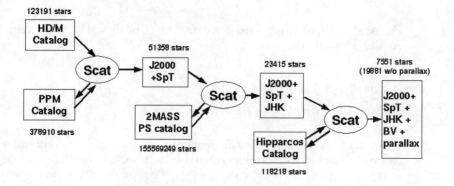

Figure 1.   Matching the HD/Houk catalog (spectral class) with PPM, Hipparcos, and 2MASS catalogs gives current positions, parallax, and V and K magnitudes.

2.   Combining Spectral Classes and Infrared Colors

The best star catalog for spectral types and classes is the Henry Draper catalog as updated by Houk et al. (1975-1999), but the original HD B1900 positions are kept, and the best photometric catalogs, such as the 2MASS PSC, the GSC II, and the USNO-A2.0 are in J2000 coordinates. WCSTools **scat** can convert between coordinate systems, epochs, and equinoxes, producing a final catalog with visible and IR magnitudes and spectral types. Figure 1 shows how **scat** was used iteratively by searching the PPM catalog to get 2000 positions, the 2MASS Point Source Catalog to get JHK infrared magnitudes, and the Hipparcos Catalog (ESA 1997) to get distance and V magnitudes. Figure 2 shows where stars of luminosity class V show up among the stars in the merged catalog.

3.   Serving the SAO Spectral Archives

Archive access can be implemented as a web service using legacy software and providing catalog cross-references After archiving uniformly processed spectra taken on our ground-based telescopes for over 20 years, SAO now has over 215,000 high dispersion and 110,000 low dispersion spectra archived. The Smithsonian Institution is chartered to promote the "increase and diffusion of knowledge," and that has been interpreted to mean that our data should be made as public as possible. 35,000 public spectra from two instruments are currently online, covering many interesting objects in the northern sky, and more are coming. Figure 3 shows how a user interface to the Updated Zwicky Catalog (Falco et al. 1999) archive allows searching a catalog of spectra (using the ubiquitous **scat** program through a Perl script). Once the desired spectra are located, selected spectra can be displayed and downloaded as either FITS or ASCII files.

The Virtual Observatory has been looked at as a hierarchy, with archives at the bottom and portals at the top, but that is only one way to view it. Archives can link to each other and back to the portals as well as acting as browsers into

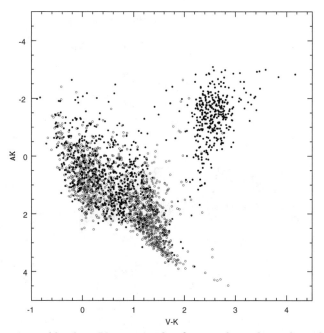

Figure 2.   Absolute K magnitude of merged catalogs plotted against (V-K) color. Circles are luminosity class V stars; filled dots are other classes.

their own data. Our spectral portal uses SIMBAD and NED to resolve named astronomical objects into coordinates, and they in turn each link from their entries for the Updated Zwicky Catalog to our spectral archive. Our displays for individual spectra act as single object portals into the virtual observatory, with links back to NED and SIMBAD, as well as the Digitized Sky Survey, and other spectra in our archives.

4.   Conclusions

Allowing input and output catalogs to be identically formatted makes merging and comparison easy. Archives should have user-friendly interfaces for browsing their data, and catalog-centric methods work well. The Virtual Observatory is a web of information; connections to and from existing portals are important. Access to the entire WCSTools package is at

    http://tdc-www.harvard.edu/software/wcstools/.

Acknowledgments.   This publication makes use of data products from the Two Micron All Sky Survey, which is a joint project of the University of Massachusetts and the Infrared Processing and Analysis Center/California Institute of Technology, funded by the National Aeronautics and Space Administration and the National Science Foundation.

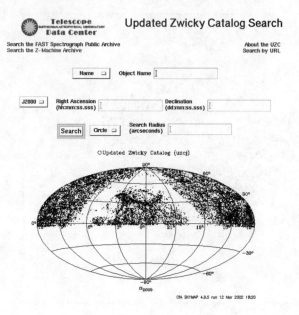

Figure 3.   User interface to the Updated Zwicky Catalog spectra.

References

European Space Agency 1997, The Hipparcos and Tycho Catalogues, ESA SP-1200

Falco, E. E., Kurtz, M. J., Geller, M. J., Huchra, J. P., Peters, J., Berlind, P., Mink, D. J., Tokarz, S. P., Elwell, B. 1999, PASP, 111, 438

Houk, N. & Cowley, A. P. 1975, Michigan Catalogue of two-dimensional spectral types for the HD stars, Ann Arbor: Dept. of Astronomy, Univ. Michigan

Houk, N. 1978, Michigan Catalogue of two-dimensional spectral types for the HD stars, Vol. 2, Ann Arbor: Dept. of Astronomy, Univ. Michigan

Houk, N. 1982, Catalogue of two-dimensional spectral types for the HD stars, Vol. 3, Michigan Spectral Survey, Ann Arbor: Dept. of Astronomy, Univ. Michigan

Houk, N. & Smith-Moore, M. 1988, Michigan catalogue of Two-Dimensional spectral types for the HD stars, Vol. 4, Michigan Spectral Survey, Ann Arbor: Dept. of Astronomy, Univ. Michigan

Houk, N. & Swift, C. 1999, Michigan catalogue of two-dimensional spectral types for the HD Stars, Vol. 5, Ann Arbor: Dept. of Astronomy, Univ. Michigan

Mink, D. J. 2002, in ASP Conf. Ser., Vol. 281, Astronomical Data Analysis Software and Systems XI, ed. D. A. Bohlender, D. Durand, & T. H. Handley (San Francisco: ASP), 169

Astronomical Data Analysis Software and Systems XII
ASP Conference Series, Vol. 295, 2003
H. E. Payne, R. I. Jedrzejewski, and R. N. Hook, eds.

Toward an AVO Interoperability Prototype

M. G. Allen[1], F. Genova[1], F. Ochsenbein[1], S. Derriere[1], C. Arviset[2], P. Didelon[3], M. Dolensky[4], S. Garrington[5], R. Mann[6], A. Micol[7], A. Richards[5], G. Rixon[8], A. Wicenec[4]

Abstract. As part of the Astrophysical Virtual Observatory (AVO) we are developing an interoperability prototype which aims to federate a set of astronomical archives, representative of a variety of techniques (space/ground, images/spectra, X-ray to radio wavelengths) into the CDS VizieR and Aladin tools. The target archives for federation are: VLT, NTT, EIS (ESO), HST/ECF, ISO, XMM (ESA), Wide field UK archives, MERLIN, and Terapix. We demonstrate the interoperability of these federated archives with examples using multi-wavelength image data and catalog overlays, and highlight new functionalities of the federation and integration tools.

1. Introduction

The Astrophysical Virtual Observatory[9] (AVO) project is a pilot program for construction of a European Virtual observatory, and participates in the International Virtual Observatory Alliance. An important first year milestone of the AVO project is to implement an interoperability prototype with the goal of federating a set of key data archives into the CDS interoperability services. The aims for the prototype system are to:

- Evaluate interoperability tools in terms of usability and function.
- Drive specifications and development of new functionalities.
- Provide a test bed for new and evolving standards (UCDs, VOTable).

---

[1]CDS

[2]European Space Agency

[3]SAP/TERAPIX

[4]European Southern Observatories

[5]University of Manchester, Jodrell Bank Observatory

[6]Royal Observatory Edinburgh

[7]ESO/ST-ECF

[8]University of Cambridge

[9]http://www.euro-vo.org

- Enable early science usage of Virtual Observatory like tools and get feedback from users.
- Heighten awareness about basic interoperability requirements among the archive providers.
- Compile a set of practical interoperability recommendations

2.   AVO Interoperability Prototype

The prototype is based on the existing interoperability tools at the CDS, namely the VizieR catalogue browser, and the Aladin sky atlas image tool. VizieR (Ochsenbein, Bauer & Marcout 2000) and Aladin (Bonnarel et al. 2000) gather and maintain metadata about catalogs, data archives and image servers. Using this metadata, the interfaces provide access to catalogs, images and remote resources for browsing, downloading data and visualization in a single environment.

The CDS systems offer a working framework in which to test and develop high level metadata definitions and standards required for Virtual Observatories. Units and Uniform Content Descriptors (UCDs) (Derriere et al. 2002, 2003) are already defined for all archives and catalog in VizieR, providing a working development platform which is complementary to parallel developments of distributed metadata systems and web-service type operations (e.g., Szalay et al. 2002).

3.   Target Archives

The target data archives for inclusion in the prototype consist of European data archives chosen to be representative of space and ground-based observations over a wide range of wavelength. The target archives include VLT, NTT, EIS (ESO), HST/ECF, ISO, XMM (ESA), Wide field UK archives, Jodrell Bank radio archives, and Terapix data.

The prototype system provides interoperability between these archives at the *data level*, meaning that coordinate systems of images from the different instruments and telescopes can be combined to create mosaics and overlays. This is done via the Aladin tool, which matches images by re-orientation and scaling, see Figure 1.

4.   Recent Enhancements

Recent enhancements have been implemented in the Aladin and VizieR tools to facilitate display of radio images, and to allow the possibility of making astrometric registration adjustments for image alignment based on common image features. Other improvements to Aladin, driven by the prototype, include a facility to generate, display and manipulate contour plots of images, and to combine registered images into a RGB colour composite.

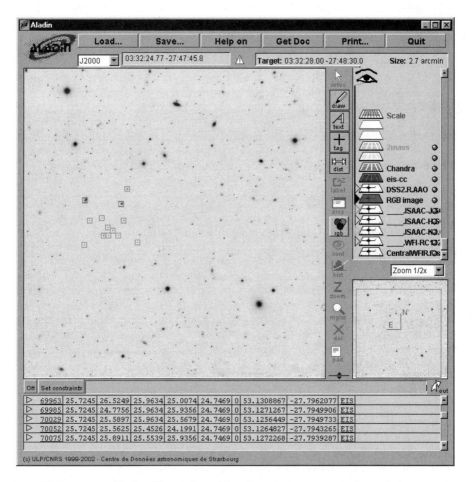

Figure 1. Aladin Sky Atlas. This figure shows a number of the interoperability prototype target archive images and catalogs loaded into Aladin. The image is a colour composite of VLT ISAAC J, H and WFI-R frames of the central part of the Chandra Deep Field South. The image is overlaid with EIS point source catalog, with selected catalog values shown in the lower panel. Also available in the image/catalog stack are locations of XMM and Chandra observations.

5.   Practical Recommendations for Interoperability

Implementation of observatory observation log files into the interoperability system currently requires significant interaction with the archive holders. This process identifies the required metadata definitions to properly describe a remote resource. In some cases this process stimulates archive holders to review their archive exposure mechanisms. Lessons learned from archive implementation are being systematically reviewed to produce a set of interoperability recommendations to archive providers. The basic requirements for implementation are the availability of direct HTTP access to archive images, and that astrometry information is supplied in the FITS World Coordinate System. For "living" archives, such as a growing observation log, a simple mechanism is required for updating the metadata. Emphasis is also placed on including uncertainties and errors on measurements where possible, and on the inclusion of auxiliary information such as filter transmission curves. Data rights and access are also key questions to be addressed by archive holders prior to interoperability implementation.

6.   Conclusions

The AVO interoperability prototype is implementing an increasing set of European data archives into the CDS VizieR and Aladin, making these data available for early science usage. The prototype provides a test bed for development of metadata descriptions and standards, and of new functionalities for working with multi-wavelength data. The requirements of the prototype have driven the developments of new functionalities such as RGB and contour displays, and additional developments and customizations are also being driven by the requirements of the AVO Early Science Demonstration foreseen for early 2003.

References

Ochsenbein, F., Bauer, P., & Marcout, J. 2000, A&AS, 143, 23

Bonnarel, F., Fernique, P., Bienayme, O., Egret, D., Genova, F., Louys, M., Ochsenbein, F., Wenger, M., & Bartlett, J. G. 2000, A&AS, 143, 33

Derriere, S. 2002, Proceedings of *Toward an International Virtual Observatory*, Garching, Germany June 10-14.

Derriere, S., Ochsenbein, F., & Boch, T. 2003, this volume, 69

Szalay, A., Budavári, T., Malik, T., Gray, J., & Thakar, A. 2002, Web Services for the Virtual Observatory, Microsoft Research Technical Report MSR-TR-2002-85

Part 3. Virtual Observatory and Archives

Astronomical Data Analysis Software and Systems XII
ASP Conference Series, Vol. 295, 2003
H. E. Payne, R. I. Jedrzejewski, and R. N. Hook, eds.

Small Theory Data in the Virtual Observatory

Jonathan C. McDowell

Smithsonian Astrophysical Observatory, 60 Garden St, Cambridge, MA 02138

Abstract. The integration of large theoretical simulation archives with the VO has been widely discussed. I suggest that it is also important to include smaller theoretical datasets and functional relationships in a structured way, and outline some possible conventions.

1. Introduction

In this article, I address the issue of resource discovery for tabular and functional theoretical and phenomenological results such as extinction laws, luminosity functions, isochrones, and distance indicators. A structured extension of the CDS concept of UCDs could make tabular data of this kind easily available not only to astronomers but also to interoperable software.

I also discuss metadata for simulations by drawing an analogy with X-ray spectral analysis, a domain in which complex new theoretical models have been rapidly integrated with the standard data analysis tools via a simple parameterized-function description. This paradigm can easily be extended to image simulations.

2. The Virtual Astrophysics Library

When I was a theorist, I spent a lot of time retyping tables from the ApJ and coding small equations from papers as subroutines; and best of all, using a ruler and pencil to digitize xeroxes of graphs. The Virtual Observatory (VO) can really help here.

My challenge to the reader is: every time you see a graph or a histogram in the ApJ or on astro-ph, I want you to ask yourself:

- How would I encode this in the VO?
- How would I locate this info in the VO?

I propose the Virtual Astrophysics Library, an on-line collection of astronomical relationships – a place to find different versions of the extinction law, the initial mass function, the Tully-Fisher relation, etc., either in tabular or subroutine form.

The near term goal is to provide coherent access to useful snippets of data, saving retyping and recoding. A longer term goal is on-the-fly manipulation of VO observational data. As presently envisaged, the VO will allow the user to say "give me this image"; I believe we should be able to say "give me this image, dereddened with an LMC extinction curve and K-corrected to redshift 2 using Smith's spectral energy distributions and the following cosmological model.."

2.1.   Step One: Small Theory or Phenomenology Tables

Much of this functionality can be encoded in fairly small lookup tables, which are easy to convert to self-describing (e.g., VOTable[1]) form. The trick is accessing (i.e., indexing) them. For example, an extinction law is a simple function (Figure 1a), but it is not analytic: rather, it is a mixture of measured and calculated values. One can consider it as a function of three parameters: wavelength, possibly metallicity, and version (Seaton et al. 1979; Morrison & McCammon 1983, etc.) Note that not all versions cover all possible wavelength ranges, so we must provide a standard which allows the function publisher to describe not only the function arguments but their allowed values.

We may wish to provide a 'VO canonical' version combining our favorite ones to cover all wavelengths (e.g., as done by Joachim Koppen's extinction web service at astro.u-strasbg.fr), although this raises problems of editorial authority. It is probably better to let such attempted syntheses be published on an equal basis with the individual fragments, and provide a mechanism for VO users to specify their defaults in a configuration file.

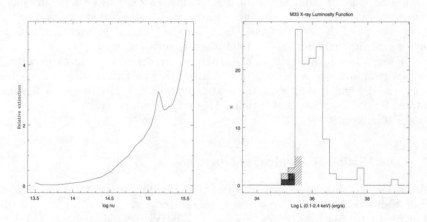

Figure 1.   (a) A sample extinction law. (b) Luminosity function of X-ray sources in M33.

2.2.   A Coordinate System for the Space of Concepts

The simplest functionality we should provide is an easy way to find all the extinction laws published to the VO. I would argue that a Google-like search is unsatisfactory, and we should have a structured way to find such information. When we are using the VO to search for information on specific objects, we can use a single, standard coordinate system (J2000/ICRS) to locate them. This

---

[1]http://cdsweb.u-strasbg.fr/doc/VOTable

coordinate system has problems as an index (for example, it breaks down for solar system objects and components of binary stars) but it solves the bulk of the problem. There is no comparable coordinate system for theoretical concepts and models, although the UCD (Unified Content Descriptor) labels in use by the Strasbourg CDS (Derriere et al. 2002) provide a first step toward such an index. By having unique identifiers for concepts they are able to meaningfully cross-match the contents of a large number of catalogs.

In the case of celestial coordinate systems, even though J2000 is the default, the VO will support different views of the sky (equatorial, galactic, ecliptic...); it is even more important to do this in theory space – we must provide a framework for indexing concepts and at least one default example, but we mustn't impose a single view of physics which might restrict the questions the user could ask. An obvious way to store the extinction law would be under 'physics; radiation; opacity; interstellar'; but an equally valid choice might be 'physics; galaxies; diffuse material; spectrum'. The Strasbourg group have emphasized the usefulness of having a unique identifier for a single concept, but perhaps it's enough to ensure that such alternate formulations are easily and automatically mapped to each other. Defining these 'concept coordinate systems' is a key technology needed for the VO, and we will have to come up with it in the near future.

Providing a way to find and download tables of this kind allows us to take more sophisticated steps. The next step is to provide the table as a web service; a user would send a spectrum and an extinction value and get back a dereddened spectrum. Rather than provide a separate web service for each such physical problem (extinction, cosmology, etc.), it should be possible to code a single web service which could apply any tabulated data, while providing a check that the input data are the right physical quantities by checking they match the correct unique tags (which I will refer to loosely as UCDs).

The final step is to register the service with the VO query language. The existence of the UCD-like tags will allow the query language to chain the tables together, allowing the user to ask questions like: 'Give me all galaxies in the Smith catalog whose dereddened B magnitudes are brighter than 14, using reddening values from the Jones sky map.' The VO now knows about reddening at a basic level.

2.3. Rawer Datasets (Histograms and Scatter Plots)

Histograms and scatter plots are also really just tables. Consider the example of the SN acceleration Hubble diagram: a scatter plot of magnitude versus redshift. This is equivalent to a catalog of objects with two columns. Although the individual objects are in fact astronomical objects with RA and Dec values, this is no longer relevant – we are idealizing them as samples from a theoretical magnitude-redshift space. Therefore, the diagram (or rather the table it represents) will be indexed in physics space, not celestial coordinate space, perhaps as 'physics; cosmology; expansion; Hubble Diagram; data'. Predictive curves would be stored 'close by'.

Another example: the luminosity function histogram of X-ray sources in a galaxy (Figure 1b). The corresponding table would have metadata linking it back to the original catalog used to make the histogram, and forward to the broken power law fit used as an idealization of the data.

2.4.   Publishing and Archiving Subroutines

Much of the simple machinery used to integrate tabular theory heuristics into the VO can be extended to handle code. A subroutine which requires no interaction and has a consistent set of input and output arguments (numbers, strings or files) is equivalent to a table with an infinite number of rows in which each argument corresponds to a table column. In particular, we can use the same kind of metadata used to define table columns to define the subroutine input and output arguments. The UCDs can be used to ensure that the arguments are of the appropriate astrophysical type and not just the approprate computer data type. One could even define an enhanced VOTable XML format with a stream parameter of type 'external code'.

3.   Big Theory Data: Metadata for Simulation Archives

Most discussion of theory data for the VO to date has focussed on the large theoretical simulation datasets, but the community has not yet established common metadata conventions for describing these datasets, or even decided what information is important enough to be recorded. We must **soon** decide how to encode (XML, FITS header) these metadata in a standard way.

I suggest that the X-ray spectral fitting community has relevant experience which can guide our thinking. In X-ray astronomy, our inability to deconvolve the instrumental spectral response has driven us to parameterized fitting of theoretical model spectra folded through the instrument simulator. The standard packages (XSPEC, Arnaud 1996; Freeman et al. 2001) share a large code base of 1-dimensional spectral simulation codes contributed by the user community. The key idea is that the simulation is described only by its parameters; the user must understand the scientific algorithm used by the simulation by reading text documentation – all the computer needs to know is a unique identifier for the simulation and the parameters that need to be fed to it. A second key idea is that all parameters are equal (in the sense that they are described in the same way), even though some are physical (temperature, abundance, density) and some are control-related (method name, number of iterations). A similar approach may be useful to describe particle simulations.

Acknowledgments.   This project is supported by the Chandra X-ray Center under NASA contract NAS8-39073.

References

Arnaud, K. A. 1996, in ASP Conf. Ser., Vol. 101, Astronomical Data Analysis Software and Systems V, ed. G. H. Jacoby & J. Barnes (San Francisco: ASP), 17

Derriere, S., Boch, T., Ochsenbein F. & Ortiz P. 2002, in "Toward an International Virtual Observatory" (Springer-Verlag).

Freeman, P., Doe S., & Siemiginowska A. 2001, SPIE 4477, 76

Astronomical Data Analysis Software and Systems XII
ASP Conference Series, Vol. 295, 2003
H. E. Payne, R. I. Jedrzejewski, and R. N. Hook, eds.

National Virtual Observatory Efforts at SAO

Mark Cresitello-Dittmar, Janet DePonte Evans, Ian Evans, Michael
Harris, Stephen Lowe, Jonathan McDowell

Harvard-Smithsonian Center for Astrophysics

Michael Noble

Massachusetts Institute of Technology

Abstract.   The National Virtual Observatory (NVO) project is an effort to federate astronomical resources, to provide seamless access to heterogeneous data at various centers throughout the world, and make them
appear to the user as a homogeneous set. The NVO will reduce the user's
need to obtain, recall and manage details such as passwords, band coverage, instrument specificity and access methodologies for each archive
site in order to get and analyze data. The project will employ Grid technology and distributed computing techniques to manage enormous data
volumes and processing needs.

At the Harvard-Smithsonian Center for Astrophysics (CfA), we are
developing a small scale prototype implementation of the NVO paradigm.
This demonstration will illustrate the directions being pursued toward
this goal by allowing a user to request data from various resources, display
the returned data, and interactively perform analysis on that data.

1.   Portal

At the Harvard-Smithsonian Center for Astrophysics, we are defining the datamodel protocol for the NVO project. As a test case, we have implemented an
end-to-end prototype of an NVO Portal. This portal will aid in defining/refining
the datamodel by applying the concepts to a real-world application.

This NVO portal allows the user to query and retrieve data from a variety
of archive centers for a particular object or location in the sky. The returned
data may then be displayed as a multi-color overlay image on which the user
selects a region of interest and executes an analysis task to determine the flux
from that region in various wavebands.

The GUI itself is written in S-lang using GTK for the graphics. It manages
the communication between the user and the various modules used to perform
this task. It knows how to find and communicate with a service registry, but
does not have prior knowledge of which services are available.

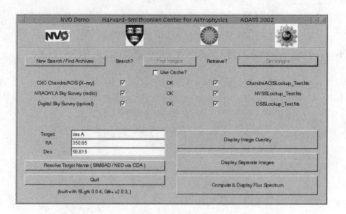

Figure 1.   NVO Portal GUI

2.   Resource Discovery

This portal makes use of a Java tuplespace as the service registry. The services and the client communicate to each other through this space. (For more information about tuple space, see Noble, this volume3.) A service must advertise its availability by leasing a "tuple" in the tuplespace. These tuples expire after a certain amount of time unless the service renews this lease to keep them active. When the user clicks the 'Find Archives' button of the portal, a query is sent to the tuplespace asking which archive services are available for searching. The server responds with the list of currently active services (Figure 2). If a service provider has hardware issues or simply needs their resources, they can stop renewing the leased tuple and the service will no longer be visible to the outside world.

3.   Query

The user may either input an object name and use the namespace resolver service or enter the coordinates manually (in decimal degrees). If an object name is entered, the portal queries the tuplespace server to determine if a name resolver service is available. If so, the portal constructs a query request for the name resolver service and sends that request to the tuplespace. The name resolver service notices that the request has been registered and processes it, returning the coordinates of the object (Figure 3).

When the user clicks 'Find Images,' the portal forms queries for each of the archive services that were selected by the user. These requests are in a standard form and are submitted individually to the tuplespace server. Each archive service retrieves its tuple, performs the search, and returns the tuple with the results. The tuple server conveys the results back to the user (Figure 4).

The query services return Metadata describing the data and the means to retrieve the file (e.g., a URL or ftp link). The interface collects this information and indicates to the user which images were found. The user then selects which images to retrieve.

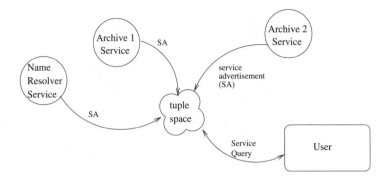

Figure 2.   Services advertise to tuple space, client queries for available services.

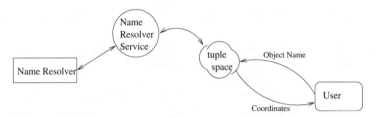

Figure 3.   Communication flow for name resolver service.

4.   Data Retrieval

Peer-to-Peer Data Transfer   Each archive search delivers an information packet to the portal that is sufficient for the portal to retrieve the data file directly from its hosting site. Since this transfer involves large amounts of data, the retrieval process is done peer-to-peer between the portal and the data-hosting site, bypassing the tuplespace registry.

Site-Specific Extractors (SSEs)   The data stored at the hosting sites exist in a variety of formats. For interoperability purposes, data used in VO applications should be delivered in a uniform format. In the VO paradigm, each archive service will create a Site-Specific Extractor (SSE), which is a processing pipeline to transform the requested data from its native format to the VO standard format. Since these VO format standards are still being developed and for reasons of convenience, for the present demo, we have written stand-ins for these components which run on the local portal.

5.   Data Analysis

While not specifically "VO," this segment highlights the interoperability advantage that VO formatted data can provide. We created some simple tools to operate on VO formatted data. These tools are local to the user's computer.

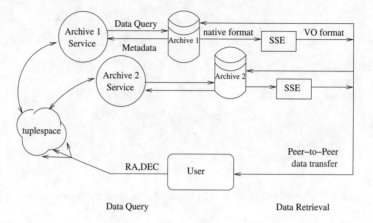

Figure 4.   Archive query

Generate Composite Image: An IDL tool to generate a tri-color image of the returned data sorted by energy band. The Lowest=red, Mid=green, Highest=blue. The resulting image is displayed in a DS9 window where the user can select a region on which to perform further analysis.

Display Individual Images: Simple invocation of DS9 with multiple frames so the user can view the individual images.

Flux Calculation: Executes routines that calculate the flux within the specified region for all retrieved data and displays a plot of the results.

6.   Future Work

Since this demo provides an end-to-end thread, it will be very helpful in developing and refining the VO Datamodel, which is the focus of our work.

This software was developed with a very modular design. As VO standards for VO file format, query model, data model, etc. evolve, we will replace existing modules with ones conforming to those standards.

Several enhancements to the interface will be needed as we pull more and varied services into the thread.

For more information about the NVO project, please refer to these web sites: CfA NVO home,[1] US National VO home,[2] and International VO home.[3]

Acknowledgments. This material is based upon work supported by the National Science Foundation under Cooperative Agreement No. AST-0122449. This project is supported by the Chandra X-ray Center under NASA contract NAS8-39073

---

[1]http://cfa-www.harvard.edu/nvo

[2]http://www.us-vo.org/

[3]http://www.ivoa.net/

Astronomical Data Analysis Software and Systems XII
ASP Conference Series, Vol. 295, 2003
H. E. Payne, R. I. Jedrzejewski, and R. N. Hook, eds.

Metadata for the VO: The Case of UCDs

Sébastien Derriere, François Ochsenbein, Thomas Boch

CDS, Observatoire Astronomique de Strasbourg, 11 rue de l'Université, F-67000 Strasbourg, France

Guy T. Rixon

Institute of Astronomy, University of Cambridge, Madingley Road, Cambridge. CB3 0HA, U.K.

Abstract. The UCDs (Unified Content Descriptors) were first developed in the ESO/CDS data mining project, to describe precisely the contents of the individual fields (columns) of tables available from a data center. They have been used to describe the content of the 10^5 columns available in the different VizieR tables. Owing to the wide diversity and high heterogeneity of table contents, UCDs constitute an excellent starting point for a hierarchical description of astronomy, for general data mining purposes. We present different applications of UCDs: selection of catalogues, based on their content; identification of catalogues having similar fields; automated data conversion allowing direct comparison of data in cross-identifications. The compatibility of UCDs with semantic descriptions developed in other contexts (data models for space-time coordinates or image datasets) will also be addressed.

1. Introduction

Astronomical tables can come from many different sources, and the original descriptions are therefore very heterogeneous. Automated processing of the contents of these datasets, which is one of the Virtual Observatory (VO) applications, requires a uniform description for the catalogues (with standardized metadata).

The UCDs (Unified Content Descriptors), first developed in the ESO/CDS data mining project (Ortiz et al. 1999), are metadata describing precisely the contents of the individual fields (columns) of tables available from a data center. They have been applied to describe the content of the 10^5 columns available in the different VizieR tables (Ochsenbein, Bauer & Marcout 2000).

Some tools using UCDs have been developed and are available online: http://vizier.u-strasbg.fr/UCD/.

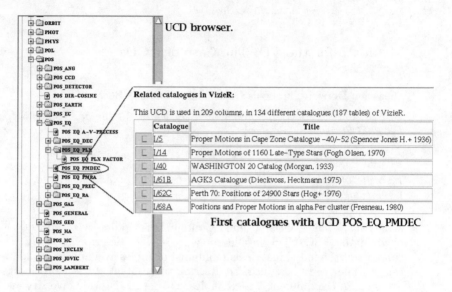

Figure 1.   The UCD browser, on the left, is used to locate relevant
UCDs in the hierarchical structure. For each UCD, the list of VizieR
catalogues containing this UCD in at least one field can be displayed
and queried.

2.   Usage of UCDs

2.1.   Browsing the UCD Tree

The UCDs consist of a 4-level hierarchical structure, with approximately 1500
elements. Different branches of the tree correspond to different domains of the
semantic classification (e.g., time, position, instrument).

A tool has been developed to visualize and explore the tree (Figure 1). A
javascript and an applet version of the browser are available. The presentation
of the tree is similar to a file system browsing engine, with folders being nodes
of the UCD tree and documents being the UCD leaves, actually describing the
catalogue columns.

Clicking on a leaf gives access to:

- a definition of the corresponding UCD;
- statistics on column labels and units associated to this UCD (Figure 2);
- usage statistics for this UCD in VizieR (catalogues and tables where it
  occurs).

2.2.   Data Validation

The wide heterogeneity of the original description of astronomical data is clearly
visible when making statistics on the column names and units used to represent
a single physical quantity (Figure 2). These statistics help pointing out possible
errors in the catalogue description, or in the UCD assignation, and are thus
useful for data validation.

UCD **POS_EQ_PMDEC** represents: **Proper Motion in Declination (pmdec)**

Statistics for this UCD:

Column names and units associated to UCD: POS_EQ_PMDEC
(there are 14 different column names and 16 different units).

Frequency: column name	Frequency: unit
185 pmDE	91 mas/yr
6 CvarDE	38 arcsec/yr
5 pmDE2000	21 arcsec/ha
3 pmDE1950	18 arcsec/a
1 pmDER	13 mas/a
1 pmDE-ACr	9 10mas/yr
1 pmDE-NPM1	6 10-4arcsec/yr
1 pmDEJ	2 10-5arcsec/yr
1 pmDE-NPM1r	2 10mas/a
1 pmDE-AC	2 10-2arcsec/yr
1 pmDE-HIP	2 carcsec/yr
	1 marcsec/a
	1 0.01arcsec/yr
	1 mag/yr
	1 10uas/yr
	1 ---

Figure 2.   Example of statistics on the different column names and units used in all VizieR tables for one UCD.

2.3.   Selection of Catalogues

One of the most important use of UCDs is that they allow to select catalogues which exactly contain a given measurement. Instead of searching all the "infrared" catalogues for a K-band magnitude, all catalogues with a Johnson K magnitude can be retrieved instantly.

This selection can be done with the browser (see Figure 1). It is also possible to translate plain text into relevant UCDs. One provides one or several terms to describe in natural language the desired quantity (e.g., 'proper motion'). The answer is a list of corresponding UCDs, tentatively ordered by relevance. These can be used to select the relevant catalogues.

2.4.   Automated Data Conversion

If two fields in two tables are described by the same UCD, these fields can be compared because they contain the same quantity. Automated data conversion can then be applied if these fields are expressed in different units (Figure 3).

2.5.   Finding Similar Catalogues

Because UCDs precisely describe the contents of catalogues, they can be used to find similar catalogues. Given a reference catalogue, the list of UCDs which are present in this catalogue is used as criteria to perform a search among all other catalogues: similar catalogues are those that will have many UCDs in common with the reference one.

I/146/ppm1	Positions and Proper Motions – North (Roeser+, 1988) Catalogue PPM–North		
RAJ2000	**DEJ2000**	**pmRA**	**pmDE**
"h:m:s"	"d:m:s"	s/yr	arcsec/yr
17 57 24.373	+04 36 09.20	–0.0014	0.032

I/239/tyc_main	The Hipparcos and Tycho Catalogues (ESA 1997) The main part of Tycho Catalogue				
RAhms	**DEdms**	**RA(ICRS)**	**DE(ICRS)**	**pmRA**	**pmDE**
		deg	deg	mas/yr	mas/yr
17 57 24.42	+04 36 09.0	269.35174824	4.60249678	41.60	37.50

I/239/tyc_main *converted columns :*

recno	**pmDE**
	arcsec/yr
35715	0.0375
35741	

Figure 3.   Example of automated conversion for columns with the same UCD.

3. Possible Evolution of UCDs

Suggestions have been made to improve the current structure of UCDs. The evolution towards an "atomic" rather than hierarchical structure is studied. UCDs could be built by assembling atomic elements (principal nouns, adjectives, complementary nouns) selected among a predefined set of standard atoms. This scheme allows more flexibility in defining new UCDs, avoids dispersion of related quantities in different branches of the tree, and describes the data more completely.

Examples of combinations of atoms (compared to current UCDs):

- angle/declination (current UCD is POS_EQ_DEC);
- length/wavelength/johnson-V (central wavelength of the band, no UCD);
- length/wavelength/extent/johnson-V (bandwidth of the band);
- energy-flux-density/uncertainty/johnson-V (current UCD is ERROR).

4. Conclusions

UCDs are currently used in VizieR to describe the semantics of astronomical content. They offer new ways of selecting relevant datasets, and enable cross catalogue/archive interoperability. Owing to the wide diversity of table contents, UCDs constitute an excellent starting point for a hierarchical description of astronomy, for general data mining purposes. An improved structure relying, for example on atomic keywords, could provide building blocks for the development of astronomical ontologies.

References

Ortiz, P. et al. 1999, in ASP Conf. Ser., Vol. 172, Astronomical Data Analysis Software and Systems VIII, ed. D. M. Mehringer, R. L. Plante, & D. A. Roberts (San Francisco: ASP), 379

Ochsenbein, F., Bauer, P. & Marcout, J. 2000, A&AS, 143, 23

Astronomical Data Analysis Software and Systems XII
ASP Conference Series, Vol. 295, 2003
H. E. Payne, R. I. Jedrzejewski, and R. N. Hook, eds.

Russian and fSU Resources to be Integrated in the IVO

Alexander Kilpio, Olga Dluzhnevskaya, Oleg Malkov, Elena Kilpio,
Dana Kovaleva, Pavel Kaigorodov, Lyudmila Sat

Institute of Astronomy, Russian Academy of Sciences , Moscow, Russia

Abstract. The goal of the Russian Virtual Observatory[1] (RVO) initiative is to provide every astronomer with on-line access to the rich volumes of data and metadata that have been and will continue to be produced by astronomical survey projects. The information hub of the RVO has a main goal of integrating resources of astronomical data accumulated in Russian observatories and institutions, and providing transparent access for scientific and educational purposes to the distributed information and data services that comprise its content.

One of the general purpose data centres for astronomy is the Moscow Centre for Astronomical Data (CAD). CAD has been systematically collecting and distributing astronomical data for more than 20 years. The CAD staff will carry out the activities on construction of the information hub of the Russian Virtual Observatory.

1. Introduction

A virtual observatory (VO) is a collection of interoperating data archives and software tools which utilize the Internet to form a scientific research environment in which astronomical research programs can be conducted. The VO consists of a number of data centres each with unique collections of astronomical data, software systems and processing capabilities. In the past months, three major international projects (NVO,[2] AVO,[3] AstroGrid[4]) and a number of smaller ones have been funded to develop and realize the vision of using astronomical data repositories as virtual observatories.

Recently, the Scientific Council on Astronomy of the Russian Academy of Sciences (RAS) strongly endorsed the RVO initiative with CAD (Institute of Astronomy, RAS) and Special Astrophysical Observatory (RAS) as coordinators. The RVO will be an integral component of the International Virtual Observatory (IVO), which will link the archives of all the world's major observatories into one

---

[1]http://www.inasan.rssi.ru/eng/rvo/

[2]http://us-vo.org/

[3]http://www.eso.org/projects/avo/

[4]http://www.astrogrid.org/

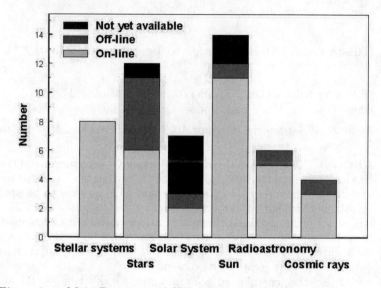

Figure 1.   Main Russian and fSU astronomical data resources.

distributed database, with powerful tools to optimize the extraction of science from the data.

The Russian contribution will be in the following areas:

- To provide the Russian astronomical community with a convenient access to the world data grid.
- To unite Russian and former Soviet Union (fSU) data, to provide them to the rest of the world and to integrate them into the IVO.
- To take part in developing of software, techniques, standards, and formats necessary for the establishment of the IVO.
- To use Russian instrumentation to provide observational data in remote mode when needed.
- To strengthen education and public applications of world astronomical data.

CAD contributes mostly in the first three points. The first is one of the main tasks of CAD as the national data centre and the work in this direction has been carried out for many years. The activity is rather manifold: mirroring of principal world databases (e.g., ADS,[5] VizieR,[6] INES[7]), providing access to off-line astronomical resources, visualization and cross-identification of catalogues, review and expert evaluation of data sets, etc.

CAD contribution to the second and the third items of the list is described below in two corresponding chapters.

---

[5]http://ads.harvard.edu/

[6]http://vizier.u-strasbg.fr/viz-bin/VizieR

[7]http://ines.vilspa.esa.es/

Main Russian astronomical organisations

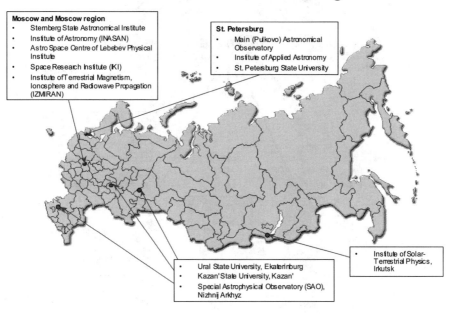

Moscow and Moscow region
- Sternberg State Astronomical Institute
- Institute of Astronomy (INASAN)
- Astro Space Centre of Lebedev Physical Institute
- Space Research Institute (IKI)
- Institute of Terrestrial Magnetism, Ionosphere and Radiowave Propagation (IZMIRAN)

St. Petersburg
- Main (Pulkovo) Astronomical Observatory
- Institute of Applied Astronomy
- St. Petersburg State University

- Ural State University, Ekaterinburg
- Kazan' State University, Kazan'
- Special Astrophysical Observatory (SAO), Nizhnij Arkhyz

- Institute of Solar-Terrestrial Physics, Irkutsk

Figure 2.   Main Russian astronomical organisations holding astronomical data resources.

2.   Russian Data to be Integrated into the IVO

There are about 30 astronomical institutes and organizations in Russia. Many of them maintain extensive data archives. But the main value of Russian astronomical observational data is their large time scale of observation. Russia is the most extended in latitude country in the world (11 time zones) and lies just on the opposite site of the globe in respect to the major world observational facilities. This allows, for instance, to obtain continuous observations of variable objects.

We collect information about all available (both Russian and some former Soviet Union) resources and classify them. Figure 1 presents distribution of the resources, kept in a dozen of Russian (see Figure 2) and some fSU astronomical organisations, according to the types and to a degree of availability.

The list of Russian and fSU astronomical resources is compiled for the first time and will be kept up to date. This list is available on the RVO web page.

Other CAD activities in this direction are:

- To provide an access to electronic tables published in main Russian astronomical journals.
- To produce (in collaboration with Russian astronomical organizations) machine-readable versions of catalogues, glass libraries, printed papers.
- To construct catalogues and databases and to provide scientific and technical support to authors of catalogues.

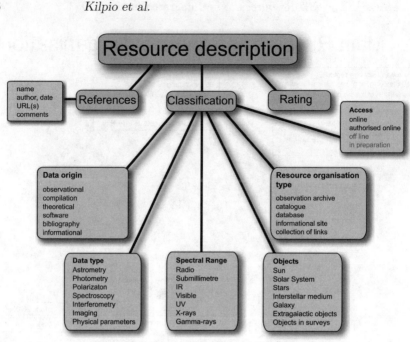

Figure 3.   Resource classification scheme.

3.   Standards and Formats Development

The RVO project starts a couple of years later than other principal VOs, and, therefore, should follow interoperability standards of various kinds already established. We must enable the open exchange of information and share our experiences among other VO projects.

One of CAD's immediate tasks in the frame of this project is standardization and unification of information on national resources, their rating and completing of a (meta-)database of Russian astronomical resources.

The development of a special collection of links to useful astronomical data resources, called Internet Resources in Astronomy (IRinA), is under way. This collection will be based on an original multi-level classification scheme and will include reviews and expert analysis, comprehensive list of national resources and bilingual resource descriptions.

The classification scheme for astronomical resources has been worked out and is presented in Figure 3. This scheme will be used as a foundation for the two described databases: IRinA and the database of Russian astronomical resources. The only difference in schemes for these databases is that in the case of Russian resources we collect information about all the resources available (off-line and online), while IRinA will contain only online ones.

Another our future goal is to construct interoperability tools, particularly, for national observational archives.

Acknowledgments. The work is supported by RFBR grants No 02-07-90391 and 02-07-93544, as well as by ADASS Organizing Committee.

Astronomical Data Analysis Software and Systems XII
ASP Conference Series, Vol. 295, 2003
H. E. Payne, R. I. Jedrzejewski, and R. N. Hook, eds.

The MAST Pointings Tables Project

Karen Levay, Paolo Padovani[1], Randall Thompson, Megan Donahue, Michael Corbin

Space Telescope Science Institute, 3700 San Martin Drive, Baltimore, MD 21218

Abstract. We have undertaken a project to create a database of all HST imaging observations organized by position on the sky. A World Wide Web (WWW)-based interface to this database has also been created, in supplement to the existing interface to the HST archive. These "pointings tables" enable quick identification of overlapping fields that can be used for multi-wavelength studies of objects and for variability studies by comparing images at given positions over different epochs. They will also allow for "mini-surveys" by providing lists of images over a specified coordinate range, such as above and below the Galactic plane. We plan to develop pointings tables for other MAST missions besides HST and expect these tables to form an important part of the upcoming virtual observatories.

1. Introduction

A question often asked of the HST archive has been: "Is there an easy way to find out how many times a region of the sky has been observed with more than one filter?" Now that question and others may be easily answered using the HST "pointings" tables and interface.

The first task was to decide how to organize the observations into sky regions. Initially this task was done as part of the MAST Scrapbook project where "representative" observations were chosen in a set of well defined "bands" for a sky region for the WFPC2 instrument. Each sky region was called a "pointing." A "pointing" is defined as an area of the sky falling within an instrument's field of view. The project realized that once we had divided the sky into pointings, it would be a simple matter to count the observations and filters falling within a pointing, thus enabling the questions our users had been asking to be answered.

2. Creating the Tables

The first step in creating the tables is to determine the sky regions that have been observed by a specific HST imaging instrument. The coordinates for all observations made with a specific instrument are selected and sorted. The first

---

[1]ESA Space Telescope Division

WFPC2 Pointings

Coordinates: Choose either a more traditional search by Target Name/Coordinate, or the serendipitous approach, to search by RA/Dec/Galactic Latitude and/or Ecliptic Latitude ranges. You do not have to search by coordinates at all.

Target Name/Coordinates [ ]   Resolver [SIMBAD ▭]   Radius (arcmin) [3.0]

RA Range [ ] degrees   Dec Range [ ] degrees

Galactic Latitude [Above & Below Plane > ± ▭] [ ] degrees

Ecliptic Latitude [Above & Below Plane > ± ▭] [ ] degrees

Number of Unique Bands [ ]   Total Number of Exposures [ ]   Num of Days between first and last exp. [ ]

Band: To search for specific bands, enter the number of exposures required per band (e.g. 4, >1, or <10). Specify if the search is to be for all specified bands (and) or any of the specified bands (or).

Exposure Times: To query on exposure times, enter exposure limits (in seconds) for the total exposure time in each band (e.g. >1000, or <10). Specify if the search is to be for all specified bands (and) or any of the specified bands (or).

WFPC2 (primary)	
Expsures per Band	Exposure Times
⊙ And (Or	⊙ And (Or
U [ ]	[ ]
B [ ]	[ ]
V [ ]	[ ]
R [ ]	[ ]
I [ ]	[ ]
Line [ ]	[ ]

Figure 1.   Pointing search specification page.

set of coordinates in the list are automatically defined as the coordinates for the first pointing. All coordinates within the defined "field of view" for that instrument are removed from the list of potential pointings. The next unselected observation becomes the second pointing and the same procedure is followed until all observations are assigned as a member of a pointing. It should be noted that while the method for defining a pointing is defined, the individual pointings may change over time as new observations are added for active instruments. During the second step, individual observations are assigned to pointings. An observation may fall in more than one pointing and is then counted as a member of all appropriate pointings. The filter is used to determine which "band" the observation is assigned to. The values for the total exposure time for each band in the pointing, the first and last observation date/time, the total number of exposures and the total number of different bands found for that pointing are also calculated. A table containing the list of dataset names with the pointing and band assignments is also created. Currently, pointings tables are available for the WFPC2, STIS (images), and FOC instruments.

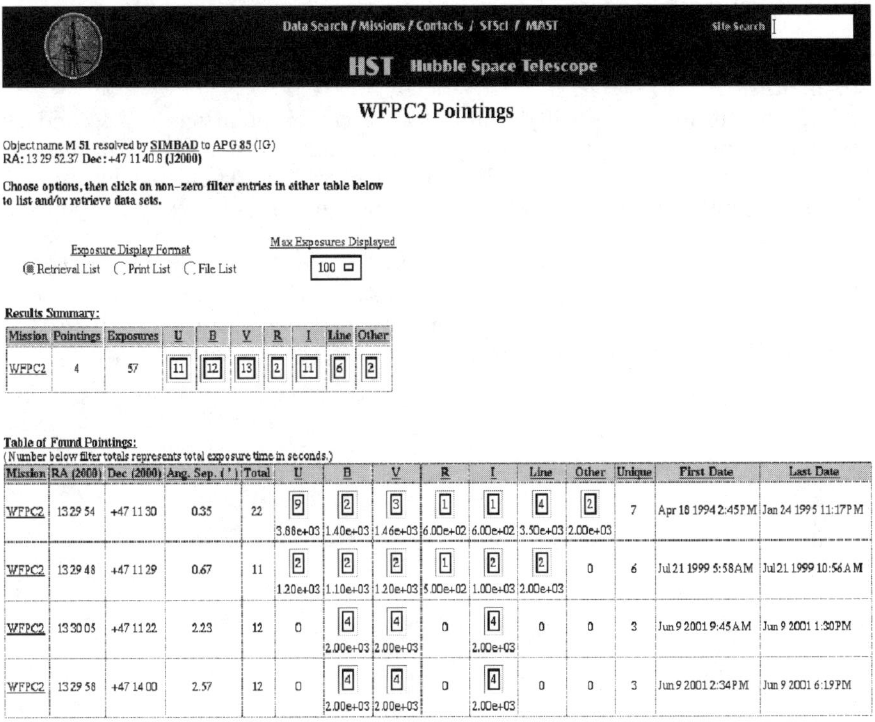

Data Search / Missions / Contacts / STScI / MAST

Site Search

HST Hubble Space Telescope

WFPC2 Pointings

Object name **M 51** resolved by SIMBAD to APG 85 (IG)
RA: 13 29 52.37 **Dec**: +47 11 40.8 **(J2000)**

Choose options, then click on non-zero filter entries in either table below to list and/or retrieve data sets.

Exposure Display Format
Retrieval List   Print List   File List

Max Exposures Displayed
100

Results Summary:

Mission	Pointings	Exposures	U	B	V	R	I	Line	Other
WFPC2	4	57	11	12	13	2	11	6	2

Table of Found Pointings:
(Number below filter totals represents total exposure time in seconds.)

Mission	RA (2000)	Dec (2000)	Ang. Sep. (')	Total	U	B	V	R	I	Line	Other	Unique	First Date	Last Date
WFPC2	13 29 54	+47 11 30	0.35	22	9 3.88e+03	2 1.40e+03	3 1.46e+03	1 6.00e+02	1 6.00e+02	4 3.50e+03	2 2.00e+03	7	Apr 18 1994 2:45PM	Jan 24 1995 11:17PM
WFPC2	13 29 48	+47 11 29	0.67	11	2 1.20e+03	2 1.10e+03	2 1.20e+03	1 5.00e+02	2 1.00e+03	2 2.00e+03	0	6	Jul 21 1999 5:58AM	Jul 21 1999 10:56AM
WFPC2	13 30 05	+47 11 22	2.23	12	0	4 2.00e+03	4 2.00e+03	0	4 2.00e+03	0	0	3	Jun 9 2001 9:45AM	Jun 9 2001 1:30PM
WFPC2	13 29 58	+47 14 00	2.57	12	0	4 2.00e+03	4 2.00e+03	0	4 2.00e+03	0	0	3	Jun 9 2001 2:34PM	Jun 9 2001 6:19PM

Figure 2. Pointings search output.

3. The Interface

The interface for the pointings table is a WWW form which can be found at `http://archive.stsci.edu/cgi-bin/point`, together with the definition of the pointing radii and filter/band assignments. Users select the instrument pointings table they wish to search. On the subsequent form, users may select a specific target, coordinate ranges, or might decide to search above/below the Galactic or ecliptic plane. They may choose to look for pointings with observations in more than one filter with or without exposure time constraints in each filter. Users may choose to do time-variability searches by specifying the number of days between the first and last observations in a pointing. See Figure 1 for an example of the form. The search results are displayed as two tables (see Figure 2). The top table is a summary of all pointings found by the search. The second table has a row for each pointing found fitting the search criteria. The number of observations within each band is also a link. When this link is executed, a list of the specific datasets for that pointing/band is displayed. Users may look at previews and also submit archive requests for those data.

4.   Future Plans

We plan to add pointings tables for NICMOS and ACS instruments in the next six months.

In the future, users will be able to search for pointings of "secondary" instruments in the context of pointings for a "primary" instrument. For instance, perhaps a user is interested in WFPC2 observations, but would also like to know if there are any STIS image observations within the field of view of the pointing. A search will be made of the WFPC2 pointings table. Then a secondary search of the STIS pointings table will be made looking for STIS pointings within the WFPC2 field of view for each WFPC2 pointing. Users will be able to specify filters and exposure times for all secondary instruments in addition to those specified for the primary instrument.

Astronomical Data Analysis Software and Systems XII
ASP Conference Series, Vol. 295, 2003
H. E. Payne, R. I. Jedrzejewski, and R. N. Hook, eds.

The AXAF (Chandra) Guide and Acquisition Star Catalog V1.5 (AGASC 1.5)

Dennis Schmidt and Paul Green

Harvard-Smithsonian Center for Astrophysics, 60 Garden Street, Cambridge, MA 02138

Abstract. Chandra's Aspect Camera Assembly (ACA) measures positions of selected stars to acquire and hold target pointings, and for post facto aspect determination. The selection and matching of the guide stars is governed by data in the AXAF (Chandra) Guide and Acquisition Star Catalog (AGASC). Based originally on version 1.1 of the Guide Star Catalog for the Hubble Space Telescope, the AGASC has been extended and refined in several stages, with data from additional catalogs and with recalibrations using on-orbit ACA observations.

In 2002 the Chandra X-ray Center (CXC) completed a major upgrade of AGASC. We merged data from three catalogs—Tycho-2, GSC-ACT, and 2MASS. The Tycho-2 data substantially improve the photometric and astrometric measurements of stars as faint as $V=12$, while the GSC-ACT merge decreases by about half the systematic astrometric errors down to the catalog limit of about $V=14.5$. The 2MASS data identify galaxies down to $J=12.5$. These new catalog data enhance the value of AGASC for scientific as well as operational purposes.

Specifically for Chandra's operational use of AGASC, we recalibrated the estimated ACA magnitudes based on Chandra on-orbit measurements, and implemented a more sophisticated calculation of the effect of nearby stars on the best-fit centroid of a guide star.

This paper presents the rationale for and the process of updating the AGASC. We then discuss the improvements in performance that we expect to result, and introduce the online AGASC 1.5 query tool http://cxc.harvard.edu/agasc.

1. Introduction

The AXAF (Chandra) Guide and Acquisition Star Catalog (AGASC) governs the selection and recognition of stars used by Chandra's Aspect Camera Assembly (ACA) to acquire and hold Chandra target pointings. The selected stars' positional data also enable post facto aspect determination and reconstruction of sharp images from dithered observations.

AGASC originated with version 1.1 of the Guide Star Catalog for the Hubble Space Telescope[1], and has been extended and refined in several stages. The Chandra X-ray Center (CXC) completed a major upgrade in 2002. The upgrade corrected errors introduced in earlier versions; incorporated data from additional catalogs; recalibrated ACA magnitudes based on accumulated on-orbit star observations with Chandra; and improved estimates of stellar centroid spoiling by nearby objects.

2.   Merges from Three Catalogs

AGASC previously incorporated data from the GSC 1.1, PPM, Tycho-1, and ACT catalogs. The recent upgrade merged data from three additional catalogs—Tycho-2, GSC-ACT, and 2MASS—into AGASC.

2.1.   Tycho-2

The Tycho-2 Catalog (Høg et al. 2000) is an astrometric reference catalog containing positions and proper motions as well as two-color photometric data for the 2.5 million brightest stars in the sky. Components of double stars with separations down to 0.8 arcsec are included. Tycho-2 supersedes Tycho-1, and the ACT and TRC catalogs based on Tycho-1.

Proper motions precise to about 2.5 mas/yr are given as derived from a comparison with the Astrographic Catalog (AC) and 143 other ground-based astrometric catalogs, all reduced to the Hipparcos celestial coordinate system. For only about 4% of stars, no proper motion could be derived.

2.2.   GSC-ACT

The original GSC 1.1 positions have random position errors of about 0.4 arcsec, but also systematic position errors of about 0.3 arcsec, due to errors in the reference catalogs (AGK3, SAO, CPC) and also to their low stellar density. STScI performed a recalibration of the GSC 1.1, using the PPM catalog for a denser reference star network, resulting in the GSC 1.2.

In the GSC-ACT project[2], Bill Gray also recalibrated the GSC 1.1, but using the ACT (Astrographic Catalog/Tycho) data from the U.S. Naval Observatory. In the GSC-ACT, GSC 1.1 systematic errors were reduced via recalibration of 42 plate coefficients plate-by-plate, using the proper-motion-corrected ACT stars for reference.

In creating AGASC 1.5, we matched (2 arcsec search radius) both the GSC-ACT and GSC 1.2 against the radio source positions that define the International Celestial Reference System (ICRS, Gambis 1999). From 43 independent sources matched, the GSC 1.2 showed a mean positional difference of 0.″40, RMS 0.″35. From 44 sources, the GSC-ACT showed mean 0.″28, RMS 0.″25. The denser

---

[1] The Guide Star Catalog (GSC) was prepared by the Space Telescope Science Institute (STScI), 3700 San Martin Drive, Baltimore, MD 21218, USA. STScI is operated by the Association of Universities for Research in Astronomy, Inc. (AURA), under contract with the National Aeronautics and Space Administration (NASA).

[2] http://www.projectpluto.com/gsc_act.htm

reference star network of the GSC-ACT results in a superior calibration; this is the catalog we chose to improve AGASC positions for stars that had only GSC 1.1 (no Tycho or PPM) data.

2.3. 2MASS

Using a pre-release (June 2001) tabulation of extended objects in the 2MASS catalog (Jarrett et al. 2002), kindly provided by Tom Jarrett (IPAC) and John Huchra (CfA), we improved AGASC's identification of galaxies and objects near galaxies. For reliability of AGASC, any AGASC object with an extended 2MASS object within 5 arcsec was judged to be a galaxy. Just 70% of 2MASS galaxies have matches within that distance in AGASC.

Examination of 2MASS galaxies on the Digital Sky Survey optical images indicated that optical galaxy brightness extends visibly to about twice r_{20} on average, and in about 25% of cases to $3r_{20}$. Any AGASC object within $3r_{20}$ of a 2MASS galaxy was marked as close to an extended object.

3. Recalibration

3.1. Recalibrating Aspect Camera Magnitude

A poorly estimated AGASC magnitude has sometimes resulted in Chandra's failing to acquire a star. More importantly, large star magnitude errors caused too many stars to be rejected from consideration, with the result that targets either were rejected or had a number of guide stars that was less than optimal.

Inclusion of Tycho-2 data to a completeness limit of $V=11.5$ (rather than the previous $V=10$ limit of Tycho) significantly lowers the magnitude and position errors on an additional 1.5 million stars in AGASC. The most significant improvement in Aspect Camera magnitude estimates results from the accurate tabulated colors available.

Experience in operating Chandra for a year also gave the opportunity to do a new polynomial fit, by comparison with colors from Tycho-1, to observed Aspect Camera magnitudes for 1939 stars. In AGASC 1.5, *MAG_ACA*—the estimated magnitude for the Aspect Camera Assembly—is derived from V and $B - V$ via the polynomial color equation

$$MAG\_ACA = V + C_0 + C_1(B - V) + C_2(B - V)^2 + C_3(B - V)^3$$

For published magnitudes from Tycho catalogs, we use $C_0 = 0.428638$, $C_1 = -0.774029$, $C_2 = 0.283002$, and $C_3 = -0.267284$.

3.2. Recalibrating Spoiler Codes

AGASC 1.5 incorporates the results of a study by David Morris of the offset induced in the computed centroid of a guide star by a nearby star. The study considered the effects of distance between star and spoiler, rotation angle between the two, magnitude difference between them, and their position on the ACA focal plane. High Resolution PSFs were produced both by raytrace simulations and by centroid aligning and stacking many thousand actual ACA star images. The study showed good agreement among combinations of the two PSF models and two algorithms. In AGASC 1.5, the aspect quality ("spoiler") code assigned to a star is the maximum centroid offset (in units of 50 milliarcsec) expected to be induced by any star within 80 arcsec, as a function of their magnitude difference and separation. For Chandra operations, stars whose centroid offsets would reach 50 milliarcsec are rejected as guide stars.

4. Stellar Surface Density

AGASC 1.5 is in everyday use for guiding Chandra and for reconstruction of dithered X-ray images to Chandra's unprecedented spatial imaging resolution.

The new catalog has an average stellar surface density of 9.5 per square degree, for unspoiled stars that have color information and are brighter than $MAG\_ACA = 10.2$. Near the galactic poles ($b > 80°$), where the stellar surface density is lowest, there are 4.1 such stars per square degree. The desired Chandra figure of merit (FOM) of 5.1 per square degree over 95% of the sky is not quite achievable with these original selection criteria. With accurate ACA magnitudes included, however, Chandra now routinely uses stars to mag 10.8, for which the FOM is easily met.

5. Conclusions

AGASC 1.5 currently represents the only available catalog that *combines* high quality astrometry on the ICRS system down to 14.5 mag with detailed color and proper motion information down to about 12th mag. In addition, the "spoiler codes" that indicate the degree to which any stellar centroid might be disturbed by nearby objects is a unique feature.

These properties make AGASC 1.5 a potentially important catalog for guide star selection for other space- and ground-based telescopes (e.g., for telescope guiding or Adaptive Optics). AGASC 1.5 should also prove useful for a variety of scientific purposes.

AGASC 1.5 may be queried online at http://cxc.harvard.edu/agasc.

Acknowledgments. We gratefully acknowledge the help and input provided by Emily Blecksmith, Melanie Clarke, John Grimes, David Morris, Tom Aldcroft, and Rob Cameron. The Chandra X-ray Center is supported through NASA Contract NAS8-39073.

References

Gambis, D. (ed.) 1999, First Extension of the ICRF, ICRF-Ext.1, in 1998 IERS Annual Report, Chapter VI, Observatoire de Paris, 87

Høg, E., Fabricius, C., Makarov, V. V., Urban, S., Corbin, T., Wycoff, G., Bastian, U., Schwekendiek, P., & Wicenec, A. 2000, A&A, 355.2, L19

Jarrett, T. H., Chester, T., Cutri, R., Schneider, S., & Huchra, J. 2002, AJ, submitted

Astronomical Data Analysis Software and Systems XII
ASP Conference Series, Vol. 295, 2003
H. E. Payne, R. I. Jedrzejewski, and R. N. Hook, eds.

SkyDOT: A Publicly Accessible Variability Database, Containing Multiple Sky Surveys and Real-Time Data

D. Starr, P. Wozniak, W. T. Vestrand

Los Alamos National Laboratory, Los Alamos, NM, USA

Abstract. SkyDOT (Sky Database for Objects in Time-Domain) is a Virtual Observatory currently comprised of data from the RAPTOR, ROTSE I, and OGLE II survey projects. This makes it a very large time domain database. In addition, the RAPTOR project provides SkyDOT with real-time variability data as well as stereoscopic information. With its web interface, we believe SkyDOT will be a very useful tool for both astronomers and the public.

Our main task has been to construct an efficient relational database containing all existing data, while handling a real-time inflow of data. We also provide a useful web interface allowing easy access to both astronomers and the public. Initially, this server will allow common searches, specific queries, and access to light curves. In the future we will include machine learning classification tools and access to spectral information.

1. Introduction

A new phase in optical astronomy research is occurring from increases in computing power and the financial feasibility of massive data collecting projects. Successful experiments such as micro lensing searches and galactic surveys have developed because of this availability of measurements. But, the rapid increase in these types of projects creates a need to organize and commonly collect their data. With such a resource then publicly available, it can be queried and used to its fullest potential. These collections of datasets are often called "virtual observatories."

Although there are currently dozens of variability sky surveys underway, the usefulness of their datasets is often limited by their frequency of observations, spatial coverage of the sky, and their availability to other astronomers. To this date, there are very few large sky surveys which are collecting high temporal-resolution variable datasets, while also providing its access to the public. SkyDOT will fill this niche by allowing general access to a large spatial database built from multiple sky surveys. One of which continually produces new data with a frequency of around once a minute.

2.   Surveys Currently Used

Within the database, SkyDOT's component surveys will be similarly structured, making them compatible with it and each other. This makes integrating additional projects fairly easy, and multi-survey queries simpler to implement. Although, of the three currently available datasets, the OGLE-II project's relative simplicity requires a slightly less complicated table structure.

2.1.   OGLE II

OGLE II is a galactic bulge variable star survey (Wozniak, Udalski et al. 2002) which was conducted with the 1.3 m Warsaw telescope at Las Champanas Observatory, Chile. Started in 1997, this 3 year project covers 11 square degrees and contains over 220,000 I-band light curves with magnitudes between 10.5 and 20.0. The 49 constituent fields contain between 200–300 measurement frames: although 10% of the objects recorded are spurious and most likely non-stellar.

2.2.   ROTSE I

Our database will also contain a year of data from the Robotic Optical Transient Search Experiment I (ROTSE-I) (Wozniak, Akerlof et al. 2002), which operated for four years in Los Alamos, NM. This survey contains 644 fields, each being 8×8 degrees in size and sampled with between 300 and 40 frames, for declinations of +90 and −30 degrees, respectively. The total number of objects with time histories is expected to be 20 million and it is estimated that around 32,000 of these will be periodic variable stars.

2.3.   RAPTOR

The Rapid Telescopes for Optical Response (RAPTOR) sky monitoring experiment (Vestrand et al. 2002) will be our database's third source of data. This LANL optical transient search project will run concurrently with SkyDOT, providing a real-time stream of photometric measurements. RAPTOR uses two identical telescopes, separated by 38 km, to stereoscopically view the same region of sky. After software processing, this binocular information can be used to separate potentially interesting objects, leaving the more distant, stellar data.

Each of the telescope pair has 4 85 mm cameras, which cover 1500 square degrees and reach a depth of 13th magnitude (Wren et al. 2002). They also contain a central 400 mm camera with a sensitivity to 16th magnitude. The combined pair's 10 cameras take 30–60 second exposures which are then immediately reduced, the sources extracted, and an object catalog is updated—before the next image is received. Transient objects found for a camera are then compared with concurrent data from the sister telescope, to determine whether the object is a possible celestial transient. If so, these interesting objects can be used to alert the rest of the project and possibly other astronomical institutions.

Besides the telescope pair, RAPTOR also has a separate large field "Patrol" telescope, as well as a rapid response spectroscopic telescope. The patrol telescope can record up to 16th magnitude objects and will independently cover the local sky in about 2–3 days. This will provide roughly 30 million objects with time histories. Our 0.3 m Ritchey-Chretien rapid response telescope is equipped

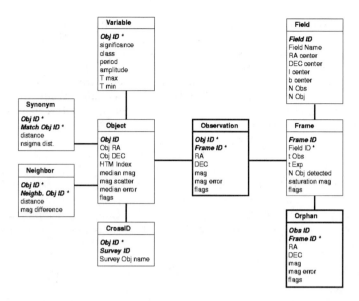

Figure 1.   Database Schema.

with a transmission grating, allowing low resolution spectroscopy. This will be
used to respond to our alerts and other selected objects.

3.   Database Design

Our database is built using PostgreSQL, a free, open source, relational system
that also has object oriented capabilities. Although an object oriented model is
most natural for using classes containing parameters and their transformations,
performance problems were reported (Szalay et al. 2002). For our task, the
relational system is more successful.

The database is structured around the "Observation" main event table
which contains all measurements. This table is indexed with two primary keys
(Obj ID & Frame ID) creating access points for the "Object" and "Frame" dimension tables. Most searches utilize the object information in tables surrounding the dimension tables. When a query is made, the observed data is retrieved
through the dimension table's link to the observation table. This snowflake
structured database results in a fairly compact system. Although a star shaped
scheme with more redundancy of data would allow faster general queries, we
chose to conserve disk space since much of our searches will be done with an
optimized index for spatiality.

Spatial queries are expected to be our most common searches. So we need
an efficient method for finding objects within a circle on a sphere. PostgreSQL
contains a few tree searching methods, but they do not pertain to 2D searches
of high resolution positions. For this reason, we implemented Hierarchical Triangular Mesh (HTM) indexing, developed at Johns Hopkins University (Kunszt
et al. 2000).

The HTM search algorithm partitions a sphere up into triangles, which are recursively divided into finer triangles. The algorithm identifies every triangle with a position related HTM ID. So, a triangle with a specific position and resolution will contain within its HTM ID the shorter IDs of its parent triangles. HTM IDs are also B-tree indexed, allowing efficient searches for objects within a triangle. Thus a circular query will return large and small triangles within the circle, which can then be searched for the individual object IDs they contain.

Tables surrounding the "Object" and "Frame" dimension tables allow a variety of searches. The "Variable" table contains typical periodic characteristics, as well as computer generated classes: created through machine learning algorithms. The "Synonym" table is used to relate an object which resides in multiple fields. This effect is fairly common in sky surveys especially in fields near the poles. Additionally, RAPTOR's overlapping cameras also compound the effect. This often leads to duplicate information, which may lead to improvements in data quality for that object. To search using the data from all three surveys, the "Cross ID" table is joined to the query. This then links an object to its counterpart in the other survey, if it exists.

On the other side of the primary observation data table is the "Frame" dimension table. It is related to the field table by the field ID index. The field Table is intended for system diagnostics and is not to be used in normal database queries. On the other hand, the "Orphan" table contains objects that are temporally unique and could not be matched with existing data. These objects, when processed using information from RAPTOR's stereoscopic system, can produce interesting alerts.

4. Summary

SkyDOT will be a powerful tool for astronomers. Its planned combination of three datasets makes it one of the largest variability databases. Plus, it will be able to include additional surveys, when they become available. The synoptic information from RAPTOR's binocular telescopes provides a wealth of information that might be used for intra-solar system searches. SkyDOT is also unique because its database will be updated by the minute with data from RAPTOR's real-time pipeline.

References

Kunszt, P. Z., Szalay, A. S., Csabai, I. & Thakar, A. R. 2000, in ASP Conf. Ser., Vol. 216, Astronomical Data Analysis Software and Systems IX, ed. N. Manset, C. Veillet, & D. Crabtree (San Francisco: ASP), 141

Szalay, A. S. et al. 2002, Proc. of ACM SIGMOD Int. Conf.

Vestrand, W. T. et al. 2002, Proc. SPIE, 4845

Wren, J. et al. 2002, Proc. SPIE, 4845

Wozniak, P. R., Akerlof, C. et al. 2002, Bull. Am. Astron. Soc., 200

Wozniak, P. R., Udalski, A. et al. 2002, Acta Astronomica, 52, 129

Astronomical Data Analysis Software and Systems XII
ASP Conference Series, Vol. 295, 2003
H. E. Payne, R. I. Jedrzejewski, and R. N. Hook, eds.

OASIS: A Data Fusion System Optimized for Access to Distributed Archives

J. C. Good, M. Kong and G. B. Berriman

IRSA/IPAC, California Institute of Technology, Pasadena, CA 91125

Abstract. The On-Line Archive Science Information Services (OASIS) uses Geographic Information Systems (GIS) technology to provide data fusion and interaction services for astronomers. These services include the ability to process and display arbitrarily large image files with user controlled contouring, overlay generation, and multi-table/image interaction. In addition, OASIS can be thoroughly integrated with web pages, active data services, and static data on any server by means of a suite of linking functionality. This functionality turns OASIS into a tool that can be used by anyone to make their data or services more accessible and integrable with other data from around the world.

1. Interactive Data Fusion using OASIS

OASIS contains a fairly complete suite of functionality for viewing and manipulating images, source catalogs (as tables and as overlays), sky drawings (e.g., contour plots), and XY plots (e.g., spectra, light curves, scatter plots). It has custom interfaces for accessing specific archives (images from various sources, catalogs from IRSA and CDS VizieR). OASIS runs as a JAVA applet/application and when running as an applet has specialized interfaces for interacting with browser forms. In this mode it relies on the JAVA 1.3 (or later) plug-in and has been tested on Solaris, LINUX and Windows using Netscape, Mozilla, and IE. It has also been successfully used on the latest version of Mac OS X (10.2) but not fully tested.

For more information on the complete suite of OASIS GIS functionality the reader is directed to the OASIS web site available through IRSA[1]. The remainder of this paper is primarily aimed at service/data providers and describes the ways in which OASIS can be used to augment or interact with other systems.

OASIS has been optimized for access to distributed archives and data sets. However, rather than build an ever-increasing suite of custom interfaces to remote archives, the OASIS remote access model is based on the idea of allowing data and service providers to control the flow of data to OASIS. In this way, the range of data services available in association with OASIS can grow organically without IRSA's direct involvement and future OASIS development can be focussed on better data visualization and data fusion functionality.

---

[1] http://irsa.ipac.caltech.edu/

This architectural difference can best be appreciated from the data provider point of view. By "data provider" we include everyone from the builder of an extensive archive system to the astronomer who simply wants to include an image, interactive plot, or data table reference on a web page. For example, a data provider who creates a query form to an archive containing a collection of data can direct the result files from the query into OASIS where it can be either viewed on its own or in conjunction with data from other sources.

This kind of interaction is possible because all OASIS data links feed into a single copy of OASIS on the client machine. In this way any data or service provider is given access to the full suite of capabilities in OASIS and the ability to include all other available datasets by reference from his web page.

As an example, Davy Kirkpatrick has included OASIS references to plot his collection of known L dwarf stars in the solar vicinity[2]. Other examples of this third-party access feature include queries involving the high-energy image datasets accessible from GSFC SkyView, links to image data that are returned from a target-based query to the NASA Extragalactic Database (NED), and AAVSO light curves.

2. Using OASIS with Your Data and Services

OASIS has been designed to serve as a presentation and data fusion tool that can be used in conjunction with existing data services. Images, source lists, etc. that are kept on-line (or even just local files) can be displayed using OASIS just by adding an extra HTML link on any web page that references them. If a service provider has data services that produce such files dynamically, these can be handled the same way. Finally, with minor adjustments an existing form interface can be modified to use attributes of the current image, etc. being displayed by OASIS (e.g., image center and size) as initialization parameters for a service. In this section, we will describe in more detail how this can be accomplished.

2.1. Basic OASIS Links

By far the most common OASIS link is for the purposes of displaying a data file. For example, suppose a data supplier has an image `orion.fits` that they wish to display. Currently, they would create a link to it on some web page which would tell the Browser to retrieve the file:

```
<a href="http://a.server.edu/images/orion.fits">Orion image</a>
```

If the browser has been told which application can handle this file, it will fire up a copy.

For an OASIS link, we use an extra level of indirection where the reference is handed off to OASIS (which is started automatically by the Browser if necessary) and OASIS retrieves the data and adds it to the current display. In this way, a

---

[2]`http://spider.ipac.caltech.edu/staff/davy/ARCHIVE/index_l_spec.html`

whole data collection (image, catalog overlays, contours, etc.) can be fused in a single client instance of OASIS even if the data all come from different locations.

The above can be converted to an OASIS link simply by sending the existing URL to the OASIS proxy service:

```
<a href="http://irsa.ipac.caltech.edu/cgi-bin/OasisLink/
nph-oasislink?ref=http://server.dummy.edu/images/orion.fits">
Orion image</a>
```

To be safe, the "`ref`" parameter should be url-encoded. Multiple data references and references to services rather than static files can also be sent. The "`file://`" construct can also be used to work with local data.

OASIS links work by generating an extra (small) Browser page which contains an OASIS applet reference (for OASIS links to work, JavaScript must be active on the Browser). After a brief delay (longer if OASIS has not been loaded), the "calling" window returns to the original page, the new applet page (the small browser window) contacts or starts OASIS, and OASIS is given the data reference(s).

OASIS forwards all such references to its File Transfer Management toolkit and they appear as parallel threads in the File Transfer Manager GUI window (requests made through OASIS will be shown here as well). As data arrives it is stored in a cache (cleared every session) and added to the current display. Since different files (and services; see below) take different amounts of time, there is no guarantee in which order the data will arrive.

2.2. Putting the Applet Button on Your Own Page

The proxy Browser window that is created dynamically in the above scenario contains a simple (if somewhat lengthy) standard plug-in applet reference. Such references can be hardcoded onto any page. This has the advantages that the process does not then need to go through the OasisLink proxy generator, have JavaScript active, or have extra browser windows appear on the user's screen. It has the disadvantages that the service provider has to understand and accommodate the applet information construct and load OASIS when the page comes up (as opposed to it only coming up if a link is activated).

2.3. Interacting with Web Forms

OASIS can also be used in conjunction with web pages containing HTML forms. Any form can be used; the only constraint being that the form must have an ID (standard but not required for HTML `form` tags). As in the previous section, an OASIS "button" is included on the page, only this time a base URL is given in the `formurl` parameter and OASIS interacts with the Browser to collect the form parameters and complete the URL (much as the Browser does when the HTML submit button is pushed). You can have multiple forms on the same page, each with its own "OASIS submit" button keyed to a specific "`formid`". See the online OASIS documentation on the IRSA web site for more details.

In addition to this, OASIS checks the form inputs on startup looking for specific names (such as "`oasisImCenter`" and "`oasisImRadius`"). When OASIS finds one of these fields, it updates it with the current display value. In this way, OASIS can be used as an integral part of many processing scenarios.

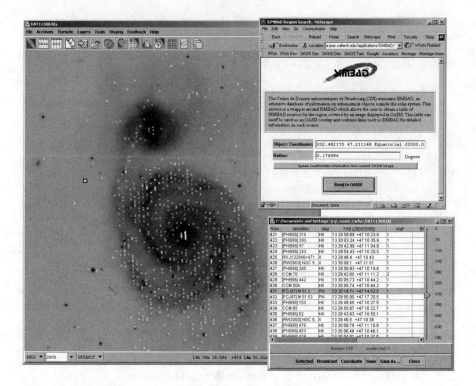

Figure 1.   SIMBAD as an OASIS User.

2.4. Future Plans

In addition to ongoing efforts to augment OASIS' visualization and interaction functionality IRSA is currently involved in several projects relating to the National Virtual Observatory (NVO), including a request manager for long-running or more complex jobs and a data collection/inventory mechanism, and we expect OASIS to be one of the primary portals to this functionality.

Acknowledgments.   OASIS was funded by the Science Applications of Information Technology Program at JPL.

Astronomical Data Analysis Software and Systems XII
ASP Conference Series, Vol. 295, 2003
H. E. Payne, R. I. Jedrzejewski, and R. N. Hook, eds.

Digital Access to Aero- and Astrophotographic Archives

Jean-Pierre De Cuyper, Edwin van Dessel, Thierry Pauwels

Royal Observatory of Belgium, Ringlaan 3, B1180 Ukkel, Belgium

Joost Vanommeslaeghe, Herman Prils, Georges De Decker, Olivier Pierre

National Geographic Institute of Belgium, Abdij ter Kameren 13, B1000 Brussel, Belgium

Johan Lavreau, Max Fernandez, Tan Tran

Royal Museum of Central Africa, Leuvense Steenweg 13, B3080 Tervuren, Belgium

Christiaan Sterken

Free University of Brussels VUB, Pleinlaan 2, B1050 Brussel, Belgium

Mark David

University of Antwerp, UA-RUCA, Groenerborgerlaan 171, 2020 Antwerpen, Belgium

Michel Schots, Gert Daelemans

AGFA-Gevaert NV, Septestraat 27, B2640 Mortsel, Belgium

Abstract. The aim of this test-bed project, initiated and financed by the Belgian Federal Services for Scientific, Technical and Cultural Affairs (SSTC Project I2/AE/103), is to acquire within the coming 4 years, the necessary know-how, hardware and software in order (*i*) to preserve the historic and the scientific information contained in aero- and astrophotographic archives, both on glass plates and on film; (*ii*) to provide a user-friendly intranet and internet access to the catalogue and the (meta)data; (*iii*) to make the photographic information exploitable again for scientific applications, by means of a high resolution digitisation technique.

1. Prescanning

Quick-look images are created for future distribution on the web and to save the hand-written notes from previous measurements, that are present on the glass/film side of part of the astro-photographs, by prescanning at low resolution (250ppi and an 8bit grey scale), using commercial preprint flatbed scanners in transmission mode. At this resolution the notes are clearly readable. Furthermore these digital images contain important information for making the digital catalogue as these images, although deformed, can be used for the redetermination of the coordinates of the plate center and of the measurable magnitude interval, allowing to determine the objects/stars visual on the plate.

The geometric deformation is due to the fact that these preprint scanners are equipped with 1-D CCD rows at a fixed optical resolution. For example, a scanner with a 1000ppi optical resolution used in 250ppi mode will only read out one pixel out of four to construct the digital image. At resolutions that are not a fraction of the optical one also (interpolated) rebinning is applied. Due to the fact that the original remains at rest and is projected by a moving mirror onto the detector, this type of scanners are suffering from scanner seeing. Hence these prescan images are not suited for scientific measurements.

2.   Plate Errors

The deviations from a perfect mapping of the sky or ground area onto the perfect image plane, have a clear hierarchy:
  • global (whole plate),
  • large scale (extending over cm range),
  • local (mm to sub-mm) and
  • emulsion structure (granularity noise).
The origin of those errors can be:
  • mapping defects of the optics,
  • large scale systematics due to centering errors of the optical system,
  • effects from the mechanical and darkroom processes, non homogeneous developing, rinsing and drying of the plates.
All this can and will produce systematic and random errors of any correlation length (i.e., the emulsion shifts are correlated over a mm or cm range).

To determine these effects reference stars or points are used. Some effects can also be calibrated by clever measuring setups at the telescope or camera (tilt of the image plane, position of the optical axes on the plate). Unfortunately these setup data are often not available. The size of these errors is in the 1–2μm range, the question is how regular they are to be calibrated to $< 0.5\mu$m.

Therefore it is important how precise the images of the reference stars or points can be measured (locally) on the emulsion. Depending on the granularity of the emulsion this is possible down to a few tenths of a micrometer. (See also the notes on SuperCosmos (Hambley et al. 1998) and on StarScan (Winter & Holdenried 2001)).

So we are facing a bandwidth of error contributions from the micrometer to the submicrometer range on the plate. These systematic errors can be calibrated successfully only in case the plate is measured precisely to at least a factor of ten better than their size. This is implied by the fact that if one tries to determine errors with a measuring accuracy of the same order, the unknowns in the calibration model will be meaningless statistically. Thus regardless what type of plates one is measuring, this is the essential condition.

3. High Resolution Scanner

Hence, in order to get the full information content from the plate, the measuring machine must have an absolute positioning accuracy of at least $0.5\mu m$ over the whole measuring area. This implies that a $0.1\mu m$ class positioning table is needed. The aim of this project is to construct a scanner using a XY airbearing table with an open frame structure and laser interferometer steering in a temperature (0.1K) and humidity (1% RH) stabilised clean room, giving submicrometer absolute positioning accuracy of the photographic plate with respect to the fixed telecentric objective and digital camera unit.

4. Testing

In order to determine their applicability depending on the introduced geometric and radiometric deformations this project will also study in detail: (*i*) the technique of first making an analogue copy of the plates on duplication roll film, this in order to have an analogue backup and to be able to automate the digitisation process by using an unattended all time scanning technique; (*ii*) the effects of the photochemical cleaning of plates containing fungi or aging deterioration.

5. Database Design

One of the essential aspects of this project is the elaboration—after a preliminary inventory—of a catalogue of the available images including all related data necessary for the exploitation of these images. The archives concerned are the astrophotographic plate archive of the Royal Observatory of Belgium and the aerophotographic archives of the National Geographic Institute of Belgium and of the Royal Museum of Central Africa (Congo, Rwanda, Burundi). All contain photographs on glass plates as well as on film sheets.

Digital catalogues are being generated in the form of ODBC relational databases. HTML files, ActiveX objects, C++ and JavaScript programming are used to create a user-friendly interface that allows easy searching and gives a straightforward overview about the available (meta)data.

The different types of data have been put together in tables. In order to prevent data duplications, several lookup tables were created. The database of the aerial archives for example, is constructed on two types of principle tables:

- Flight Tables (containing all the data concerning a particular aerial flight)
- Aerial Photograph Tables (containing the data concerning an individual aerial photograph)

The aerial photographic missions consist of one or more flights. The Mission Tables contain the flights making up one particular mission.

References

Hambley, N. C. Miller, L. MacGillivray, H. T. Herd, J. T. & Cormack, W. A. 1998, MNRAS, 298, 897

Winter, L. & Holdenried, E. 2001, BAAS, 33-4, Section 129,3

Astronomical Data Analysis Software and Systems XII
ASP Conference Series, Vol. 295, 2003
H. E. Payne, R. I. Jedrzejewski, and R. N. Hook, eds.

Construction of the Japanese Virtual Observatory (JVO)

Yoshihiko Mizumoto, Masatoshi Ohishi, Naoki Yasuda, Yuji Shirasaki
and Masahiro Tanaka

*National Astronomical Observatory of Japan, 2-21-1, Osawa, Mitaka,
Tokyo 181-8588, Japan*

Yoshifumi Masunaga

Ochanomizu University, 2-1-1, Otsuka, Bunkyo, Tokyo 112-8610, Japan

Ken Miura, Hirokuni Monzen, Kenji Kawarai, Yasuhide Ishihara,
Yasushi Yamaguchi and Hiroshi Yanaka

Fujitsu Ltd., 1-9-3, Nakase, Mihama, Chiba 261-8588, Japan

Abstract. The National Astronomical Observatory of Japan (NAOJ)
has been operating several large astronomical facilities, such as the Subaru telescope, the 45 m radio telescope and the Nobeyama Millimeter
Array, and plans to construct the ALMA under close collaborations with
the US and the EU. Since January 2002, the NAOJ has been connected
to the Super SINET[1] with 10 Gbps, and it has become possible to provide a huge amount of observed multi-color data and analysis facilities
to other astronomical institutions. We therefore started the Japanese
Virtual Observatory[2] (JVO) project in April 2002. JVO utilizes the
Grid technology to combine several remote computational facilities. We
have completed defining the query language for the JVO (JVOQL), and
have been designing the JVO components. We plan to construct a JVO-
prototype by the end of 2002.

1. Introduction

The National Astronomical Observatory of Japan operates the Subaru telescope
(optical and infrared) in Hawaii and large radio telescopes in Nobeyama. All
the observed data are digitally archived and are accessible via the Internet,
and the data archives have strongly supported many researchers on astronomy
and astrophysics. The radio telescopes of Nobeyama produce ~ 1 TBytes per
year, and the Subaru telescope outputs ~ 20 TBytes per year. However, until recently, there was a severe restriction to access such amount of data—the
network bandwidth between the NAOJ and the Internet was only 10 Mbps.

---

[1]http://www.sinet.ad.jp/english/

[2]http://jvo.nao.ac.jp/english/

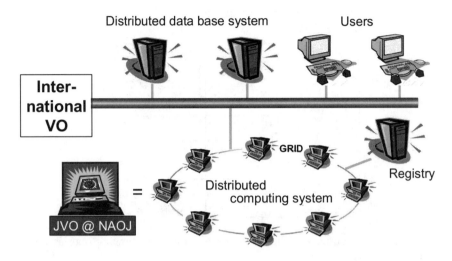

Figure 1.   The schematic diagram of the JVO system.

The National Institute of Informatics has started to operate a new network, the Super SINET since January 4, 2002, and the NAOJ has become an important node for the Super SINET. The Super SINET is an ultrahigh-speed network intended to develop and promote Japanese academic research by strengthening collaborations among leading academic research institutes. The backbone network connects research institutes with a bandwidth of 10 Gbps, and leading research facilities in Japan are directly connected with a 1 Gbps network.

The JVO is designed to seamlessly link the distributed database (DB) and data analyses system for Subaru, Nobeyama observatories, and other observational data for astronomers in research institutes by utilizing the state-of-the-art GRID technology through the 10Gbps Super SINET. This paper briefly describes our overall concept and future plans of the Japanese Virtual Observatory.

2.   Structure of the JVO System

Figure 1 shows the schematic diagram of the JVO system. JVO consists of a distributed computing system (DCS) which is deployed over the high-speed network such as the Super SINET by utilizing the GRID technology. The registry plays quite an important role in the JVO system, which provides information required for DCS to resolve the URLs of distributed DB systems, data analysis servers, and so on. All the computers of the DCS may have independent functions. However many of them need to have redundant functions with others to guarantee robustness of the JVO system. The Resource Manager automatically selects the most appropriate machine for a given task requested by the JVO users through GRID Resource Information Service. It is inevitable that the JVO has an interoperability with the other VOs, such as the NVO, the AVO, the AstroGrid, and so on, to enable researchers to access databases around the world.

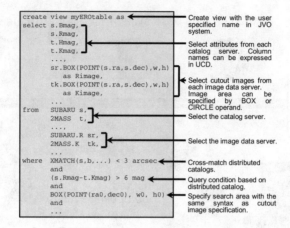

Figure 2.   Samples of the JVO Query Language showing queries for catalog searches.

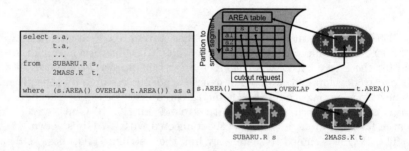

Figure 3.   Samples of the JVO Query Language showing queries to search for images.

3. The JVO Query Language

The JVO Query Language (JVOQL) is used in JVO as a language to specify a variety of user queries. The samples are illustrated in Figures 2 and 3.

The JVOQL is designed to keep upward-compatibility with the standard relational database language, Structured Query Language (SQL), to enable handling image data and cross-matching among distributed databases. The interpreter of JVOQL communicates with the registry of available databases and issues query sequences to distributed databases.

JVOQL has an ability to query image data without referring to catalogs. This function is useful for multi-color or multi-epoch analyses. The JVOQL example (Figure 2) shows how to obtain R-band images taken by Subaru and K-band images by 2MASS in an area where both Subaru and 2MASS observed. The operand "OVERLAP" returns overlapped area of the two data. Figure 3 shows an example to search for required images. Similar to Figure 2, the operand "X.AREA()" returns the observed area of server X.

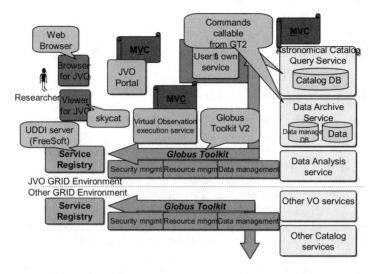

Figure 4.   The schematic diagram showing interrelations among components of the JVO system.

4.   Three-Tiered Design of the JVO Prototype

The JVO prototype is now under development. The first prototype is scheduled to be completed by the end of 2002. The design of the JVO prototype is shown as a schematic diagram (Figure 4). We adopted Globus Toolkit V2 for our prototype. However we also take into account the Web service concept which will be included in Globus Toolkit V3.

Researchers provide the JVO with simple instructions on how they plan to use their own "Virtual Observation" through the JVO portal. The JVO portal interprets them and generates a work-flow through consulting the UDDI servers, where available JVO services are registered. Based on the work-flow, built-in or user-defined services are called. The GRID framework is used for dynamical assignment of distributed resources according to their availabilities. Execution results of the work-flow are transferred through GridFTP, and are presented to the researchers with skycat, etc.

5.   Future Plans

When our first prototype is completed, we will assess it and then modify and re-implement it as a second prototype. We plan to federate more Subaru open use/Nobeyama Radio Observatory data, to implement interoperability with other VOs and with CPU intensive image analysis tools such as deconvolution, image subtraction, and so on.

We also plan to implement data mining/visualization tools to manage the huge amount of data for new discoveries through statistical data analyses on the operational version of the JVO system. The JVO is intended to be a core system of the Regional Support Center in Japan for the ALMA in the near future.

Astronomical Data Analysis Software and Systems XII
ASP Conference Series, Vol. 295, 2003
H. E. Payne, R. I. Jedrzejewski, and R. N. Hook, eds.

The NOAO Science Archive, Version 2.0

R. Seaman, N. Zárate, T. Lauer, P. B. Warner

*Data Products Program, National Optical Astronomy Observatory[1], 950
North Cherry Ave., Tucson, AZ 85719*

Abstract. The NOAO Science Archive (NSA) is a major step toward
building a comprehensive scientific archive of the optical and infrared
data holdings of the National Optical Astronomy Observatory. The goals
for the NSA are to rapidly create a scientifically useful archive of NOAO
Survey data, to develop in-house expertise in the relevant technologies, to
identify requirements for NOAO's developing comprehensive archive, and
to create a high level of visibility as well as utility for both the NOAO
Archive and NOAO Surveys, for example, through new Web services.

The holdings of the NSA[1] are drawn from the NOAO Survey program
as well as from other coherent imaging or spectral, optical/IR reduced
datasets that may be identified as candidates from NOAO or community
facilities. Catalogs and other derived data products will be included in
addition to images, spectra and the tools necessary to evaluate them.
Synoptic, time-domain data is a special focus in anticipation of the needs
of the LSST.

The NSA team is working in coordination with other groups at
NOAO who are focusing on data handling and data pipeline systems in
the context of supporting NOAO instrumentation as well as the emerging
National Virtual Observatory infrastructure.

Planning for the NSA was started in November of 2001 by the Science
Data Systems Group of the NOAO Data Products Program. Version 1.0
of the NSA was released in April, version 1.1 in July and version 1.2 in
October of 2002. We discuss plans for Version 2.0 of NSA to be released
in January of 2003.

1. NOAO Science Archive Overview

The NOAO Science Archive (NSA) provides a rapid prototyping environment
of techniques, hardware and software while at the same time building an operational archive of scientifically interesting data sets. NSA represents the first
major project of the newly established NOAO Data Products Program that

---

[1]National Optical Astronomy Observatory, operated by the Association of Universities for Research in Astronomy, Inc. (AURA) under cooperative agreement with the National Science
Foundation

[1]http://archive.noao.edu/nsa

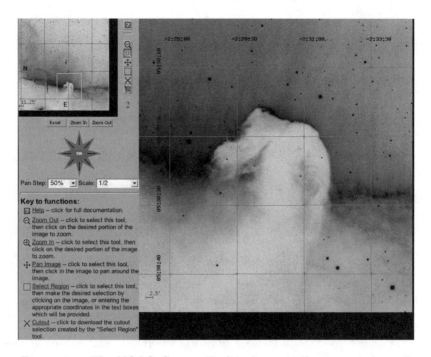

Figure 1.   The NOAO Cutout Tool is dynamically connected to all data holdings – over 15,000 calibrated images as of January 2003.

seeks to construct a complete data handling system from data capture to public archiving of the resulting data products, anticipating the requirements and possibilities of the National Virtual Observatory and the Large Synoptic Survey Telescope.

Data products contained in the NSA are the results of the successful NOAO Survey Program.[2] Survey teams provide the key to the NSA by providing a wide range of extremely useful datasets. The survey teams reduce and calibrate the data before it is ingested into the archive.

A major requirement of NSA is to not only build an archive system—but to build the community who will use that system. In such a case it is highly desirable to keep the development team in close communication with all the users of the system, including the survey teams themselves. In general, the NOAO Data Products Program seeks to build community partnerships wherever possible with both data providers and data customers.

2. NSA Web Interface

The NOAO Science Archive is accessed through a Web interface using HTML and JavaScript for the client interface, and Apache, MySQL, PHP, C and IRAF

---

[2]http://www.noao.edu/gateway/surveys/programs.html

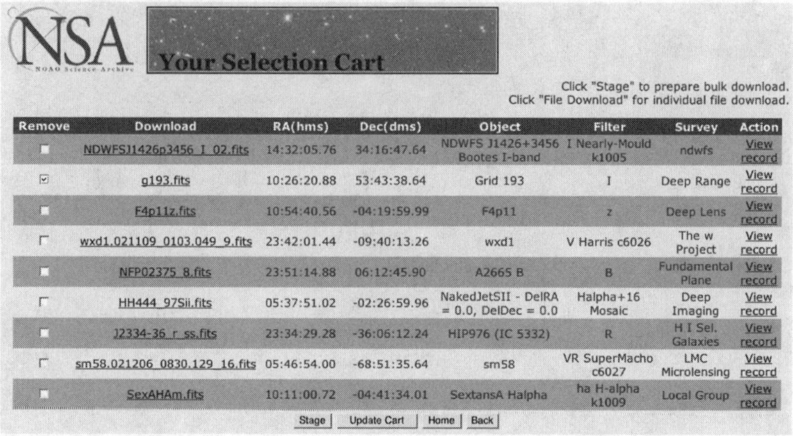

Figure 2.   The NOAO Science Archive Shopping Cart.

task executables for server-side procedures. The interface provides the user the capability to search the NSA via coordinate information, object name, observation date, photometric depth, survey name, and filter. Access to SIMBAD or NED is enabled through C client libraries, kindly provided by each of these projects.

The NOAO Science Archive Image Viewer and Cutout Service[3] was derived from the NOAO Deep-Wide Field Survey[4] Image Viewer and benefits from ongoing work for NOAO's National Virtual Observatory efforts.

Search results include the ability to view the full FITS header, download the FITS file, create a cutout region of the image for download, and a shopping cart mechanism to assemble datasets (that is, either full images or cutout regions) for bulk download.

3.   NOAO Science Archive Status

Work on the NSA project started in the Fall of 2001 with a part time team of four. Current staffing has grown to about seven. The initial version 1.0 of NSA was finished and released in April of 2002 and included data from three survey projects and the ability to search the database, retrieve data files and perform various utility chores such as ingesting data and logging traffic. Static preview images and the ability to display the FITS headers were also included.

A follow-up NSA version 1.1 was immediately initiated and was released in June of 2002. This version was principally a support release for the NOAO Deep-Wide Field Survey and included a revised version of their release 1 data products along with data quality masks and related improvements. Version 1.2

---

[3]http://www.archive.noao.edu/ndwfs/data-cutout.html

[4]http://www.archive.noao.edu/ndwfs

of NSA was released in October of 2002. Even incremental releases like version 1.2 include significant new data holdings—version 1.2 approximately doubled the data holdings. This release also marked the first appearance of the new database-enabled NOAO image cutout server.

In addition to including data from many more of the NOAO survey projects, version 2.0 will include full support for the NOAO cutout server for all data holdings. This is being implemented dynamically directly from the NSA MySQL database information, rather than using a static index file as was originally done for the NDWFS data. An "NSA Shopping Cart" is being implemented to service "push" requests for multiple data files. A mirror archive will be hosted at CTIO in La Serena, Chile. The hardware, including a one Terabyte class RAID array, is in the process of being configured. The data, database, software and web pages will be copied onto the new disks before the system is shipped to the Southern hemisphere.

The long term goal is a fully engineered archive to serve as a major component of the Virtual Observatory. Planning activities for how to transition subsystems of the NSA onto the corresponding engineered subsystems are in progress. It is likely that significant portions of the NSA—and large amounts of data holdings—will remain in operation indefinitely.

Acknowledgments. IRAF is distributed by the National Optical Astronomy Observatory, which is operated by the Association of Universities for Research in Astronomy, Inc., under cooperative agreement with the National Science Foundation.

This research has made use of the NASA/IPAC Extragalactic Database (NED) which is operated by the Jet Propulsion Laboratory, California Institute of Technology, under contract with the National Aeronautics and Space Administration.

This service is provided in collaboration with the SIMBAD project, Centre de Données Astronomiques de Strasbourg, France.

References

Davis, L., Fitzpatrick, M. & Tody, D. 2002, in ASP Conf. Ser., Vol. 281, Astronomical Data Analysis Software and Systems XI, ed. D. A. Bohlender, D. Durand, & T. H. Handley (San Francisco: ASP), 367

Seaman, R. 1994, in ASP Conf. Ser., Vol. 77, Astronomical Data Analysis Software and Systems IV, ed. R. A. Shaw, H. E. Payne, & J. J. E. Hayes (San Francisco: ASP), 119

Seaman, R. 2000, in ASP Conf. Ser., Vol. 238, Astronomical Data Analysis Software and Systems X, ed. F. R. Harnden, Jr., F. A. Primini, & H. E. Payne (San Francisco: ASP), 133

Shaw, R., Boroson, T., & Smith, C. 2002, in Information Technologies: Observatory Operations to Optimize Scientific Return III, ed. P. Quinn, Proc. SPIE, 4844, in press

Tody, D. & Fitzpatrick, M. 2002, in ASP Conf. Ser., Vol. 281, Astronomical Data Analysis Software and Systems XI, ed. D. A. Bohlender, D. Durand, & T. H. Handley (San Francisco: ASP), 177

Part 4. Sky Surveys

Astronomical Data Analysis Software and Systems XII
ASP Conference Series, Vol. 295, 2003
H. E. Payne, R. I. Jedrzejewski, and R. N. Hook, eds.

The XMM-Newton Serendipitous Sky Survey

M. G. Watson

Department of Physics and Astronomy, University of Leicester,
Leicester LE1 7RH, UK on behalf of the XMM-Newton *Survey Science*
Centre (SSC)

Abstract. The main properties of the *XMM-Newton* serendipitous sky
survey are outlined. The *XMM-Newton* Survey Science Centre's role in
the survey is described with emphasis on its follow-up and identification
programme and the production of the *XMM-Newton* catalogue.

1. Introduction

Serendipitous X-ray sky surveys have been pursued with most X-ray astronomy
satellites since the *Einstein* Observatory. The resultant serendipitous source catalogues have made a significant contribution to our knowledge of the X-ray sky
and our understanding of the nature of the various Galactic and extragalactic
source populations. The *XMM-Newton* Observatory (Jansen et al. 2001) provides unrivaled capabilities for serendipitous X-ray surveys by virtue of the large
field of view of the X-ray telescopes with the EPIC X-ray cameras[1] (Turner et
al. 2001; Strüder et al. 2001), and the high throughput afforded by the heavily nested telescope modules. This capability ensures that each *XMM-Newton*
observation provides significant numbers of previously unknown serendipitous
X-ray sources in addition to data on the original target (Watson et al. 2001).

A follow-up and identification programme for the *XMM-Newton* sources
and the compilation of a high quality serendipitous source catalogue from the
XMM-Newton EPIC observations are major responsibilities of the *XMM-Newton*
Survey Science Centre (SSC; Watson et al. 2001). This paper describes these
two aspects of the SSC's activities, both of which are ongoing projects.

2. The Role of the XMM-Newton Survey Science Centre (SSC)

The SSC is an international collaboration involving a consortium of ten institutions in the UK, France, Germany, Italy and Spain. The SSC has several
major roles in the project: the development of the scientific processing and
analysis software for *XMM-Newton*, the routine 'pipeline' processing of all the
observations, a follow-up and identification programme for the *XMM-Newton*

---

[1]There are three EPIC cameras on-board *XMM-Newton*, one in the focal plane of each of the
co-aligned X-ray telescope modules: two EPIC MOS cameras and one EPIC pn camera. In
normal operations observations are made with all three cameras simultaneously.

Figure 1.   Example *XMM-Newton* X-ray image. Data shown are the combined images from all three EPIC cameras in the 0.5–4.5 keV band. The target of the observation is a relatively faint quasar.

serendipitous survey and the compilation of the *XMM-Newton* Serendipitous Source Catalogue. Here I briefly outline the SSC's activities in the first two areas, the others being covered in later sections.

Working closely with ESA's Science Operations Centre (SOC) staff, the SSC has played a large role in the development of the scientific analysis software for the *XMM-Newton* project: the 'SAS.' SAS modules are used in a fixed configuration for the routine processing of the *XMM-Newton* data, and in an interactive configuration to carry out custom analysis of the data. The SSC also carries out the routine 'pipeline' processing of all the *XMM-Newton* observations from each of the three science instrument packages. The aim of this processing is to provide a set of data products which will be of immediate value for the *XMM-Newton* observer as well as for the science archive. The *XMM-Newton* data products include calibrated, 'cleaned' event lists which provide the starting point for most interactive analysis of the data as well as a number of secondary high-level products such as sky images, source lists, cross-correlations with archival catalogues, source spectra and time series. The data products also constitute the starting point for the compilation of the serendipitous catalogue (see section 5.).

3.   Serendipitous Science with XMM-Newton

The high throughput, large field of view and good imaging capabilities of *XMM-Newton* mean that it detects significant numbers of serendipitous X-ray sources in each pointing in addition to the main target of the observation, as is illustrated in Figure 1. Typical observations yield $\sim$ 50 serendipitous sources per field. As *XMM-Newton* makes of the order 700 observations per year, covering $\sim$ 150 sq.deg. of the sky, the number of serendipitous sources is thus growing at a rate of $\sim$ 50000 sources per year, i.e., the annual rate is comparable in size to the complete *ROSAT* All Sky Survey, but reaches fluxes 2–3 orders of magnitude fainter. *XMM-Newton* data thus provides a deep, large area sky survey which represents a major resource for a wide range of programmes (see section 7.). The extended energy range of *XMM-Newton*, compared with previous imaging X-ray missions such as *ROSAT* and the *Einstein* Observatory, means that *XMM-Newton* detects significant numbers of obscured and hard-spectrum objects (e.g., obscured AGNs) which are absent from earlier studies.

In comparison with *Chandra*, typical *XMM-Newton* observations cover a significantly larger sky area but do not go as deep due to the superior imaging provided by the *Chandra* mirrors. *XMM-Newton* has a very significant advantage at photon energies above 4–5 keV: at low energies the ratio of *XMM-Newton/Chandra* effective areas is 3–4 but this increases to $\sim$ 6 at 5 keV and $>$ 10 at 7 keV.

4. The 'XID' Follow-up Programme

4.1. Need for Follow-up Studies

In order to exploit the full potential of the *XMM-Newton* serendipitous survey in the context of a wide range of scientific programmes, the key initial step is the 'identification' of the X-ray sources, i.e., a knowledge of the likely classification into different object types. For *XMM-Newton* serendipitous sources, the X-ray observations themselves will provide the basic parameters of each object: the celestial position, X-ray flux and colours for all sources and information on the X-ray spectrum, spatial extent and temporal variability for the brighter objects detected. This information alone will, in some cases, be sufficient to provide a clear indication of the type of object, but for the vast majority of sources, additional information will be required before a confident classification of the object can be made. Some of this information can come from existing astronomical catalogues, or from existing or planned large-scale optical, IR and radio surveys (e.g., SDSS, 2MASS, Denis, FIRST/NVSS), but full exploitation of the *XMM-Newton* serendipitous survey requires a substantial programme of new observations, primarily in the optical and IR using ground-based facilities. The SSC's XID follow-up programme is designed to meet these aims. The main new observational elements of the XID programme, the 'Core Programme' and the 'Imaging Programme' are outlined below.

4.2. The XID Core Programme

The aim of the Core Programme is to obtain the identifications for a well-defined sample of X-ray sources drawn from selected *XMM-Newton* fields, primarily using optical/IR imaging and spectroscopy. Imaging is required both to locate potential candidates accurately and reveal their morphology, whilst the optical spectroscopy provides the diagnostics needed both for object classification and for determining basic object parameters such as redshift and spectral slope. The principal objective is to obtain a completely identified sample which can be used to characterise the *XMM-Newton* source population overall sufficiently well that we can use the basic X-ray and optical parameters to assign a 'statistical' identification for a large fraction of **all** the sources in the *XMM-Newton* serendipitous source catalogue.

Table 1.   XID Core Programme samples.

Sample	Flux range[a]	Sky dens.[b]	# EPIC[c]	r/ mag.[d]
FAINT	$\geq 10^{-15}$	2200	5–10	23–25
MEDIUM	$\geq 10^{-14}$	340	30–50	21–23
BRIGHT	$\geq 10^{-13}$	10	1000	17–21
GALACTIC	$\geq 5 \; 10^{-15}$	~ 300	40	wide range

[a] X-ray flux in erg cm^{-2} s^{-1} in the 0.5–4.5 keV band

[b]source density (deg^{-2})

[c]no.of EPIC fields required

[d]typical r' magnitude range of counterparts

   The Core Programme has two main parts: one for the high and one for the low galactic latitude sky. The high galactic latitude part consists of three samples, each containing $\approx$ 1000 X-ray sources in three broad flux ranges as summarised in Table 1. The size of the subsamples is dictated by the need to identify enough objects to reveal minority populations. Studying sources at a range of X-ray fluxes is necessary because we already know that the importance of different source populations changes with X-ray flux level.

   Substantial progress has been made on the XID Core Programme over the last two years, in particular in the medium, bright and Galactic samples (Barcons et al. 2002a,b; Della Ceca et al. 2002; Motch et al. 2002). A large fraction of the ground-based observations needed to support this programme have come from the AXIS programme which gained a substantial international time allocation on the Canary Islands telescopes (Barcons et al. 2001). For example a significant number of identifications have already been made in 19 medium sample fields included in the XID programme. Of the 239 medium sample sources in these fields around 2/3 of these have already been identified (see Figure 2); the remaining sources are typically too faint for 4m-class telescopes and will be pursued with larger facilities over the next year. When complete, the XID medium sample will bridge the gap between the deepest surveys aimed at studying the most distant Universe, and shallower surveys which aim to characterise the local and high luminosity X-ray source populations.

4.3.   The XID Imaging Programme

The XID imaging programme aims to obtain optical/IR photometry and colours for a large number of *XMM-Newton* fields. The rationale is that a combination of X-ray flux & X-ray colours (from the *XMM-Newton* data) and optical magnitude

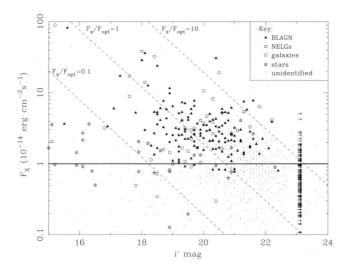

Figure 2. Distribution of X-ray and optical fluxes for serendipitous sources identified in the XID programme. The symbols indicate object classifications as given in the key. The nominal limit for the XID **medium** sample is indicated by the horizontal line.

and optical colours (from new ground-based observations) will provide the key parameters which make possible an accurate 'statistical' identification of the *XMM-Newton* sources. This will be possible using the results from the Core Programme to provide the 'calibration' of the basic parameters for different object types.

To date deep multi-colour optical imaging has been obtained for more than 150 *XMM-Newton* fields using 2m-class telescopes in both hemispheres. The prospects are good to expand this to 250–300 fields over the next two years.

5. The XMM-Newton Catalogue

5.1. Catalogue fields

The first installment of the catalogue (Watson et al. 2002) will include around 700 *XMM-Newton* observations ('fields') selected purely on the public availability of the fields at the planned release date (end 2002) and the observation being made in one of the appropriate EPIC imaging modes. No other selection of fields, e.g., in terms of sky location, exposure time etc., has been made. Figure 3 shows the sky distribution of the catalogue fields. The overall sky distribution is reasonably uniform, although there are some biases such as the paucity of fields in the Cygnus region due to *XMM-Newton* visibility constraints. The average exposure time per catalogue field is ~ 20 ksec for the EPIC MOS cameras and ~ 15 ksec for the EPIC pn camera.

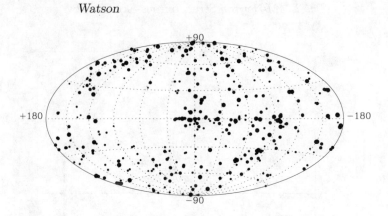

Figure 3.   Sky distribution of the *XMM-Newton* fields in the catalogue shown in Galactic coordinates. Size of the symbols reflects the
total number of serendipitous sources detected: the average number is
~ 50 per field.

5.2. Data Processing

Data processing for the production of the *XMM-Newton* catalogue is based
closely on the standard SSC pipeline (see section 2.) used to process each *XMM-
Newton* dataset for distribution to the observer, and population of the *XMM-
Newton* Science Archive. Catalogue processing uses a fixed software and calibration data configuration in order to guarantee uniformity. The main processing
stages for each *XMM-Newton* observation are:

- production of calibrated events from the ODF science frames;
- generation of the appropriate low-background time intervals using a threshold optimized for point source detection;
- generation of multi-energy-band X-ray images and exposure maps from
  the calibrated events;
- a four-stage source detection and parameterization procedure:
  - generation of a preliminary source list using a
    sliding-box technique and local background estimation;
  - generation of a background map from 2-D spline fits to the images
    with bright sources excised;
  - generation of a refined source list again using a sliding-box technique
    but employing the background map; and
  - maximum-likelihood fitting and parameterization of sources in the
    refined list.
- merging of the three camera-level source lists into an EPIC-level source
  list with merging on the basis of positional coincidence alone; and
- cross-correlation of the source list with a variety of archival catalogues and
  other resources using the CDS facilities in Strasbourg.

The source search approach utilized involves simultaneous fitting of five energy
band images for each EPIC camera, thus producing a source list for each camera
which contains source and detection information in each energy band (as well as
the total band). The camera lists combined in the penultimate stage described

above thus produce a merged source list which forms the reference source list for that observation.

5.3.   Quality Control

Although the source detection algorithm described above is now mature, typically producing reliable source lists from most *XMM-Newton* observations, the approach is not perfect and is known to have problems in producing reliable results in a number of (rare) circumstances. Each *XMM-Newton* field included in the catalogue is therefore visually screened to locate such defects. Where problems are noted the sources affected are 'flagged' and the flag values transferred to the source lists. In rare cases ($< 10\%$ of the total) the entire field has significant problems, e.g., very high background or very high surface brightness diffuse sources, which mean that it is of marginal value for detecting serendipitous sources. Such fields will be excluded from the final catalogue. Apart from these rare cases, the median fraction of sources flagged as being spurious amounts to only 4% overall, reflecting the maturity of the source detection approach.

6.   Catalogue Properties

6.1.   Source Numbers

The working catalogue contains a total of ~ 78000 source detections in any EPIC camera (i.e., in one or more cameras) and a total of ~ 11000 sources detected in all three EPIC cameras. These numbers refer to a broad-band (0.2–12 keV) detection above a likelihood of 10, corresponding to $\approx 4\sigma$. At this significance the *a priori* probability of spurious detections is low, corresponding to < 1 spurious source per field, although simulations are underway to verify the calibration of the likelihood parameterisation. The total sky area covered for detections in any camera is ~ 130 sq.deg., whilst for detection in all three cameras the area is ~ 90 sq.deg.

For the released version of the catalogue these numbers will be reduced by the fraction flagged as spurious (and the small number of fields totally excluded). We also anticipate setting a somewhat higher likelihood threshold once we have completed our investigation of the reliability of detections as a function of likelihood, being pursued by simulations.

6.2.   Source Count Distribution

Figure 4 shows the $\log N - \log S$ distribution for all EPIC pn sources in the working catalogue. The distribution is **not** corrected for sky coverage, i.e., how the actual sky area covered varies with X-ray flux. Comparing the uncorrected $\log N - \log S$ with the expected source counts demonstrates that the catalogue is essentially complete down to an X-ray flux $f_X \approx 4 \times 10^{-14}$ erg cm^{-2} s^{-1} (0.2–12 keV) (equivalent to $f_X \approx 2 \times 10^{-14}$ erg cm^{-2} s^{-1} in the 0.5–2 keV band and $f_X \approx 8 \times 10^{-15}$ erg cm^{-2} s^{-1} in the 2–10 keV band). This limit is in line with expectations given the exposure time distribution of catalogue fields. Around 30% of the catalogue sky area is covered to $f_X \approx 10^{-14}$ erg cm^{-2} s^{-1} (0.2–12 keV). Work to establish the definitive coverage corrections is underway and will

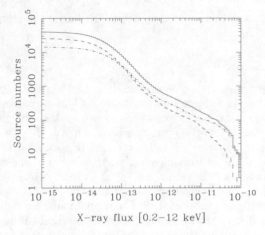

Figure 4.   Uncorrected $\log N - \log S$ distribution for all EPIC pn detections in the working catalogue. The solid curve is for all sources, the dashed curve is for high latitude sources ($|b| > 20°$) and the dashed-dot curve for low latitude sources ($|b| < 20°$).

be part of the ancillary information included with the released version of the catalogue.

6.3.   Astrometry

For each *XMM-Newton* field, the catalogue processing (section 5.2.) attempts to correct the astrometric reference frame using cross-correlation of the *XMM-Newton* source list with the USNO A2.0 catalogue (Monet et al. 1998). The technique employed involves finding the maximum likelihood in a grid of trial astrometric shifts and rotations with a likelihood function depending on the angular separation between each potential *XMM-Newton*–USNO object match. If an acceptable solution is found ($> 70\%$ of fields) the resultant astrometric correction is applied to the *XMM-Newton* source list for that field. (The cases where an acceptable solution is not found are primarily fields with low numbers of X-ray sources and/or fields with high optical object density).

The results of applying this technique to the catalogue fields can be employed to quantify the initial accuracy of the astrometry of each *XMM-Newton* field (i.e., before correction). Fits to the distribution of shifts in RA, Dec and field rotation imply that the intrinsic accuracy of the *XMM-Newton* field astrometry (as determined solely from the in-orbit attitude solution) can be characterized by a Gaussian with $\sigma \approx 1.5$ arcsec. *After* correction using this technique, the residual field astrometric errors are of the order 0.5–1 arcsec, close to the nominal 1 arcsec astrometric accuracy of the USNO catalogue itself.

As the typical *statistical* error-circle for a faint *XMM-Newton* source has $\sigma_{\mathrm{stat}} \approx 1 - -2$ arcsec, the size of the field systematic component determined justifies the ~ 5 arcsec positional accuracy which has been assumed to date as the effective $\sim 90\%$ confidence radius of uncorrected positions, e.g., for the identification of *XMM-Newton* source counterparts (see section 4.).

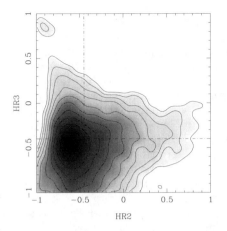

Figure 5.   X-ray colour-colour plot showing the distribution of HR2-HR3 values for EPIC pn catalogue sources ($|b| > 20°$ only). The grayscale and contours indicate the logarithmic density of points down to $\sim 1\%$ of the peak. The dashed-dot lines indicate the approximate HR2, HR3 values for the X-ray background. HR2 is the ratio (B-A)/(A+B) and HR3 is the ratio (C-B)/(B+C) where A= 0.5–2 keV count rate, B=2–4.5 keV count rate and C=4.5–7.5 keV count rate.

7.   Scientific Potential of the Catalogue

The *XMM-Newton* catalogue represents a significant resource that can be used for a variety of astrophysical projects. Although deep Chandra and *XMM-Newton* pencil-beam surveys (e.g., Mushotzky et al. 2000; Hasinger et al. 2001; Giacconi et al. 2001; Brandt et al. 2001) have probed the faintest parts of the extragalactic source population, the *XMM-Newton* catalogue also can make a major contribution. The *XMM-Newton* catalogue reaches modest depths ($f_X \approx 10^{-14}$ erg cm^{-2} s^{-1}) at high coverage (tens of square degrees). As this flux limit is where the bulk of the objects that contribute to the X-ray background lie (due to the fact the $\log N - \log S$ distribution breaks to a flatter slope at around this flux), the large samples of medium-deep flux sources that the *XMM-Newton* catalogue provides will thus be a significant resource for X-ray background studies.

The *XMM-Newton* catalogue also provides a rich resource for generating well-defined samples for specific studies, utilizing the fact that X-ray selection is a highly efficient (arguably the most efficient) way of selecting certain types of object, notably AGN, clusters of galaxies, interacting compact binaries and very active stellar coronae. AGN samples have obvious value in evolution studies and cluster samples can provide, potentially, key measurements of cosmological parameters. Selecting 'clean' samples requires knowledge of the likely parameter ranges of different types of object: some of this is already known but further 'calibration' of this concept is one of the key aims of the SSC's XID programme (section 4.; Watson et al. 2001; Barcons et al. 2002a,b). The inclusion of matches with archival catalogues for each *XMM-Newton* catalogue source also provides a valuable starting point for investigation of well-defined samples.

To illustrate some of the potential described above, Figure 5 shows the overall distribution of X-ray colours in the catalogue. This figure provides a glimpse of the power of the *XMM-Newton* catalogue for providing interesting samples. The spectrum of the X-ray background corresponds to HR2 ≈ -0.45, HR3 ≈ -0.4, but evidently the bulk of the catalogue sources have spectra softer than this. Thus merely by extracting a subset of *XMM-Newton* sources with X-ray colours harder than these limits, one automatically selects those objects that must be an important constituent of the background. Optical and near-IR observing programmes to investigate the nature of the hard source samples constructed in this manner are already underway.

As well as the potential for building up large samples, the brighter sources in the *XMM-Newton* catalogue also provide the prospect of obtaining high quality X-ray spectra and time series data (and morphology). Amongst the catalogue sources more than 15% have more than 200 EPIC pn counts, enough for a reasonable spectral characterization and crude variability indications, whilst 3% have more than 1000 counts, sufficient for a very good X-ray spectral measurement or variability analysis.

Acknowledgments. The SSC's activities relating to the *XMM-Newton* serendipitous sky survey are a consortium effort involving all the SSC institutions. I gratefully acknowledge the efforts of many colleagues which continue to contribute to the success of these projects.

References

Barcons, X. et al. 2001, New Century of X-ray Astronomy, eds. H. Inoue & H. Kunieda (San Francisco: ASP), 160

Barcons, X. et al. 2002a, A&A, 382, 522

Barcons, X. et al. 2002b, Astron Nachr., in press

Brandt, W. N. et al. 2001, AJ, 122, 1

Della Ceca, R. et al. 2002, New visions of the X-ray Universe in the XMM-Newton and Chandra era, in press, astro-ph/0202150

Giacconi, R. et al. 2001, ApJ, 551, 624

Hasinger, G. et al. 2001, A&A, 365, L45

Jansen, F. et al. 2001, A&A, 365, L1

Monet, D. et al. 1998, The USNO-A2.0 Catalogue, (U.S. Naval Observatory, Washington DC; VizieR Online Data Catalog, 1252)

Motch, C. et al. 2002, New visions of the X-ray Universe in the XMM-Newton and Chandra era, in press, astro-ph/0203025

Strüder, L. et al. 2001, A&A, 365, L18

Turner, M. J. L. et al. 2001, A&A, 365, L110

Watson, M. G. et al. 2001, A&A, 365, L51

Watson, M. G. et al. 2002, Astron Nachr., in press

Astronomical Data Analysis Software and Systems XII
ASP Conference Series, Vol. 295, 2003
H. E. Payne, R. I. Jedrzejewski, and R. N. Hook, eds.

The ISOCAM Parallel Mode Survey

Stephan Ott[1]

*Herschel Science Centre, ESA Research and Scientific Support
Department, PO Box 299, 2200 AG Noordwijk, The Netherlands*

Ralf Siebenmorgen

ESO, Karl-Schwarzschild-Str. 2, 85748 Garching, Germany

Norbert Schartel

*XMM-Newton Science Operations Centre, ESA Research and Scientific
Support Department, PO Box 50727, 28080 Madrid, Spain*

Thúy Võ

*ISO Data Centre, ESA Research and Scientific Support Department,
PO Box 50727, 28080 Madrid, Spain*

Abstract. During most of ESA's ISO mission, the mid-infrared camera
ISOCAM continued to observe the sky mainly around 6.7μm with a pixel
field of view of 6″ in its so-called "parallel mode" while another instrument
was prime.

This permitted an serendipitous survey of limited areas of the infrared sky, with varying depth and wavelength per field due to the different instrumental configurations used and the highly variable time spent
per pointed observation.

Dedicated calibration, data reduction and source extraction methods
were developed to analyse these serendipitously recorded data: 37000 individual pointings, taken during 6700 hours of observation. Using sophisticated merging algorithms, over 42 square degrees of the sky — roughly
one per mille of the celestial sphere — are currently being processed and
catalogued.

For the final catalogue around 30000 distinct point sources are expected. Their mid-infrared flux goes down to 0.5 mJy. Sources observed
with the most sensitive instrumental configuration have a median flux of
2.7 mJy outside the galactic plane, and a median flux of 6.3 mJy inside
the galactic plane.

---

[1]ISO Data Centre, ESA Research and Scientific Support Department, PO Box 50727, 28080
Madrid, Spain

1. Overview of the ISOCAM Parallel Survey

During most of ESA's Infrared Space Observatory (ISO) mission (Kessler et al. 1996), the mid-infrared camera ISOCAM (Cesarsky et al. 1996), continued to observe the sky in its so-called "parallel mode" while another of the three instruments (LWS, ISOPHOT or SWS) was prime, during both normal pointed observations and satellite slews between targets (Siebenmorgen et al. 1996).

In parallel mode, routine use was made of broad band filters centred around $6\mu m$ with the $6''$ pixel field of view (PFOV). As only a restricted telemetry band-width was available, 12 readouts with 2.1 seconds integration time were accumulated on board and down-linked as one image every 25 seconds. Depending on the prime instrument, ISOCAM observed the sky $12'-17'$ from the prime target. In order to avoid saturation of the detector, the optical configuration was adapted to the expected flux level of field sources using one of several modes.

Effectively, this permitted an serendipitous survey of limited areas of the infrared sky: Around 9700 hours of data were taken in the ISOCAM parallel mode; out of these 400 hours were used for calibration measurements, with ISOCAM in dark configuration.

For the work on the ISOCAM parallel catalogue only pointed observations lasting longer than 100 seconds were considered, i.e., such that at least four ISOCAM parallel readouts view the same part of the sky with the same instrumental configuration. Additionally, 617 hours of observation time had to be excluded for various reasons. Consequently 37000 pointings, representing in total 6700 hours of observation time, or 72% of all ISOCAM parallel data taken in pointed mode, could be processed. This makes the ISOCAM parallel survey the ISOCAM programme with by far the longest observing time. With an observed area of approximately 42 square degrees, it yields a sky-coverage double as large as any other ISO proposal for this wavelength range. Compared to IRAS (Beichman et al. 1988), areas covered by ISOCAM parallel are surveyed with up to 500 times more sensitivity, and a 50 times higher spatial resolution.

2. Status of the Point Source Catalogue

Dedicated data reduction and source extraction techniques, combined with major calibration, simulation and verification efforts, had to be developed to generate a catalogue of mid-infrared point sources candidates from data taken in the ISOCAM parallel survey (Ott 2002).

The deglitching methods are based on improved sigma-clipping algorithms, adapted for ISOCAM observations and its temporal glitch distribution, and were particularly efficient to deglitch ISOCAM parallel data down to four readouts. Major calibration efforts led to the generation of 11 master flat-fields, which enabled the detection of true sources close to the array borders and significantly reduced the number of spurious detections at the same area.

The source extraction method is based on an iterative, multi-step "search and destroy" algorithm, that combines source detection with classification into point and extended sources. This technique was particularly powerful to detect point sources in crowded areas and within extended sources, without missing any significant sources.

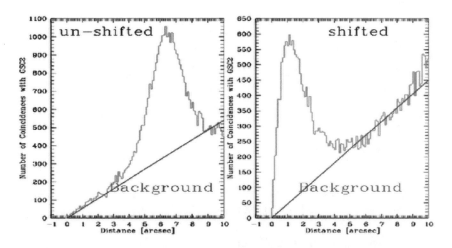

Figure 1.   Position coincidence between ISO and optical sources before **(left)** and after **(right)** astrometric correction for the lens-wheel jitter. For the corrected coordinates the peak of the distribution is $\approx 1.3''$, i.e., the magnitude of ISO's pointing error, and not at $\approx 6.5''$ as seen for sources without correction

A variety of simulations, performed at different flux levels, covered all aspects of the data processing. These validated the algorithmic approach, and permitted to predict the flux and positional accuracy of the extracted sources, and the completeness limits for each pointing of the ISOCAM parallel survey.

Major efforts were spent on quality checks and source classification. Over 74000 source candidates and 24000 individual pointings were eye-balled. The manual classification of source candidates is used to determine the cut-off parameters in order to statistically clean the detected source candidates.

Sources found in pointings which are characterised by a high number of readouts are accepted for the final catalogue if they are compliant with the cut-off parameters. This method isn't sufficient for sources detected in pointings with a small number of read-outs. Therefore, such sources are only accepted if they show a distance coincidence with sources known from optical (Guide Star Catalogue II), or near infrared (2MASS, k-band) observations.

Due to the lens-wheel jitter, which leads to an astrometric shift of ± 1 PFOV (e.g., $\pm 6''$ for most observations), direct merging is not possible, as there are sources which are observed several times and might be interpreted as independent sources, or two independent sources might be wrongly identified as one source. The final merging is based on ISO-ISO distance coincidences as provided in Figure 2 (left).

Currently we are in the process to merge multiple detected sources into unique sources. We hope to complete the merging, and the simulation of bias effects, and an additional completeness estimate on the whole catalogue end 2002, so that the catalogue can be published and released to the community spring 2003.

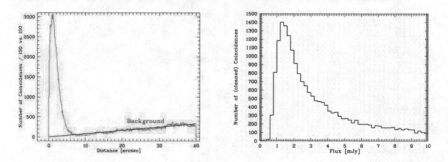

Figure 2.   **Left:** Position coincidence between ISO / ISO sources
Right: Flux distribution of ISOCAM parallel LW2 point sources.

3.   Description of the Catalogue

For the final catalogue, we expect 30000 unique point sources, and a reliability of
at least 99%. The detection threshold is limited by the flat-field noise. Using the
most sensitive instrumental configuration (the broad band filter LW2, covering a
wavelength range between 5–8.5μm, and 6″ PFOV), sources with a flux down to
0.5 mJy can be detected. The median flux of sources outside the galactic plane
(galactic latitude outside $\pm20°$) is 2.7mJy. The vast majority of these sources
are new detections in the infrared. 30 square degrees are mapped completely
down to 4 mJy, while 0.4 square degrees could be mapped completely down to
1.0 mJy.

Acknowledgments.   ISO is an ESA project with instruments funded by
ESA member states (especially the PI countries: France, Germany, the Nether-
lands and the United Kingdom) and with the participation of ISAS and NASA.
CIA is a joint development by the ESA Astrophysics Division and the ISOCAM
Consortium. The ISOCAM consortium is led by the ISOCAM PI, C. Cesarsky.

References

Beichman C. et al., eds. 1988, IRAS Catalogs and Atlases Explanatory Supple-
    ment, NASA RP-1190, (Washington, DC: GPO), vol 1

Cesarsky, C. et al. 1996, A&A, 315, L32

Kessler, M. F. et al. 1996, A&A, 315, L27

Ott, S. et al. 1997, in ASP Conf. Ser., Vol. 125, Astronomical Data Analysis
    Software and Systems VI, ed. G. Hunt & H. E. Payne (San Francisco:
    ASP), 34

Ott, S. 2002, Observations of the infrared sky with the ISOCAM parallel mode,
    PhD Thesis, Université Paris 6

Siebenmorgen, R. et al. 1996, A&A, 315, L169

Astronomical Data Analysis Software and Systems XII
ASP Conference Series, Vol. 295, 2003
H. E. Payne, R. I. Jedrzejewski, and R. N. Hook, eds.

Photometric and Astrometric Calibration of the Southern H-alpha Sky Survey Atlas

Peter R. McCullough

Space Telescope Science Institute, Baltimore, MD 21218

Abstract. The Southern H-Alpha Sky Survey Atlas (SHASSA) is the primary data product of a robotic wide-angle imaging survey of the southern sky at 656.3 nm wavelength, the H-alpha emission line of hydrogen. The scientific motivation for the survey and its photometric and astrometric calibration were described in this ADASS presentation and in Gaustad et al. (2001). The latter's Section 5 describes a mosaicing process by which foreground emission is removed from hundreds of overlapping images. Some scientific uses of the SHASSA are listed in the references below. SHASSA's web site can be found by typing "SHASSA" into Google.

References

Gaustad, J. E., McCullough, P. R., Rosing, W., & Van Buren, D. 2001, PASP, 113, 1326

McCullough, P. R., Bender, C., Gaustad, J. E., Rosing, W., & Van Buren, D. 2001, AJ, 121, 1578

McCullough, P. R., Fields, B. D., & Pavlidou, V. 2002, ApJ, 576, L41

Speck, A. K., Meixner, M., Fong, D., McCullough, P. R., Moser, D. E., & Ueta, T. 2002, AJ, 123, 346

Part 5. Telescopes and Observatory Operations

Astronomical Data Analysis Software and Systems XII
ASP Conference Series, Vol. 295, 2003
H. E. Payne, R. I. Jedrzejewski, and R. N. Hook, eds.

Conceptual Design for the Square Kilometer Array

R. D. Ekers

CSIRO, Australia Telescope National Facility, Sydney, NSW 2121, Australia

Abstract. New technologies have made it possible to construct an affordable radio telescope with collecting area of one square km: the SKA. Such a telescope would be so powerful that we could expand our knowledge of the universe from the earliest stages of its formation through to planetary exploration with greatly enhanced spacecraft communications. The SKA will join the new generation of telescopes at other wavebands with the sensitivity and resolution to image the earliest phases of galaxy formation, as well as greatly extending the range of unique science accessible at radio wavelengths. We already know how to build an SKA, the issue is how to build the most cost effective SKA, and how to maximize the science we can do with it. This project was born International and a number of countries are now comparing conceptual designs. All implementations call on Moore's law to satisfy the computationally demanding requirements. Some are more demanding than others and involve technologies and operational procedures never previously implemented in an astronomical facility.

1. The Development of Radio Astronomy

1.1. Exponential Growth in Science

It is well known that most scientific advances follow technical innovation. For astronomy this is well documented by Harwit (1981). De Solla Price (1963), had also reached this conclusion from his application of quantitative measurement to the progress of science in general. His analysis also showed that the normal mode of growth of science is exponential and showed examples from many areas. Moore's law, describing the 18 month doubling of transistor density on semiconductor chips, is a more recent re-discovery of this effect.

A famous example of exponential growth is the rate of increase of the operating beam energy in particle accelerators, as illustrated by Livingstone and Blewett (1962) and updated by Sessler (1988). Starting in 1930, each particle accelerator technology initially provided exponential growth up to a ceiling where the growth rate leveled off. At that point, a new technology was introduced. The envelope of the set of curves is itself an exponential curve, with an increase in energy of 10^{10} in 60 years. This example, originally presented by Fermi, has become known as the *Livingstone Curve* and is shown in Figure 1a.

1.2. Radio Telescope Sensitivity

A plot of the continuum sensitivity of telescopes used for radioastronomy since the discovery of extra-terrestrial radio emission in 1933 shows this exponential character (Figure 1b) with an increase in sensitivity of 10^5 since 1940, doubling every three years. As with the previous example, particular radio telescope technologies reach ceilings and new technologies are introduced. In particular, there was a transition (about 1980) from large single dishes to arrays of smaller dishes. To maintain the extraordinary momentum of discovery of the last few decades a very large new radio telescope will be needed in the next decade.

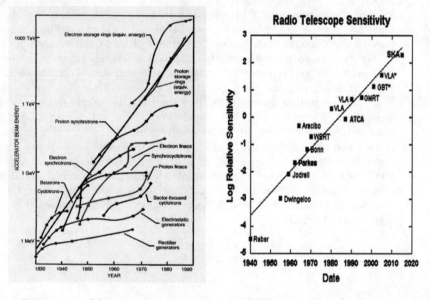

Figure 1.   (a) Livingstone curves   (b) Radio telescope sensitivity

1.3. The Square Kilometre Array (SKA)

An increase in sensitivity needed to maintain this exponential growth until 2010 cannot be achieved by improving the electronics or receiver systems in existing telescopes, but only by *increasing the total effective collecting area of radio telescopes to about a million square metres.* The project has therefore acquired the appellation, the Square Kilometre Array (http://www.skatelescope.org).

1.4. The Epoch of Re-Ionization

By the end of this decade one of the biggest questions remaining in astronomy will be the state of the Universe when the neutral hydrogen which recombined after the Big Bang is being re-ionized. This epoch of the Universe is totally opaque to optical radiation but can be probed by the 21-cm H line. The first structures will appear as inhomogeneities in the primordial hydrogen, heated by infalling gas or the first generation of stars and quasars. A patchwork of either 21-cm emission or absorption against the cosmic background radiation

Table 1.   Instrumental Design Goals

Parameter	Design Goal
Sensitivity	100 times the VLA
Total Frequency Range	0.03 – 20 GHz
Imaging Field of View	1 square deg. @ 1.4 GHz
Angular Resolution	0.1 arcsec @ 1.4 GHz
Surface Brightness Sensitivity	1 K @ 0.1 arcsec (continuum)
Instantaneous Bandwidth	$0.5 + \nu/5$ GHz
Number of Spectral Channels	10^4
Number of Instantaneous Pencil Beams	100 (at lower frequencies)

will result. This structure and its evolution with z will depend on the nature of the re-ionization sources. A large population of low mass stars have a completely different effect than a small number of QSOs. From $z \sim 6$ we expect to see a growing 'cosmic web' of neutral hydrogen and galaxy halos forming and evolving (e.g., Tozzi et al. 2000). A radio telescope with a square kilometer of collecting area operating in the 100–200 MHz frequency range will have the sensitivity to detect and study this web in HI emission!

2.   The Square Kilometre Array

2.1.   The Concept

The SKA is a unique radio telescope now being planned by an international consortium. Extensive discussion of the science drivers and of the evolving technical possibilities led to a set of design goals for the Square Kilometre Array (Taylor & Braun 1999). Some of the basic system parameters required to meet these goals are summarized in Table 1.

3.   Building the Square Kilometre Array

Costs of major astronomy facilities have now reached $US 1 billion levels. International funding is unlikely to exceed this value implying it has to be built at a cost $< \$US1000$ per square metre for 10^6 square metres. If we compare the costs per square metre of existing radio telescopes (Table 2) we see that we will need innovative design to reduce cost.

One new technology that helps is the combination of transistor amplifiers and their large-scale integration into systems which can be duplicated inexpensively. Another essential technology is our recently acquired ability to apply digital processing at high bandwidth. This enables us to realize processes, such as multiple adaptive beam formation and active interference rejection, in ways not previously conceivable.

Some aspects of the technology needed are still in the development stage. Institutions participating in the SKA are designing and building prototype sys-

Table 2.   Cost / sq metre

Telescope	$US/sqm	ν_{max}
GBT	10,000	100 GHz
VLA	10,000	50 GHz
ATA	3,000	11 GHz
GMRT	1,000	1 GHz

tems and the key technologies will be determined from these. The time frame during which a new radio facility is needed to complement other planned instruments will be in the years around 2010.

4.   How to Build the SKA?

We have the technology to build the SKA now, we have decades of experience with diffraction limited interferometry and self calibration (Adaptive Optics). The issue for the SKA is not whether we can build it, but how to find the most cost effective solution. Options under consideration include: arrays of small dishes; planar phased arrays; single adaptive reflector; multiple Arecibos; arrays of Luneburg lenses.

4.1.   Focal and Aperture Plane Arrays

There is an equivalence between focal plane arrays and aperture plane arrays. For a given number N of receiver elements, these two approaches are exactly equivalent for contiguous aperture. However, achieving the maximum compactness without either shadowing or geometric projection losses is only possible if the aperture plane array is on a tilting platform. For unfilled aperture arrays the synthesis approach trades resolution for brightness sensitivity.

The single dish forms its image with real time delays and is inherently wide band while an array with only electronic phasing (or Fourier transform of the complex coherence function) will be monochromatic. The aperture plane array can be made achromatic by dividing the band into sufficiently narrow spectral channels ($\Delta\nu/\nu <$ element size/aperture size), and with the rapidly decreasing cost of digital electronics this becomes increasingly affordable.

There are major differences in implementation for the two approaches. A single dish uses optics to combine the analog signal (wave front) at the focus whereas a modern aperture synthesis telescope uses digital signal processing. This difference leads to a very big shift in cost between mechanical structures for a big dish and computers for an aperture plane array. These two cost drivers have a very different time dependence, with the decreasing cost of digital processing shifting the most cost effective designs from big dishes to arrays. At higher frequencies the increased cost contribution of the lowest noise receivers and the cost of the backend signal processing for the larger bandwidth, shift the balance back to arrays with larger dish size. A recent analysis by Weinreb & D'Addario (2001) shows that the optimum centimetre telescope in 2010 will be an array of 8m dishes.

4.2. Mass-produced Parabolas: The Allen Telescope Array

The Allen Telescope Array (ATA) being built by the SETI Institute and UC Berkeley is a modern example of an aperture plane array with 350×6.1 m parabolic antennas giving aperture synthesis capability with a very large primary beam (2°50 field of view at 1.4 GHz) and the equivalent of a 100m aperture. Taking advantage of modern electronics and wide band optical communication it will cover 0.5–11 GHz and generate four simultaneous beams. The planned completion date is 2005.

4.3. Phased Array

In the extreme aperture plane array with element size comparable to a wavelength it is possible, with no moving parts, to electronically steer beams to any part of the sky. It is also possible to generate simultaneous independent beams anywhere in the sky.

Figure 2.   NFRA phased array with director Harvey Butcher and the Dwingeloo 25m dish in the background.

The Netherlands have now produced a pure phased array with significant collecting area and no moving parts. (Figure 2). The juxtaposition of the 25m dish and the phased array nicely illustrates 50 years of technology development.

4.4. Software and Computing Power

Much more computing capacity is needed for these telescopes with large numbers of elements but with computing power doubling every 18 months (Moore's Law) the required capacity looks achievable. However, software development time scales are now much longer than hardware development time scales so software should be treated as a capital cost and hardware, which needs to be upgraded continually to obtain maximum performance, becomes an operating cost.

5. Sensitivity

The most obvious impact of the SKA will be its sensitivity, almost 100 times that of any existing radio telescope. For example, the current deepest VLA integration in the HDF detects about a dozen sources. In the same region the SKA will detect many hundreds of galaxies and AGNs (Hopkins et al. 2000).

5.1. Computing Demand : Sensitivity

The increased sensitivity makes indirect demands on computational capacity and software systems. Interference rejection of up to 10^4 will be needed to reach sensitivity limits, and the suppression of sidelobes from stronger sources will require a dynamic range of 10^6. Achieving full sensitivity will also require reliable operation of a great many elements, putting pressure on the monitoring and debugging software needed to maintain the system.

6. Interference

Ironically, the very developments in communications that drive Moore's Law and make these radio telescopes possible also generate radio interference at levels far in excess of the weak signals detectable with an SKA. The future of radio observations with this high sensitivity will depend on our ability to mitigate against interference. A combination of adaptive cancelation, regulation and geographic protection will be required to let us access the faint signals from the early universe (Ekers & Bell 2001). These techniques will make critical and complex demands on computational requirements and are discussed further in the next section.

6.1. Mitigation Strategies and Issues

Undesired interfering signals and astronomy signals can differ (be orthogonal) in a range of parameters, including: frequency, time, position, polarization, distance, coding, positivity, and multi path. It is extremely rare that interfering and astronomy signals do not possess some level of orthogonality in this ≥ 8 dimensional parameter space.

Figure 3.   ATA in nulls, Bower(2002).

We are developing signal processing systems to take advantage of the orthogonality and separate the astronomy and interfering signals. Antenna arrays and focal plane arrays are particularly powerful because they can take advantage of the position, and even distance (curvature of wavefront) phase space (Ekers & Bell 2002).

The adaptive filter is one of the most promising areas of interference mitigation. The characteristics of the interfering signal in the astronomical data are used to derive the parameters of the filter which removes or reduces the interference. Two implementations of the adaptive filter are currently being studied (Kesteven 2002): the pre-detection filters which are well known in the signal processing field and a post-correlation filter which is well adapted to radio astronomy needs.

When these filter concepts are applied to arrays they are equivalent to the generation of spatial nulls in the direction of the interfering signals. A dramatic illustration of the potential to generate very complex patterns of nulls has been provided by Geoff Bowers who generated 'ATA' in nulls with the 350 element of the Allen Telescope Array. (Figure 3).

7. Dynamic Range

Achieving the 10^6 dynamic range needed to realize full sensitivity will be a very demanding and computationally intensive requirement. The SKA is unusual because in many implementations the 'primary beam' is also generated by aperture synthesis hence it will be necessary to calibrate a synthesized time-variable primary beam with precision. The measurement equation formalism (Sault & Cornwell 1999) implemented in AIPS++ allows correction for such image-plane calibration effects. Self calibration (adaptive optics) will be needed.

The radio interferometry group at MIT/Haystack is studying the design of arrays made up of a very large number of small telescopes. These designs might have several thousand elements implying millions of baselines, and antenna elements are less than several meters. Such large-N configurations have extremely dense u-v coverage, and because of the small elements very large primary beams. This results in a massive correlation problem, but from these characteristics spring a startling number of benefits. The sidelobes due to (u,v) coverage are naturally very low, the achievable dynamic range is very high and there is great flexibility to generate nulls in order to remove interference. Of course the computational requirements are also correspondingly larger.

8. Resolution and Field of View (FOV)

Both focal and aperture plane arrays dramatically increase the throughput for surveys. The Square Kilometre Array will be the world's premier instrument for astronomical imaging. No other instrument, existing or currently planned, on the ground or in space, at any wavelength, will provide simultaneously: a wide instantaneous field of view (1 square degree) and exquisite and well defined angular resolution (0.1–0.001 arcsec); and wide instantaneous bandwidth ($\Delta\nu/\nu > 50\%$), coupled with high spectral resolution ($\nu/d\nu > 10^4$) for detecting small variations in velocity.

8.1.   Computing Demand : Resolution

For observations with the full field of view the maximum practical baselines used would be limited to about 300 km, corresponding to 0.1 arcsec at 1.4 GHz. Full resolution observations in subfields which contain structure could use up to 5000 km baselines providing milli arcsec resolution.

Signal distribution will involve transport of GHz bandwidth signals over 1000 km to hundreds of stations. Achieving this will be expensive and will be one of the key factors limiting ultimate performance.

8.2.   Computing Demand : FOV

The image size for the highest resolution likely to be used over the full FOV is about $10^5 \times 10^5$ pixels. This is about $400 \times$ VLA and should be achieved in 10–15 years. For the higher resolution available with SKA it is neither practical nor sensible to image the full FOV so hierarchical beamforming will be used to only image regions with signals of interest.

Wide field synthesis will require corrections for non planar effects and chromatic aberration. These are discussed in Cotton (1999).

8.3.   Computing Demand : Spectral Line Imaging

An ambitious SKA spectral imaging correlator could require correlations of 8000 antennas (3.2×10^7 baselines) each with 1 GHz band width and 1000 spectral line channels.

Fortunately, extrapolation of the historical rate of correlator development (Figure 4) Wright (2002) shows that achieving this is not an unreasonable projection.

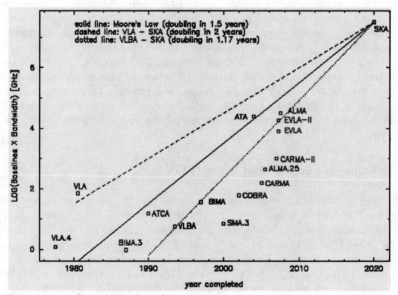

Figure 4.   Correlator Development

9. Multiple Beams

The reduction in the cost and size of the electronics in telescopes of the future will allow radio astronomers to take increasing advantage of multibeaming through either focal plane or aperture plane arrays. In the extreme aperture plane array with element size comparable to a wavelength it is even possible to generate simultaneous independent beams anywhere in the sky changing the whole sociology of big telescope astronomy (Figure 5).

Figure 5.   SKA Multibeaming

9.1.   Computing Demand : Multiple Beams

Many simultaneous beams can be generated by signal processing from the output of an array of small dishes. For example, for an array which contains 500 dishes connected with 2 GHz bandwidth, it requires about 4,000 Gops to form each beam by direction summation. In early 1999 that was quite expensive! At $US250 per digital signal processing Gop, it amounted to $US10M per beam. However, the processing costs are dropping rapidly. Assuming that Moore's law continues to hold, then in about 2008 the processing cost will only be $US2/Gop, corresponding to <$US0.1 M per beam.

One of the exciting advantages of the multiple beam operation is the diversity of backend configurations. Different beams could be configured with: spectral line imaging correlators; pulsar timing devices, pulse detectors or SETI processors. Correspondingly diverse software support would be needed.

We can have remotely configurable configurations for making parallel simultaneous observations with multiple backend configurations, and multiple users. Control software for such a facility will present challenging opportunities.

9.2.   Observing Transients Before They Happen

Entirely new ways of doing astronomy may be possible with the SKA. With an array that is pointed electronically, the raw, 'undetected' signals can be recorded in memory. These stored signals could be used to construct virtual beams pointing anywhere in the sky. Using such beams astronomers could literally go back in time and use the full collecting area to study pulsar glitches, supernovae and gamma-ray bursts or SETI candidate signals, following a trigger from a subarray of the SKA or from other wavelength domains.

10. International

Even with the dramatic reduction in cost of unit aperture, future telescopes such as the SKA will be expensive. One path to achieving this vision is through international collaboration. While the additional overhead of a collaborative project is a penalty, the advantages are also great. It can avoid wasteful duplication and competition; provide access to a broader knowledge base; generate innovation through cross fertilization; and create wealth for the nations involved.

References

Bower, G 2002, ATA memo Series, UC Berkeley

Cotton, W. D. 1999, Synthesis Imaging in Radio Astronomy II, eds. G. B. Taylor, C. L. Carilli, and R. A. Perley. ASP Conference Series, 180, 357

de Solla Price, D. J. 1963, Little Science, Big Science (New York: Columbia University Press)

Ekers, R. D., & Bell, J. F. 2001, in IAU Symp. 196, Preserving the Astronomical Sky, Vienna, ed. R.J. Cohen and W.T. Sullivan (San Francisco: ASP)

Ekers, R. D., & Bell, J. F., 2002, in IAU Symp. 199, The Universe at Low Radio Frequencies, ed. P. Rao (San Francisco: ASP)

Harwit, M. 1981, Cosmic Discovery (New York: Basic Books, Inc)

Hopkins, A., Windhorst, R., Cram, L., & Ekers, R. 2000, Experimental Astronomy, 10, 419

Kesteven, M. 2003, New Technologies in VLBI, Gyeongju, Korea; Nov 5-8, 2002 (San Francisco: ASP)

Livingstone, M. S. & Blewet, J. P. 1962, Particle Accelerators (New York: McGraw Hill)

Sault, R. J. & Cornwell, T. J. 1999, ASP Conf. Ser. 180, Synthesis Imaging in Radio Astronomy II, eds. G. B. Taylor, C. L. Carilli, and R. A. Perley (San Francisco: ASP) 657

Sessler, A. M. 1988, Physics Today, 41, 26

Taylor, A. R., & Braun, R. eds. 1999, Science with the Square Kilometre Array[1]

Tozzi, P., Madau, P., Meiksin, A. & Rees, M. J. 2000, ApJ, 528, 597

Weinreb, S. & D'Addario, L. 2001, SKA Memo Series,[2] 1

Wright, M. 2002, SKA Memo Series,[2] 21

---

[1]http://www.skatelescope.org/ska_science.shtml

[2]http://www.skatelescope.org/ska_memos.shtml

Astronomical Data Analysis Software and Systems XII
ASP Conference Series, Vol. 295, 2003
H. E. Payne, R. I. Jedrzejewski, and R. N. Hook, eds.

Adaptive Optics at the VLT: NAOS-CONICA

Chris Lidman

European Southern Observatory, Alonso de Cordova 3107, P.O. 19001 Santiago 19 Chile

Abstract. NAOS-CONICA is the first adaptive optics instrument to be offered to the community at the ESO VLT. This instrument is capable of diffraction limited imaging, spectroscopy, polarimetry and coronography in the 1 to 5 micron wavelength region. In this paper, I will provide a description of the instrument and summarize NAOS-CONICA "end-to-end" operations.

1. Introduction

NAOS-CONICA is the first adaptive optics (AO) instrument to begin operations at the ESO VLT, and the fifth instrument overall since operations began with ISAAC and FORS1 as the first two instruments on Antu[1] in 1999. NAOS-CONICA is located on Yepun, which also hosts FORS2 and came into operations in 2001.

2. NAOS-CONICA

An image of NAOS-CONICA attached to the Nasmyth B focus of Yepun is shown in Figure 1. NAOS-CONICA consists of two instruments: NAOS (Rousset et al. 2002, Lacombe et al. 2002), which is the AO part of NAOS-CONICA (in Figure 1 it can be seen attached directly to the telescope) and CONICA (Lenzen et al. 2002), which is the IR camera and spectrograph that is attached to the back of NAOS.

The process of bringing an instrument into operations on the VLT follows a process of commissioning, where the instrument is integrated, attached to the telescope and tested, and *Paranalization*, where operational procedures are defined, calibration methods are tested, and readiness for science operations is assessed. Commissioning of NAOS-CONICA started in November, 2001; first light occurred on November 25th; Paranalization started in May 2002 and Operations started on September 30th, 2002.

---

[1]The four 8m telescopes are called Antu (VLT-UT1), Kueyen (VLT-UT2), Melipal (VLT-UT3) and Yepun (VLT-UT4), which, in the Mapuche language, translate to The Sun, The Moon, The Southern Cross and The Evening Star.

Figure 1.   NAOS-CONICA on the Nasmyth B focus of Yepun. From left to right, one can identify the Nasmyth B rotator (dark blue), NAOS (light blue), the back-end of NAOS (white), CONICA (red) and the cables that transport coolant, power and signals between NAOS-CONICA and the co-rotator.

2.1. NAOS

NAOS takes the uncorrected beam from the telescope and provides a turbulence compensated F/15 beam and a 2 arc-minutes FOV to CONICA. The wavefront distortions are measured with sensors that use Shack-Hartmann screens and compensated via tip-tilt and deformable mirrors, the latter of which has 185 actuators. NAOS can work with natural reference sources that are either point like or extended and can select them over a 2 arc-minute FOV. Provisions have been made for it to work with a laser guide star.

NAOS can do the wavefront sensing either in visible (0.4–1.0 microns) or IR light (1.0–2.5 microns) and can perform partial correction for reference sources as faint at $V \approx 17$ and $K \approx 12$. Full correction, where the PSF core becomes diffraction limited, occurs with brighter reference sources.

Five dichroics can be used to split different fractions of visible and IR light between the wave front sensors (reflection) and CONICA (transmission). Currently, only two dichroics are offered; the remainder will be offered in future periods.

2.2. CONICA

CONICA takes the corrected beam from NAOS and can be used for

- imaging with 34 broad, intermediate and narrow-band filters,
- low-resolution long-slit spectroscopy with four grisms,
- polarimetry with Wollaston prisms or wire grids,
- coronography with masks in the focal plane and apodising masks in the pupil plane and
- Fabry-Perot imaging.

There are seven objectives in the camera wheel, which allow one to do all of the above at pixel scales ranging from 13 to 110 milli-arcseconds per pixel.

The array is an Aladdin detector and is sensitive over the 1–5 micron wavelength range. Depending on which elements are in the light path, the background on the array can vary by six order of magnitude. To cope with this, a number of readout modes and bias voltage settings are used.

The total number of instrument and detector configurations is very, very large. Currently, only a small subset of all possible configurations are offered. Additional configurations will be offered as their usefulness are assessed.

3. NOAS-CONICA (VLT) Operations

NAOS-CONICA is operated like any other instrument on the VLT, so when one refers to NAOS-CONICA operations, one is really referring to VLT operations (Hanuschik et al. 2002; Mathys et al. 2002; Quinn et al. 2002, Silva et al. 2002). Given the number of instruments on Paranal, their complexity and the number of operators who are likely to operate any one instrument, a successful and efficient operation demands a very high degree of uniformity in instrument operations.

Operations are guided by the following principles:

- All observations and calibrations are done with Observing Blocks (OBs).
- All calibrations are done by the observatory staff according to a calibration plan.
- Daily tasks are managed through checklists.
- Instrument (and telescope) performance is monitored and recorded.
- All data is checked and archived.

3.1. Observing Tools - The Life-cycle of an OB

The astronomer and the observatory have a number of tools to prepare and execute observations, to monitor instrument performance and assess data quality. These tools are illustrated in Figure 2, where we follow the life-cycle of an OB.

After carefully reading the User Manual and the Calibration Plan, the astronomer uses the preparation software (PS) to determine the optimal configuration of NAOS for a given set of observing conditions and reference parameters, the Exposure Time Calculator (ETC) to compute S/N estimates and the phase II preparation (P2PP) tool to prepare OBs.

The astronomer specifies under which conditions the observations should take place. Constraints generally include the seeing, the transparency of the atmosphere, the airmass, the distance to the moon and the lunar phase. For

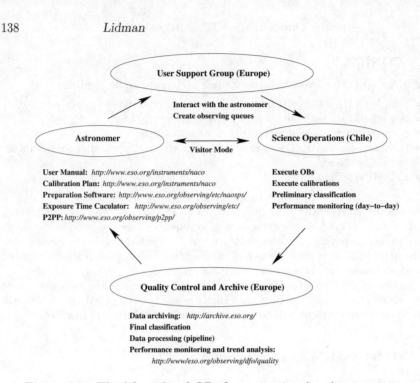

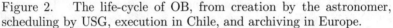

Figure 2.   The life-cycle of OB, from creation by the astronomer, scheduling by USG, execution in Chile, and archiving in Europe.

observations with NAOS-CONICA, the user also lists the Strehl ratio, which is a measure of the quality of the correction. The Strehl ratio is determined by the PS, and it depends on the characteristics of the atmospheric turbulence, the brightness and morphology of the reference source and the distance of the reference source to the target. The use of PS is obligatory for all NAOS-CONICA observations. It is discussed in more detail in Section 3.3.

In service (queue) mode, the OBs, the finding charts and a file describing the observations are submitted to the User Support Group (USG) in Europe. USG checks the validity of the submitted material and inserts the OBs into queues that are updated on a daily basis. In visitor mode the OBs are usually prepared a few days before the observations take place. In this case, USG and QC are not directly involved, but all data is still archived. The OBs, whether it be service or visitor mode, are executed by ESO staff in Chile. Calibrations are taken the following day according to the calibration plan.

In service mode, OBs are started if the seeing, airmass, etc., are with the limits specified by the astronomer. At this point, there is no information about the Strehl ratio. This is evaluated during the acquisition of the target and during execution of the OB, both through direct measurements on the data (if possible) and through inferred estimates provided by the real time computer, which is the computer that measures the wavefront distortions and controls the tip-tilt and deformable mirrors. The operator assigns a preliminary classification according to measured or inferred Strehl, airmass, etc. Three classification classes are used: A - meets all specifications, B - does not meet all specifications but should not be repeated, C - does not meet all specifications and should be repeated. In general, the seeing is not used to classify OBs.

OBs that were classified as C are immediately re-queued. The data from OBs that were classified A or B are examined by quality control in Europe, where a final classification is made. These OBs can be reclassified as C and, as such, will be re-queued. All data, regardless of the classification, is archived and passed onto the user. The data is usually sent to the astronomer once the program is complete and is available to the entire community one year later.

The performance of the instrument is monitored by the observatory staff on a daily basis. All information is collected into a central database which can be queried. The database contains information from telescope and instrument subsystems, pipeline processing of the data and the meteorological station. The monitoring is primarily designed to detect sudden changes in instrument performance. The performance of the instrument is also monitored in Europe. Here, the emphasis is on long term trending. Results are fed back into the system as improvements to operations.

3.2. The NAOS-CONICA Calibration Plan

The calibration plan is an important document and this is particularly true for a complex instrument like NAOS-CONICA, where the number of modes is very large and the amount of time to do calibrations can be limited. The calibration plan describes:

- which calibrations are supported, and which are not,
- how they are done,
- how frequently they are done,
- how accurately they are done, and
- how they are processed, if some sort of processing is required.

Twilight flats provide a pertinent example of what is in the calibration plan. In principle, with 7 objectives, 34 filters, 3 neutral density filters and 5 dichroics, one could have $7 \times 34 \times 3 \times 5 = 3570$ combinations. To calibrate all possible combinations is an impossible task. As an alternative, twilight flats are taken with a single dichroic and without neutral density filters. The calibration plan states this and discusses how useful the flats are if a different dichroic or a neutral density filter was used during the observations. All of this needs to be tested and characterized during *Paranalization*.

3.3. The Preparation Software

In addition to the standard observing tools, such as P2PP and the Exposure Time Calculator (ETC), users have to use the preparation software (PS).

As input, the PS takes:

- the wavelength of the observation,
- the seeing (at Zenith) and airmass of the observation,
- the brightness and morphology of the reference source,
- the spectral type or black body temperature of the reference source,
- the distance between the reference source and the scientific target and
- any user constraints (if any) that the user sets with regards to the configuration of NAOS.

Table 1.   The future of adaptive optics at the VLT.

Instrument Name	Purpose	Year
Laser Guide Star	For NAOS-CONICA and SINFONI	04
MACAO (6 will be built)	Curvature sensing AO system	02–04
MACAO + SPIFFI (SINFONI)	AO assisted 3D system IR Spectroscopy	02–04
MACAO + CRIRES	AO assisted high resolution IR Spectroscopy	04
MAD	Multi-conjugate AO Demonstrator	04

As output, the PS delivers:

- the Strehl ratio on the target and the reference source at the wavelength of observation,
- the Strehl ratio on the reference source at 2.16 microns (this corresponds to the wavelength of the Br_γ filter),
- a model PSF which is used by the ETC for estimating exposure times,
- the optimal NAOS configuration, and
- a P2PP parameter file containing all of the above information.

In this way, the user does not need to know anything about NAOS.

The PS consists of a PS GUI and a PS server. The PS GUI is available from the ESO web pages.[2] The server receives requests from the GUI, does all the necessary calculations and sends the results back to the GUI for inspection.

Currently, three servers are running: one in Europe for OB preparation, one in the control room for real time OB preparation, and one on the instrument workstation for real time optimization of NAOS. Real time optimization is the default mode of operations.

The estimate of the Strehl ratio provided by the PS is critical, since it is compared directly to the one measured in the data. The two values are compared and the OB is classified accordingly. If the PS over-estimates the performance of NAOS, very few OBs will be successfully executed according to the rules which are currently in use.

4.   Adaptive Optics at the VLT: Future Prospects

Over the next few years, ESO will install, commission and operate a number of facilities/instruments that are either AO systems or will be feeding to/from AO systems. The instruments and their commissioning dates are listed in Table 1.

As these lines are being written, NAOS-CONICA has been in operations for six weeks. The experience in operating NAOS-CONICA, the first AO system at the VLT, should prove to be very useful in optimising the operations of the many AO instruments to come.

---

[2]http://www.eso.org/observing/etc/naosps/

References

Hanuschik, R. W., Hummel, W., Sartoretti, P., & Silva, D. R. 2002, "Quality Control of the ESO-VLT instruments," in Observatory Operations to Optimize Scientific Return III, P. J. Quinn, ed., Proc SPIE 4844, in press

Lacombe, F., Zins, G., Charton, J., Chauvin, G., Dumont, G., Feautrier, P., Fusco, T., Gendron, E., Hubin, N. N., Kern, P. Y., Lagrange, A. M., Mouillet, D., Puget, P., Rabaud, D., Rabou, P., Rousset, G., & Beuzit, J. 2002, "NAOS: from an AO system to an astronomical instrument," in Adaptive Optical System Technologies II, P. L. Wizinowich, ed., Proc SPIE 4839, in press

Lenzen, R., Hartung, M., Brandner, W., Finger, G., Hubin, N. N., Lacombe, F., Lagrange, A., Lehnert, M. D., Moorwood, A., & Mouillet, D. 2002, "NAOS/CONICA first on sky results in a variety of observing modes," in Instrument Design and Performance for Optical/Infrared Ground-Based Telescopes, A. Moorwoed, ed., Proc SPIE 4841, in press

Mathys, G., Gilmozzi, R., Hurtado, N., Kaufer, A., Lidman, C. & Parra, J. 2002, "Paranal science operations: running the four 8m unit telescopes of ESO's VLT" in Observatory Operations to Optimize Scientific Return III, P. J. Quinn, ed., Proc SPIE 4844, in press

Quinn, P. J., Gilmozzi, R., Comeron, G., Mathys, G., & Silva, D. R. 2002, "VLT end-to-end science operations: the first three years," in Observatory Operations to Optimize Scientific Return III, P. J. Quinn, ed., Proc SPIE 4844, in press

Rousset, G., Lacombe, F., Puget, P., Hubin, N. N., Gendron, E., Fusco, T., Charton, J., Feautrier, P., Kern, P. Y., Lagrange, A. M., Madec, P. Y., Mouillet, D., Rabaud, D., Rabou, P., Stadler, E., & Zins, G. 2002, "NAOS, the first AO system of the VLT: on-sky performance," in Adaptive Optical System Technologies II. P. L. Wizinowich, ed., Proc SPIE 4839, in press

Silva, D. R. 2002, "Service Mode Scheduling at the ESO VLT," in Observatory Operations to Optimize Scientific Return III, P. J. Quinn, ed., Proc SPIE 4844, in press

Astronomical Data Analysis Software and Systems XII
ASP Conference Series, Vol. 295, 2003
H. E. Payne, R. I. Jedrzejewski, and R. N. Hook, eds.

The Subaru Telescope Software Trinity System

R. Ogasawara, G. Kosugi, T. Takata, J. Noumaru, T. Sasaki

Subaru Telescope, NAOJ, 650 N. Aohoku Pl., Hilo HI 96720

Y. Chikada[2], Y. Mizumoto[3], M. Yagi[3], N. Yasuda[4], S. Ichikawa[4], M. Yoshida[5]

NAOJ, Osawa 2-21-1, Mitaka 181-8588 Tokyo, Japan

K. Kawarai, Y. Ishihara, A. Kawai[6]

Fujitsu Ltd., Nakase 1-9-3, Mihama, Chiba 261-8588, Japan

Abstract. In order to support observations made with the Subaru Telescope located atop Mauna Kea, Hawaii, a synthesized software system has been developed in the past several years. It consists of the Subaru Observation Software System, the Subaru Telescope Archive System, and the Data Analysis System Hierarchy. This was a challenging project of the Japanese astronomical community and it contributes to the operational data flow and quality control of observational data of the Subaru Telescope.

1. Introduction

The Subaru Telescope is an optical infrared telescope with 8.2m monolithic mirror located at the summit of Mauna Kea, Hawaii, funded 100% by the Japanese government, Ministry of the Education, Culture, Sports, Science, and Technology (MEXT). The Subaru Telescope began operation in January 1999, and began the Open Use program for astronomers all over the world in December 2000 (Kaifu 1998; Noumaru 2002; Iye 2002).

The essence of the Subaru Telescope can be summarized as follows.

- 8.2 meter monolithic mirror, 20cm thick and weighing 24 tons, made of ULE glass.

---

[1] E-Mail:ryu@subarutelescope.org

[2] Radio Astronomy Division

[3] Optical Infrared Astronomy and Observation System Division

[4] Astronomical Data Analysis and Computing Center

[5] Okayama Astrophysical Observatory

[6] Fujitsu America Inc.

- Active Mirror Support to maintain the accurate mirror surface.
- Multiple foci (Prime, Cassegrain,and two Nasmyth foci)
- Air Flushing Dome to stabilize the air flow.
- Temperature Control of Mirror and Dome to reduce turbulence.

The construction of the dome structure at the summit of Mauna Kea, Hawaii, began on July 6, 1992, and the telescope was brought in 1997 December. Meanwhile, the Subaru Headquarters at Hilo, Hawaii (Hilo Base Facility) opened in April 1997. The 8.2m monolithic mirror blank was transported to the summit November 1998, and the mirror emerged after a successful onsite aluminization on November 8, 1998. All eight facility instruments have successfully survived the commissioning process in the following two years to open a new era of astronomy in December 2000; complete open use for all astronomers in the world.

2.   Strategy of Software System Design and Development

The Subaru Telescope is characterized as a complex system of various mechanisms; telescope structure, enclosing dome structure, air flow and temperature control, and many instruments and the huge amount of data produced by those instruments.

An operational model of the Subaru Telescope was defined as follows.

- To achieve uniform operation and maintenance for each of the instruments and telescope.
- To establish an effective and easy-to-handle operational system, not only for the staff but also for visiting astronomers.
- To archive all data.
- To assure a proper proprietary time for observers, and then open all observing data.
- To construct pipeline analysis software with suitable quality control.
- To provide sufficient support for the observation process both for observers and for the observatory.

The three main components of the core system have been abstracted; an observation control system to support the whole observation process, an archive system to support data management, and a data analysis system to support data analysis including automatic pipeline analysis. Through this operation, the quality control of observed data is considered to be a most important concern.

The control system of the telescope and dome structure was developed in close conjunction with the construction of the telescope and dome by Mitsubishi Electric Co. Ltd.(Tanaka 1998), the main contractor of the construction of the Telescope from 1992–1998. The first generation instruments, three in visible wavelengths and five infra-red instruments had been planned to be developed by each instrument team after 1995 (Iye 1998; Iye & Yamashita 2000).

When we started a project to develop a software system for the telescope operation in 1992, none of those instruments was existing, nor was the telescope control system. The telescope control system and instrument control systems were treated as plug-in applications to the core system and an application interface layer was defined. It is advantageous to complete the core software system during the construction of the telescope itself, because the software system could then be used for data acquisition in the final adjustment of the telescope construction.

The milestones were planned and performed as follows.

- 1995 Apr–1998 Dec   Control system development
- 1998 Dec 24   Subaru Telescope Engineering First light
- 1997 Apr–1999 Jan   Archive system development
- 1999 Jan 28   Scientific First Light
- 1996 Apr–2000 Mar   Data Analysis system development
- 2000 Dec 4   Open Use began

We named the core software system of the Subaru Telescope data flow operation as the Subaru Telescope Software Trinity System(STsTS) to symbolize that none of those three software components could be considered removable from the system.

3.   Subaru Software Trinity System — STsTS

The Subaru Software Trinity System(STsTS), consisting of the Subaru Observation Software (SOSS), the Subaru Telescope Archive System (STARS), and the Data Analysis System Hierarchy (DASH) has been developed as another systematic software system of the telescope operation in Japan (Morita 2002). Performing effective observation with a user-friendly environment is the primary purpose of SOSS at the summit of Mauna Kea, 4200 m in the altitude, where there is 40% less oxygen in the atmosphere in comparison with that at sea level.

Observed data is kept in the tape library storage as an archive managed by STARS. DASH is waiting for all observed frames to be treated from series of observations, and invokes an automatic data analysis pipeline process. A supercomputer system STN-I and STN-II has been installed to support STsTS operation at the Hilo Base Facility.

3.1.   Subaru Operation Software System — SOSS

The SOSS is designed to perform effective operations on the Subaru Telescope (Kosugi 1997; Sasaki 1996; Sasaki 1997). The SOSS system consists of five subsystems; Observation Control System (Sasaki 1998), Data Acquisition System (DAQ, Noumaru 1995), Quick Look Analysis (QDAS, Kosugi 1996), Data Base system, and Tool Kit (Noumaru 1997). The Observation Control System controls the interface with the Telescope control system, in a loose network connection on the Ethernet, and the Tool Kit defines the interface with the instrument control systems (OBCP) that has been developed independently by the instrument development teams. Even for testing facility instruments and private instruments, the Tool Kit has been provided and adopted as a standard interface between SOSS and the instruments. Simulator software of the telescope control system is provided in the Tool Kit so that OBCP could have done testing even without the actual connection of the telescope control system to SOSS.

During the commissioning procedure of eight facility instruments, the testing dedicated for the software interface between SOSS and OBCP took a few days at the simulator laboratory in Hilo Base Facility and another couple of days at the summit telescope site, and the introduction of Tool Kit Interface to instruments were quite successful.

The actual observation process continues based on the Observation Procedure, that is prepared by observers based on the observation plan in advance. A supporting interface for creation of Observation Procedures is provided. The Observation Procedure includes the Observation Data Set (ODS) detailing relationships among various frames (target frames, standard star frames, flat frames, and other calibration frames) with IF-THEN rules. The ODS is a key component in data flow in STsTS operation (Kosugi 2000; Kosugi 2002) as described in Section 4.

The ODS is written with Abstract Commands which are defined to be a common language among various kind of instruments (Kosugi 1998). The Abstract Commands are expanded by the Observation Control Subsystem into specific commands for each instrument. Execution of ODS could be dynamically optimized by adopting an optimization process (Sasaki 2000) based on SPIKE. Using Abstract Commands, observers can use the same language such as "Get_Object", "Begin_Exposure" and so on for all instruments attached to the Subaru Telescope.

The operation of the SOSS runs on the closed system at the summit site in order to maintain a secure environment as well as stable operation. A synthesized GUI for observers or operators (even in the case of usage during the engineering & maintenance period of the telescope or instruments) are prepared. A quick look analysis of observed data is supported by the QDAS subsystem which is developed on DASH & SASH (see Section 3.3) environment. Monitoring functions of various kinds of status information of telescope, dome condition, and environmental conditions has been equipped.

The SOSS system has been designed to work as an autonomous software system and interfaces with instruments and telescope are implemented independently, so it is rather simple to run SOSS remotely from Hilo Base Facility or even from Mitaka Headquarters in Japan as far as a critical condition of the interface can be satisfied. Since the interface is defined on the basis of *command & status* protocol, the condition is written as short enough round trip time among relevant processes. Testing of remote operation has been successfully carried on from Hilo Base Facility and it will be open to Open Use in near future. We are planning to realize the remote operation from Japan in near future.

SOSS consists of 3200 modules, 690,000 steps approximately.

3.2.   Subaru Telescope Archive System — STARS

STARS supports online registration of observation data in close relation with SOSS, and offline data retrieving with DASH as well as a WWW interface for astronomers. The design of STARS began in 1997 to achieve the following features (Takata 1996; Takata 1998; Takata 2000 ASP; Takata 2000 SPIE):

- Online Data Archive with OC12 optical fiber link from SOSS DAQ subsystem including raw data, telescope logging, skymonitor, and environmental data
- FITS header to define index in the Oracle Data Base

- Open Data Management after 18 months of proprietary period for observers
- Replica Operation in Mitaka satellite system in Japan
- Quick look image production(QP) and server(QLIS)
- Name resolver and link to other data bases
- WWW interface for users with authentication

Oracle 7 had been adopted initially as the database management system in STN-I, and it is running with Oracle 8 on STN-II. Several terabytes of raw data have been archived so far, and will be increasing by a few terabytes per year, due to the enhancement of data production rate by improved instruments.

In STARS, all observation proposals are assigned with UNIX group attributes which is common among SOSS and DASH. Each observer can handle data through a WWW interface of STARS during and after the observation, by accessing both servers at Hilo or at Mitaka with suitable authentication according to the UNIX group assignment. Each item in the FITS header of frames is categorized suitably for retrieving.

An interface between STARS and DASH is provided so that STARS can handle not only the observed data, but also environmental data, Observation Data Set (see Section 4), and telescope logging data. The primary purpose of STARS is to provide fast and automatic retrieval through the DASH pipeline processing. The baseline of the design is to use the high performance computing power of STN-II for the analysis particularly as an automated pipeline process, and no bulk transfer of observation data to the other site is supported so far. Various kind of removable media instead, such as DLT, DAT, ATL, and so on, are available for remote users.

As for the communication between Hilo and Mitaka, STARS has been designed to support loosely coupled remote database management from the beginning. The faster the network bandwidth between Subaru Hilo Base Facility and Subaru Mitaka Headquarters, the closer the relation between two databases (Takata 2002). As of December 2001, there has been established STM1/OC3 cable network between Hilo and Mitaka Headquarters, and a closely coupled operation of STARS and MASTARS, the replica of STARS at Mitaka, began operation as a standard communication. In Japan, an academic 10 Gbps backbone network, Super-SINET[1] is utilized to deliver data among researchers in universities and institutes.

STARS consists of 600 modules, 90,000 steps approximately.

3.3.   Data Analysis System Hierarchy — DASH

The DASH project, based on the Object Oriented Method and CORBA, began in 1996 (Mizumoto 1998 ASP; Mizumoto 1998 SPIE; Yagi 1998), and completed in March 2002 (Mizumoto 2000; Yagi 2000; Yagi 2002).

The basic concept of DASH can be summarized as follows.

- Research target oriented analysis
- Seamless operation on heterogeneous computer systems
- To manage huge amounts of data of different types

---

[1]http://www.sinet.ad.jp/english/super-sinet.html

- Previous results should be easily reproduced
- Able to use existing data analysis engines wrapping
- Easy to construct pipeline processing
- Easy to execute trial-and-error processing by researcher
- To reduce/analyze data produced by various instruments

In order to develop the project, we adopted an Object Oriented Method (OOM) for research target oriented purpose. Prototyping began in 1996 to show how the concept of DASH can be implemented on a distributed computer environment. A metaphor of Restaurant Model has been developed to clarify how the astronomer needs to treat or analyze data. The model can be easily mapped into OOM modeling for programmers who were belonging to the software house, not to the astronomical observatory. The model has three tiers; 1) user interface (waiter and dish) 2) process agents (chef and manager) 3) database (warehouse), where the restaurant metaphor is shown in parentheses.

A unit of processing in DASH is defined as a PROCube (an abbreviation of PROcess Cube). The PROCube contains all information required for the data analysis as frame categories in the X-axis, number of frames in the Y-axis and reduction flows in Z-axis. Reduction in the Z-direction runs with various engines, that need to be wrapped for existing generic modules (e.g., *eclipse*), or newly developed for each of Subaru's instruments.

Furthermore, in order to support a typical application of the DASH pipeline for the mosaic CCD frames, the Hierarchy which contains PROCubes as components are implemented. Thus, there are three classes of reduction procedure, Engine, PROCube, and Hierarchy in the DASH pipelines, where PROCube contains Engines, and Hierarchy contains PROCubes.

The logging and management information of PROCube execution is stored in the PROCube itself to make reproduction of the result of analysis possible. Since engines are stateless, all parameters necessary for the execution of engines need to be kept in the PROCube.

The concept of PROCube can be useful even without a complete set of database and engines with CORBA naming services. Then, a single user interface of DASH (it is named as SASH) can be detached from the DASH system to make available to observers offline analysis locally on her/his lap-top PC with the same interface as DASH. This is actually applied to the quick-look analysis subsystem(QDAS) of SOSS during the observation. JavaIDL is running as an Object Request Broker for SASH.

As for base of the DASH, the Object Director of Fujitsu INTERSTAGE (initially CORBA 1.0, then CORBA 2.3) has been implemented. JAVA2 (initially JDK 1.2.0, then JDK 1.3.1) has been used for the user interface. As browsers, *ESO-skycat* and *SAOimage-DS9* are implemented.

Subaru is equipped with eight standard facility instruments and observational data taken with five of those instruments (Suprime-Cam, CIAO, HDS, OHS/CISCO and FOCAS) are now ready to be analyzed by dedicated pipelines constructed on the DASH platform. We are opening a new production phase of pipeline packages for numerous variations of observation modes, and will be adopted to the big survey project planned in collaboration with several other telescopes.

DASH consists of 4000 modules, 110,000 steps approximately.

3.4.   Subaru Telescope Network — STN-I & STN-II

The amount of observing data produced by the Subaru Telescope had been estimated to be 50GB/night in the beginning of the development of STsTS, and actually, more than 30GB of data/night was produced in the year 2001 by the Suprime-Cam imaging observations. For handling huge amount of data with STsTS, we have introduced a super computer system, the Subaru Telescope Network with hierarchical storage capability up to several petabytes. The first system, STN-I, was installed in March 1997 (Ogasawara 1998), with 150TB storage, and successfully having supported the STsTS operation, then upgraded in 2002 March (Ogasawara 2002 SPIE 4844-44), STN-II with 600TB tape library. A satellite system at Mitaka Headquarters with 120TB storage has been installed.

SOSS is operating on the summit subsystem of STN that is connected by OC12 optical fiber network with the Supercomputer system at the Hilo Base Facility. Gigabit Ethernets are installed as backbones on each subsystem, and Storage Area Network with fiber channel switches are supporting reliable and secure data transfer among networks.

STARS and DASH are running on the supercomputer system in Hilo, as well as on the satellite system located in Mitaka. A high speed OC3 network over the Pacific Ocean has been in use since December 2001 (Ogasawara 2002 SPIE 4845-02).

Thus, STN-II is supporting full function of STsTS on distributed locations among the summit telescope site, Hilo Base Facility, and Mitaka Headquarters. The network connections among sites are operated by Subaru and the STN-II system is installed from Fujitsu Ltd. as a limited term operational contract[2]. Real time quality control using nearly tera-flops computing power to find suitable parameters for proceeding observations is planned and will be introduced on STsTS in near future.

4.   Data Flow Operation and Quality Control

According to the observation procedure defined in SOSS, all information of data frames in principle can be described in the Observation Dataset (ODS). In a modern CCD observation, a target frame needs to be verified after several calibration processes. Since the quality of calibration frames directly reflects the quality of the target frames, it is important to gather enough qualified calibration frames during observations. By adopting ODS-rules properly, the observer could get sufficient calibration frames.

As the observation proceeds, frames that match the rule described in the ODS ensemble could be filled and the DASH pipeline will begin automatically to execute proper PROCubes, or Hierarchies. DASH issues a retrieving request to STARS to find relevant frames, either target frames or calibration frames, according to the description of the ODS and fulfilled the data frames in PROCube. Thus, the quality control of the target frame can be achieved automatically by

---

[2]A standard contract in Japan for universities and institutes. The system belongs to the vendor and the organization pays for the function of the system.

the cooperative function of SOSS, STARS, and DASH through the concept of the Observation Data Set.

After completion of development of the three components of STsTS, we did observe using the Suprime-Cam instrument, the mosaic CCD attached to the prime focus of the Subaru Telescope (Miyazaki 1998). An observation procedure was prepared according to the observation plan and ODS rules were applied. The observation began around 02:00am HST on June 22, 2001 and automatic calibration ended around 09:30am HST to get images of 8192×10240 pixels without any human interruption. This was another first light of the Subaru Telescope by STsTS, that is the software first light.

Since there is no direct link at this moment with the environmental data, observers are careful enough to watch the weather conditions. However, we hope it is possible to detect a change of several key variables, e.g., seeing, transparency, point-spread-function and so on, it is not impossible to maintain the quality by the software to a certain degree. It would be advantageous in a survey observation in which homogeneous quality is one of the most important features of the survey data. We are planning to apply the quality controlled data flow with STsTS in several survey projects using the Subaru Telsecope.

Since the data flow operation based on the ODS runs automatically in principle, it will be possible to control the quality by applying suitable observation parameters such as exposure time, interval for calibration frames and so on, by real time, and detailed analysis of observing data. For this purpose, a huge amount of computation power is required, using the supercomputers of STN-II.

Not only a real time response during the observation, but also for preparation of the next observation plan, the STARS archive and DASH can be helpful for retrieving previous results (Noumaru 1998; Noumaru 2000; Ogasawara 2000). Even without actual observations, STsTS is available to find suitable calibration frames from the STARS archive, then re-analyze the target frames afterward, to achieve a required quality level. This is a most important feature of STsTS; to keep the data obtained by the Subaru Telescope precious enough to be fed to the Japanese Virtual Observatories (Mizumoto 2002) as reliable data.

The archive in STsTS is basically raw frames so far, it is strongly desired to prepare a scientific archive that keeps well-calibrated frames. What can be achieved by STsTS is to use CPU power to analyze frames according to the re-defined ODS-rules recursively to get a scientific result repeatedly, and it would be implemented as a basic tool for browsing Subaru data.

5. Summary and Future Prospects

The development and operation of STsTS is summarized as follows.

- Development of Subaru Software Trinity System StsTS began in 1993
- SOSS began operation 1998 March
- STARS began operation 1999 January
- DASH began operation 2000 April
- Observation & Analysis Pipeline with Observation Dataset succeeded 2001 June on Suprime-Cam

The total module number of STsTS exceeds 8,000 with nearly 900,000 steps in total.

The STsTS project has been a close collaboration with a software house, Fujitsu Ltd., and related corporations. In considering the situation in Japan, such a contract seems to have been the only possible way to develop a complicated software system, with foolproof or need to work basis.

After the three years successful operation of the Subaru Telescope, the next generation of the STsTS components; SOSS, STARS, and DASH will be developed based on experiences of the STsTS operation especially taking the possibility of a much more efficient system to support data flow operation of the Subaru Telescope into account. For example, development of a more user-friendly GUI, a supporting system of remote observations, and more efficient observation including optimization of ODS could be the possible targets of improvement in the future. Current STsTS is running on the Solaris-based UNIX system, and selection of operating system would be another important issue.

Acknowledgments. Since the development and operation of the Subaru Software Trinity System is a long-term project, there have been many collaborators. We are thankful to Mr. Y. Kosaka and Mr. H. Monzen of Fujitsu Ltd. and Dr. N. Kaifu, the Director-general of National Astronomical Observatory of Japan. The members who were attending discussion and contributed to the basic design of the Subaru Software Trinity System was as following; Dr. T. Kato (Kyoto University), Dr. T. Aoki (University of Tokyo), Dr. H. Baba (ISAS), Dr. M. Taga (Waseda University), Dr. T. Horaguchi (National Science Museum, Tokyo), Dr. M. Hamabe (Nippon Univ.), Mr. N. Koura, Mr. S. Honma (Fujitsu Ltd.), Mr. M. Furuichi, Mr. T. Yamamoto (Fujitsu America Inc.), Mr. T. Kusumoto (FFC Ltd.), Mr. I. Akiyama, Mr. Y. Kusama, Mr. S. Iwai, Mr. K. Ooto, Mr. Y. Morita, Mr. N. Watanabe, Mr. K. Ukawa, Mr. H. Nakamoto, Mr. T. Yagasaki (Systems Engineering Consultants Co. Ltd.), Mr. S. Wakabayashi, and Mr. T. Goto (MAIN Corp.).

Without the precious ideas and comments given by those collaborators, and without the stellar effort of them in coding and testing, the Subaru Telescope Software Trinity System could not have been achieved successfully as it is. The project has been supported by the budget for the construction of the Subaru Telescope during 1995–2001, and now goes into the stable era of operation since 2002 Apr. We are grateful for Dr. K. Kodaira, Dr. H. Karoji, Dr. H. Ando, Dr. M. Iye and all Subaru related personnel for supporting and helping the project.

References

Iye, M. 1998, in SPIE Proc., Vol. 3355, 344

Iye, M. & Yamashita, T. 2000, in SPIE Proc., Vol. 4008, 18

Iye, M. et al. 2002, PASJ December, in Press

Kaifu, N. 1998, in SPIE Proc., Vol. 3352, 14

Kosugi, G., et al. 1996, in ASP Conf. Ser., Vol. 101, Astronomical Data Analysis Software and Systems V, ed. G. H. Jacoby & J. Barnes (San Francisco: ASP), 404

Kosugi, G., et al. 1997, in SPIE Proc., Vol. 3112, 284

Kosugi, G., et al. 1998, in SPIE Proc., Vol. 3349, 426

Kosugi, G. et al. 2000, in SPIE Proc., Vol. 4010, 174

Kosugi, G. et al. 2002, in SPIE Proc., Vol. 4833, in Press

Miyazaki, S. et al. 1998, in SPIE Proc., Vol. 3355, 363

Mizumoto, Y. et al. 1998, in ASP Conf. Ser., Vol. 145, Astronomical Data Analysis Software and Systems VII, ed. R. Albrecht, R. N. Hook, & H. A. Bushouse (San Francisco: ASP), 332

Mizumoto, Y. et al. 1998, in SPIE Proc., Vol. 3349, 173

Mizumoto, Y. et al. 2000, in SPIE Proc., Vol. 4009, 429

Mizumoto, Y. et al. 2003, this volume, 96

Morita, K. et al. 2003, this volume, 166

Noumaru, J. et al. 1995, in SPIE Proc., Vol. 2479, 453

Noumaru, J. et al. 1997, in SPIE Proc., Vol. 3112, 52

Noumaru, J. et al. 1998, in SPIE Proc., Vol. 3349, 195

Noumaru, J. 2000, in SPIE Proc., Vol. 4010, 10

Noumaru, J. 2002, in SPIE Proc., Vol. 4844-02, in Press

Ogasawara, R. et al. 1998, in SPIE Proc., Vol. 3349, 255

Ogasawara, R. et al. 2000, in SPIE Proc., Vol. 4010, 159

Ogasawara, R. et al. 2002, in SPIE Proc., Vol. 4845-02, in Press

Ogasawara, R. et al. 2002, in SPIE Proc., Vol. 4844-44, in Press

Sasaki, T. et al. 1996, in ASP Conf. Ser., Vol. 125, Astronomical Data Analysis Software and Systems VI, ed. G. Hunt & H. E. Payne (San Francisco: ASP), 196

Sasaki, T. et al. 1997, in SPIE Proc., Vol. 3112, 267

Sasaki, T. et al. 1998, in SPIE Proc., Vol. 3349, 427

Sasaki, T. et al. 2000, in SPIE Proc., Vol. 4009, 350

Takata, T. et al. 1996, in ASP Conf. Ser., Vol. 101, Astronomical Data Analysis Software and Systems V, ed. G. H. Jacoby & J. Barnes (San Francisco: ASP), 251

Takata, T. et al. 1998, in SPIE Proc., Vol. 3349, 247

Takata, T. et al. 2000, in ASP Conf. Ser., Vol. 216, Astronomical Data Analysis Software and Systems IX, ed. N. Manset, C. Veillet, & D. Crabtree (San Francisco: ASP), 157

Takata, T. et al. 2000, in SPIE Proc., Vol. 4010, 181

Takata, T. et al. 2002, in SPIE Proc., Vol. 4844-52, in Press

Tanaka, W. et al. 1998, in SPIE Proc., Vol. 3351, 478

Yagi, M. et al. 1998, in ASP Conf. Ser., Vol. 172, Astronomical Data Analysis Software and Systems VIII, ed. D. M. Mehringer, R. L. Plante, & D. A. Roberts (San Francisco: ASP), 375

Yagi, M. et al. 2000, in ASP Conf. Ser., Vol. 216, Astronomical Data Analysis Software and Systems IX, ed. N. Manset, C. Veillet, & D. Crabtree (San Francisco: ASP), 510

Yagi, M. et al. 2002, in SPIE Proc., Vol. 4847-33, in Press

Astronomical Data Analysis Software and Systems XII
ASP Conference Series, Vol. 295, 2003
H. E. Payne, R. I. Jedrzejewski, and R. N. Hook, eds.

Science Goal Driven Observing

Anuradha Koratkar

Space Telescope Science Institute

Sandy Grosvenor

Booz Allen Hamilton

Jeremy Jones

NASA/Goddard Space Flight Center

Karl Wolf

Aquilent

Abstract. In the coming decade, we will be forced to automate many of the scientific tasks that are done manually today because observatories will have to be managed in a fiscally tight environment. Thus, spacecraft autonomy will become a part of mission operations. In such an environment, observing campaigns of inherently variable targets and targets of opportunity will need flexible scheduling to focus observing time and data download on exposures that are scientifically interesting and useful. The ability to quickly recognize and react to such events by re-prioritizing the observing schedule will be an essential characteristic for maximizing scientific returns from the observatory.

The science goal monitoring (SGM) system is a proof-of-concept effort to address these challenges. The SGM will have an interface to help capture higher level science goals from the scientists and translate them into a flexible observing strategy that SGM can execute and monitor. We are developing an interactive distributed system that will use on-board processing and storage combined with event-driven interfaces with ground-based processing and operations, to enable fast re-prioritization of observing schedules, and to minimize time spent on non-optimized observations.

1. Introduction

In the last fifteen years astronomers have come to depend on software tools to operate observatories/missions, and also to obtain, analyze, archive and reanalyze data. In the coming decade due to limited funding, observatories must work with smaller and smaller operations staff, even as instrument complexities and data volumes are increasing. Many of the scientific tasks that have traditionally been manually overseen will have to be automated. In such an environment, software tools are an essential component for increasing scientific productivity and developing cost-effective techniques for obtaining and assimilating data.

Thus, spacecraft autonomy will become an even greater part of mission operations. While recent missions have made great strides in the ability to autonomously monitor and react to changing health and physical status of spacecraft, little progress has been made in responding quickly to science driven events.

The current spacecraft operations are reasonable for simple pointed observations. For observations of inherently variable targets, monitoring projects and targets of opportunity, the ability to recognize early if an observation will meet the science goals, and react accordingly, can have a major positive impact on the overall scientific returns of an observatory and on its operational costs. Thus, for at least a class of targets there is a need for flexible scheduling to capture quality data to achieve science goals.

2. The Science Goal Monitor Project

The Science Goal Monitor (SGM) project is a research effort funded by NASA Code R to determine if it is feasible to "get the eye back to the telescope" and to develop prototype software that will enable this. In the first phase of our study, we have determined that there is a subset of space science problems that are conducive to the philosophy of science goal driven observing. These problems are related to objects that are time variable and are often monitored for long periods. Using these problems as test cases for our prototype, we are in the process of designing and developing the SGM system which is a set of tools that have the ability to capture the underlying science goals of an observation, translate them into a machine interpretable format, and then autonomously recognize and react in a timely fashion when goals are met. SGM will provide astronomers with visual tools to capture their scientific goals in terms of measurable objectives and be able to autonomously monitor the data stream in near-real time to see if these goals are being met. Our prototype is designed for use in a distributed environment where some analysis can be performed onboard a spacecraft, while other analyses can be performed on the ground.

To testbed our proof-of-concept prototype, we have determined that an observatory that has the following conditions would get the most benefit from an SGM-like system: a typical target is intrinsically variable, targets are monitored for long periods of time, and spacecraft are designed for scheduling flexibility.

2.1. The Science Goal Monitor (SGM) Project Overview

The Science Goal Monitor (SGM) system will interact with not only the data processing pipeline for a mission, but when used on board the spacecraft, it will also interact with the raw data from the detector. Figure 1 shows the high-level concept of the SGM. At present, we are concentrating on designing the Science Goal Capture Tool (SGCT). We hope to design and develop an underlying architecture and framework for the SGM system (see Figure 1). The three key modules include:

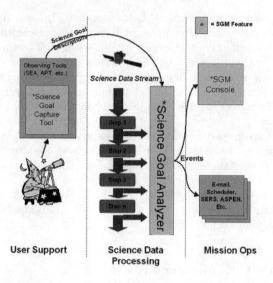

Figure 1.   SGM System Overview (ground-based)

- The Science Goal Capture Tool (SGCT) will capture the user's science goals in an intuitive and easily understandable manner while simultaneously storing them in a format for easy machine processing. To achieve this mix of capabilities we are modeling the SGCT after "state diagrams" commonly used in computer science. An example of an early design overview of the SGCT interface is shown in Figure 2.
- The Science Goal Analyzer (SGA) will interpret the science data stream from the observatory and interact with its processing pipeline to analyze whether or not a set of science goals are being satisfied. When goals are met, the SGA will fire events notifying any registered observer of the event and provide access to the details. While usability will be the key in the capture tool, the analyzer will place a premium on efficiency and speed. We anticipate that the SGA will work in cooperation with an onboard scheduler. The SGA will also monitor messages and data from the spacecraft flight software and update the status of its monitored campaigns accordingly. This partnership will allow the SGM to introduce progressive autonomy and dynamic behavior while the instrument and flight software continue to provide their traditional safety and control checks.
- The Science Goal Monitor Console (SGMC) will provide a visual interface and console for mission operations to query, monitor, and interact with the SGA. We currently anticipate that this feature will be used primarily as a testing module to observe and validate the workings of the SGA and also as the "reference implementation" of an event monitor.

An important component of the SGM will be the ability to send alerts to interested scientists and operations managers, alerting them when SGM has recognized an interesting event. There are already several event notification systems in development or operation. We propose to provide an interface to one

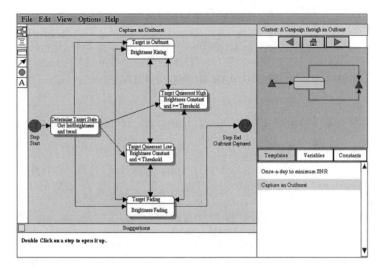

Figure 2.   SGM Science Goal Capture Tool

or more of these systems, but do not plan to develop one specifically for the SGM.

2.2.   The Science Goal Monitor (SGM) Project Future Plans

We are currently prototyping user interfaces to capture science goals in a fashion that the scientist can use and understand. We are also evaluating existing and emerging software to dynamically evaluate science data on board the spacecraft. The prototype will be used to evaluate the effectiveness of an SGM and to understand the risks involved for such a system to be implemented. We plan to implement and test the prototype using the Small and Medium ApertuRe TelescopeS (SMARTS) project.

3.   Conclusions

Introduction of flexible scheduling and autonomously reacting to science driven events inherently infuses automation technologies into mission operations. Missions, especially complex high-profile missions, are more culturally and politically averse to risk when it comes to automation. Clearly, the capture of science goals rather than the mechanics of an observation while developing observing programs, and the subsequent automatic analysis of the data stream to determine if goals are met, represents not just a leap forward in automation, but a large change in the operations paradigm. We are in the early stages of the Science Goal Monitor project to develop prototypes, evaluate their effectiveness, and understand the risks.

Acknowledgments.   This work is funded by NASA Code R under the Computing, Information and Communication Technologies (CICT) program.

Astronomical Data Analysis Software and Systems XII
ASP Conference Series, Vol. 295, 2003
H. E. Payne, R. I. Jedrzejewski, and R. N. Hook, eds.

The Digital Zenith Camera TZK2-D - A Modern High-Precision Geodetic Instrument for Automatic Geographic Positioning in Real-Time

Christian Hirt

Institut für Erdmessung, Universität Hannover, Schneiderberg 50, 30167 Hannover, Germany

Abstract. The digital zenith camera TZK2-D is a geodetic state-of-the-art instrument for determining geographic longitude and latitude fully automatically. Using CCD technology for imaging stars and a GPS-receiver for precise time measurement, this instrument allows real-time geographic positioning with an accuracy of 0.2 seconds of arc. The digital zenith camera is used for fast and high-precision determination of the plumb line and its vertical deflection applied for the local gravity field determination in geodesy. In astronomy, high-precision pointing of large telescopes can be supported by the knowledge of the plumb line and its vertical deflection provided by the digital zenith camera in combination with a GPS receiver.

1. Introduction

Determining geographic longitude and latitude used to be one of the main tasks of practical astronomy in the past. Whereas the basic principle of geographic positioning remained unvaried throughout the centuries, application fields and observation techniques altered thoroughly. In geodesy, the application of celestial position determination changed during the last decades. Celestial methods used to be the only way to determine geographic positions on the Earth's surface until modern satellite systems like the Global Positioning System GPS (e.g., Seeber 2003) took over this traditional task of practical astronomy. Today, classical celestial positioning methods are applied in geodesy for economic and high-precision gravity field determination using modern transportable instruments like digital zenith cameras (e.g., Hirt & Buerki 2002).

The aim of this paper is to introduce the digital zenith camera system TZK2-D (Transportable Zenith Camera 2-Digital) developed at the Institut für Erdmessung, University of Hanover as an efficient state-of-the-art instrument for the astronomical determination of geographic longitude and latitude with an accuracy of 0.2 seconds of arc.

Photographic zenith cameras, developed at Universities in Europe in the 1970's and 1980's (e.g., Wissel 1982), have been applied to the local and regional determination of the Earth's gravity field in many geodetical projects in countries all over Europe and America. Compared to standards of today, these analogue instruments are inefficient since analogue data acquisition and the partly manual data processing required high efforts regarding time, manpower and consequently costs. In recent time, the availability of digital image sensors (CCD) at reasonable prices initiated the development of a digital zenith camera system in Hanover (Hirt 2001, Hirt & Buerki 2002). Compared to classical photographic zenith cameras, this automated instrumentation is a fundamental improvement in terms of automation, real-time capability, accuracy and efficiency.

2. Zenith Camera, GPS and Geographic Coordinates

The basic difference between satellite-based and astronomically determined geographic coordinates is as follows. Geographic coordinates determined with GPS refer to the ellipsoid as a simplified geometrical model of the Earth. Hence, they are called *ellipsoidal* latitude φ and longitude λ. Geographic coordinates determined with astronomical instruments such as a zenith camera are called *astronomical* latitude Φ and longitude Λ. They define the local plumb line and depend on the gravity field of the Earth in contrast to ellipsoidal coordinates (cf. Hirt 2001 or Torge 2001). Hence, astronomical methods of geographic positioning can be used for the determination of the Earth's gravity field, a basic task of geodesy.

Considering an arbitrary point at the Earth's surface, its astronomical and ellipsoidal coordinates are usually not identical. The differences are called *deflections of the vertical* and they reflect anomalies of the Earth's gravity field, caused by inhomogeneous mass distribution. Deflections of the vertical vary between a few seconds of arc in rather flat regions up to a maximum of approximately one arc minute in mountainous areas. More detailed information on this subject can be found in Torge (2001).

3. System Design

Figure 1. The digital zenith camera TZK2-D

The digital zenith camera TZK2-D (Figure 1) is composed of a lens directed towards zenith, a CCD-sensor, a GPS equipment, a pair of electronic tiltmeters and an industrial computer. The zenith camera is designed as a portable measurement system. It is characterized by its robust and compact architecture and can be applied even under rough conditions. Since a GPS equipment is integrated in the zenith camera system, both astronomical coordinates (Φ, Λ) and ellipsoidal coordinates (φ, λ) can be determined. Thus, deflections of the vertical are directly provided by the system.

A lens type Mirotar by Zeiss is used as optical component with an aperture of about 200 mm. It achieves 1020 mm focal length by shortened architecture similar to Maksutov Cassegrain. A CCD camera KX2E by Apogee used for image data acquisition is located in the focal plane. The CCD's array with a size of 1530×1020 pixel corresponds to a celestial area of 47.2×31.5 minutes of arc. The CCD camera is equipped with an electronic shutter for exposure time control using a logical TTL signal. In contrast to other telescopes, the zenith camera is a non-tracking system. Therefore, the instrument's limiting magnitude of 14.0 is achieved within short exposure intervals between 0.2 and 1.0 seconds of time.

Celestial position determination requires the exposure epochs for longitude determination. For high-precision time keeping, a GPS equipment consisting of antenna and receiver is connected to the electronic shutter of the CCD camera via a hardware link. Utilizing the TTL signal, the epoch of every exposure is marked at the GPS time scale.

A pair of electronic tiltmeters of type High Resolution Tiltmeter (HRTM) by Lippmann is used in orthogonal orientation to level the zenith camera. Minor deviations between the zenith camera's optical axis and the plumb line are measured during exposure and corrected in order to get reference to the plumb line. The tilt measurement is done with an accuracy of approximately 0.05 seconds of arc.

An industrial computer for device steering, data acquisition, data storage and real-time data processing in combination with a wireless display for visualization and remote system control completes the digital zenith camera system.

4.   Data Processing

The processing chain starts with the astrometric reduction of the observations. Using image moment analysis, the extraction of imaged stars is quickly performed achieving an position accuracy of $0.2 - 0.4$ arc seconds. Due to the camera's light-sensitivity of about 14th magnitude allowing to image a total of 14 million stars, dense star catalogues are required providing the celestial reference. Currently, the catalogues Tycho-2, the Guide Star Catalogue (GSC) and the First USNO CCD Astrograph Catalogue (UCAC) are used as reference. Extracted stars and their match from the catalogue are related through projective transformation formulae. After astrometric data reduction, astronomical latitude Φ and longitude Λ are obtained by interpolation of the zenith point into the field of zenithal stars.

Both data acquisition and astrometric data processing is performed with the software package AURIGA (Automatic Real-Time Image Processing System for Geodetic Astronomy). This real-time capable package has a modular design. It consists of executable programs (C,C++) for data processing and graphical user interfaces (Tcl/Tk) for data management, visualization and analysis. Since AURIGA allows fast and automated data processing, astronomical latitude Φ and longitude Λ are provided practically in real-time. A more detailed description of the data processing is given in Hirt (2001).

5. Applications in Geodesy and Astronomy

In geodesy, the digital zenith camera system is applied for the determination of deflections of the vertical used for local high-precision geoid[1] and high-resolution gravity field determinations. Due to the efficiency of the system, deflections of the vertical can be determined at $8 - 12$ stations per night or even more by measuring along a profile with densely distributed stations. In addition to geodetic applications, the system can be used for monitoring and analysis of atmospheric effects such as systematic zenith refraction and scintillation.

In astronomy, the knowledge of astronomical latitude Φ and longitude Λ is very useful for the high-precision pointing of large telescopes. The knowledge of astronomical coordinates (Φ, Λ) allows the separation of the deflection of the vertical from instrumental errors both resulting in pointing errors of the telescope. If only ellipsoidal coordinates (φ, λ) are available, one can not distinguish whether pointing errors come from neglecting the deflection of the vertical or from instrumental effects. The availability of coordinates (Φ, Λ) might be of interest for acceptance testing or it helps understanding physical effects happening to the telescope such as tilting of the pier due to settling of its foundation. Furthermore, if portable telescopes are used, the knowledge of deflections of the vertical and instrumental errors could produce better "out of the box" pointing.

Acknowledgments. The development of the digital zenith camera system is supported by the Deutsche Forschungsgemeinschaft DFG (German national research foundation). The author is grateful to Prof. Dr.-Ing. Günter Seeber for the continuous and encouraging support of his work.

References

Hirt, C. 2001, Automatic Determination of Vertical Deflections in Real-Time by Combining GPS and Digital Zenith Camera for Solving the GPS-Height-Problem. Proceed. 14th International Technical Meeting of the Satellite Division of the Institute of Navigation, Alexandria, VA, pp. $2540-2551$

Hirt, C. & Buerki, B. 2002, The Digital Zenith Camera – A New High-Precision And Economic Astrogeodetic Observation System for Real-Time Measurement of Deflections of the Vertical. Proceed. of the 3rd Meeting of the International Gravity and Geoid Commission of the International Association of Geodesy, Thessaloniki, Greece (in press)

Seeber, G. 2003, Satellite Geodesy, Second Edition. Foundations, Methods, and Applications. W. de Gruyter, Berlin, New York

Torge, W. 2001, Geodesy, Third Edition. W. de Gruyter, Berlin, New York

Wissel, H. 1982, Zur Leistungsfähigkeit von transportablen Zenitkameras bei der Lotabweichungsbestimmung. Wiss. Arb. Fach. Vermessungswesen Univ. Hannover, Nr. 107, Hannover

---

[1]The geoid is the equipotential surface of the Earth's gravity field at mean sea level (cf. Torge 2001)

Astronomical Data Analysis Software and Systems XII
ASP Conference Series, Vol. 295, 2003
H. E. Payne, R. I. Jedrzejewski, and R. N. Hook, eds.

SIRTF Web Based Tools for QA and Instrument Performance Monitoring

Bob Narron, Irene Bregman, John H. White, Mehrdad Moshir

California Institute of Technology, Pasadena, CA 91125

Abstract. The SIRTF Science Center is developing two Web-based tools that will be used during operations. One tool is for Quality Analysis. It will allow the analysts to display images and plots of new data and then to record status and comments in the central database. The other tool is for display of Instrument Performance Monitoring data. It provides an easy-to-use way for the science staff to create plots and ASCII files of this data. Both tools use Java applets to display images and plots and Perl for everything else. The standard Perl DBI interface is used to access the database.

1. Introduction

SIRTF launch is scheduled for January 2003. Two Web based tools have been developed for SIRTF operations in anticipation of launch in January 2003. After launch, these tools will be used during routine operations to perform QA on the data products and to analyze satellite engineering data.

2. Quality Analysis ("QA")

The basic design requirements for the QA tool are (1) that it provide an easy way of looking at all the data, observation by observation, and (2) that it provide an easy way to specify status and comments for each observation. Advanced visualization capabilities are not provided by this tool. To perform more sophisticated analysis, users may download the data into their own favorite analysis package.

2.1. The QA Data

The data accessed by this tool consists of meta-data in the central database as well as the actual data files in the archive. The central database contains an accounting of all files associated with each observation along with status information and QA statistical profiles for each data file. The archive contains both raw and processed data such as image files and extracted spectra files.

2.2. The QA Interactive Tool

A session with the QA Tool starts with the selection of a set of observations of interest. This selection may be made on the basis of such things as status, time, and which analyst is assigned. The observations may then be inspected one by one. For each observation, the inspection starts with the composite products and allows "drilling down" to the individual products used in the production of the composite products.

For visualization of image products a few basic functions are provided. These include display with contrast enhancement, histogram calculation, zoom, and plots of horizontal and vertical "cuts", There is also a "movie" display provided for multi-plane images. Visualization of spectra is a multi-color plot of flux vs. wavelength.

After inspecting the elements of an observation, the observation status may be set and important comments may be recorded.

3. Instrument Performance Monitoring ("IPM")

The design requirement for the IPM tool is easy access and visualization of the IPM data.

3.1. The IPM Data

When the IPM data arrives, it is resampled to standard intervals and stored in the central database. For each interval values are saved for mean, standard deviation, minimum, and maximum of all samples in the interval. The data is organized by time tag and "channel" number. Each channel number corresponds to one sampled value, such as baffle temperature. The amount of such data received is expected to be between 50GB and 500GB per day (between about 20TB and 200TB per year), depending on how much data is deemed important enough to save.

3.2. The IPM Interactive Tool

The IPM interactive tool allows selection of data by channel number and time range. It allows the user to select either (1) value vs. time plot, (2) two channel value vs. value scatter plot, or (3) ASCII table output.

4. Software Architecture

Both of the tools described above are Web based tools running on an Apache server. They use CGI and are coded Perl. For the visualization functions, Java applets are used. The data files used for visualization are accessed on the client machine where the browser is running rather than being served up by the server. Access to the Informix database is via the Perl DBI interface. As of this writing, these tools will be running within the operations firewall and will therefore not be available for use to the outside world.

Acknowledgments. This work was carried out at the SIRTF Science Center, with funding from NASA under contract to the California Institute of Technology and the Jet Propulsion Laboratory.

Astronomical Data Analysis Software and Systems XII
ASP Conference Series, Vol. 295, 2003
H. E. Payne, R. I. Jedrzejewski, and R. N. Hook, eds.

Monitoring the Chandra X-ray Observatory via the Wireless Internet

Bradley D. Spitzbart, Scott J. Wolk, Robert A. Cameron

Chandra X-ray Center, Harvard-Smithsonian Center for Astrophysics, 60 Garden St., Cambridge, MA 02138

Abstract. The *Chandra X-ray Observatory*, launched in July 1999, continues to provide unprecedented high energy astrophysical discoveries with efficiency and reliability. From time to time, though, urgent operational decisions must be made by engineers, instrument teams, and scientists, often on short notice and at odd hours. There are several real-time, mostly Internet-based data resources available to aid in the decision-making discussions when a crisis arises. *Chandra's* Science Operations Team (SOT) has been experimenting with emerging Wireless Application Protocol (WAP) technologies to create yet another pathway for data flow. Our WAP Internet pages provide anytime, anywhere access to critical spacecraft information through cellular phones or other WAP-enabled devices. There are, of course, many challenges in attempting to present useful, meaningful content on a 5 × 12 character screen over limited bandwidth in a way that is user-friendly and beneficial. This paper will discuss our experience with this developing and promising new medium, design strategies, and future enhancements.

1. Introduction

The *Chandra* wireless web pages were conceived and have evolved to provide ready access to the most relevant spacecraft information at critical, decision-making times. In its first incarnation, data were requested and passed through two-way pagers. Here we describe our next generation approach of using Wireless Application Protocol (WAP)-enabled devices and Wireless Markup Language (WML) for a more comprehensive and accessible application. At present the pages are customized for viewing on cell phones. These same devices are also capable of acting as pagers through text messaging and in fact most of the team uses the phone to its full, versatile convenience for voice, text, and web browsing. E-mails are sent directly to the devices by SOT monitoring software, alerting to high radiation conditions, and other spacecraft or system anomalies. As with any emerging technology, the learning curve is quite steep, but we have solved several technical and design issues along the way. The URL for the SOT wireless home is http://cxc.harvard.edu/mta/WL/sot.wml.

Figure 1. [left to right] The *Chandra* Snapshot main page, CCDM subsystem snapshot, support schedule, and observing schedule.

2. Content and Design

The wireless pages are essentially WML mirrors of the most mission-critical of our myriad standard web pages[1]. Examples of these pages are shown in Figure 1 and described below. By emphasizing a simple, server-side approach, we are able to create and maintain our wireless web quickly and efficiently. Performance has been more than satisfactory as we utilize the server for computations and pass only small amounts (< 2Kbytes) of data at a time.

Several design issues had to be considered to map full HTML pages to WML. For instance, most devices are limited to only about 12 characters across and 5 characters down each screen. To compensate, many mnemonics are shortened, long pages are broken into multiple pages, and navigation links are positioned atop and occasionally throughout long pages. To counter the color and font non-capability we provide separate pages for a reference to each colored mnemonic (see section 2.1.). Most devices also attempt to efficiently cache and redisplay previously called pages. To prevent this action, an always-expired header is added so that the most current data are displayed on each invocation during real-time contacts. Finally, the wide variety of device types and manufacturers make on-line emulators[2] invaluable for testing as well as for saving air time charges.

2.1. Chandra Snapshot

Our main real-time web page is the *Chandra* Snapshot. This page is created by reading the *Chandra* telemetry stream through a C++ based decommutator, then formatting the HTML output with PERL scripts. State checking occurs in the PERL code and values are color coded on the web to indicate any limit violations. To implement the WML version of the Snapshot, we simply added a module to output a plain text log of telemetry values. The WAP pages then run an underlying PERL (CGI) code to extract and format the user requested data. An example of the output WML code is given in Figure 2. The CGI is also used to handle "browser" buttons which make data available from the past three days. The color coding of the original pages is preserved in the black and white only WAP pages by displaying separate pages for each color. That is, the "RED Flags" link shows all values that are colored red indicating a limit violation or unexpected state.

---

[1]http://cxc.harvard.edu/mta/sot.html

[2]http://www.gelon.net has one; there are many others.

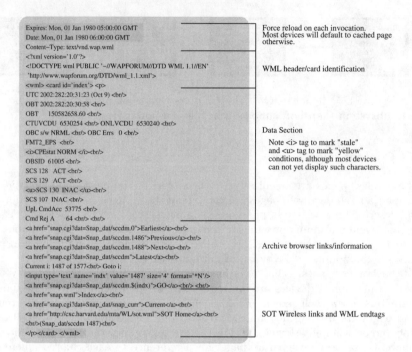

Figure 2.   Example WML code of SOT wireless Snapshot. This is
output from a CGI script and displays the CCDM subsystem mnemonics.

2.2.   Radiation Monitoring

The radiation environment in which *Chandra* operates is closely monitored. During times of elevated solar activity it is often necessary to consider stopping
observations in order to protect the science instruments. We provide renderings
of Advanced Composition Explorer (ACE) spacecraft data and Chandra Radiation Model (CRM) predictions along with the current spacecraft configuration
and ephemeris to aid in these decisions. These pages are autonomously updated
every five minutes and are available as static WML pages.

2.3.   On-line Schedules

When crises arise it is often helpful to have ready access to various schedules.
The *Chandra* wireless web provides links to the spacecraft support schedule. This
lists the times of our thrice daily, one-hour contacts for the past day and the
next two days, with the current or next pass highlighted for easy reference. This
page is autonomously updated every ten minutes. We also create a simplified
version of the observing schedule to assist when replan decisions must be made.
The main page gives links to a daily listing of observations for the current week
and the next scheduled week. The start time, observation id, target name,
instrument, and grating parameters are listed for each observation. These pages
are updated manually upon the approval of each weekly schedule.

3. Conclusions and Future Work

Wireless Internet technology will continue to advance with more bandwidth, larger displays, greater graphical capability, and code standardization being made available incrementally. This will allow us to offer more *Chandra* systems and scientific data quickly and conveniently via wireless devices.

Some of our short and long term visions include the following:

- Make more text-only pages accessible.
- Explore adding some simple graphical representations (ACE data, for instance) in the near future.
- Expanded graphical services as we convert our many monitoring and trending plots for wireless access.
- Enhanced user interactivity for searching and requesting specific data values and timeframes for trending and analysis.
- Supply products appropriate to a wide variety of devices. Compatibility and translation issues will be investigated to implement our wireless web on upgraded cell phones, PDAs and other devices.

While relatively quick and easy to implement and maintain, the wireless web has proven to be a valuable resource for *Chandra* Operations and will continue to evolve and expand.

Acknowledgments. We acknowledge valuable user feedback and bug reports. This work is supported by the *Chandra X-ray Center* under NASA contract NAS8-39073.

Astronomical Data Analysis Software and Systems XII
ASP Conference Series, Vol. 295, 2003
H. E. Payne, R. I. Jedrzejewski, and R. N. Hook, eds.

COSMOS-3: The Third Generation Telescope Control Software System of Nobeyama Radio Observatory

Koh-Ichiro Morita, Naomasa Nakai, Toshikazu Takahashi,
Kazuhiko Miyazawa

*Nobeyama Radio Observatory, National Astronomical Observatory
Japan, Minamimaki, Minamisaku, Nagano 384-1305, Japan*

Masatoshi Ohishi, Takahiro Tsutsumi

*National Astronomical Observatory Japan, Osawa, Mitaka, Tokyo
181-8588, Japan*

Shigehisa Takakuwa

*Academia Sinica Institute of Astronomy and Astrophysics, P.O. Box
1-87, Nankang, Taipei 11529, Taiwan*

Hiroyuki Ohta

*Fujitsu Limited, 1-9-3, Nakase, Mihama-ku, Chiba, Chiba 261-8588,
Japan*

Kiyohiko Yanagisawa

*Fujitsu Nagano System Engineering Limited 1403-3 Tsuruganabeyata,
Nagano, Nagano 380-0813, Japan*

Abstract. COSMOS-3 is the third generation telescope software system of Nobeyama Radio Observatory, which was designed to control and to monitor the 45 m telescope and Nobeyama Millimeter Array and to acquire observing data from receiver backends.

COSMOS-3 is functionally divided into three layers. Tools at the top layer provide user interfaces for many kinds of observing requirements and various displays of observing results and system monitors. There are MANAGER and MERGER at a middle layer, which control message/data flow between upper layer and lower layers. At a bottom layer, there are many Local Controllers to communicate with each device.

For flexibility and system stability, COSMOS-3 has simple communication interfaces between different layers and no direct connection between subsystems at the bottom layer. For non-expert software engineers, it provides a wrapping mechanism at the bottom layer which makes it easy for non-expert people to develop Local Controllers.

1.   Introduction

The Nobeyama 45 m telescope and Nobeyama Millimeter Array has been operated since 1982 at Nobeyama Radio Observatory (NRO), National Astronomical Observatory Japan (NAOJ). COSMOS (*C*ontrol and *O*peration *S*oftware system for *M*illimeter *O*bservation*S*) is the control system for these telescopes, which has evolved from a centralized mainframe architecture to the current hierarchical distributed system running on a distributed environment of workstations and PCs (Morita et al. 1995).

COSMOS was expected to be used for both the single dish telescope and interferometer. Therefore, it must control and monitor a wide range of instruments, and various kinds of observing modes should be available for use by observers.

The first and second generation systems (COSMOS-1 and COSMOS-2) basically had centralized architectures based on IBM compatible mainframe hardware. To realize realtime performance on the mainframe environments, these system were complicated and not flexible. Therefore, it was not easy for maintenance and it took a long time to add new instruments to the system. To overcome these defects, COSMOS-3 has been developed since 1995. That was when NRO replaced the computer hardware with a network of workstations and PCs.

2.   Concepts of COSMOS-3

Design goals of COSMOS-3 are to improve flexibility, reliability, and user friendliness. COSMOS-3 runs on the new hardware system. To achieve these goals, we designed the system based on a three layered hierarchical architecture as shown in Figure 1. Important points of this design are:

- The top layer provides user interfaces,
- The middle layer controls message and data flow between layers,
- The bottom layer is directly connected to telescope instruments,
- Sequence control at the middle layer is done by a simple script generated at the top layer,
- There is a simple interface between layers, and
- There is no direct connection between modules in the bottom layer.

3.   Architecture

3.1.   Top Layer

Modules in this layer are for preparing the observing sequence and monitoring observing status with a user friendly interface.

Communication with the observing system is quite different between the 45 m telescope and NMA. Therefore, we have used different modules for the 45 m telescope and NMA.

There are several tools for preparing observation preparations in a scripting language (OBSTBL) with GUI's for each telescope and various observing modes.

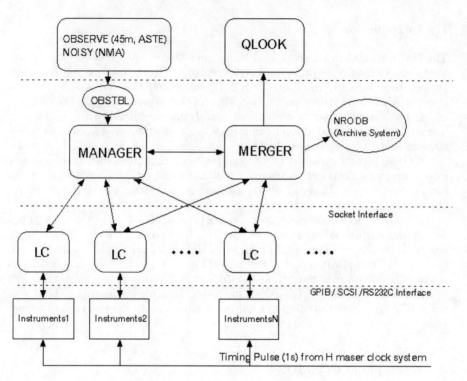

Figure 1.   COSMOS-3 three layers hierarchical architecture.

3.2.   Middle Layer

This layer consists of MANAGER and MERGER. MANAGER is a concentrator for control information flow. MANAGER reads, checks, and expands an OB-STBL. Then, according to the expanded OBSTBL, it sends control messages to requested Local Controller (LC) at appropriate timing. MERGER receives backend data and monitor data from LCs and generates archive data or QLOOK data.

3.3.   Bottom Layer

At the bottom layer, there are many LCs, which are directly connected to tele-scope instruments mostly via GPIB. An LC analyzes each message from MAN-AGER, converts it to device commands if necessary, and sends it to the instru-ment with timing accuracy of about 50 msec. For exact realtime operation, a 1 second timing pulse from H-maser clock system is distributed to each instru-ment. The system provides a wrapping mechanism for simple PC programs. Instrument developers do not need expert software skills to make LCs for their instruments.

4. OBSTBL: A Simple Scripting Language for Observations

Observing sequence information for MANAGER is written in OBSTBL, which is a simple scripting language. Observing preparation tools in the top layer automatically generate OBSTBLs for typical observing modes according to a few input parameters from observers. In the case of special observing modes, experienced observers can directly write their OBSTBLs with editor tools.

As an example, a simple position switch observation is as follows:

```
OPEN ANT
OPEN AOSW
SET ANT TRK_TYPE 'RADEC'
SET ANT SCAN_COOD 'AZEL'
SET ANT SRC_POS (149.645883,55.920967)
SET AOSW INTEG_TIME 20
EXECUTE ANT OFFSET(0.00, 0.00)
WAIT_READY ANT
REPEAT 10
    EXECUTE ANT OFFSET(0.00, 0.00)
    WAIT_READY ANT
    EXECUTE AOSW
    EXECUTE ANT OFFSET(0.05, 0.00)
    WAIT_READY ANT
    EXECUTE AOSW
REPEAT_END
CLOSE ANT
CLOSE AOSW
```

5. Summary

COSMOS-3 is the third generation telescope operation software system at NRO, which was designed based on a three layered hierarchical architecture. In about five years of operation at Nobeyama it has showed its excellent performance and reliability. Recently we have started to use a modified version of COSMOS-3 for remote operation of a new sub-millimeter 10 m telescope in the Atacama desert in northern Chile.

References

Morita, K.-I., et al. 1995, in Telescope Control Systems, ed. P. T. Wallace, Proc. SPIE Vol. 2479, 70

Astronomical Data Analysis Software and Systems XII
ASP Conference Series, Vol. 295, 2003
H. E. Payne, R. I. Jedrzejewski, and R. N. Hook, eds.

Remote Observing on the Keck Telescopes

Patrick L. Shopbell

California Institute of Technology, Pasadena, CA 91125

Robert Kibrick, Steve Allen, Brian Hayes

UCO/Lick Observatory, Santa Cruz, CA 95064

Abstract. Remote observing has long been a part of the Keck Observatory operating plan. Remote observing from the Keck Headquarters, in Waimea, HI, has been operational since 1996, before the second Keck Telescope came on-line. Remote observing from the Keck HQ now encompasses over 95% of observing runs at the Keck Observatory.

Recently, additional efforts have been made to enable remote observing on the Keck Telescopes from the U.S. mainland. Driven primarily by financial motivations, and enabled by recent increases in the available bandwidth between the mainland and Hawaii, remote runs from the mainland are now provided to observers at UC Santa Cruz (UCSC) and Caltech. Additional locations are in preparation.

In this paper, we present a brief summary of the Keck remote observing efforts from the U.S. mainland, with an emphasis on the system at Caltech, which is the most recent to come on-line. We describe the history and motivation for remote observing with the Keck Telescopes, outline the remote observing system and hardware, and describe plans for the future implementation of remote observing on a broader scale.

1. Historical Background

Remote operation of the Keck Telescopes has always been part of the long-range plan for the observatory. Remote operations of Keck I from the Keck headquarters in Waimea began before the Keck II telescope opened for observations. See Table 1 for a summary of the history of observing modes at Keck.

The last few years have seen the emergence of remote observing with Keck from the U.S. mainland. This effort had been spearheaded by a group of us from UCO/Lick Observatory. An essentially identical observing system has been installed at Caltech; it is now operational and used in a testing mode approximately two nights per month. Additional remote observing stations, following the same system parameters, are being established at other sites, including UC San Diego and UC Berkeley.

1993	Keck I science first light
1995	remote control rooms installed at Keck HQ
1996	videoconferencing between summit and HQ
	Keck I HQ remote observing first light
	Keck II science first light
1997	> 50% of Keck I operation is remote from HQ
1998	HQ-summit bandwidth upgraded to 45 Mbit/sec
	mainland (UCSC) remote observing first light
1999	> 90% of Keck I/II operation is remote from HQ
2000	HQ remote operation is default mode
2001	mainland (Caltech) remote observing first light

Table 1.   Keck Observatory remote observing timeline

2. Motivation for Mainland Observing

When the Keck Telescopes began to be used remotely from the Keck HQ in Waimea, HI, the motivations were twofold: First, to increase service for the observers by providing a direct link between HQ observatory staff and the observers at the telescope. Second, remote observing at Keck HQ provides a much less demanding observing environment, due to its altitude of a mere 2,500 feet above sea level. In extreme cases, Keck HQ provides a safe alternative to those unable to ascend the mountain (e.g., those with heart conditions). In the average case, Keck HQ simply provides a much more comfortable environment, with 60% more oxygen than the summit of Mauna Kea.

In recent years, additional factors have arisen which have motivated remote observing from the U.S. mainland, even from the home institutions of the observers. The primary impetus here has been financial: Some hundreds of thousands of dollars are spent each year on observing travel alone. In more than half of cases, these costs are for runs of one night or less. The cost is increased if one includes lost time for travel (usually 2 days). Finally, remote observing from the mainland provides a way for increased involvement by large groups, students, and collaborators.

3. Remote Observing System

The remote observing system has been designed for a high level of redundancy, to ensure minimal loss of observing time in case of failure. It is functionally equivalent to the systems at the Keck HQ and the Keck summit control rooms:

- Sun Ultra 10 instrument computer with 3 LCD monitors
- Sun Ultra 10 backup instrument computer with 1 LCD monitor
- Redundant graphics and SCSI cards
- Exabyte Eliant 820 tape drive for data backup
- Polycom 512MP videoconferencing station
- Cisco 2600 router with 4-port ISDN card

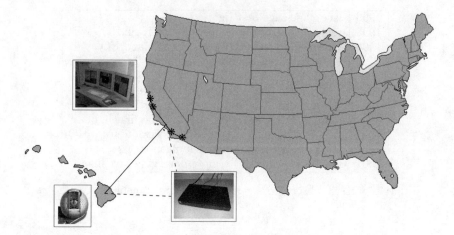

Figure 1.   Schematic representation of the Keck remote observing network. The asterisks denote the four remote observing stations currently operational or under development. The dotted line denotes the backup network link via a group of ISDN lines.

The videoconferencing unit is a critical component of the remote observing system. Remote operations typically involve three sites: observers at the remote mainland location, observers at Keck HQ, and the telescope operators on the summit of Mauna Kea. The videoconferencing system provides a crucial link between these parties, allowing for much better communication than a simple voice line. When problems arise, the videoconferencing system can be used to share paper documents, audible noises, and computer output screens (thus the use of LCD panel displays on the computers).

To ensure complete redundancy of the remote observing system, a Cisco 2600 router with a 4-port ISDN card has been installed. During normal operation, the router is configured to pass all traffic over the standard Internet. (As of the year 2000, the Internet-2 project has enabled a peak bandwidth of approximately 35 Mbit/sec between the mainland and the summit of Mauna Kea.) If the router senses at any time that the Internet connection to Keck has failed, this route is disabled and a set of ISDN lines to the summit are activated. Although the ISDN lines provide much lower bandwidth (128 Kbit/sec per line), it is sufficient to ensure that critical traffic is passed. In particular, the observing software contains a number of timeouts that are triggered after inactivity for ~ 90 seconds. Given that network traffic between the mainland and Mauna Kea must traverse some dozen different networks, approximately one third of the remote runs from Caltech (thus far) experience a network dropout. These dropouts typically last 2-3 minutes, but are easily handled by the ISDN failover system.

4. Summary and Future Work

Remote observing with the Keck Telescopes is expected to slowly expand, to encompass additional remote sites and more flexible observing modes:

- Reliable remote observing with the Keck Telescopes is now possible from the U.S. mainland. Observing sites include UCSC and Caltech, with UCSD and UC Berkeley coming soon. Current redundancy requirements effectively prohibit remote observing from arbitrary home institutions, and there are no plans in this direction.

- Observatory policy currently requires at least one observer to be on-site at Keck HQ, to ensure that telescope time is not lost in case of remote system failure. As reliability is increased and experience gained, this restriction may be relaxed.

- Hardware for remote observing is easily affordable, especially when the cost savings are included (i.e., from travel). The available network resources are currently sufficient for observing with first-generation instruments on Keck. It remains to be seen how well advances in networking will keep pace with the next generation of larger detectors and more complicated instruments.

- The social implications of remote observing are complex and not yet fully understood. On the negative side, one must appreciate the impact of further distancing the observer from the telescope and observatory staff. On the positive side, the possibilities for group collaboration and education are clearly vast. Understanding the importance of such issues may be the key to a successful remote observing system.

Astronomical Data Analysis Software and Systems XII
ASP Conference Series, Vol. 295, 2003
H. E. Payne, R. I. Jedrzejewski, and R. N. Hook, eds.

Chandra Monitoring, Trending, and Response

Scott J. Wolk, Bradley D. Spitzbart and Takashi Isobe

Harvard-Smithsonian Center for Astrophysics, 60 Garden St., Cambridge, MA 02138

Abstract. The *Chandra* X-ray Observatory was launched in July, 1999 and has yielded extraordinary scientific results. As part of *Chandra's* Science Operations Team, the primary goal of Monitoring and Trends Analysis (MTA) is to provide tools for effective decision making leading to the most efficient production of quality science output from the observatory. MTA tools, products, and services include real-time monitoring and alert generation for the most mission critical components, long term trending of all spacecraft systems, detailed analysis of various subsystems for life expectancy or anomaly resolution, and the creation and maintenance of a large SQL database of relevant information. This is accomplished through the use of a wide variety of input data sources and flexible, accessible programming and analysis techniques.

1. Introduction

The Monitoring and Trends Analysis (MTA) subdivision within the science operations team (SOT) of the *Chandra X-ray Center* (CXC) is charged with providing an overview of telescope performance as it affects the science quality and efficiency of the observatory. The group often serves as a clearinghouse of data and analysis tools for *Chandra* with the engineers, instrument experts, and calibration scientists. The MTA tasks make fervent use of the World Wide Web. We maintain thousands of dynamic web pages as well as a similar number updated on a daily basis. All the data and many on-line tools can be accessed through our home page `http://cxc.harvard.edu/mta/sot.html` which has links to all of the products described below, as well as to many other MTA and CXC resources.

2. Inputs

The MTA system is designed to use a variety of interchangeable inputs. New data arrives at the CXC approximately every eight hours. Data are stored onboard and dumped during ground supports, roughly three times a day. During real-time contacts data feeds are sent directly to the CXC. Dumped data generally arrives within a few hours.

For raw telemetry decommutation we use ACORN (Wolk et al. 2000). ACORN is capable of reading from both the real-time telemetry stream or from several types of archived dump files. *Chandra* telemetry is coded in over 11,000 MSIDs (mnemonic string identifiers). Each spacecraft meter, sensor, thermistor, boolean value, etc. can be identified and tracked with an unique MSID. ACORN decodes the telemetry stream and provides times, MSIDs, and values to either the standard output or to a tab-delimited file, for other tools to use as input.

Input data is also obtained from CXC standard processing pipeline products. We frequently use files from all levels of available processing (see Plummer et al. (2001) for a full description of pipeline data products.) All of these standard products are easily accessible from the *Chandra* data archive in FITS format.

In addition to *Chandra* data, the MTA system gathers data from outside sources, most notably the NOAA GOES and ACE missions, using lynx and anonymous ftp commands.

3. Processes

The standard MTA data processing pipeline is run as part of standard *Chandra* automated processing (Plummer et al. 2001). For more customized applications, the focus of the current effort is to create simple data products which can be massaged to allow intuitive visualization. Our programming tools of choice are UNIX shell scripts, Perl, IDL, and HTML. These often are used to write wrapper tools around *Chandra's* suite of data analysis programs (CIAO[1]). Programming is approached with the intent of eventual automation. We rely heavily on the UNIX time daemon (cron) to autonomously run jobs at various times of the day and night, updating data files and web pages and monitoring processing status and telemetry. MTA's crontab consists of over 50 periodic tasks. Jobs are divided among three UNIX machines, all running Solaris 5.8. The main real-time analysis and standard processing occurs on a Sun Ultra10/440, with a completely independent real-time data flow on an UltraE450 for redundancy. A separate UltraE450 handles daily tasks and individual cron jobs.

4. Outputs

MTA data and analyses are provided to the community in three forms: Time- and mission-critical alerts are sent via e-mail to pagers, standard and custom presentations are posted on the world wide web, and all monitored values are archived in a database.

4.1. Alerts

We have created a number of e-mail aliases to which alert messages can be sent when spacecraft state violations or other problems are detected. Data are monitored in real-time and dump data is processed on receipt in a near real-time mode.

Real-time Alerts During each real-time support, MTA runs Perl scripts which create a dynamic web page known as the *Chandra* Snapshot (see Sect. 4.2.). The

---

[1]http://cxc.harvard.edu/ciao/documents.html

Perl code incorporates selected limit checks to color code the display, indicating any state violations. In addition, these limit checks will generate alerts if certain persistent conditions are found. Once a message is sent, a semaphore is created which prevents further alerts for the same violation. This semaphore is autonomously removed when the condition subsides for three minutes. Similar alerts are triggered if limits are exceeded on other spacecraft which monitor the radiation environment.

Near Real-time Alerts　　We have developed a separate customizable Perl-based package called *config_mon*. This software acts on the spacecraft playback data when it arrives at the CXC (a few hours after the completion of each communications pass). This data contains the record of spacecraft state for the time period since the previous data dump. The values are reviewed and compared against as-planned values and operational limits using output products from mission planning and a limits database. When violations are found, alerts are sent. *Config_mon* currently monitors science instrument position, focus position, pointing, gratings positions, wheel rates and particular temperatures of concern.

4.2. World Wide Web

Our main vehicle for data dissemination is the world wide web. We maintain a large suite of dynamic web pages presenting real-time data feeds, standard processing displays, customized studies, and weekly and monthly reports. To the extent possible these pages are updated automatically. We are also experimenting with emerging WAP (Wireless Application Protocol). Spitzbart et al. (2003) have a complete report on this aspect of the project.

Real-time Web Pages　　Real-time data is viewed through a variety of web pages. Each one is run using a dedicated ACORN feed and underlying Perl code to format the ASCII output and color code particular items of interest. The *Chandra* Snapshot[2] provides easy access to the most relevant information from the current telemetry. Other real-time displays cover over 1000 additional MSIDs and data from the science instruments.

Standard Web Pages　　Spacecraft subsystem monitoring pages are produced each day as part of the standard data processing pipeline. Plots and statistics are displayed for each mnemonic and values are highlighted according to a green-yellow-red color scheme. These plots are reviewed daily by the SOT and a summary of violations or other concerns are reported to the project each week. We provide quick-look images and statistics of all observations. Certain calibration observations are further processed in specialized pipelines. The flexibility of MTA tools and data allows for the timely creation and presentation of customized studies as called for by various teams in response to current spacecraft needs or anomalies. These have included details on the radiation environment, spacecraft mechanisms and instrument performance.

---

[2]http://cxc.harvard.edu/cgi-gen/mta/Snap/snap.cgi

4.3. MTA Databases

At the end of the standard data processing pipeline, a five minute average and standard deviation is computed for each monitored MSID. This is ingested into an SQL database. Currently there are eight databases and 43 individual tables, divided by subsystem (Wolk et al. 2002). The DataSeeker (Overbeck et al. 2002) is used to extract and merge tables from the MTA databases. This tool is available with either a web interface or command line mode, which makes it convenient for first-time users or incorporation into automated scripts. DataSeeker seamlessly merges data keying on time. This allows users to cross-correlate data to find trends relating to temperatures, attitude, power consumption, etc. in addition to temporal trends. Another important feature of the DataSeeker is the ability to incorporate non-SQL tables. Easily generated RDB files can be merged with existing SQL database tables. This has proven valuable for rapid implementation of new tables for which the need had not been foreseen.

In practice, we call the DataSeeker via an automated trending script. The script provides plots and statistics for all the monitored MSIDs. The system attempts to predict the next six months' behavior by performing simple fitting to data and extrapolating. Past and predicted future limit violations are highlighted.

5. Conclusions

The main lesson learned from the MTA experience is that simple, uniform access to data is paramount. Unfortunately today's spacecraft and instruments, with their programmable telemetry, do not lend themselves to uniformity. What we have done is to impose uniformity on the ground data such that separate systems can be analyzed and displayed as a unit using fairly simple scripts. The next phases feature expanded databases which will include more higher level data products as well as more sophisticated trending tools. We will continue to respond to and attempt to anticipate spacecraft issues.

References

Overbeck, R.S. et al. 2002, in ASP Conf. Ser., Vol. 281, Astronomical Data Analysis Software and Systems XI, ed. D. A. Bohlender, D. Durand, & T. H. Handley (San Francisco: ASP), 449

Plummer, D.A. et al. 2001, in ASP Conf. Ser., Vol. 238, Astronomical Data Analysis Software and Systems X, ed. F. R. Harnden, Jr., F. A. Primini, & H. E. Payne (San Francisco: ASP), 475

Spitzbart, B.D. et al. 2003, this volume, 162

Wolk, S.J. et al. 2000, in ASP Conf. Ser., Vol. 216, Astronomical Data Analysis Software and Systems IX, ed. N. Manset, C. Veillet, & D. Crabtree (San Francisco: ASP), 453

Wolk, S.J. et al. 2002, in ASP Conf. Ser., Vol. 281, Astronomical Data Analysis Software and Systems XI, ed. D. A. Bohlender, D. Durand, & T. H. Handley (San Francisco: ASP), 341

Part 6. Calibration

Astronomical Data Analysis Software and Systems XII
ASP Conference Series, Vol. 295, 2003
H. E. Payne, R. I. Jedrzejewski, and R. N. Hook, eds.

Uncertainty Estimation and Propagation in SIRTF Pipelines

Mehrdad Moshir, John Fowler, David Henderson

SIRTF Science Center, California Institute of Technology, Pasadena, CA 91125

Abstract. In the course of reducing raw data from SIRTF into properly calibrated science products, many automated pipelines are utilized. In a typical pipeline, instrumental signatures are successively removed, and previously computed calibration values are applied. For such a large-scale automated process one needs to estimate quantitatively the results of data reduction to facilitate quality assessment, for example to verify that requirements are met. Furthermore, higher level science products such as point source extraction or mosaicking are dependent on trustable estimates of uncertainties in the data. In addition, it is essential that the end-user is supplied with statistically meaningful measures of confidence in the quoted fluxes or positions to allow full scientific utilization. For these reasons all of SIRTF pipelines have been designed to estimate and propagate uncertainties in each step. Here we will discuss the methods that have been adopted for estimating and propagating uncertainties. Our approach is based on sound statistical reasoning while taking into account the implications of inherent uncertainties in the characterization of the instrumental signatures that we are trying to remove.

1. Introduction

The *Space Infrared Telescope Facility* (SIRTF), the last member of the four Great Observatories program, will be launched in January, 2003. Multiple instruments covering a wide range of wavelengths, from $\sim 3\mu$m to $\sim 160\mu$m, will be utilized to gather data in both imaging and spectroscopic modes during the expected five-year life of the mission.

The data from individual observations will be processed through a set of pipelines specific to the particular data collection mode, and an infrastructure has been implemented to enable the processing and quality assessment in a lights-out fashion (Moshir 2001). Typically for a given instrument, calibration data are first processed through a set of calibration pipelines and then the resulting calibration terms are employed during the reduction and calibration of regular science data products. A paper at this conference discusses the spectroscopic mode pipelines (Fang et al. 2003). The *SIRTF Science Center* (SSC) is committed to providing the user community the most up-to-date calibrated data products. As part of this commitment it is also planned to provide the users

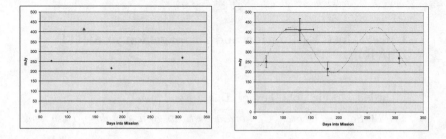

Figure 1.   Illustration of flux density measurements with informative uncertainties. The data point at a flux density of ~ 400 mJy is from the *IRAS* Faint Source Survey, the remainder are from pointed observations. Data are consistent with a variable source.

with estimates of product uncertainties that are traceable, reasonable, and at the same time *informative*.

In Section 2 we will first discuss some of the motivating concepts for this undertaking, and in Section 3 we will discuss the statistics and practical aspects of approaching the problem. Section 4 is devoted to a discussion of examples and complications. In Section 5 we discuss the issue of uncertainty propagation when calibration data are interpolated.

2.   Motivation

In many undertakings it is customary (due to diverse circumstances such as lack of resources, compressed schedules, etc.) to quote *reasonable* uncertainties—at times using somewhat *ad-hoc* methods. In our discussion, besides the requirement of reasonableness we wish to emphasize the adjective *informative*. It signifies that it is possible to make statistically significant statements regarding the quality of the data. An example of when correct and informative uncertainties provide significant aid in scientific utilization of the data can be seen in Figure 1. In the left panel the flux densities for a source quoted in the *IRAS* Faint Source Survey (Moshir et al. 1992) and *IRAS* pointed observations are shown. Without the "error bars" it would not be possible to conclude much about the detections, or even *whether the data are trustable at all*. However, with the uncertainties shown, it is possible to consider and evaluate several hypotheses to explain the disagreement between the two datasets. Here the hypothesis of a variable source appears to fit the data well (right panel). Later follow up of the source revealed that the object was in fact a variable star.

In passing we note some areas where uncertainty analysis has been proven to be of significant utility:

- It provides ways to limit the effects of low quality data (do not ruin good data with bad ones!)
- By assuming normal distribution of uncertainties many standard analysis tools could be invoked.
- Inspection of uncertainties reveals problems early, for example significantly larger than expected uncertainties point to a problem upstream.

- It allows quantitative assessment of whether requirements are being met. Alarms could be raised when requirements specify unreasonable goals.
- It permits optimal usage of products in hypothesis testing scenarios (e.g., radiation-hit detection, variability analysis, position-based merging, etc.). For an application see Masci et al. (2003).

3. Statistics and Practical Considerations

In order to proceed with the program of uncertainty estimation and propagation, a few preliminaries need to be considered:

- Incoming data need to have uncertainties. A *noise* model is desired.
- While performing mathematical steps, propagate the uncertainties as indicated by the arithmetical operations. But be aware of the pitfalls of blindly following mathematical procedures.
- When applying calibration terms, propagate their uncertainties appropriately. Take into account the epoch differences between calibration measurements and their application. Pay attention to the implications of calibration *models*.
- While cognizant of the previous points, follow the "trust but verify" approach. Do the final uncertainties make sense?
- Appreciate the unknown. Systematic errors may be lurking here and there!

In many cases in the discussion of uncertainties there is an unspoken assumption that prevails, namely that of *normality*. There are many reasons for this. For example, Gaussian distributions are part of every science curriculum. They are easy to manipulate and lead to rigorous justification for least squares fit, χ^2 minimization, and goodness of fit tests. The second moments can be tied to confidence levels (1-σ and 68% probability becoming interchangeable). And finally, under reasonable (*but not all*) conditions, many scenarios lead to Normal distributions.

It needs to be kept in mind that the assumptions of normality should not cloud practical situations (where the statement "let $N \to \infty$" does not clearly apply!) There are cases when uncertainties can not be treated as Gaussian because data are a mixture of different distributions, for example there are radiation hits, transients in the field of view, etc. There are also cases where the instrumental noise does not follow a Gaussian model. And an important often encountered situation is that mathematical operations on Gaussian data can easily turn them into non-Gaussian constructs.

Despite all of the previous points and potential complications, one still needs to estimate σs that are reasonable and informative so they can be used to signify confidence bands. These complications only make the subject more interesting and reveal some new approaches in the field of practical applications of statistics.

As an illustration of the scenarios we encounter, two pipelines, one for science and the other for calibration are shown in Figure 2. The science pipeline consists of a series of well defined arithmetical operations for which the rules of mathematical statistics provide the means of propagating the uncertainties. The science pipeline also applies calibration terms to the products using well defined mathematical operations; these steps are shown with a thick arrow. In these

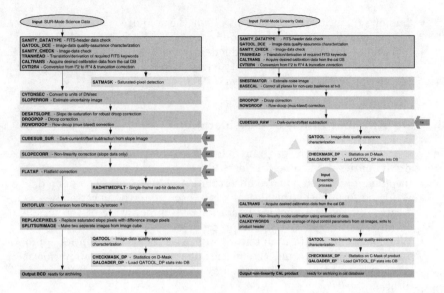

Figure 2.   Pipelines for MIPS 24μm science data (left panel) and for MIPS 24μm non-linearity calibration.

stages one must be aware of epoch differences between when the calibration measurements are performed and when the science data are collected. This leads to the issues of uncertainty propagation with sparse calibration terms, a subject that will be discussed in section 5. Similar considerations apply to the calibration pipeline shown in the right hand side panel of Figure 2.

3.1.   Noise Modeling

With the advent of sophisticated (and *expensive!*) instrumentation, they are also becoming generally well characterizable. The noise model is usually known to a reasonable extent. The model is generally verified in lab tests, for example through repeatability experiments. For a measured DN value one can write a formula for the uncertainty that depends on the measured DN and a few other characterized parameters (independent of DN value). For example via a simple formula such as $\sigma^2 = g \times DN + \sigma_r^2$, where σ is in electrons, g is the gain (in e-/DN) and σ_r is the "read noise" expressed in electrons; thus one may assign an *a priori* uncertainty to each measured value. For a given measurement $\phi = DN \pm \sigma'$ ($\sigma' = \sigma/g$) it becomes possible to propagate the uncertainties as the measurement progresses through pipelines. Now suppose that the instrument's gain is not known at a given instance (the physics of the detector would lead to a variable gain, for example the transients in a Ge:Ga array). As a case study we consider the scenario where it is only known that the gain is varying somewhere in the range of 3 to 8 e-/DN.

We desire the uncertainty distribution appropriate for photon noise (following the common model of Poisson statistics) with a gain that is variable or unknown. Photo-electron number is DN multiplied by the gain g. The gain is

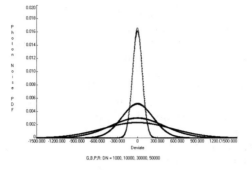

Figure 3. The expected distributions when the "gain" in the noise model is only known to fall within some range.

normally treated as a constant, but here the problem is defined such that our lack of knowledge of the gain (except that it is somewhere between 3 and 8!) leads us to treat the gain as a random variable with a uniform distribution. For example, a DN value of 1 may imply anything from 3 to 8 photo-electrons with equal probability (again we emphasize that the instrument is *not* acting randomly, it is our state of knowledge that is incomplete).

The situation may be thought of as one in which the gain varies smoothly from 3 to 8 over the integration period. There is no resolution into what happens within one integration time, so the gain could actually be jumping instantaneously from one value to another, but after the integration is complete, the gain must have spent a fraction $\Delta g/5$ of the integration time within the range from g to $g + \Delta g$ for all values of g from 3 to $8 - \Delta g$ and for all values of Δg greater than zero and less than or equal to 5. This follows from the assumption of g being uniformly distributed over $[3, 8]$. With no evidence to the contrary, so we can think of g as varying smoothly over $[3, 8]$.

Think of the range $[3, 8]$ as subdivided into N equal sections, with N large enough so that $1/N \ll g$. The gain at the center of the nth section is $3 + (n - 1/2)/N$. The total distribution is then the sum of N Poisson distributions with mean and variance equal to $DN(3 + (n - 1/2)/N)$, $n = 1, 2, 3, ...N$.

A representative read noise value to use in this example is 350 electrons, so photon noise very much smaller than this is negligible, and therefore any photon noise worth considering may be assumed to be in the Gaussian limit of the Poisson distribution. This assumption is not necessary, but it simplifies the numerical construction of the above total distribution. We note in passing that the sum of two or more Gaussian populations is algebraically non-Gaussian, but this does not preclude numerical properties that may resemble a single Gaussian distribution to a sufficiently good approximation (and similarly for Poisson distributions).

To study this approximation, total distributions were computed for DN values of 1000, 10000, 30000, and 50000 DN. Renormalized histograms were made for each of the N = 1000 distributions described above. These are shown in Figure 3 as solid lines with colors green, blue, purple, and red, respectively. Then the pure Gaussian density function was evaluated at the center of each cell; these values are shown in the figure as black dots in all cases (the black dots along each curve are the pure Gaussian values for that curve's DN value). It is obvious from the figure that the pure Gaussian distributions based on the average gain are extremely good approximations to the distributions based on uniform mixtures over the gain range.

This model of the photon noise is applicable even when the gain is not actually varying but is merely unknown and equally likely to be anywhere in the range used. Once a measurement is made, whatever error occurred is always some unknown constant. The distribution of possible values represents the uncertainty in what the error was, not the error itself, which either cannot be known or else could be removed.

4. Examples and Complications

As stated earlier, the rules of mathematics and statistics allow one to formally propagate uncertainties, but in the process one should be aware of some pitfalls. A given measurement $\phi = DN \pm \sigma'$ undergoes many arithmetic operations until a final calibrated value appears out of a pipeline. Some mathematical operations are safe in the use of the *central limit theorem* to assume a normal distribution for the resultant. However, in general, caution is advised in the invocation of asymptotic normalcy. We observe that when $x \in N(\mu_1, \sigma_1)$, and $y \in N(\mu_2, \sigma_2)$ then both of the primitive arithmetic operations $+$ and $-$ result in $x+y$ and $x-y$ following a normal distribution. The other two primitive operations of multiply and divide lead to *non*-Gaussian results when $x \times y$ and x/y are calculated.

An interesting case to consider is when we divide two values which we have reason to believe are each following the Normal distribution. For example, a value in a pixel is divided by a flat-field to obtain a flattened image. The pixel value (in the numerator) prior to this operation has undergone many operations and is seen empirically to follow very closely a Gaussian distribution. The flat-field has very likely come from the process of super-medianing or trimmed-averaging of a *large* number of independent values, thus it is expected to be a good candidate for invoking the *central limit theorem*, and is expected to follow a Gaussian as well. With these preambles we form the flat-fielded value $z = x/y$. With a bit of effort one can derive the probability distribution for $z = x/y$, when $x \in N(\mu_1, \sigma_1)$, and $y \in N(\mu_2, \sigma_2)$; $P(z)$ has the following form:

$$
\frac{e^{-\frac{\mu_1^2}{2\sigma_1^2} - \frac{\mu_2^2}{2\sigma_2^2}} \left(2\sigma_1\sigma_2 + \frac{e^{\frac{\left(\mu_2\sigma_1^2 + z\mu_1\sigma_2^2\right)^2}{2\sigma_1^2\sigma_2^2(\sigma_1^2 + z^2\sigma_2^2)}} \sqrt{2\pi}\,(\mu_2\sigma_1^2 + z\mu_1\sigma_2^2)\, Erf(\frac{\frac{\mu_2\sigma_1}{\sigma_2} + \frac{z\mu_1\sigma_2}{\sigma_1}}{\sqrt{2}\sqrt{\sigma_1^2 + z^2\sigma_2^2}})}{\sqrt{\sigma_1^2 + z^2\sigma_2^2}} \right)}{2\pi\,(\sigma_1^2 + z^2\,\sigma_2^2)}
$$

Asymptotically, as $z \to \pm\infty$, the distribution becomes Cauchy-like

$$
\frac{e^{-\frac{\mu_1^2}{2\sigma_1^2} - \frac{\mu_2^2}{2\sigma_2^2}} \left(2\sigma_1\sigma_2 + e^{\frac{\mu_1^2}{2\sigma_1^2}} \sqrt{2\pi}\,\mu_1\sigma_2\, Erf(\frac{\mu_1}{\sqrt{2}\sigma_1}) \right)}{2\pi(\sigma_1^2 + z^2\sigma_2^2)}
$$

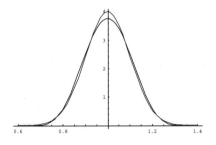

Figure 4.   A Gaussian distribution (red curve), along with another distribution of compact support with same mean and standard deviation (lower-peaked) which also *looks* very Gaussian.

It is well known that the Cauchy distribution does not possess first or higher order moments. Thus we can neither claim an expected value nor an uncertainty for the flat-fielded result! From experience we know this to be an absurd proposition; for years people have used flat-fielded images and have even come up with "error bars." From this exercise it is clear that assuming Gaussian behavior for the numerator and denominator (which appeared to be reasonable) can lead to erroneous conclusions if one attempts to strictly adhere to mathematical rigor. Instead we must use the rules of *plausible reasoning*, because we are dealing with real world scenarios. For one thing, the flat-field frame is a positive definite quantity, the algorithms that produce the flat-field must ensure that this is the case. If arithmetic leads to a non-physical value, that value must be masked appropriately so that when the result is used in pipeline processing, its non-physical nature could be communicated. SIRTF calibration pipelines produce such calibration quality mask files, and use them for quality assessment (see the step called CHECKMASK_DP in the example calibration pipeline in Figure 2.) For another thing, while the denominator (the flat-field frame) is thought to be Gaussian, this is only in appearance. It is possible to come up with a function that *looks* very much Gaussian, but in fact has a compact support (mathematically speaking). This is illustrated in Figure 4. If we follow the approach of *plausible reasoning* and use the lower-peaked curve in Figure 4 as the distribution of flat-field uncertainties, then the ratio $z = x/y$ will be very well behaved, asymptotically it will decay rapidly, and will possess moments as well. Following this approach, since the ratio is now expected to have a second moment, it is possible to use an equation such as $\sigma_z^2/z^2 = \sigma_x^2/x^2 + \sigma_y^2/y^2 + 3\sigma_x^2/x^2\sigma_y^2/y^2$ to derive the formal variance of the ratio (which is very accurate even when the numerator and denominator have large uncertainties).

As an application, let us consider again the case of flat fielding. Suppose that the pixel to be flattened has a value of 1,000 and an uncertainty of 1.4%, this measurement has a sharp symmetric distribution. Next suppose the flat-field for that pixel has an uncertainty of 25%,[1] the denominator also has a symmetric

---

[1]There will be instances during estimating a spectral flat-field that the reference object's spectrum is not known accurately over a given wavelength range; this lack of knowledge is thus transferred into the estimated flat-field frame.

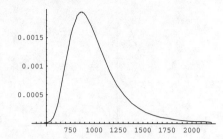

Figure 5.   The distribution function for a flat fielded pixel when the input pixel has a sharp symmetric distribution with $\sigma = 1.4\%$ and the flat-field has a wide symmetric distribution with $\sigma = 25\%$.

distribution (similar to the blue curve in Figure 4). Under this scenario the probability distribution for the flat fielded value has the form shown in Figure 5. The important point to note is that the distribution is asymmetric (due to the large uncertainty in the denominator). If a minimum range corresponding to 68% probability is calculated from the distribution of P(z), the resulting 'σ' agrees very closely with the expression for σ_z^2/z^2 that was discussed earlier.

A library of functions dealing with the four primary arithmetic operations has been developed and used by pipeline modules. For more complex operations, each module propagates the uncertainty according to the specific algorithmic form. As example consider detector non-linearity. The non-linearity coefficient α has been estimated for each pixel in a calibration pipeline (see Figure 2); the science pipeline estimates a linearized DN from the observed DN. The model is simple, $DN_{obs} = \alpha DN_{true}^2 + DN_{true}$. In this case, performing a few reduction steps, the uncertainty due to the application of the algorithm with the given α becomes

$$\sigma_{DN_{linear}} \approx \frac{\sigma_\alpha DN_{linear}^2}{2\alpha DN_{linear} + 1}$$

The input data, DN_{obs} are originally accompanied by uncertainties; the final uncertainty of the result is obtained by "rss-ing" the two quantities (neglecting first order terms in error expansion, which is valid in this particular case).

5.   Calibration Extension and Uncertainties

As part of pipeline processing, calibration terms need be applied to the data. In general only a finite number of calibration measurements are performed over a given time period. From those discrete observations, calibration terms must be extended beyond their original domain. Of course with modern instrumentation the builders do their utmost to set up stable and calibratable instruments. The instrument builders count heavily on the power of calibration extension. The process of calibration can fall into two general categories discussed below.

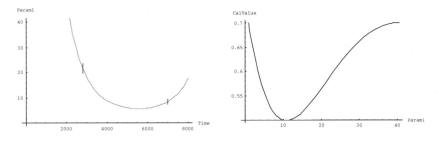

Figure 6. Left, control parameter versus time. Right, the *known* correlation of a calibration term with the control parameter.

5.1. Calibration Extension with Control Parameters

In this scenario, the measured calibration terms are known to be correlated with *known* control parameters (an instrument builder's dream!) Here, only *occasional* calibration measurements are performed to *verify* that the correlation is still valid. The correlation curve is characterized along with uncertainties. At any given time, the calibration term can be "looked up" by measuring the control parameter (which could be a frequently sampled House-Keeping parameter) and then using that value to estimate the calibration term and its uncertainty, as illustrated in Figure 6. As stated earlier this is almost dream-like for an instrument builder. With few calibration measurements it is possible to periodically *validate* the model and continue using a deterministic calibration *model*.

5.2. Calibration Extension with Calibration Rules

The case just discussed is usually the exception rather than the rule! More frequently, the dependence of calibration on control parameters is not known well, or there are too many control parameters, each with its own "seemingly random" variation. In this case it is difficult, if not impossible, to reach the same level of luxury as in previous section. The purpose of a mission is to *maximize* science time while staying well calibrated, not to spend most of the time to *fully* characterize calibration. Thus a few calibration measurements are performed on a routine basis and the principle of "calibration extension" is invoked, resulting in a set of *calibration rules*, for example

- Fallback (one and same for all times).
- Nearest in time (past, future, either)
- Interpolation or extrapolation (various orders)
- ...

Each of these rules leads to different quotes for uncertainties. For example in the case of fallback, there is no sense of *context*, thus extend the uncertainty the same way as the fallback term itself. A more non-trivial case is when two calibration measurements have been performed at two different times, and the two calibration products are different without there being an apparent reason (happens so often!). A calibration rule is then invoked and the pipelines use a nearest in time value or perhaps an interpolation between the two. Taking the latter case, in the absence of evidence to the contrary, assume calibration

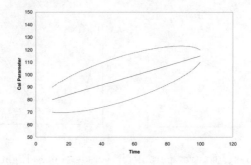

Figure 7.   The uncertainty growth as a result of interpolation of a calibration term at two discrete epochs.

term changes continuously from value C_1 at time t_1 to value C_2 at time t_2 (plausible reasoning). The simplest continuous function is a straight line. So the calibration extended to time t is $C_t = (1 - \alpha)C_1 + \alpha C_2$ where $\alpha = (t - t_1)/(t_2 - t_1)$. The next issue is what to use for the uncertainty of C_t. We stated that in the absence of information the least costly path from C_1 at t_1 to C_2 at t_2 appears to be a straight line, but other possibilities exist as well. A random walk could take us from C_1 at t_1 to C_2 at t_2 also! In fact instruments are known to have drifts, often times expressible by fractional Brownian Motion (fBM processes). We can postulate that the variance of C_1 *used at time t* is $V_t(C_1) = V_{t_1}(C_1) + V_{rw}|t - t_1|/|t_2 - t_1|$, where $V_{rw} = (C1 - C2)^2$, similarly for $V_t(C_2)$. This results in the growth of uncertainty in the interpolation scheme that is seen in Figure 7. Plausible reasoning has led to a growth of uncertainty as we go farther away from the epoch of calibration measurement.

6.   Summary

Plausible reasoning leads to consistent and sufficiently accurate uncertainty propagation methods, even in seemingly dead-end scenarios. Expenditure of resources on uncertainty characterization is highly recommended to all projects.

Acknowledgments.   This work was carried out at the SIRTF Science Center, with funding from NASA under contract to the California Institute of Technology and the Jet Propulsion Laboratory.

References

Moshir, M. 2001, in ASP Conf. Ser., Vol. 281, Astronomical Data Analysis Software and Systems XI, ed. D. A. Bohlender, D. Durand, & T. H. Handley (San Francisco: ASP), 336

Fang, F. et al. 2003, this volume, 253

Moshir, M. et al. 1992, Explanatory Supplement to the IRAS Faint Source Survey, Version2, JPL D-10015 8/92 (Pasadena:JPL)

Masci, F. et al. 2003, this volume, 391

Astronomical Data Analysis Software and Systems XII
ASP Conference Series, Vol. 295, 2003
H. E. Payne, R. I. Jedrzejewski, and R. N. Hook, eds.

Generalized Self-Calibration for Space VLBI Image Reconstruction

Sergey F. Likhachev

Astro Space Center, Profsojuznaya 84/32, GSP-7, 117997, Moscow, Russia

Abstract. Generalized self-calibration (GSC) algorithm as a solution of a non-linear optimization problem is considered. The algorithm allows to work easily with the first and the second derivatives of a visibility function phases and amplitudes. This approach is important for high orbiting Space VLBI data processing. The implementation of the GSC-algorithm for radio astronomy image restoration is shown. The comparison with other self-calibration algorithms is demonstrated. The GSC-algorithm was implemented in the radio astronomy imaging software project Astro Space Locator (ASL) for Windows developed at the Astro Space Center.

1. Image reconstruction: Basic concepts

Definition 1.1. A space of complex functions $V(\mathbf{u})$ dual to the brightness distribution $I(\mathbf{x})$ and risen by an operator F, is called a space of *visibility functions* or *spatial coherency*.

$$V(\mathbf{u}) = F\{\mathbf{I}(\mathbf{x})\} = \int_{-\infty}^{\infty} \mathbf{I}(\mathbf{x}) \exp\{-2\pi i \langle \mathbf{x}, \mathbf{u} \rangle\} \, d\mathbf{x} \qquad (1)$$

Definition 1.2. Let us define *an object* as a domain of the Universe that is a subject of the investigation whose brightness distribution could be represented as a 2-D function with infinite spatial frequency spectra.

Definition 1.3. Let us define *an image* of the object as a result of creation *by unknown spatial brightness distribution*

$$\mathbf{I}_{true}(\mathbf{x})$$

(the object) of *an illumination distribution*

$$\mathbf{J}_{true}(\mathbf{x}),$$

i.e.,

$$\mathbf{J}_{true}(\mathbf{x}) = (H\mathbf{I}_{true})(\mathbf{x}).$$

In other words, we have an original object located somewhere in the space (Universe) and we can observe only some projection of this object on this space. For example, one of the projections of the object can be its electromagnetic emission of the object in a given spectral band and in a given moment of time.

2. VLBI Image Restoration as an Approximation Procedure

Let us consider a metrics

$$\rho = \sum_{ij} w_{ij} \left[V_{ij} - \hat{V}_{ij} \right]^2 \Rightarrow \min \qquad (2)$$

where V_{ij} is a measurements of the visibility function and $\hat{V}_{ij}$ is an approximating function.

There exist a few possible approximating functions:

1. Orthogonal approximation:

$$\hat{V}_{ij} = \sum_{ij} c_{ij}\varphi_{ij}$$

If φ_{ij} is a Fourier basis, the orthogonal approximation is known in VLBI as a CLEAN algorithm.

2. Bi-orthogonal approximation:

$$\hat{\mathbf{V}} = \mathbf{g} \cdot \psi \cdot \bar{\mathbf{g}}$$

If ψ_{ij} is a 2-D complex function (a model), the bi-orthogonal approximation is known in VLBI as a self-calibration algorithm.

3. Non-parametrical approximation:

$$\sum_{i} \lg I_i - \lambda \cdot \rho \max$$

(known in VLBI as a MEM algorithm).

4. Mathematical programming approximation:

$$\mathbf{D} = \mathbf{B} \cdot \mathbf{I}$$

$$\mathbf{I} \geq 0$$

(known in VLBI as a so-called NNLS algorithm).

3. Generalized Self-Calibration (GSC) as a Problem of Non-linear Optimization

Let us consider an expression

$$\mathbf{V}_{t\nu} = \mathbf{g}_{t\nu} \mathbf{V}_{t\nu}^{true} \bar{\mathbf{g}}_{t\nu} + \varepsilon_{t\nu} \qquad (3)$$

where $\mathbf{g}_{t\nu} = diag\,[g_i]$, $\dim\{\mathbf{g}_{t\nu}\} = [N-1 \times N-1]$, $\mathbf{V}_{t\nu} = \{V_{ijkl}\}$ visibility matrix was measured on the baseline (i,j) for a given moment of time t_k and frequency ν_l, $\dim\{\mathbf{V}_{t\nu}\} = [N-1 \times N-1]$, $\mathbf{V}_{t\nu}^{true}$ true visibility function for the baseline (i,j), for a given moment of time t_k and frequency ν_l, $\dim\{\mathbf{V}_{t\nu}\} = [N-1 \times N-1]$, $\varepsilon_{t\nu}$ additive noise.

Let us consider a discrepancy

$$\mathbf{z}_{tv} = \mathbf{g}_{tv}\hat{\mathbf{V}}_{tv}\bar{\mathbf{g}}_{tv} - \mathbf{V}_{tv} \tag{4}$$

It is necessary to obtain:

$$\arg\min_{g_i} \rho = \|\mathbf{z}_{tv}\|^2 \tag{5}$$

where $\hat{\mathbf{V}}_{tv}$ is a model of $\mathbf{V}_{tv}^{true}$, $\hat{\mathbf{V}}_{tv}$ is upper triangular matrix with $\hat{V}_{ij} = 0$. The solution $\mathbf{g}_{tv}$ obtained on the basis generalized Newton's algorithm with pseudo-inversion.

4. Local Approximation of Gains

Let us represent *a complex function* $g_i(t', \nu')$ as a time series in the neighborhood of a point (t_0', ν_0'). Then

$$g_i(t_0' + \Delta t, \nu_0' + \Delta\nu) = g_i(t_0, \nu_0) + \frac{\partial g_i(t_0, \nu_0)}{\partial t'}\Delta t + \frac{\partial g_i(t_0, \nu_0)}{\partial \nu'}\Delta\nu +$$
$$O\left(\Delta t^2 + \Delta\nu^2\right) \tag{6}$$

Let us introduce the following notations:
- let us call

$$r_i = \frac{\partial\varphi_i(t_0, \nu_0)}{\partial t}$$

as *a fringe rate*;
- let us call

$$\tau_i = \frac{\partial\varphi_i(t_0, \nu_0)}{\partial \nu}$$

as *a fringe delay.*

Both values are complex ones and can be represented as

$$g_i(t_0' + \Delta t, \nu_0' + \Delta\nu) =$$
$$\left\{\left[a_i(t_0, \nu_0) + \frac{\partial a_i(t_0, \nu_0)}{\partial t'}\Delta t + \frac{\partial a_i(t_0, \nu_0)}{\partial \nu'}\Delta\nu\right] + \right.$$
$$\left. i \cdot [a_i(t_0, \nu_0) r_i\Delta t + a_i(t_0, \nu_0)\tau\Delta\nu]\right\} \times \exp\left\{i \cdot \varphi_i(t_0, \nu_0)\right\} +$$
$$O\left(\Delta t^2 + \Delta\nu^2\right) \tag{7}$$

Example. If $a_i(t_0, \nu_0) = const$ (no amplitude calibration) then

$$g_i(t_0' + \Delta t, \nu_0' + \Delta\nu) =$$
$$\left\{const \cdot [r_i\Delta t + \tau\Delta\nu]\right\} \times \exp\left\{i \cdot \left[\varphi_i(t_0, \nu_0) + \frac{\pi}{2} + 2k\pi\right]\right\} +$$
$$O\left(\Delta t^2 + \Delta\nu^2\right) \tag{8}$$

and obtain a well-known expression for phase calibration (see Schwab 1981).

A value $O\left(\Delta t^2 + \Delta\nu^2\right)$ describes derivatives of the second order that is necessary to take into account for Space VLBI imaging.

5.   Some Imaging Problems for High Orbiting Space VLBI

Definition 5.1. If for any three radio telescopes
1. there exists its closing, i.e.,

$$\vec{\varphi}_1 + \vec{\varphi}_2 + \vec{\varphi}_3 = 0;$$

2. any two baselines

$$\|\mathbf{b}_{13}\| \,\&\, \|\mathbf{b}_{23}\| > D_{Earth},$$

3. and

$$\|\mathbf{b}_{23} - \mathbf{b}_{13}\| / \|\mathbf{b}_{12}\| \to 1,$$

then the VLBI can be called *high orbiting space VLBI*.

In case of a High Orbiting SVLB mission a good (u,v)-coverage does not guarantee high quality images because

$$\Delta\varphi_{12} \approx \delta\varphi_{rms}$$

is an "apogee phase gap."

6.   Implementation of GSC in the ASL for Windows

The software project, Astro Space Locator (ASL) for Windows 9x/NT/2000 (code name ASL_Spider 1.0) is developed by the Laboratory for Mathematical Methods[1] of the ASC to provide a free software package for VLBI data processing. We used the Microsoft Windows NT/2000 and MS Visual C++ 6.0 on IBM compatible PCs as the platform from which to make data processing and reconstruction of VLBI images.

7.   Outcomes

A generalized self-calibration (GSC) algorithm was developed. The solution was obtained as a non-linear optimization in the Hilbert space L_2. GCS describes not only the first derivatives but also of the second derivatives that is necessary to take into account for Space VLBI imaging. A global fringe fitting procedure is just an initialization (zero iteration) of GSC. GSC allows to obtain more stable and reliable results than traditional self-calibration algorithms.

References

Schwab, F. R. 1981, VLA Scientific Memorandum, No. 136, NRAO

---

[1]http://platon.asc.rssi.ru/dpd/asl/asl.html

Astronomical Data Analysis Software and Systems XII
ASP Conference Series, Vol. 295, 2003
H. E. Payne, R. I. Jedrzejewski, and R. N. Hook, eds.

Calibration of BIMA Data in AIPS++

Daniel Goscha, David M. Mehringer, Raymond L. Plante

National Center for Supercomputing Applications

Anuj Sarma

University of Illinois

Abstract. We summarize the general approach adopted for the calibration of millimeter interferometer data from the BIMA telescope using AIPS++ and illustrate the use of the relevant software tools. In particular, we will discuss flagging, phase calibration, flux calibration, and polarization calibration, and we will show how we take advantage of the unique capabilities of AIPS++ to meet the special needs of BIMA data. We will show how BIMA calibration tools can be used to hide some of the complexity of the processes while still allowing access to specialized variations if desired. We will illustrate how these tools are pipelined together for end-to-end processing both within the BIMA Image Pipeline and on the user's desktop. Finally, we will present a comparison of data calibrated in MIRIAD and AIPS++.

1. Introduction

We present the results of a comparison of calibrated millimeter data from the Berkeley-Illinois-Maryland Association (BIMA) Array using both AIPS++ and MIRIAD. In addition, we discuss the unique calibration capabilities of AIPS++ in calibrating BIMA data both on the user's desktop and in an end-to-end (e2e) pipeline. In particular we present:

- A brief discussion of calibration of BIMA data using AIPS++;
- A qualitative comparison of data calibrated and cleaned in AIPS++ and MIRIAD;
- A quantitative comparison of the RMS and dynamic range of data calibrated and cleaned in AIPS++ and MIRIAD.

2. Calibration of BIMA Data with AIPS++

AIPS++ allows for the concealment of some of the complexity of calibrating BIMA data through the use of custom tools. The *bimacalibrater* tool in AIPS++ is such a tool. *bimacalibrater* contains several functions needed in the calibration process, many of which are friendly wrappers around functions of the AIPS++ *calibrater* tool. These wrappers hide parameters not normally needed in the calibration of BIMA data and provide more suitable defaults for other parameters.

The *bimacalibrater* functions hide much of the complexity of the calibration process while still allowing a high degree of customization for varied data.

One of the important aspects of the calibration process is the ability to view the antenna based gain solutions, flag bad data in the solution, and fit the solutions. Gain solutions are written to a gain table that can be accessed by the AIPS++ table tool, allowing for a high level of accessibility to the data. Once this has been done, an interactive user can use the *plotcal* function of the *bimacalibrater* tool to examine the gain table. If any bad data were noted after examining the gain table, a user could simply flag the bad data using the *autoflag* tool, or, interactively using the *msplot* tool (both part of AIPS++). In addition, it is also possible to flag and fit gain table solutions using the *gainpolyfitter* tool.

2.1. Calibration Process

The calibration process consists of three primary steps:
  1. Filling;
  2. Flagging/Editing;
  3. Calibration.
All of these steps can be carried out interactively on the user's desktop using the AIPS++ GUI, interactively using the Glish (the scripting language front end to AIPS++) command line interface, or in an automated fashion using custom Glish scripts. The BIMA Image Pipeline currently employs the *bimacalibrater* tool to do automated calibration of BIMA data.

3. Comparison of Data Calibration with AIPS++ and MIRIAD

In order to assess the robustness of calibration of BIMA data within AIPS++, several comparisons were made between data calibrated with and cleaned within AIPS++ and MIRIAD. Great care was taken at each step of the calibration process to ensure we were comparing "apples to apples" – data that were flagged in one data set were flagged in the other, the same clean algorithms were used in both cases, gain solution fits were both two point interpolations, etc. The following comparisons were carried out:
  • Peak fluxes of calibrated versions of the calibrator were compared;
  • Antenna based gain solutions were compared;
  • Contour maps with the contours chosen to highlight the noise levels were made for qualitative comparison;
  • The data were cleaned using the same number of iteration and noise and dynamic range calculations were made;
  • The data were cleaned to the same peak residual level and the number of iterations needed to reach that level was noted and subsequent image noise and dynamic range measurements were made.

As a check on the flux density calibration, images of the calibrator 1733-130 were made. The specified flux density of this source during calibration was 2.8 Jy. The flux densities of the dirty maps were compared. The MIRIAD image produced a peak flux density of 2.66 Jy, while the AIPS++ data yielded a flux density of 2.81 Jy. In this particular case, AIPS++ did a better job in reproducing the correct flux density during calibration.

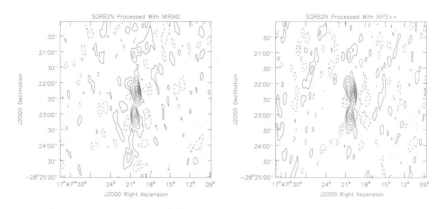

Figure 1. SGRB2N calibrated and cleaned in MIRIAD and in AIPS++.

The next step in the calibration comparison was to examine the gain solutions produced in the two packages. There was no noteworthy difference in the gain solutions other than the fact that gain solution amplitudes in MIRIAD are the reciprocals of their AIPS++ counterparts.

A qualitative comparison of the images after a 1000 iteration clean (using the Clark clean algorithm) was then performed. The same data were calibrated and cleaned in AIPS++ and MIRIAD and then imaged. Figure 1 shows the results. In both cases, contour levels were chosen to highlight the background noise levels so qualitative comparisons between the calibrations could be seen more clearly. The contour levels are the same for both images.

Using the *imstat* command in MIRIAD and the image analysis tool in AIPS++, the RMS noise level for each cleaned image was measured. In both cases, the same off-source region was used. The results of this comparison are summarized in Table 1.

Table 1. Image quality after calibration and cleaning (1000 iterations)

	AIPS++	MIRIAD
RMS (Jy/beam)	0.06	0.06
Peak Flux (Jy/beam)	5.50	5.25
Dynamic Range	91	90

Lastly the data were cleaned to a maximum residual cutoff of 0.115 Jy/beam and a similar comparison of background noise done. It should be noted that AIPS++ cleaned to that level faster than MIRIAD – 1437 iterations in AIPS++ and 4451 iterations in MIRIAD. The results are summarized in Table 2.

Table 2. Image quality after calibration and cleaning (maximum residual cutoff of 0.115 Jy)

	AIPS++	MIRIAD
NITER	1437	4451
RMS (Jy/beam)	0.05	0.05
Peak Flux (Jy/beam)	5.5	5.4
Dynamic Range	112	117

4. Summary

Comparison of calibration of BIMA Array data in MIRIAD and in AIPS++ has been carried out. We found no significant difference in the gain solutions and images made from calibrated data from either package. Specifically we found the following:

- The AIPS++ *bimacalibrater* tool and associated functions provide a useful interactive GUI, command line, or pipeline solution for calibrating BIMA data;
- In comparing antenna based gain solutions, it was found that gain solution amplitudes in MIRIAD are the recipricals of their AIPS++ counterparts;
- In comparing flux densities of the phase-calibrator from maps made using each package, AIPS++ did a better job reproducing the correct density;
- When the target data were calibrated and cleaned using the same number of iterations, the dynamic range of the image is roughly 2% higher in the AIPS++ image;
- When the target data were calibrated and cleaned to the same intensity cutoff whilst AIPS++ required fewer iterations, the dynamic range of the MIRIAD image was 4% higher than the AIPS++ image.

Astronomical Data Analysis Software and Systems XII
ASP Conference Series, Vol. 295, 2003
H. E. Payne, R. I. Jedrzejewski, and R. N. Hook, eds.

Self-calibration for the SIRTF GOODS Legacy Project

D. Grumm and S. Casertano

Space Telescope Science Institute, Baltimore, MD 21218

Abstract. Data analysis for the SIRTF GOODS Legacy Project must be able to achieve a level of calibration noise well below a part in 10,000. To achieve such a high level of fidelity, a form of self-calibration may be required in which the sky intensity and the instrumental effects are derived simultaneously. Two methods being investigated are a least squares approach based on the work of Fixsen and Arendt at GSFC, and an iterative method. Both methods have been applied to derive the sky, flat field, and offset from simulated data for instruments to be flown on SIRTF; the results will be discussed.

1. Introduction

The Great Observatories Origins Deep Survey (GOODS) incorporates a SIRTF Legacy project designed to study galaxy formation and evolution over a wide range of redshift and cosmic lookback time. Our current understanding is that the standard pipeline developed by the SIRTF Science Center may not achieve the levels of fidelity required for the analysis of the deepest GOODS data, which translate into a level of calibration noise well below a part in 10,000. Self-calibration may be required to achieve the necessary level of calibration.

2. Algorithms

Two algorithms have been used to simultaneously solve for the sky, gain, and offset for simulated sets of dithered images. These techniques are the Fixsen-Arendt least squares self-calibration code (Arendt et al. 2000) and an iterative code.

Fixsen-Arendt code:

- Written in IDL using C matrix routines; handles ideal case (integer pixel shifts, no geometric distortion), solves data=gain*sky+offset. Code incorporating geometric distortion is under development.
- When solving for sky and gain, achieves machine precision on noiseless data; for noisy data, solution within noise.
- Memory limitations become a problem when attempting to use all dither positions for GOODS.
- Additional instrumental effects are difficult to add to code, and the amount of memory and execution time required roughly triple with each effect.

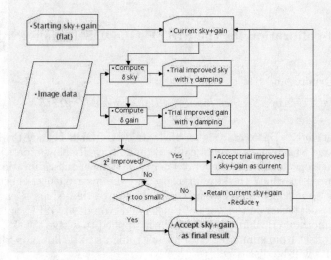

Figure 1.   Iterative self-calibration method.

Iterative code:

- Written in IDL; handles ideal case (integer pixel shifts, no geometric distortion), solves for data=gain*sky+offset.
- Tests on simulated MIPS HDF-N campaign (1440 pointings) converge to shot-noise-limited sky in 2 hours (single-processor 440 MHz Sun Blade 1000)
- When solving for sky and gain, achieves machine precision on noiseless data; for noisy data, solution slightly different from Fixsen-Arendt solution, but within noise.
- Run times slightly better than the Fixsen-Arendt code.
- We are developing a version in which subpixel shifts and geometric distortion are included.
- Somewhat inefficient since there is no built-in independence between successive steps.

Compared to the Fixsen-Arendt technique, the iterative approach may scale more favorably with dataset size and complexity of the observing process (i.e., presence of instrumental artifacts), and is less memory intensive. In the iterative algorithm, the sky and gain are alternately updated, as shown in Figure 1.

3.   Approach

In lieu of actual data, we've used SIRTF's MIPS instrument simulator[1] to generate truth images. The simulator generates images which include sky background,

---

[1]Ranga-Ram Chary, private communication

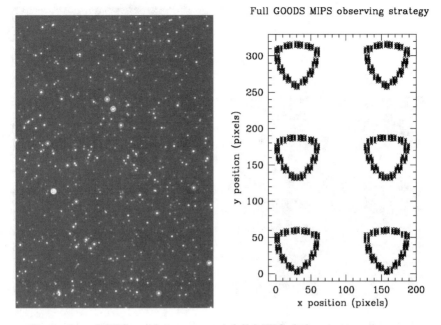

Figure 2.   MIPS truth image, and full MIPS dither pattern

Poisson noise, readout noise, and dark current. The MIPS truth image (316×453 pixels) is shown in Figure 2; 94% of the pixels are greater than 0.01% above the background.

From a truth image, sets of individual images (128×128 pixels for MIPS) were generated from a table of integer dither positions. For a self-calibration run in which the sky and gain are to be derived, each individual image is multiplied by the input gain. (If the offset is also to be derived, it is also incorporated). The input gain image used has ±30% large-scale variation, and ±5% rms pixel-to-pixel variation.

4.   Results

For the sky and gain runs, the goodness of fit was quantified by comparing the derived gain to the input gain. Tests were done by varying the dither pattern, varying the number of dither positions, and varying the tightness of the pattern. The full MIPS dither pattern of 1440 pointings (6 major pointings with 18 minor pointings each) is shown in Figure 2. Several dither patterns were compared for a subset of these observations.

With a poor dither pattern (4 sets of only 3 chosen positions from the 18-point Reuleaux pattern), the gain ratio shows vertical artifacts due to an insufficient number of x-positions. With a better dither pattern (4 sets of 7 chosen positions from the 18-point Reuleaux pattern), there are no visible artifacts in the gain ratio.

Figure 3.   Sky noise (rms=1.5E-4) and gain ratio (rms=6.4E-5)

Using the full MIPS dither pattern shown in Figure 2, the derived sky and gain have no unexpected features. The sky is reproduced with the expected noise level, and is within a few percent of the combined shot and read noise. The derived sky noise and the gain ratio for this case are shown in Figure 3.

5.   Discussion

Our tests indicate that for reasonable dithering strategies, the results of the derived sky and gain are close to shot-noise-limited sensitivity. If there are too few dither positions, periodic artifacts are introduced into the derived quantities at approximately the 1-sigma level. If the dither pattern is too tight, the large-scale variation in the gain is not constrained.

The iterative method offers flexibility to incorporate additional instrumental effects which may occur in the actual data. We are currently modifying the routine to accommodate subpixel dither positions and geometric distortion.

Acknowledgments.   We are grateful for many fruitful discussions with Rick Arendt, Richard Hook, and the GOODS team.

References

Arendt, R. G., Fixsen, D. J., & Moseley, S. H. 2000, ApJ, 536, 500

Astronomical Data Analysis Software and Systems XII
ASP Conference Series, Vol. 295, 2003
H. E. Payne, R. I. Jedrzejewski, and R. N. Hook, eds.

Calibration of COS data at STScI

Philip E. Hodge

Space Telescope Science Institute, Baltimore, MD 21218

Abstract. This paper describes the program for pipeline calibration of Cosmic Origins Spectrograph (COS) data at the Space Telescope Science Institute. CALCOS is written in Python. Image and table data are read from and written to FITS files using PyFITS, and the data arrays are manipulated using the numarray module, with C extension code for special cases not included in numarray.

1. Introduction

The Cosmic Origins Spectrograph is an ultraviolet spectrograph for installation in the Hubble Space Telescope in 2005. COS is being built by the Center for Astrophysics and Space Astronomy (CASA) at the University of Colorado, and Ball Aerospace. The far ultraviolet (FUV) detector system was built by the Experimental Astrophysics Group (EAG) at the University of California, Berkeley. For further information on the instrument, see http://cos.colorado.edu/ and http://ozma.ssl.berkeley.edu/~eagcos/.

CALCOS performs the basic calibration of COS data, producing a flat fielded 2-D image and a 1-D flux calibrated spectrum. The high level portion of CALCOS uses three classes: Association, Observation, and Calibration. The Association class contains a list of Observation instances and information about the relationships between files in the association. It checks for consistency in the header keywords of all the input files, for example that they were taken with the same detector and grating, and that they use the same reference files. The Observation class contains information for an individual input file. The Calibration class contains the high level calibration methods. The lower level functions that do the actual calibration are procedural.

Further information can be found in Hodge (2002).

2. Processing

COS data may be taken in time-tag format (a table of photon events) or in image format (referred to as accum, or histogram mode). Some of the processing by CALCOS is identical for these two formats, partly for consistency but also to reduce duplication of code.

For time-tag data, tabular format is retained for the basic calibration steps. The thermal and geometric corrections are applied by changing the X and Y pixel coordinates of each photon event. Orbital and heliocentric Doppler corrections are done by changing the pixel coordinate in the dispersion direction (X for FUV, Y for NUV). Bad regions on the detector, bad time intervals, and events rejected because the pulse height is out of range are flagged by setting a bit in the data quality column. Flat field and deadtime corrections are applied by assigning a value in a weight column. After applying these corrections, the results are written to an output events table, which is similar in format to the input events table but with additional columns and different data types for some columns. The corrected table of photon events is also binned into an image. For each row in the table, the pixel nearest to the corrected X,Y position of the photon is incremented by the value in the weight column.

For accum image data, if the FUV detector was used, the image will be temporarily converted into a pseudo-time-tag list. For each count in the raw image, the X and Y coordinates of the pixel will be appended to in-memory lists; the time of arrival of the photon cannot be known, so there is no list of times. A pseudo-random number on the interval $[-0.5, +0.5]$ is added to each pixel coordinate to reduce aliasing effects. Thermal and geometric corrections are then applied using the same code as for time-tag data. The lists of X and Y coordinates are then binned back into an image, and subsequent calibration steps (flat field, deadtime) are performed on the image. The heliocentric correction for accum data is done by writing the radial velocity to a header keyword, which is later used during 1-D spectral extraction to shift the wavelengths.

After the basic calibration described above, a 1-D spectrum is extracted from the calibrated image. A wavelength is assigned to each pixel of the extracted spectrum, and the wavelength scale can be shifted to correct for an error in the grating adjustment (see below). One exposure yields two or three noncontiguous sections of spectrum. The FUV detector consists of two separate "segments" with a narrow gap between them. For NUV, three separate "stripes" of the spectrum are focussed onto the detector at one time. The gap between NUV stripes is large, approximately twice the length of a stripe. Each extracted 1-D spectrum is stored as one row in the output table, i.e., two rows for FUV and three rows for NUV, with the wavelength, flux, etc., stored as arrays in each row.

The mechanism to select or reposition a grating is not perfectly repeatable. For each exposure at a given position, the offset from the nominal position is determined using a "wavecal," an exposure using an internal emission-line lamp. A cross correlation of the 1-D extracted wavecal spectrum with a template spectrum gives the offset. The individual spectra within an exposure (for the two FUV detector segments or the three NUV spectral stripes) are processed independently, rather than averaging them to yield one offset per exposure. If multiple wavecal observations are available and two wavecals bracket a science observation, the offset to apply to the wavelength scale for the science observation is determined by linear interpolation with time. Two diagnostic tests have been implemented, to catch gross errors such as a failure of the grating mechanism: (1) the width of the cross correlation should be small, comparable to the spectral resolution; and (2) the maximum value of the cross correlation should be much larger than the median value.

The default observing mode is to take multiple exposures at four slightly different positions, offset in the dispersion direction, to smooth out flat-field irregularities and avoid detector defects. It is also possible to take multiple exposures at the same grating position, or to take single exposures. When multiple exposures were taken, an additional output file will be written that contains the averages of the individual 1-D extracted spectra. The flat-fielded images will also be averaged, for repeated exposures at the same grating position.

3. Python, PyFITS, Numarray, C

FITS files are used for raw data input, reference files (such as flat fields and dispersion coefficients), and calibrated output files. In all cases, the data are stored in FITS extensions, not in the primary header/data unit. Keywords in the primary header of COS data files specify the instrument configuration, which calibration steps to perform, and the names of the reference files to use for calibration. Binary table extensions are used for input time-tag data, calibrated time-tag data, output 1-D extracted spectra, and most reference files. Image extensions are used for input accum data, calibrated accum data, calibrated time-tag event data after binning into an image, and flat field and geometric distortion reference files.

CALCOS is written in Python, with some C code for row-by-row or pixel-by-pixel operations. The PyFITS module is used for FITS file I/O. The numarray module supports efficient array operations, and array arithmetic is as simple as scalar arithmetic. An image data array is represented in PyFITS as a numarray object, and a table is a 1-D array of records (rows). Each column of a table is a numarray object (or chararray for text strings). The numarray 'strides' attribute allows column access directly within the table data, without making a separate copy of the column. The total size and structure of a numarray object are fixed when the array is created (e.g., the columns and their data types, and the number of rows). Rather than actually deleting rows that are rejected during processing, CALCOS flags them as bad in the data quality column, because this doesn't change the number of rows; it also has the advantage of being reversible.

Most arithmetic operations use numarray. There are some operations that are not sufficiently generic to have been implemented in numarray, however, and for these a C extension module was written. A comparison of the flat field calibration step for time-tag and for accum data illustrates this issue. Time-tag data are corrected individually for each photon event (table row), and the entire procedure uses C code. For each row, the pixel coordinates of the event are gotten from the X and Y columns. The coordinates are rounded to the nearest integer, and the value is taken at that pixel in the flat field reference image. The weight for the event is then set equal to the reciprocal of the flat field value. A combination of C code and numarray operations are used for accum data. The first step is to convolve the flat field image in the dispersion direction, to account for the orbital Doppler shift during the exposure. (The on-board software shifts the pixel location before incrementing the image array in memory, so the flat field should be shifted by the same amount before being applied to the image.) This is done using C code, because it is a 1-D convolution of a 2-D image. After this, however, the actual flat-field calibration is just a division of two arrays, using numarray arithmetic. If the flat field is a subset of the entire detector (which would be the case for FUV data), just the matching subset of the input image will be corrected by using standard Python slice notation.

4. Memory Considerations

CALCOS processes the data in-memory, and some of the data files are in the 100-Mb range. The NUV detector is only 1K by 1K pixels, but the FUV detector is 16K by 1K. CALCOS writes error and data quality arrays in addition to the science data. Calibration takes approximately five minutes for a 100-Mb FUV time-tag file on a fast Sun or on an Intel/Linux machine. A typical FUV observation would include four exposures at slightly different positions, with perhaps four associated wavecal exposures. Since there are two FUV detector segments per exposure, this would involve a total of 16 files for the raw data. These 16 files are related, and CALCOS calibrates them as a set (one at a time, but within the same process), rather than independently. In-memory arrays (numarray objects) will be repeatedly created and destroyed as these files are processed. Memory allocation is handled efficiently on Intel/Linux machines, and 0.5 Gb of memory is sufficient for calibrating 100-Mb time-tag files. Using Sun/Solaris, however, memory is not necessarily available for reuse after being freed. Processing appears normal for the first few files (depending on the available real memory), but then it bogs down and may grind to a halt. Two Gb of memory appears to be sufficient, but 0.5 Gb is clearly not enough, due to the accumulation of allocated memory while processing multiple files. If sufficient memory is not available, a fallback option is to spawn a separate process for doing the basic calibration of each file. After that has completed for all of the files, the remainder of the calibration (wavecal processing, 1-D extraction, averaging of results) can be done. At the present time, memory mapping has been partially implemented in PyFITS, and further development is planned. Initial tests show that memory mapping does help. Raw accum image data use BZERO (in order to store unsigned 16-bit data in FITS files), and they need to be copied to scratch in order for the zero-point offset to be applied. This would defeat memory mapping for the raw data, but accum mode is expected to be used far less frequently than time-tag. It is likely that the CALCOS Python code will need to be customized in order to take full advantage of memory mapping.

Acknowledgments. The calibration algorithms were developed by the COS instrument development team together with COS instrument scientists at STScI.

References

Hodge, P. 2002, in ASP Conf. Ser., Vol. 281, Astronomical Data Analysis Software and Systems XI, ed. D. A. Bohlender, D. Durand, & T. H. Handley (San Francisco: ASP), 273

Part 7. Data Management and Pipelines

Astronomical Data Analysis Software and Systems XII
ASP Conference Series, Vol. 295, 2003
H. E. Payne, R. I. Jedrzejewski, and R. N. Hook, eds.

Data Management for the VO

Patrick D. Dowler

Canadian Astronomy Data Centre, Herzberg Institute of Astrophysics
5071 W. Saanich Rd. Victoria, BC, Canada

Abstract. The Canadian Astronomy Data Centre has developed a general purpose scientific data model and an API for accessing a scientific data warehouse. The Catalog API defines a general mechanism for exploring and querying scientific content using a constraint-based design. The API provides access to separate but related catalogs and allows for entries in one catalog to be related to (usually derived from) entries in another catalog. The purpose of the API is to provide storage-neutral and content-neutral access methods for scientific data. The API defines a network-accessible Jini service.

We have developed the Canadian Virtual Observatory (CVO) as Jini services that implement the Catalog API. These catalogs store astronomical content: the pixel catalog provides uniform access to our many archival data holdings, the source catalog stores the results of image analysis, and the processing catalog stores metadata describing exactly how sources are extracted from pixel data. Entries in the source catalog are connected to entries in the processing and pixel catalogs from which they are derived.

1. Introduction

The primary design goal of the CVO is to enable science across the entire electromagnetic spectrum. We have achieved this by recognizing that the engineering principles at work in different wavebands are quite different and by developing a system which abstracts various types of VO content in order to remove these engineering details and complexity. The result is a data model that is sufficiently general to be used by all astronomers.

Reproducibility is the cornerstone of good science. As such, all content in the CVO includes a pedigree so that astronomers can examine exactly how any quantity was computed. This transparency allows for peer review by the user community and open, objective science.

The Catalog API developed at CADC provides a mechanism for programmatic remote access, discovery, and exploration of scientific content. The API models both the content and the data flow and allows full pedigree navigation via *derived from* links.

The CVO site holds a collection of catalogs: pixel data, processing instances, source, objects, and other products of processing. Each of these catalogs is an

209

implementation of the Catalog API; they service as an excellent test-bed for VO content management and interoperability issues.

2. Abstraction

The reality of astronomical data services is that they are either data archives storing pixel data or they are static catalogs reproduced from referred publications. In the case of data archives, these services are filled with engineering concepts and terminology[1] which varies from one archive to the next, even from a single service provider. Furthermore, differences in the engineering challenges across the spectrum remain as artifacts in the archives, making multiwavelength[2] science difficult if not impossible. Every archive is different and cross-archive research suffers as a result.

One can abstract all of these technical details into a relatively simple set of pixel data properties that describe the spatial, spectral, and temporal coverage and resolution of the observation. These *sampling properties* recognize the three-dimensional nature of astronomical observations and provides an analog description that is useful across the entire spectrum.

It is also useful to include some description of the actual content of the observation distinct from the intended content (usually derived from the observing program). These *content properties* would normally be measured from the pixel data and include quantities like the number of point sources, number of extended sources, density of sources, and detection limit for point sources.

For derived catalogs, the situation is not much better than for data archives. The catalog properties tend to carry their engineering heritage (baggage). In the optical regime, magnitudes are commonly used and each is named for the filter or filter system from which it is derived. With new filter systems being deployed for specific scientific goals - typically in large surveys - the list of different magnitude systems is growing and there is no straightforward way to aggregate the information. Astronomers working in other parts of the spectrum tend to use flux density rather than magnitude as a measure of brightness. Across the spectrum, there is no consistent use of wavelength, frequency, or energy - pick your favorite. In order to place all derived properties on the same *coordinate system* we have adopted a multi-dimensional approach. For all wavelength-dependent properties, we store and work with a function[3] $f(\lambda)$ and retain the analog nature of the spectral sampling. Clearly this is derived from the abstraction used for pixel data and avoids dragging the engineering heritage into derived catalog content.

---

[1]telescope, instrument, CCD, filter, grating, grism, etc.

[2]even wavelength is only commonly used in part of the spectrum

[3]the choice of λ is arbitrary ; we could use ν or E instead

3. Data Types

The abstractions described above for pixel data and derived catalog content require a set of data types not normally used for catalogs. In choosing the data types, we have to consider whether the types capture all of the information and whether they can be used in the context of a scientific data warehouse. That is, we must choose data types that can be indexed for fast access and searching within available database management systems

3.1. Pixel Properties

The required data types for describing the observational sampling are (1) a polygon on the surface of a unit sphere for spatial coverage, (2) an interval of floating point values for spectral coverage, and (3) an interval of date and time values for temporal coverage. In addition, one must also store the spatial, spectral, and temporal *span* (the size of the coverage) and the spatial, spectral, and temporal *resolution* (the size of the one resolution element), all of which are scalar (floating point or integer) values.

The content description properties are generally integer or floating point values; the dataset name and archive name are strings (or URLs) which enable retrieval of the data. All of these are primitive types easily stored and indexed by database systems.

3.2. Source Properties

The required data types for source properties fall into three categories: positional, wavelength-dependent, and wavelength-independent quantities.

For positional information, we require a point on the surface of a unit sphere and, for extended sources, an ellipse or other polygon (also on a sphere). The error value for points is typically an ellipse.

For wavelength-dependent properties (flux, size, shape, etc.) we are actually storing the floating point interval (spectral coverage) from the pixel data and a floating point value (scalar). This is a function evaluated (estimated, measured) over a fixed interval. In graphical terms, it is a horizontal line segment (λ_1, y) to (λ_2, y) where y is the *value* of the property in question. For our purposes, we can consider these wavelength-dependent source properties as functions and we can index them as *2D line segments in Cartesian coordinates* using one of several spatial indexing schemes (e.g., R-Trees, spatial decomposition); a general multi-dimensional indexing scheme would also be effective in accessing this functional information.

The wavelength-independent properties (redshift, spectral indices, object type, etc.) are scalar values and easily stored and indexed by database systems.

4. Reproducibility

The scientific method requires that all results be reproducible by the scientific community. This is necessary to verify correctness and, in the case of scientific data services, to build trust and confidence in the quality of the service. To this end, every piece of information in the VO must have a pedigree that users can follow in order to discover exactly where a value came from and exactly how it was produced.

5.   Goals of the CVO

The primary goal of the CVO project is to create a system for scientists. Specifically, the system enables astronomers to do more than just find data; they must be able to produce scientific results and to produce results that cannot be (easily) obtained through other means. The CVO captures the information content and the data flow and enables a sophisticated level of exploration and discovery.

From a technology standpoint, the CVO project uses best practices and technologies to attain its scientific goals. This means the CVO is unencumbered by backwards compatibility and some content may never find its way into the system. To these ends, the CVO is implemented as a set of Jini services using the Java programming language (Edwards 1999, Sun Microsystems[4]).

Finally, from a practical point of view, we have implemented the system in order to find all the hidden details and complexity that must be dealt with in order for the VO to be a productive scientific instrument.

6.   Catalog API

The CVO data model is defined by the Catalog API. The API can be divided into three components: content, discovery, and exploration.

6.1.   Content

The content of the CVO is captured in three types of objects: `Entry`, `EntryProp`, and `EntryLink`. An `Entry` is a single *thing* in a catalog. An `EntryProp` is one property of an `Entry`. An `EntryLink` is a link between an `EntryProp` and another `EntryProp`, possibly in a different catalog. Thus, the `EntryProp` is the *unit of information* in a catalog; it is made up of:

```
link - an EntryLink denoting the origin of this EntryProp

prop_id - used to query the EntryPropMap

tuple_id - used to distinguish between multiple values

value - the value of the property

error - the error in the value
```

---

[4]http://www.sun.com/jini

```
rank - arbitrary way to denote multiple values as
       better or best
```

The `EntryLink` contains sufficient information to look up an `EntryProp` or an `Entry` in an arbitrary catalog. It contains:

```
entry_id - the unique ID of the linked Entry

prop_id - the prop_id of the linked EntryPropMap

tuple_id - the tuple_id of the linked EntryProp

catalog - the name of the catalog that contains the linked
          Entry
```

Finally, the `Entry` is simply a container for `EntryProps` with a unique ID (the `entry_id`). Thus, the data model for the CVO is quite simple, keeping in mind the variety of value types permitted within an `EntryProp`.

6.2. Discovery

The CVO discovery model operates at two levels. The first level is service discovery, which is implemented using standard Jini *discovery and join* semantics. The core Jini platform provides the capability to find a *service registrar* on the network using either unicast discovery (basically a URL to the service registrar) or multicast discovery, where the client (1) requests that service registrar(s) contact it and (2) listens for service registrar announcements. In either case, once the client software contacts a service registrar, it can use the service registrar API to look up services by *type* and/or *attributes* (like name). To access the CVO, the client would look up services of type `ExplorableCatalog` (see below).

The second level of discovery is that of discovering the type of content available in an `ExplorableCatalog`. This is done by accessing the `EntryPropMap` for the catalog and looking at the `EntryPropDescriptors` it contains. Each `EntryPropDescriptor` describes one property of `Entrys` in the catalog; it reveals information like the name, type, units, and a description of the property. All of the information needed to query an `ExplorableCatalog` and interpret the results is available in the `EntryPropMap`.

6.3. Exploration

The base features of the API are the methods of the `Catalog` interface:

```
public EntryPropMap getPropMap();

public Entry get(Long entry_id);
```

The `ExplorableCatalog` interface extends the `Catalog` interface, adding the following exploration methods:

```
public DataModel[] getCount(ConstraintSet cs);

public DataModel[] getRange(ConstraintSet cs,
                            Property prop);

public DataModel[] getHistogram(ConstraintSet cs,
                                Property prop,
                                Interval range,
                                int nbins);

public DataModel[] getTable(ConstraintSet cs);
```

The arguments and return types specified above require some explanation. The `ConstraintSet` argument is a set of simple `Constraints` on one or more properties in the catalog (see below). The `Property` arguments specify a single property of interest (by name). The `Interval` argument defines the range of values to be included in the histogram. The `DataModel` return type is the interface implemented by all content container types; the contract for each of the above methods is that they must return the specified `DataModel` (`Count`, `Range`, `Histogram`, or `Table`) but they can optionally return other `DataModels`. This allows implementations of the `ExplorableCatalog` interface to provide extra information if it is not costly to do so. For example, if the query to get the count is essentially the same as to get the range of values, the implementation is free to return both in order to avoid executing a very similar query in the near future. Each of the methods in the `ExplorableCatalog` interface is a request for a progressively more detailed summary or view of the set of `Entrys` specified by the `ConstraintSet`.

The Catalog API also includes a `MutableCatalog` interface that defines the methods used to add, update, and remove content. This interface is described elsewhere.

6.4.   Constraints

The `ConstraintSet` argument used in exploratory queries holds a collection of `Constraints`. These `Constraints` are simple query predicate components that can be put together to build arbitrarily complex queries. For all data types, one can use the `Known` and `Unknown` constraints to require the existence or non-existence of the property. For scalar data types (int, float, date, string) one can use the `Eq`, `Leq`, `Geq`, and `Between` constraints to select certain value(s). For interval types (date and float intervals are currently supported) one can use the `Intersect` constraint to specify that the interval property value contains a scalar value of the same base type (i.e., `Intersect(Interval.Date, Date)` and `Intersect(Interval.Float, Float)`). Finally, for geometric types (points, lines, circles, ellipses, and polygons) one can use the `Intersect` constraint to test for intersection of a geometric type with another geometric type. In addition, one can construct arbitrary algebraic expressions with numeric scalar data types and use them with any constraints that work with scalar data types. Thus, the constraint system is a toolbox of simple `Constraint` types which work with `Property`, `Constant`, and `Operator` arguments to specify the query predicate.

7. The CVO Experiment

The CVO project is an experiment in developing and deploying VO functionality. Our base content that has motivated the design is the CNOC1 catalog (Yee et al. 1996) and the WFPC2 Association project[5], but we have also kept in mind other survey catalogs (2MASS, SDSS, etc.) and future telescopes and instruments (CFHT Megacam, IFUs, etc.) as they all add scale and complexity to the VO content.

The CVO is an experiment in VO content management. The scale and complexity underlines the need for dynamic discovery and exploration, automation of processing, and bi-directional linkage between data and results: data flow in one direction and pedigree navigation in the other.

The CVO is an experiment in interoperability. By building the tools and infrastructure for various interdependent catalogs, we have learned many lessons about what information must be stored, what things can remain implementation details (internal), and what things must be agreed upon by all participants. The abstractions of observational data to spatial, spectral, and temporal sampling are the primary result of this interoperability experiment. In addition, we have developed an architecture which allows for remote catalog services and arbitrary linkages between the content within different catalogs.

The CVO is an experiment in integrating VO with operational systems. We treat archives as external (legacy) systems that *publish* their content to the VO. Users can initiate data retrieval (from an archive) after exploring the pixel catalog. Although we use our processing catalog to store processing details and track execution status, the data processing itself occurs in the CADC Distributed Processing System (also a Jini service).

8. Summary

The primary design goal of the CVO is to use abstraction to separate engineering and science - hide the engineering, in fact - in order to deliver uniform access across the entire spectrum. The most important aspect of the design is that pixel data should be described by the spatial, spectral, and temporal sampling of the observation. It is vital to characterize both the coverage and resolution of the sampling of an observation. In addition, data analysis can provide some useful and interesting summary information about the content of pixel data. For example, one could measure the number of point and extended sources, source density, detection limits, to name a few. All of these properties of the pixel data help astronomers to find data that is useful for their specific scientific goals in a telescope and instrument-agnostic fashion.

Reproducibility is the cornerstone of good science. As such, the VO must include access to the pedigree of every piece of information so that astronomers

---

[5] `http://cadcwww.dao.nrc.ca/wfpc2/`

can examine exactly how any quantity was computed. The astronomer must be able to retrieve the input data and reproduce the result. This detailed pedigree requirement is necessary so that VO content may be peer-reviewed by the user community and so that the VO can gain the confidence and trust of the users.

The Catalog API developed at CADC provides a mechanism for programmatic remote access, discovery, and exploration of scientific content. The current version is very general and not astronomy-specific; it could be used in many fields of science. The API models both the content and the data flow and allows full pedigree navigation via *derived from* links.

CVO is a collection of 3-5 catalogs: pixel data, processing instances, sources, objects, and other products of processing. Archives publish abstracted pixel data to the pixel catalog. Software agents find new pixel data and create processing catalog entries for them. The processing catalog entries are eventually executed to produce processing products and source catalog entries. Finally, source catalog entries are cross-identified to produce object catalog entries. Pixel content from a variety of CADC archives and external catalogs will be published to the CVO pixel catalog; this and the subsequent processing will make the CVO a rich playground for astronomers.

Acknowledgments. The entire CADC group has provided invaluable assistance in developing the concepts and ideas that have resulted in the CVO.

References

Edwards, K. 1999, Core Jini, Sun Microsystems Press

Yee, H. K. C., Ellingson, E., & Carlberg, R. G. 1996, ApJS, 102, 269

Astronomical Data Analysis Software and Systems XII
ASP Conference Series, Vol. 295, 2003
H. E. Payne, R. I. Jedrzejewski, and R. N. Hook, eds.

Data Organization in the SDSS Data Release 1

A.R. Thakar, A.S. Szalay, and J.V. vandenBerg

Johns Hopkins University, Baltimore, MD 21218

Jim Gray

Microsoft Research

Chris Stoughton

FermiLab, Batavia, IL 60510

Abstract. The first official public data release from the Sloan Digital Sky Survey (www.sdss.org) is scheduled for Spring 2003. Due to the unprecedented size and complexity of the data, we face unique challenges in organizing and distributing the data to a large user community. We discuss the data organization, the archive loading and backup strategy, and the data mining tools available to the public and the astronomical community, in the overall context of large databases and the VO.

1. Introduction

The SDSS Data Release 1 (DR1) is the first officially scheduled public data release of the SDSS data. It is the successor to the Early Data Release (EDR) released in June 2001 (`archive.stsci.edu/sdss`). DR1 is scheduled for release in Spring 2003, and covers more than 20% of the total survey area (>2k square degrees). The raw data size is about 5 times that of the EDR, i.e., several Terabytes. The catalog data will be about the same size because there will be 3 datasets with several versions of each dataset.

This is the first single release of such a large dataset to the public, and naturally it presents unprecedented challenges. Simply distributing the data and making it available 24/7/365 will be quite an undertaking for the SDSS collaboration. Providing competent data mining tools on this multi-TB dataset, especially within the context and evolving framework of the Virtual Observatory, will be an even more daunting challenge. The SDSS database loading software and data mining tools are being developed at JHU (`www.sdss.jhu.edu`).

2. Data Distribution

The master copy of the raw data (FITS files) will be stored at FermiLab. In addition to the master archive at FermiLab, there will be several mirror sites for the DR1 data hosted by SDSS and other institutions. Replication and synchronization of the mirrors will therefore be required. We describe below the configuration of the master archive site. Mirror sites will probably be scaled-down replicas of the master site.

2.1. Data Products

There will be three separate datasets made available to the public - two versions of the imaging data and one version of the spectra:

- **Target dataset** - this is the calibration of the raw data from which spectral **targets** were chosen;
- **Best dataset** - this is the latest, greatest calibration and represents the **best** processing of the data from a science perspective;
- **Spectro dataset** - these are the spectra of the target objects chosen from the target dataset.

Within each dataset, the raw imaging data will consist of the Atlas Images, Corrected Frames, Binned Images, Reconstructed Frames and the Image Cutouts in addition to the **Imaging Catalogs** for the Target and Best versions. The spectroscopic data consists of the Raw spectra along with the **Spectro Catalog** and the **Tiling Catalog**.

2.2. Data Volume

Table 1 shows the total expected size for a single instance of the DR1 archive - about 1TB. In practice, however, the overall size of the catalog data at a given archive site will be several TB, i.e., comparable to the size of the raw data, since more than one copy of the data will be required for performance and redundancy.

Table 1.   Data sizes of the DR1 datasets.

BEST Catalog	Jpegs	TARGET Catalog	Jpegs	SPECTRO Spectra	Tiling	Indices	Misc. Catalogs	TOTAL
400 Gb	50 Gb	300 Gb	50 Gb	10 Gb	10 Gb	150 Gb	20-30 Gb	1 TB

3.   Archive Operations

3.1.   Archive Redundancy, Backups and Loading

It will be necessary to have several copies of the archive at least at the master site, to ensure high data availability and adequate data mining performance. Figure 1 shows the physical organization of the archive data and the loading data flow. Backups will be kept in a deep store tape facility, and legacy datasets will be maintained so that all versions of the data ever published will be available for science if needed. The loading process will be completely automated using a combination of VB and DTS scripts and SQL stored procedures, and a admin web interface will be provided to the **Load Monitor** which controls the entire loading process. Data will be first converted from FITS to CSV (comma-separated values) before being transferred from Linux to Windows.

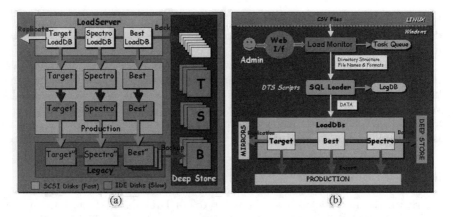

Figure 1.   (a) Production archive components, (b) loading data flow.

3.2.   Current Hardware Plan

The proposed hardware plan for the master DR1 site at FermiLab reflects the function that each copy of the archive must provide, but it also makes the most effective use of the existing SDSS hardware resources at FermiLab. Table 2 shows the plan for the various DR1 components.

Table 2.   Hardware for DR1 Archive.

	Load Servers	Production Servers	Legacy	Deep Store
Priority	Hi Perf/Lo Capacity	Hi Perf/Hi Capacity	Lo Perf/Hi Capacity	Hi Capacity
Vendor	Dell PowerEdge 4600	Intel E7500	Dell PowerEdge 4400	Enstore
CPU	Dual 2.6 GHz Xeon	Dual 2.4 GHz Xeon	Dual 1 GHz PIII Xeon	
Memory	2-4 Gb	4-8-12 Gb	2 Gb	
Disks	2 × 120MB/s SCSI software RAID	2 × 8 × 160GB 3ware 7500 ATA RAID	14 × 73GB SCSI across 4 ultra 160 channels	Tape Silo
Options	Parallelize with multiple servers	Cluster of these for redundancy (warm sp.)	May use slower IDE Disks	

4.   Databases

In January 2002, the SDSS collaboration made the decision to migrate to Microsoft SQL Server as the DB engine based on our dissatisfaction with Objectivity/DB's features and performance (Thakar et al. 2002). SQL Server meets our performance needs much better and offers the full power of SQL to the database users. SQL Server is also known for its self-optimizing capabilities, and provides a rich set of optimization and indexing options. We have further significantly augmented the power of SQL Server by adding the HTM spatial index (Kunszt et al. 2001) to it along with a pre-computed neighbors table that enables fast spatial lookups and proximity searches of the data. Additional features like built-in aggregate functions, extensive stored procedures and functions, and indexed and partitioned views of the data make SQL Server a much better choice for data mining.

As the size of the SDSS data grows with future releases, we will be experimenting with more advanced SQL Server performance enhancements, such as horizontal partitioning and distributed partition views (DPVs). We are also developing a plan to provide load-sharing with a cluster of DR1 copies rather than a single copy. This kills two birds with one stone - it also removes the need to have warm spares of the databases, since each copy can serve as a warm spare.

5. Data Mining Tools

There will be a single web access point to all DR1 data. Our data mining tools will be integrated into a VO-ready framework of hierarchical Web Services (Szalay et al. 2002).

5.1. Catalog Access

Access to catalog data will be via a variety of tools for different levels of users.
1. The **SkyServer** is a web front end that provides search, navigate and explore tools, and is aimed at the public and casual astronomy users.
2. The **sdssQA** is a portable Java client that sends HTTP SOAP requests to the database, and is meant for serious users with complex queries.
3. An **Emacs** interface (.el file) to submit SQL directly to the databases.
4. **SkyCL** is a python command-line interface for submitting SQL queries.
5. **SkyQuery** is a distributed query and cross-matching service implemented via hierarchical Web Services (see Budavari et al. 2003).

5.2. Raw data

1. The **Data Archive Server (DAS)** will be a no-frills web page for downloading raw data files (FITS) for the various raw data products.
2. A Web Form or Web Service interface to upload results of SQL queries to the DAS and retrieve the corresponding raw images and spectra.
3. An **Image Cutout Service** (jpeg and FITS/VOTable) which will be implemented as a Web Service.

References

Budavari, T., et al. 2003, this volume, 31

Kunszt, P. Z., Szalay, A. S., and Thakar, A. 2001, Mining the Sky: Proc. of the MPA/ESO/MPE workshop, Garching, A.J.Banday, S. Zaroubi, M. Bartelmann (ed.), (Springer-Verlag Berlin Heidelberg), 631.

Szalay, A. S., et al. 2002, Proceedings of SPIE "Astronomical Telescopes and Instrumentation", 4846, in press.

Thakar, A. R., et al. 2002, in ASP Conf. Ser., Vol. 281, Astronomical Data Analysis Software and Systems XI, ed. D. A. Bohlender, D. Durand, & T. H. Handley (San Francisco: ASP), 112

Astronomical Data Analysis Software and Systems XII
ASP Conference Series, Vol. 295, 2003
H. E. Payne, R. I. Jedrzejewski, and R. N. Hook, eds.

HDX Data Model: FITS, NDF and XML Implementation

David Giaretta, Mark Taylor, Peter Draper, Norman Gray, Brian McIlwrath

Starlink Project, UK

Abstract. A highly adaptable data model, HDX, based on the concepts embodied in FITS and various proposed XML-based formats, as well as Starlink's NDF and HDS will be described, together with the Java software that has been developed to support it. The aim is to provide a flexible model which is compatible with FITS, can be extended to accommodate VO requirements, but which maintains enough mandatory structure to make application-level interoperability relatively easy.

1. Introduction

HDX is a flexible and extensible data model for astronomical and other data. The ideas underlying HDX have been tested in a large volume of deployed software. The resulting system is designed to be highly interoperable: it is platform independent, and neutral as regards file formats, though its 'natural' (in the sense of first implemented) formats are FITS and XML. This paper is a progress report on work we have been carrying out on a Structured approach to data; updates will be available on `http://www.starlink.ac.uk/hdx`.

2. Motivation

Increasingly complex data structures are becoming necessary as more complex instrument data becomes available. Some indication of this comes from proposals for additions to the FITS format such as the Hierarchical Grouping Convention[1] proposal. On the other hand the basic FITS format does not readily lend itself to such extensions. In addition there is a growing recognition that astronomical applications must deal with data quality as well as track data errors as a matter of course.

The Virtual Observatory (VO) brings the promise of yet more complex, interrelated, distributed, data; the development of VOTable[2] shows a recognition of the importance of XML. Metadata is seen as a key component of the Virtual Observatory, as well as provenance of information gathered or created by a remote, automated process, using the VO. Complex interrelationships between

---

[1] `http://fits.gsfc.nasa.gov/group.html`

[2] `http://cdsweb.u-strasbg.fr/doc/VOTable/`

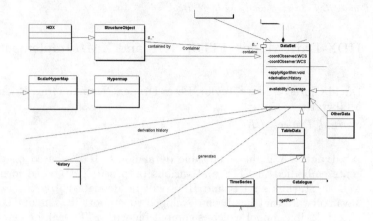

Figure 1.   Section of the Data Model

large numbers of files are likely to become commonplace in the VO. Rather than develop an astronomy specific semantic toolkit it seems sensible to position oneself to be able to use the tools which are being produced in the context of the wider WWW community, such as RDF and related standards.

We see therefore requirements for something flexible, extensible, capable of storing hierarchical information, able to deal with distributed data but usable locally, and with the backing of a sophisticated astronomical data model. In addition it should be open to the new tools and standards which are bound to be produced in the near future outside astronomy. It should also facilitate interoperation of applications—something which will become increasingly difficult as complex structures are generated.

3.   The Structure Object

Figure 1 shows an extract from a proposed hierarchy of data objects.

In addition to the data containers such as Table and N-Dimensional array, there is an additional Structure Object which can contain other objects, including other Structure Objects—allowing a hierarchical data structure to be developed.

It is important to remember that we are not talking about any particular data format such as FITS. Instead we are considering conceptual data structures which may be serialised in a number of different ways.

The advantages of separating the data container elements from the structuring elements include allowing the containers to avoid becoming more complicated than necessary. It leaves one free to consider additional metadata, which is recognised as being of fundamental importance for the VO, without being forced to think of encodings which would fit within the constraints of FITS keywords. Instead one is free to consider the use of something like XML, with its promise of a large number of standards and tools as a serialisation mechanism.

3.1. Dangers of Using of Hierarchical Data

Using hierarchical data does have dangers, at least until such time as structural metadata is adequately developed—which is probably some way off. The danger is that one application will not understand the relationship between components which another application has written out.

Starlink's experience with hierarchical data structures, based on the Hierarchical Data System[3] (HDS), over the past 10 years or more is of use here. This experience shows that one must strike a balance between being very proscriptive in what applications can write out, e.g., simple FITS files, on the one hand, and allowing anarchy on the other. The most common problem was for applications to not understand the relationships between components, leading to erroneous processing, or that pieces of metadata which were not understood were not correctly passed on to downstream applications.

Our experience is that one needs some fairly simple rules which applications must obey, and that there should be some pre-defined components within which to hide additional structures in order to allow common operations to be dealt with uniformly and correctly. An example of this is NDX (based on Starlink's NDF) which is described below. In addition it must be possible for an application to adequately check the validity of a hierarchical file with which it is presented. We refer the reader to the HDX documentation for a full discussion of these rules.

4. Candidate Structure Object: HDX

Starlink has been developing a candidate Structure Object called HDX. It embodies a flexible data model based on many years experience with HDS, which uses local data. One aim is to support distributed processing and data holding, using URI's to point to data. HDX can be serialised as XML, and in addition can be packed within a FITS file if the data are local. It is independent of the platform and format of the data containers, although for astronomical purposes its natural data holding formats are XML and FITS.

HDX is a particular, simple, Structure Object. From an applications point of view an HDX is a W3C DOM (http://www.w3.org/DOM/) which has a top-level element <hdx>, and which is valid. It is valid if each of the document element's children is either unknown to the HDX system or, if known, is validated by its declared validator (a software component which HDX can find).

The abstract HDX data model has been implemented in a Java data-access library, but others such as a Perl implementation will be produced. Note however that support for the underlying data containers is distinct from the support for the various HDX types which are defined. Further design aims are to have low (or even zero) overhead to the extent that applications can work using, for example, bare FITS files; to be easy to extend the system to support new types; to be easy to extend the system to support new data storage resources, such as new file formats or a database serving an archive; and to be able to implement these in very efficient ways.

---

[3]http://www.starlink.rl.ac.uk/star/docs/sun92.htx/sun92.html

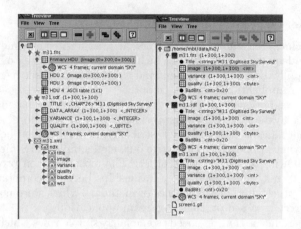

Figure 2.   Treeview of the same data as XML, HDS and FITS plus
the NDX view where they appear identical.

5.   NDX: A Generalised Astronomical N-Dimension Image

NDX represents an N-dimensional chunk of astronomical data and contains pixel
arrays for Image data plus Error estimate and pixel Quality. In addition there is
World Coordinate System information, History, Title, Units, and User-defined
extensions.

Simple operations on NDXs (e.g., ndx1.add(ndx2)) take care of variance,
quality, WCS, etc. (where these components are present). Access is available to
individual arrays (called NDArray objects) to allow more complex algorithms to
be used.

The philosophy and design goals behind NDArray/NDX included being able
to process arrays of unlimited size, comprehensive and transparent bad value
processing, direct and transparent array access between different formats and
location transparent resource naming.

To help to understand the relationship between underlying data containers
and NDX, Figure 2 shows an application (Treeview) looking at the same data
which is held as FITS, HDS and XML. On the left of the figure one sees the
individual components; on the right one sees that all the data is viewable as
identical NDX components.

6.   Summary

This is a report on work in progress, on the use of Structured data, based on
many years' experience. It is expected that there will be changes to support
developing VO standards, however we believe that the underlying ideas are
sound, practical and extensible, and unique in their format agnosticism. Finally
it is worth reiterating that HDX/NDX is aimed at supplementing such data
containers as FITS or VOTable with structure information rather than replacing
them.

Astronomical Data Analysis Software and Systems XII
ASP Conference Series, Vol. 295, 2003
H. E. Payne, R. I. Jedrzejewski, and R. N. Hook, eds.

The Raptor Real-Time Processing Architecture

Mark Galassi, Daniel Starr, Przemyslaw Wozniak, Konstantin Borozdin

Los Alamos National Laboratory, Los Alamos, NM, USA

Abstract. The primary goal of Raptor is ambitious: to identify interesting optical transients from very wide field of view telescopes in real time, and then to quickly point the higher resolution Raptor "fovea" cameras and spectrometer to the location of the optical transient. The most interesting of Raptor's many applications is the real-time search for orphan optical counterparts of Gamma Ray Bursts.

The sequence of steps (data acquisition, basic calibration, source extraction, astrometry, relative photometry, the smarts of transient identification and elimination of false positives, telescope pointing feedback, etc.) is implemented with a "component" approach. All basic elements of the pipeline functionality have been written from scratch or adapted (as in the case of SExtractor for source extraction) to form a consistent modern API operating on memory resident images and source lists. The result is a pipeline which meets our real-time requirements and which can easily operate as a monolithic or distributed processing system.

Finally, the Raptor architecture is entirely based on free software (sometimes referred to as "open source" software). In this paper we also discuss the interplay between various free software technologies in this type of astronomical problem.

1. Scientific Motivation

The January 23 1999 burst (sometimes referred to as the "Rotse Burst", Akerlof 1999; Akerlof & McKay GCN 205[1]) showed that we can detect the *prompt optical emission* of Gamma Ray Bursts (GRBs) with inexpensive wide field-of-view cameras.

The very recent October 4, 2002 burst from HETE (1) confirms this (it was seen by amateur telescopes), and it raises the stakes on the prompt optical emission.

Right now it could be said that the prompt optical emission is the holy grail of GRB science, and many satellite and ground-based experiments are being planned to help observe it.

1.1. How to Capture the Prompt Optical Emission

There are two main approaches that are being tried right now:

---

[1]http://gcn.gsfc.nasa.gov/gcn/gcn3/205.gcn3

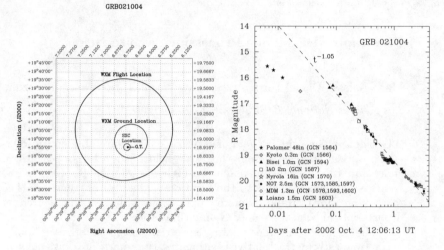

Figure 1.   The 2002-10-04 GRB real time localization by HETE-2, and the decay of the optical intensity

- rapid robotic response to HETE or Swift events, and
- capturing the optical signal when it first appears, possibly without a gamma ray or X-ray trigger at all!

The first approach can be very effective for $t0 + 45$sec but it cannot reach $t0$ except by luck.

The second approach (the search for **orphan** optical transients) is difficult because GRB optical counterparts are relatively dim in a very cluttered optical sky.

1.2.   Enter Raptor

Many systems (Rotse, Lotis, ...) are prepared to do rapid robotic response to high energy satellite triggers from HETE-2 and later on from Swift (both of these missions are dedicated to GRBs) as well as INTEGRAL and Agile.

Raptor (Vestrand et al. 2002) can do rapid robotic response, but it also has a *closed-loop self-triggering* system: it scans the optical sky (40×40 degree field of view) and triggers on potential orphan optical transients.

2.   Details: How Raptor Tackles Science Goals

2.1.   Hardware

Self-triggering requires wide field of view, thus each Raptor system has four 20×20 degree cameras (total of 40×40 degrees, 12.5th magnitude).

Optical self-triggering requires sifting through very many false transient events. Raptor uses both stereoscopic vision and intelligent back ends to sift through transients.

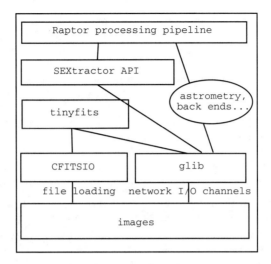

Figure 2.   Raptor processing pipeline: the layering of the APIs.

Immediate follow up by deeper instruments is important. Raptor has a central *fovea* camera (4×4 degrees, 16th magnitude) which can slew to the desired location within seconds.

2.2.   Software Pipeline

In designing the Raptor processing pipeline we face two main issues: software complexity and performance (images have to be processed and analyzed with intelligent back ends *in real time*).

Our main approach to both issues is through *abstraction* and *API design*. Each portion of the pipeline functionality is defined as an API (Application Programming Interface).

Programs are thin shells above the library APIs to move away from the classic clunky astronomy pipeline.

3.   Abstractions

The main abstractions we use in the software pipeline are:

- Abstract memory resident images.
- API to manipulate these images provided by tinyfits library.
- Plugin architecture for image-feeding front-ends.
- Plugin architecture for smart and machine-learning back-ends.

4.   Software Engineering

4.1.   Approaches

We used a particular modern point of view in developing the infrastructure and programs for the Raptor pipeline.

The software is a collection of several small libraries, firmly based on free software, with all components released under the GPL. We follow the GNU coding standards and conventions throughout (standards compliance, configure/build, test suites). We use `glib` (from the Gtk+ toolkit) as a C Rosetta stone, offering some of the standardization that STL offers on top of the C++ standard library. A certain amount of eXtreme programming philosophy permeates our approaches (Beck 1999).

Development is currently hosted on `http://sourceforge.net` (although we might shift to the GNU project hosting sites).

4.2. The Tinyfits and SEXtractor APIs

The reference implementation of the FITS data format is the CFITSIO library. This library does not lend itself to the abstractions we used, especially API we used for SEXtractor. We implemented *tinyfits*, a very thin layer over CFITSIO.

Tinyfits provides the very few FITS file manipulation operations that are used almost all the time. It uses opaque data types for FITS images and tables, which allows it to be dropped in to other applications that have their own set of data types and abstractions.

One of the largest software efforts in the Raptor pipeline was to make the very widely used SEXtractor program (which extracts source lists from star images) work in a real time pipeline. Our modifications turn SEXtractor into an embeddable library which operates on memory-resident images and tables, which is crucial for performance and adaptability.

5. Some Results

Raptor is operational and searching for triggers, as well as responding to GCN alerts.

The versatility in our approach has allowed frequent rapid rewrites of the code (we consider this crucial in a significant software effort).

The use of APIs with thin application shells, which in turn makes obvious the use of memory-resident objects, gives Raptor the performance it needs to generate alerts in real time.

The principal timing improvements come from the faster SEXtractor runs and from tighter file I/O.

Acknowledgments. We are grateful to the entire Raptor team for the work in conceiving and bringing to life this project. We also gratefully acknowledge the internal Los Alamos LDRD grant which funded the project.

References

Akerlof, K. 1999, Nature, 398

Vestrand, T. et al. 2002, "The RAPTOR Experiment: A System for Monitoring the Optical Sky in Real Time", astro-ph/0209300

Beck, K. 1999, Extreme Programming Explained: Embrace Change (Reading, MA: Addison-Wesley)

Astronomical Data Analysis Software and Systems XII
ASP Conference Series, Vol. 295, 2003
H. E. Payne, R. I. Jedrzejewski, and R. N. Hook, eds.

Image Reduction Pipeline for the Detection of Variable Sources in Highly Crowded Fields

Claus A. Gössl, Arno Riffeser

Universitäts-Sternwarte München, Scheinerstraße 1, D-81671 München, Germany

Abstract. We present a reduction pipeline for CCD (charge-coupled device) images which was built to search for variable sources in highly crowded fields such as the M 31 bulge. We describe all the steps of the standard reduction including per pixel error propagation: Bias correction, treatment of bad pixels, flatfielding, and filtering of cosmic ray events. We utilize a flux and PSF (point spread function) conserving alignment procedure and a signal-to-noise maximizing stacking method. We build difference images via image convolution with a technique called OIS (optimal image subtraction, Alard & Lupton 1998), proceed with PSF-fitting, relative photometry on all pixels and finally apply an automatic detection of variable sources. The complete per pixel error propagation allows us to give accurate errors for each measurement.

1. Introduction

The WeCAPP project (Riffeser et al. 2001), which imaged the M 31 bulge to search for Microlensing events, yielded 0.2 TB of inhomogenous raw data. Available data reduction software was not able to cope with the highly variable observing conditions (varying seeing, sky background level, and flatfield quality; different cameras, CCDs, and telescopes) and give consistent measurements with reliable error estimates. Therefore we decided to develop our own reduction pipeline. For additional information on error propagation and why it is important see also Moshir et al. (2003) and Gössl & Riffeser (2002).

2. The Reduction Pipeline

2.1. Bad Pixels & Bias Correction

We mask saturated (and blooming affected) pixels, as well as CCD-defects (hot, cold pixels etc.). We subtract the bias level of individual frames estimated from the overscan region and a masterbias ($\kappa\sigma$-clipped mean image of multiple bias level corrected bias frames).

2.2. Initial Error Estimate

The initial error estimate for each pixel in every image is calculated from the pixel's photon noise ($\sqrt{\text{signal/gain}}$), the bias noise of the image (clipped RMS of

Figure 1.   Left: 300×300 pixel window of a raw CCD image of part of the M 31 bulge taken at the Calar Alto 1.23 m telescope, 3. Feb. 2001. (WeCAPP project, Riffeser et al. 2001). Right: Stacked image after processing steps described in Sect. 2.1. to Sect. 2.5..

the overscan), and the uncertainties of bias level and bias pattern determination. Errors are propagated throughout the complete reduction pipeline with Gaussian error propagation.

2.3.   Flatfield Calibration

To achieve a high signal-to-noise ratio (S/N) for a combined flatfield of an epoch we first calculate in each pixel the error weighted mean of normalized and illumination corrected twilight flatfields. After rejecting all 5×5 pixels regions where the center pixel exceeds this mean by more than 5σ, the final calibration image is built by 3σ clipping of the remaining pixels.

2.4.   Cosmic Ray Rejection

We fit five-parameter Gaussians to all local maxima of an image. Sources with a width along one axis of the fitting function smaller than a threshold (which has to be chosen according to the PSF) and, in addition, an amplitude of the fitting function exceeding the expected noise by a certain factor (which has to be chosen according to the additional noise, i.e., due to crowding) correspond to cosmics. We mask the pixels, where the fitting function exceeds the fitted surface constant by more than two times the expected photon noise.

2.5.   Image Alignment & Stacking

Images are shifted onto a reference grid using a flux and PSF conserving algorithm. The shifted images are photometrically calibrated using the profile of the M 31 bulge. Bad pixels (except saturated) are replaced with pixels of the most similar image, but accounted for in the error image. The final stack is built by maximizing its S/N ratio using the error images and the PSF width for the calculation of weighting factors (Figure 1).

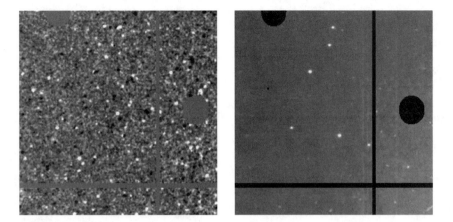

Figure 2. Left: Profile fitting photometry (cuts: -5×10^{-6} Jy, $+5 \times 10^{-6}$ Jy). Right: Corresponding error frame (cuts: $+0.6 \times 10^{-6}$ Jy, $+1.2 \times 10^{-6}$ Jy).

2.6. Image Convolution & Reference Subtraction

For the difference photometry a high S/N reference frame with a narrow PSF is convolved to the broader PSF of each science frame. The calculation of the convolution kernel is performed by a least squares linear fitting procedure optimizing 52 free parameters (OIS). The difference frame (built by subtracting the convolved reference frame from the science frame) shows a large number of positive and negative point sources.

2.7. Variable Sources Detection

Fluxes for the variable sources are extracted using PSF-fitting photometry in each pixel: The PSF of a high S/N star in the convolved reference frame is fit to a small region around each pixel in the difference image (Figure 2). This reduces the influence of neighboring variable sources to a low level. Therefore we are able to extract light curves for each pixel of the difference frame (Figure 3).

3. The Implementation

All algorithms are implemented in C++. Each individual reduction step is represented by a command line program. The pipeline is a simple shell script or Makefile. We take part in the development of a Little Template Library (LTL) which provides very fast and easy to use methods for I/O (i.e., FITS or ASCII), array operations, statistics and Linear Algebra as well as for command line flags and configuration file parameters.

Acknowledgments. Our thanks are due to Ralf Bender, Niv Drory, Jürgen Fliri, Ulrich Hopp, and Jan Snigula. This work was supported by the German *Deutsche Forschungsgemeinschaft, DFG*, SFB 375 Astroteilchenphysik.

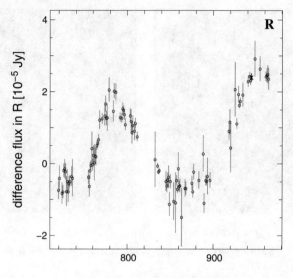

Figure 3.   Final light curve of a long period, semi-regular variable
star (in the center of Figure 2). The '×' symbol shows the epoch of
the sample images. The sample source in the sample image shows a
difference flux of $2.4(\pm0.1) \times 10^{-5}$ Jy on a background of 11×10^{-5}
Jy/arcsec^2.

References

Alard, C., & Lupton, R. H. 1998, ApJ, 503, 325

Gössl, C. A., & Riffeser A. 2002, A&A, 381, 1095

Moshir, M., Fowler, J., & Henderson, D. 2003, this volume, 181

Riffeser, A., Fliri, J., Gössl, C. A., Bender, R., Hopp, U., Bärnbantner, O.,
    Ries, C., Barwig, H., Seitz, S., & Mitsch, W. 2001, A&A, 379, 362

Astronomical Data Analysis Software and Systems XII
ASP Conference Series, Vol. 295, 2003
H. E. Payne, R. I. Jedrzejewski, and R. N. Hook, eds.

Status of the BIMA Image Pipeline

David M. Mehringer & Raymond L. Plante

National Center for Supercomputing Applications

Abstract. The BIMA Image Pipeline is nearing production mode. In this mode it will automatically process data that has recently been transferred from the telescope. Its products will be calibrated *uv* datasets, calibration tables, FITS images, etc. that will be ingested in the BIMA Data Archive and be retrievable by astronomers.

1. Introduction

The BIMA Image Pipeline[1] processes data from the BIMA Array[2] using the AIPS++ astronomical data processing package[3]. Currently, processing is initiated manually, but soon this process will start automatically after data from observing tracks have been ingested into the archive. Only single tracks can be processed at present, but in the future multiple tracks (e.g., from different telescope configurations) from the same project will be combined and processed. Processing jobs normally consist of multiple stages (e.g., serial processing for filling and calibration and parallel processing for image deconvolution). After the processing is complete, the data products are re-ingested into the BIMA Data Archive[4] where they are available for users to download.

2. Architecture of the Pipeline

Figure 1 is a block diagram of the BIMA Image Pipeline. The major components are discussed below.

2.1. The Event Server

Raw BIMA data are automatically transferred from the telescope at Hat Creek, California to NCSA over the internet where they are ingested into the BIMA Data Archive by the Ingest Engine. The Ingest Engine notifies the Event Server that new data have been archived and are ready for processing. The Event Server determines if the new data should be processed, and if so, creates a so-called

---

[1] http://monet.astro.uiuc.edu/BIP/index.html

[2] http://bima.astro.umd.edu

[3] http://aips2.nrao.edu

[4] http://bimaarch.ncsa.uiuc.edu

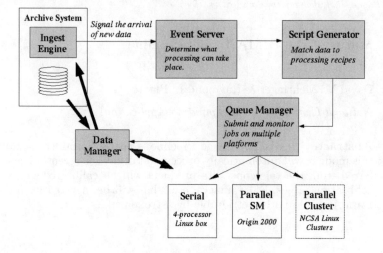

Figure 1.   Architecture of the BIMA Image Pipeline

Shot document. This document is an XML document containing the metadata for the data collection (e.g., observing track) to be processed, wrapped in a root SHOT node. The Event Server places the SHOT document in an area where the Script Generator can locate it.

2.2.   The Script Generator

The Script Generator is responsible for creating various scripts (Glish/AIPS++, shell/MIRIAD, and other shell scripts used for moving data) that are ultimately used for processing the data collection. It does this by transforming the Shot document created by the Event Server using XSLT into the various scripts to be used as well as XML metadata describing the products of the processing. Generally, a processing job is composed of several sub-stages. For example, a processing job to fill, calibrate, and image data is composed of a sub-stage that uses a shell script to copy the data to be processed to the work area, a sub-stage that uses a Glish script for filling and calibration in AIPS++ on a serial machine, a sub-stage that uses a Glish script for imaging and deconvolution on a parallel machine such as a Linux cluster, and a sub-stage that uses a shell script to archive the data products. The type of processing to be done (e.g., filling only, filling and calibration only, filling, calibration, and imaging) is encoded in the XML metadata of the collection. Each type of processing has an associated XSL stylesheet that is used to transform a Shot document to create the scripts appropriate for that specific type of processing. Upon successful generation of these files, the Script Generator notifies the Queue Manager that a collection is ready to be processed. This notification includes informing the Queue Manager in what order the scripts that were just generated should be run as well as in which queue each of these sub-stages should be placed.

2.3. The Queue Manager

The Queue Manager is responsible for scheduling, initializing, and monitoring jobs and sub-stages. The Queue Manager manages several queues. In general, each processing queue is configured to run a maximum number of jobs at any given time. A job starts out its life in the *pending queue*. When room becomes available in the queue in which the job's first sub-stage will run, the Queue Manager moves the job to the *running queue*. The first sub-stage is placed into the type of queue that is responsible for processing that type of job (e.g., the *unix queue* for processing shell scripts, the *serial queue* for processing AIPS++ jobs on serial machines, or the *parallel queue* for processing AIPS++ jobs on parallel platforms). If that sub-stage ends successfully (generally determined by the exit status of the script that it runs), the next sub-stage is started and placed in the appropriate queue. If all sub-stages complete successfully, the job finishes and is moved to the *success queue*. The data products (filled and calibrated *uv* data in AIPS++ Measurement Set 2 format, AIPS++ calibration tables, images in FITS format, etc.) of successful processing runs are ingested into the archive where they can be retrieved by users. If any sub-stage fails, the main job is terminated and moved to the *error queue* and none of the data products are ingested into the archive.

The primary means of monitoring the states of the various queues by both users and administrators is via web interfaces. These interfaces are powered by Apache Tomcat, which transforms XML documents describing the current queue state to HTML using Java Servlets. Information provided includes the start and end times of all the sub-stages associated with a job, the script used to run that stage, etc. The administrator view has the added features of allowing jobs to be purged from queues, jobs to be moved to other queues, etc.

3. Recipes

The scripts that are used for processing come from a *recipe library*. Each recipe is written to do a single phase of the processing. For example, there are standard recipes for filling, calibration, and imaging. Jobs (and their sub-stages) generally call numerous recipes. The recipes needed by a sub-stage are called by a top-level Glish script. For example, below is an example of a top-level Glish script that fills, calibrates, and images data from a single track. This script is invoked by a single sub-stage of a processing job (in this case, the sub-stage is run on a serial platform, though normally the deconvolution portion of imaging will be run on a parallel platform to take advantage of AIPS++'s ability to utilize such systems).

```
# set some project dependent parameters
sources := ['1733-130','3c84','sgb2n','venus'];
targets := ['sgb2n'];
phcals := ['1733-130'];
# include individual recipes
include 'pipelineinit.g';  # initialization
include 'filling.g';       # recipe for filling
include 'flagging.g';      # recipe for flagging
```

```
include 'calibration.g';    # recipe for calibration
bip.numprocs := 1           # number of processors
    include 'imaging.g';    # recipe for imaging
if(bip.imaging())           # main imaging function that returns
                            # true if successful
    note('Imaging completed successfully',priority='NORMAL');
else
    note('Imaging failed',priority='SEVERE');
include 'pipelinefinalize.g';      # finalization
note('Pipeline processing successful',priority=bip.note.NORMAL);

exit 0;
```

4. Summary

The BIMA Image Pipeline processes BIMA data and makes the products of this processing available to users by sending them to the BIMA Data Archive to be ingested. There are several components to the pipeline. The Event Server receives processing events and notifies the Script Generator that a data collection is awaiting processing. The Script Generator generates the various scripts that will be used to process the data as well as XML files that contain some of the metadata for the data products. The Script Generator informs the Queue Manager of the collection that is waiting to be processed and also tells how many sub-stages there are to the job and what type of processing each sub-stage requires. The Queue Manager manages the various sub-stages, and if all are successful, alerts the BIMA Data Archive of the new data products to ingest.

Astronomical Data Analysis Software and Systems XII
ASP Conference Series, Vol. 295, 2003
H. E. Payne, R. I. Jedrzejewski, and R. N. Hook, eds.

ORAC-DR: One Pipeline for Multiple Telescopes

Brad Cavanagh, Paul Hirst, Tim Jenness, Frossie Economou

Joint Astronomy Centre, 660 N. A'ohōkū Place, University Park, Hilo, HI 96720

Malcolm J. Currie

Starlink Project, Rutherford Appleton Laboratory, Chilton, Didcot, Oxon, OX11 0QX, United Kingdom

Stephen Todd

UK Astronomy Technology Centre, Blackford Hill, Edinburgh, EH9 3HJ, United Kingdom

Stuart D. Ryder

Anglo-Australian Observatory, P.O. Box 296, Epping, NSW 1710, Australia

Abstract. ORAC-DR, a flexible and extensible data reduction pipeline, has been successfully used for real-time data reduction from UFTI and IRCAM (infrared cameras), CGS4 (near-infrared spectrometer), Michelle (mid-infrared imager and echelle spectrometer), at UKIRT; and SCUBA (sub-millimeter bolometer array) at JCMT. We have now added the infrared imaging spectrometers IRIS2 at the Anglo-Australian Telescope and UIST at UKIRT to the list of officially supported instruments. We also present initial integral field unit support for UIST, along with unofficial support for the imager and multi-object spectrograph GMOS at Gemini. This paper briefly describes features of the pipeline along with details of adopting ORAC-DR for other instruments on telescopes around the world.

1. Background on ORAC-DR

ORAC-DR is the data reduction pipeline for the Observatory Reduction and Acquisition Control project (ORAC[1], Wright et al 2001). The ORAC-DR pipeline design was presented previously by Economou et al (1998) and Jenness & Economou (1999) and makes extensive reuse of existing data reduction packages (Economou et al 1999). Allan et al (2002) described groundwork for turning ORAC-DR into a truly generic data reduction pipeline. For the past

---

[1]ORAC is a joint project of the Astronomy Technology Centre, Edinburgh and the Joint Astronomy Centre, Hawaii.

three years it has been used at the United Kingdom Infrared Telescope (UKIRT) and for SCUBA observations on the James Clerk Maxwell Telescope (JCMT).

2. Reducing the Workload

When developing the ORAC-DR pipeline, we recognized that many of the tasks performed by instrument-specific pipelines are shared. File handling, calibration systems, and header translations are tasks that are often duplicated. Also, the actual data reduction tasks are similar from one instrument to the next. Repeating the implementation of these tasks by developing a specific pipeline for each new instrument was considered to be a waste of time and resources, so we sought a generic solution.

To accomplish this, we created a generic, and yet advanced, object-oriented ORAC-DR infrastructure which handles file conversions, header translations, calibration information, and other generic tasks. It also runs on a 'primitive'-based system, where one primitive (Perl script) does the work of one astronomically meaningful step. These primitives also do a bare minimum of computing; processing of bulk data is done by CCDPACK (Draper, Taylor & Allan 2000), KAPPA (Currie & Berry 2000), and Figaro (Shortridge et al 1999; Shortridge 1993), all supported by Starlink.

3. Necessary Modifications

As ORAC-DR is a data-driven data reduction pipeline, it obtains most of the information required to reduce data from the data itself. For astronomical data, this means that FITS headers need to be complete and correct. Simple instrument-specific Perl modules translate FITS headers into internal headers that are used by any code relying on headers. These translations are not limited to changes of name, and may involve combinations of headers. Through inheritance one instrument can acquire header translations from another, further reducing the number of header-translation modifications necessary to use ORAC-DR with a new instrument.

This same philosophy applies to file formats. As the actual data reduction calculations are performed by Starlink tasks whose internal data format is the Extensible N-Dimensional Data Format (NDF, Warren-Smith 2000), ORAC-DR minimizes the number of conversions from a different format (FITS, for example) by doing a conversion to NDF when it first sees a data file. Which conversion ORAC-DR does is instrument-specific, and this is programmed in such a way that adding a new instrument and new data conversions requires minimal effort.

Inheritance is also used for recipes and primitives. A large collection of generic recipes and primitives exists. Should an instrument require a new or modified recipe or primitive then this new code is placed in an instrument-specific subdirectory. When ORAC-DR searches for a primitive, it looks in the instrument-specific directory, then in the instrument-agnostic directory.

Occasionally new observing modes are needed, or instruments with different capabilities are developed. An example of this is the imaging spectrometer UIST, which also has an integral field unit. ORAC-DR had no previous IFU support, so it was necessary to develop a new set of primitives and recipes to reduce IFU data.

Modifying ORAC-DR to be used on an instrument similar to currently supported instruments takes approximately one to two weeks of programming time. If new observing modes are needed, then this time is increased to one to four months, depending on the number of recipes needed and the instrument's complexity.

4. Implementation of Modifications

4.1. IRIS2

IRIS2[2] is an infrared imager and spectrograph currently being commissioned for the 3.9-meter Anglo-Australian Telescope. In addition to wide-field imaging and long-slit spectroscopy, it also offers multi-object spectroscopy. It writes data in FITS format, not the NDF that UKIRT instruments use.

In July 2002 ORAC-DR was commissioned for imaging with IRIS2, needing only two weeks of programming effort to become fully usable. As ORAC-DR relies on FITS headers to process data, a side-effect of porting it to other instruments is an ability to find omissions and deficiencies in header information. During the commissioning of ORAC-DR it was noticed that an incorrect value for the array read noise of IRIS2 was being reported. This was traced to a bug in the data acquisition software and was immediately fixed. Had ORAC-DR not been running at the AAT at the time, this bug would have been found much later and after much more effort.

During the commissioning of ORAC-DR, IRIS2 made a deep image of a section of sky that would later be observed with the Very Large Telescope. As ORAC-DR was able to calculate a reduced mosaic of the region in real-time, it was possible to send this mosaic to the principle investigator. He then used this mosaic to select out high-z galaxy candidates from low-mass stars for follow-up VLT multi-object spectroscopy a few days later. ORAC-DR was able to save the principle investigator the time and effort necessary to reduce their data and did so needing only minimal changes.

4.2. UIST

UIST[3] is an imaging spectrometer very similar to IRIS2 in capabilities. Adapting ORAC-DR to work with imaging and spectroscopy modes with UIST was thus trivial, requiring approximately two weeks of effort to run correctly.

In addition to imaging and spectroscopy modes, UIST has an integral field unit which allows it to simultaneously obtain spectra at a number of points on a field. This mode is one that had not been previously supported by ORAC-DR, so programming effort required to get ORAC-DR properly reducing IFU data was approximately three months by a programmer with no previous experience with ORAC-DR.

---

[2]http://www.aao.gov.au/iris2/iris2.html

[3]http://www.jach.hawaii.edu/JACpublic/UKIRT/instruments/uist/uist.html

4.3. GMOS

GMOS[4] is a multi-object spectrograph with imaging, long-slit spectroscopy, and IFU modes. Basic System Verification data were released for imaging and multi-object spectrograph modes, and imaging data was used for ORAC-DR. The FITS headers for this SV data are incomplete and raw calibration data are not available, so ORAC-DR support for GMOS is minimal. However, ORAC-DR can successfully reduce publicly available GMOS data. The programming time needed to attain this level of support was eight hours.

Acknowledgments. We would like to thank STARLINK for distributing ORAC-DR and supporting many packages ORAC-DR uses. We thank Gemini for releasing GMOS System Verification data for its use with ORAC-DR.

References

Allan, A., Jenness, T., Economou, F., Currie, M. J., & Bly, M. 2002, in ASP Conf. Ser., Vol. 281, Astronomical Data Analysis Software and Systems XI, ed. D. A. Bohlender, D. Durand, & T. H. Handley (San Francisco: ASP), 311

Currie, M. J., Berry, D. S. 2000, Starlink User Note 95,[5] Starlink Project, CCLRC

Draper, P. W., Taylor, M., & Allan, A. 2000, Starlink User Note 139,[6] Starlink Project, CCLRC

Economou, F., Bridger, A., Wright, G. S., Rees, N. P., & Jenness, T. 1998, in ASP Conf. Ser., Vol. 145, Astronomical Data Analysis Software and Systems VII, ed. R. Albrecht, R. N. Hook, & H. A. Bushouse (San Francisco: ASP), 196

Jenness, T., & Economou, F. 1999, in ASP Conf. Ser., Vol. 172, Astronomical Data Analysis Software and Systems VIII, ed. D. M. Mehringer, R. L. Plante, & D. A. Roberts (San Francisco: ASP), 171

Shortridge, K. 1993, in ASP Conf. Ser., Vol. 52, Astronomical Data Analysis Software and Systems II, ed. R. J. Hanisch, R. J. V. Brissenden, & J. Barnes (San Francisco: ASP), 219

Shortridge, K., et al. 1999, Starlink User Note 86,[7] Starlink Project, CCLRC

Warren-Smith, R. F. 2000, Starlink User Note 33,[8] Starlink Project, CCLRC

Wright, G. S. et al. 2001, in ASP Conf. Ser., Vol. 238, Astronomical Data Analysis Software and Systems X, ed. F. R. Harnden, Jr., F. A. Primini, & H. E. Payne (San Francisco: ASP), 137

---

[4]http://www.gemini.edu/sciops/instruments/gmos/gmosIndex.html

[5]http://www.starlink.rl.ac.uk/star/docs/sun95.htx/sun95.html

[6]http://www.starlink.rl.ac.uk/star/docs/sun139.htx/sun139.html

[7]http://www.starlink.rl.ac.uk/star/docs/sun86.htx/sun86.html

[8]http://www.starlink.rl.ac.uk/star/docs/sun33.htx/sun33.html

Astronomical Data Analysis Software and Systems XII
ASP Conference Series, Vol. 295, 2003
H. E. Payne, R. I. Jedrzejewski, and R. N. Hook, eds.

CalFUSE v2.2: An Improved Data Calibration Pipeline for the Far Ultraviolet Spectroscopic Explorer (FUSE)

W. Van Dyke Dixon, David J. Sahnow, and the FUSE Science Data Processing Group

Department of Physics and Astronomy, The Johns Hopkins University, Baltimore, MD 21218, Email: wvd@pha.jhu.edu

Abstract. CalFUSE is the data-reduction software pipeline used at the Johns Hopkins University to process data from the *Far Ultraviolet Spectroscopic Explorer (FUSE)*. The pipeline corrects for a variety of instrumental effects, extracts target spectra, and applies wavelength and flux calibrations. We present improvements included in v2.2 of the pipeline and announce the availability of calibrated spectral files processed with CalFUSE v2.2 from the Multimission Archive at STScI (MAST).

1. Introduction

CalFUSE is the data-reduction software pipeline used at the Johns Hopkins University (JHU) to process data from *FUSE*, the Far Ultraviolet Spectroscopic Explorer. CalFUSE corrects for a variety of instrumental effects, extracts target spectra, and applies wavelength and flux calibrations. Once processed at JHU, both the raw and calibrated data files are shipped to the Multimission Archive at STScI (MAST) for distribution to observers. For the past two years, *FUSE* data have been processed with CalFUSE v1.8.7. In the mean time, the pipeline has undergone considerable development. CalFUSE v2.2, recently released, incorporates more than a dozen major improvements over v1.8.7. We are happy to announce that all new *FUSE* data are now being processed with v2.2. We have begun to reprocess archival *FUSE* data and expect that, by April of 2003, all *FUSE* data in the MAST archive will have been processed with the newest version of CalFUSE.

2. New in CalFUSE v2.2

2.1. Detection and Removal of Event Bursts

Occasionally, the *FUSE* detectors register large count rates for short periods of time. These event bursts can occur on one or more detectors and often have a complex structure, including scalloping and sharp edges (Figure 1). CalFUSE v2.2 includes a module that screens the data to identify and exclude bursts. The data are binned, then median filtered to reject time intervals whose count rates differ by more than N (user-adjustable) standard deviations from the mean. The algorithm also rejects time intervals in which there is no data or in which the

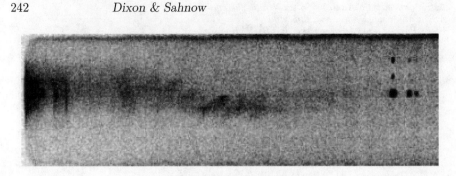

Figure 1.   An event burst on the LiF 1 detector.

background rate rises rapidly, as when an observation extends into an SAA. Burst removal is possible only for data obtained in time-tag (TTAG) mode.

2.2.   Walk Correction for Low-pulse-height Events

The *FUSE* detectors convert each ultraviolet photon into a shower of electrons, for which the detector electronics calculate the X and Y coordinates and the charge, or pulse height. Prolonged exposure to photons causes the detectors to become less efficient at this conversion (a phenomenon called "gain sag"), and the mean pulse height slowly decreases. Unfortunately, the X coordinate of low-pulse-height photon events is systematically miscalculated by the detector electronics. As the number of low-pulse-height events increases, spectral features appear to "walk" across the detector. The strength of this effect varies with location on the detector, peaking near the Lyman β airglow line at 1026 Å (Figure 2), where the detectors have received the greatest exposure. CalFUSE v2.2 incorporates a module to reposition low-pulse-height events, correcting for this effect. Histogram data, for which pulse-height information is unavailable, are only partially corrected for walk.

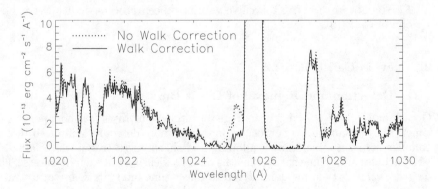

Figure 2.   LiF 1A spectrum before and after walk correction.

Figure 3.   Night-time scattered-light model for detector 1A.

2.3. Jitter-correction Module

We can now correct *FUSE* data for slow drifts resulting from a loss of pointing control during an observation. For time-tagged data, we reposition individual photon events to correct for spacecraft motion. For histogram data, we determine when the target was out of the (LiF 1) aperture and scale the flux accordingly. Both routines use information from a new file, *jitrf.fit, created by OPUS from spacecraft engineering data during level-zero processing. Because this file does not exist for any data processed before August 2002, the jitter-correction routines cannot be applied to older data sets. The incorporation of engineering data into the calibration pipeline is an innovation of CalFUSE v2.2.

2.4. Bad-pixel Maps Reflect Changes in Detector Y Scale

The detector Y scale is not constant, but changes both with time through the mission and as a function of detector count rate. As the Y scale changes, dead spots on the detector move relative to our bad-pixel maps, preventing the pipeline from properly excluding them during spectral extraction. To account for these effects, we have developed a series of bad-pixel maps that span the entire mission, reflecting the change in Y scale with time. Before being applied to the data, the bad-pixel maps are stretched in Y to account for the count-rate-dependent change in the detector Y scale.

2.5. Improved Scattered-light Model

The background has two components, detector dark count and scattered light. The dark count is spatially uniform but varies in intensity with time. The scattered light has considerable spatial structure (Figure 3) and differs between day and night-time observations. CalFUSE v1.8.7 assumes a constant background intensity across the detector. CalFUSE v2.2 scales separate day- and night-time scattered-light images and combines them with a uniform dark-count component to produce a model of the scattered light for each exposure.

2.6. Astigmatism Correction

The astigmatic height of *FUSE* spectra perpendicular to the dispersion direction is significant and varies as a function of wavelength. Moreover, spectral absorption features show considerable curvature, especially near the ends of the detectors, where the astigmatism is greatest. CalFUSE v2.2 shifts the data to correct for the spectral-line curvature introduced by the *FUSE* optics, providing

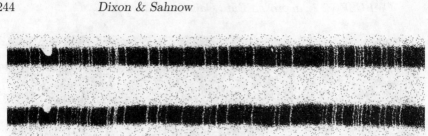

Figure 4.   Segment of LiF 1A spectrum before *(bottom)* and after *(top)* astigmatism correction.

a noticeable improvement in spectral resolution for point sources (Figure 4). At present, no astigmatism correction is defined for diffuse sources, and none is applied.

2.7. Optimal (Weighted) Spectral Extraction

The extraction algorithms used in CalFUSE v2.2 provide two important improvements over v1.8.7. First, the software determines the Y coordinate of the target spectrum by performing a cross-correlation between the data (in the form of a detector image) and the known distribution of flux on the detector. This routine greatly improves our ability to center the extraction window on the target spectrum. Second, spectra are extracted via an optimal-extraction algorithm, which produces a weighted sum of the pixels falling within the extraction window. Pixels having a quality flag of BAD_PIXEL do not contribute to the sum. The variances are weighted and summed to produce an error array. Optimal extraction improves the signal-to-noise ratio of the spectra of faint point sources.

2.8. Improved Flux Calibration

CalFUSE v1.8.7 used a single flux-calibration curve for all three apertures, scaling the effective area by the expected throughput of each. CalFUSE v2.2 uses flux-calibration curves for each aperture derived from spectra obtained through that aperture. Since the middle of 2001, we have noticed a slow degradation in the effective area of the *FUSE* spectrograph, more or less independent of wavelength. The flux-calibration files used by CalFUSE v2.2 account for this effect.

3.   Conclusions

Now that *FUSE* data processed with CalFUSE v2.2 are available from MAST, we expect that fewer users will find it necessary to download and run CalFUSE at their home institutions. This advance should make *FUSE* data easier to use than ever before.

Acknowledgments.   The NASA-CNES-CSA *FUSE* mission is operated by the Johns Hopkins University under NASA contract NAS5-32985.

Astronomical Data Analysis Software and Systems XII
ASP Conference Series, Vol. 295, 2003
H. E. Payne, R. I. Jedrzejewski, and R. N. Hook, eds.

The Next Step for the FUSE Calibration Pipeline

David J. Sahnow, W. Van Dyke Dixon, and the FUSE Science Data
Processing Group

*Department of Physics and Astronomy, The Johns Hopkins University,
Baltimore, MD 21218, Email: sahnow@pha.jhu.edu*

Abstract. The calibration pipeline for the Far Ultraviolet Spectroscopic Explorer (FUSE) satellite was designed years before it was launched. Since then, a number of unexpected instrumental features were discovered and the pipeline was modified appropriately. Eventually, these
changes made the design so cumbersome that the pipeline became difficult to maintain. In 2002, we began to develop a new pipeline concept
that takes into account the actual instrument characteristics. We present
our plans for this improved calibration pipeline.

1. Introduction

The design of the CalFUSE pipeline dates to well before the launch of FUSE.
As the primary FUSE mission draws to a close and an extended mission begins,
the resources available for maintaining the existing pipeline will diminish. Thus,
it is prudent to rethink the design, consider ways to make it easier to maintain,
and investigate changes which may improve the data quality. This process was
begun in the summer of 2002 when we proposed that for version 3 of the pipeline,
a new method for calibrating the data be used. These changes, which are described in the following sections, are intended to improve the data quality while
ensuring flexibility for future modifications. The ideas for these changes have
been prompted by our three years of experience with FUSE data, along with
information obtained during the design of the pipeline for the Cosmic Origins
Spectrograph, which will use a similar detector (Beland et al., this conference).

The present FUSE pipeline (Dixon et al. 2003) is less flexible than desired
when dealing with a number of instrument properties which were discovered
(or appreciated more clearly) after launch. These include the thermally-induced
motions of the mirrors and gratings, changes in the detector y scale as a function
of count rate, event bursts, the "worm," and the decrease in pointing stability
due to the failure of reaction wheels. Some of these effects are due to unexpected
performance of the instrument hardware, while others are a consequence of the
analog nature of the double delay line detectors. Among the shortcomings of
the original design are the fact that time-tag data was converted into a two-
dimensional image in an early step. Although this would work well if there were
no time-varying effects on the data, this is not the case for FUSE.

In addition to being developed with the instrument anomalies in mind, the
new design is more flexible, so that any new effects discovered as the instrument

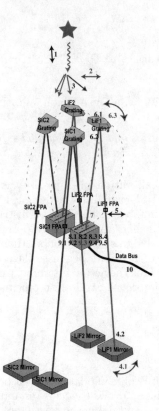

Figure 1.   A schematic view of the path of a photon through the
FUSE instrument. The steps which affect the data (and consequently,
the pipeline) are numbered; each of these must be compensated for in
the pipeline process.

ages can be dealt with more gracefully. The modular design should allow for the
addition of new modules with little or no effects on the existing ones. Although
the current design also permitted modules to be added, the fact that each created
its own output file and expected a unique format for its input made this difficult.

2.   The Life and Death of a Photon

Figure 1 shows the path of a photon through the instrument. This list describes
each effect. Items marked with an asterisk were not considered in the original
pipeline design.

    1.1   Doppler Shift due to motion of satellite.
    1.2   Wavelength shift due to heliocentric motion.
    2.   *Satellite pointing jitter.
    3.   Four Barrel design — divides incoming light among channels.

4.1 *Mirror motions due to thermal effects, which cause motion of the spots at the FPAs.

4.2 Mirror reflectivity.

5. Focal Plane Assembly (FPA) position, which shifts the location of the spectra on the detectors.

6.1 Grating efficiency.

6.2 Dispersion & astigmatism due to grating design & alignment.

6.3 *Grating motions due to thermal effects, which cause motion of the spectra on the detector.

7. *The "worm," caused by an interaction of the optical design and the detector grid wires.

8.1 Detector quantum efficiency.

8.2 Detector flat field.

8.3 Detector bad pixels.

8.4 Detector background.

9.1 *Detector "walk" — position of photon depends on pulse height.

9.2 Detector geometric distortion effects.

9.3 *Detector change in Y scale as a function of count rate.

9.4 Detector shift and stretch as a function of temperature.

9.5 Detector electronics dead time.

10. Instrument Data System (IDS) computer dead time.

3. Processing Steps

A major improvement in version 3 is the use of a single Intermediate Data File (IDF) for the entire pipeline. The IDF is a FITS file containing a binary table in the first extension. This extension contains one row per photon, and has columns for time, x, y, and pulse height from the raw data; x and y in the geometrically undistorted detector frame; a weighting factor for each photon; x and y after all motions are removed; channel; and wavelength. Nearly all of the pipeline modules operate on this one file, by reading and writing particular columns. A simplified outline of the processing steps is presented below. The numbers in parentheses refer to the steps in the previous section.

Put all photons in a rectified image frame:

- Adjust photon weight for IDS dead time (10).
- Adjust photon weight for detector electronics dead time (9.5).
- Correct (x,y) position of photon for thermal stretch & shift (9.4).
- Adjust y position of photon based on count rate (9.3).
- Correct (x,y) position of photon for geometric distortion (9.2).
- Adjust x position of photons to account for detector "walk" (9.1).

Remove Motions:

- Identify channel (LiF1, SiC1, etc.) for each photon.
- Calculate the time-dependent y centroid for each aperture.
- Adjust (x,y) position of photons to correct for grating motions (6.3).
- Adjust x position of photons to compensate for FPA offsets (5)

- Adjust (x,y) position of photons to correct for mirror motions (4.1).
- Use satellite jitter to discard data during particular times (2).
- Calculate the y centroid for all photons in each aperture.

Assign Wavelengths:

- Assign a wavelength to each photon based on position & channel (6.2).
- Correct for the heliocentric motion (1.2).
- Correct for the Doppler shift (1.1).

Screen the Data:

- Identify times when limb angle constraints are violated, or the satellite is in the SAA.
- Identify times when the detector high voltage values are outside of their nominal ranges.
- Find times when event bursts occurred.
- Exclude events which have pulse heights outside the nominal range.

Calibration:

- Convert each photon weight into units of erg cm^{-2} (4.2, 6.1, 8.1)
- Extract a one dimensional spectrum as a function of wavelength for each channel; correct for detector background and flat field (8.2, 8.4).
- Correct for the worm (7).

4.   Some Advantages of Version 3

The single Intermediate Data File means that the I/O is the same for all pipeline modules, and thus the order of modules can be changed, or new ones added, with a minimum of complication. The fact that the flow of the pipeline processing steps more closely follows the inverse of the "life of the photon" than previous version did makes it easier for users to understand the steps, and makes it easier to maintain.

Housekeeping (pointing stability, count rates, and high voltage values) data are used where appropriate to improve the quality of the data.

Since every pixel is assigned a floating point wavelength — rather than having every photon put in a wavelength bin as happens now — the final 1-dimensional spectrum can be binned to any convenient wavelength scale. This permits a straightforward addition of data from multiple segments. Because the analog photon positions (with times attached) are maintained for as long as possible, roundoff problems that currently exist will be minimized.

Acknowledgments.   The NASA-CNES-CSA FUSE mission is operated by the Johns Hopkins University under NASA contract NAS5-32985.

References

Dixon, W. V. and Sahnow, D. J. 2003, this volume, 241

Astronomical Data Analysis Software and Systems XII
ASP Conference Series, Vol. 295, 2003
H. E. Payne, R. I. Jedrzejewski, and R. N. Hook, eds.

Middle Tier Services Accessing the Chandra X-Ray Center Data Archive

Alexandra Patz, Peter Harbo, John Moran, David Van Stone, Panagoula Zografou

Harvard-Smithsonian Center for Astrophysics, 60 Garden Street, Cambridge MA 02138

Abstract. The Chandra Data Archive team at the Chandra X-ray Center[1] has developed middle tier services that are used by both our search and retrieval applications to uniformly access our data repository. Accessible through an HTTP URL interface, these services can be called by our J2EE web application (WebChaser) and our Java Swing application (Chaser), as well as any other HTTP client. Programs can call the services to retrieve observation data such as a single FITS file, a proposal abstract or a detailed report of observation parameters. Having a central interface to the archive, shared by client applications, facilitates code reusability and easier maintenance.

These middle tier services have been written in Java and packaged into a single J2EE application called the Search and Retrieval (SR) Services. The package consists of a web application front-end and an Enterprise Java Beans back-end. This paper describes the design and use of the SR Services.

1. Introduction

The Chandra Data Archive team has two search and retrieval applications: Chaser, a Java Swing application and WebChaser, a J2EE web application. Both perform similar functions: they search the Chandra Data Archive for observations matching a set of search criteria, display information about the found observations, and allow the user to download data for these observations from the archive. Until recently, they have used two different bodies of code to perform these functions causing maintenance issues. In an effort to make our code more reusable, these shared functions have been broken out into a separate middle tier that both applications can use to access and retrieve data from the archive. This middle layer is comprised of a collection of services, accessible through an HTTP URL interface, called the Search and Retrieval (SR) Services.

In addition to being used by these two internally developed applications, the SR Services can also be used by external programs needing to access the Chandra Data Archive. There is a growing need from the astronomical community for programmatic interfaces to the astronomical data archives. Interest in Web

---

[1]`http://asc.harvard.edu`

249

Services is growing with virtual observatory projects needing to query various data archives for observation data. While we have not yet implemented actual Web Services, these HTTP URL services do provide programmatic access to the Chandra Data Archive.

2.   The Interface to the SR Services

2.1.   Description of Individual SR Services

The following SR Services are available:

Observation Summary Service   Given a set of search criteria (position coordinates, target name, observation start date etc.) this service returns a summary report of the observations found. The data is returned in one of two formats: RDB table format or HTML format. In an effort to comply with emerging virtual observatory standards, there will also be a future option for the data to be returned in VO Table format.

Observation Details Service   Given the same set of search criteria used by the Observation Summary Service, this service returns a detailed observation report including instrument settings and multiple ACIS window settings if applicable. The data is returned in the same formats as the Observation Summary Service.

V&V Report Service   Given a single observation ID, this service returns the Verification and Validation Report. The data is returned as a formatted text file.

Proposal Abstract Service   Given a single observation ID, this service returns proposal information, such as the principal investigator, proposal title and abstract. The data is returned as an HTML page.

Archive File Retrieve Service   Given an observation ID, filetype and data-processing level, this service returns the content of a single file from the Data Archive. The file is returned as a stream of binary data.

Image Service   Given an observation ID and an image filetype, this service returns a JPEG image.

ADS Wrapper Service   Given a single observation ID, this service looks up the NASA Astrophysics Data System (ADS) bibcodes in our Data Archive. It then uses these bibcodes to forward to the relevant page on the ADS website[2].

2.2.   Calling the SR Services

To connect to the SR Services the HTTP URL query mechanism is used. Both Chaser and WebChaser connect to the SR Services using the HttpUrlConnection Java class, as could other Java programs. Clients running scripts could access

---

[2]http://adsabs.harvard.edu

the SR Services using an application such as wget[3] to retrieve the content via HTTP.

HTTP error codes are returned to the client application when the user passes in a bad parameter, when no data is found, when authentication fails or when proprietary data not belonging to the user is requested.

2.3. Handling proprietary data

If an observation has not yet been made public, the Image Service, the V&V Report Service and the Archive File Service require authentication to retrieve proprietary data. Client applications must send a username and password to these services using www-authentication to retrieve proprietary data, otherwise only publicly available data may be requested.

3. Applications Using the SR Services

Both internally developed applications and externally developed applications could use the SR Services.

3.1. Search and Retrieval Applications: Chaser and WebChaser

Chaser   The Java Swing application Chaser makes calls to the individual SR Services and displays the results in a manner dependent on the data type the service returns. For example, when a service, such as the Observation Details Service, returns an HTML page the results are displayed in the Swing JEditorPane widget. When a service, such as the Observation Summary Service, returns data in RDB table format the results are parsed and displayed in a JTable control.

The WebChaser Observation Viewer   After an initial observation search has been performed in WebChaser, the new Observation Viewer page can be used to examine information about these observations before products are selected for retrieval. The Observation Viewer page includes a set of menu options: Summary, Detail, V&V Report, Proposal Abstract, Images and Publications. Each menu option makes a call to the corresponding service in the SR Services middle tier to display the requested data.

3.2. Other Applications

There has been interest from other astronomical data archives in providing links to Chandra data from their client search applications. These links could be made to the SR Services through the HTTP URL interface.

There has also been interest in using these services from educational astronomy software, astronomical analysis programs and virtual observatory applications.

---

[3]http://www.gnu.org/software/wget/wget.html

4. Design of the SR Services

The SR Services have been written in Java and packaged into a single J2EE application. This consists of a web application front-end and an Enterprise Java Beans back-end.

The web application follows a Model-View-Controller design pattern implemented on top of the Apache Struts[4] framework. The Struts framework provides a *controller* for the application which invokes the relevant SR Service object. The *model* layer is made up of form beans that encapsulate the set of parameters each service accepts. The *view* layer consists of JSP pages that display the results.

The Enterprise Java Beans (EJBs) are called from the web application to do the actual archive lookup. The EJBs connect to the back-end archive servers using the Sybase JConnect JDBC driver.

Putting all the SR Services together in one application allows the services to share code. The front-end components share authentication and logging code, for example, while the back-end components share code that checks the proprietary status of the data.

Acknowledgments.   This project is supported by the Chandra Xray Center under NASA contract NAS8-39073.

---

[4]http://jakarta.apache.org/struts

Astronomical Data Analysis Software and Systems XII
ASP Conference Series, Vol. 295, 2003
H. E. Payne, R. I. Jedrzejewski, and R. N. Hook, eds.

The Automated Data Processing Pipeline for SIRTF IRS

Fan Fang, Jing Li, Bob Narron, Clare Waterson, Iffat Khan, Wen P. Lee, John Fowler, Russ Laher, & Mehrdad Moshir

SIRTF Science Center, Caltech, Pasadena, CA 91125

Abstract. We present the design, structure, and implementation of the automated data processing pipelines for the Infrared Spectrograph onboard Space Infrared Telescope Facility. This includes science data reduction pipelines that generate Basic Calibrated Data and enhanced science products, and calibration pipelines generating calibration data that allows reduction of the science data.

1. Introduction

The Infrared Spectrograph (IRS) will be one of the three instruments onboard the NASA mission Space Infrared Telescope Facility (SIRTF). Four instrument modules of IRS are built to observe the mid-infrared (5 to 40 microns) spectra of astronomical sources in four overlapping wavelength channels with low- and medium-resolution dispersion optics and As:Si and As:Sb BIB detectors. The IRS data processing pipelines have been developed at the SIRTF Science Center (SSC) to reduce IRS data. The IRS Science and Coadd pipelines remove a combination of detector electronic and optical artifacts and generate high signal-to-noise ratio (S/N) 2-dimensional science images from raw data. Calibration pipelines reduce data taken for specific calibration purposes and generate calibration images to enable science data processing. The Pointing Transfer pipeline interacts with a pointing server to provide pointing data for each Data Collection Event (DCE). These pipelines work together to provide the Basic Calibrated Data (BCD). The Post-BCD pipeline enhances data products by extracting 1-dimensional spectra from 2-dimensional BCDs.

2. IRS Pipeline Architecture

The IRS data processing involves several sub-systems interacting with each other. Figure 1 illustrates the main components involved in the process. When a DCE is received from the Flight Operations System (FOS), it is ingested and records are made in the Science Operations Database (SODB) and data archive. The PrepareDCE subsystem retrieves the records and establishes processing directories. The appropriate processing pipeline is activated based on information in SODB. Each IRS pipeline communicates with the SODB, retrieving the calibration and controlled data files appropriate for the DCE during processing. Upon completion of reducing the data, the pipeline loads product and Quality Assurance (QA) data into the SODB. Data products are physically stored in local disk and an area called Sandbox, before being moved to the archive.

Pipelines have established priorities and are executed in order. The calibration pipelines are to be executed first on calibration-specific data since they are tasked to provide calibration files for science data reduction. Among the calibration pipelines the reference dark current calibration and linearity model are needed before calculating the flatfield or efficiency frame for spectra, and therefore have higher priorities. Before a high-quality calibration product is generated, each calibration DCE is reduced by a calibration pre-processing pipeline. When a given number of DCEs are pre-processed an ensemble processing pipeline is triggered and multiple pre-processing products are combined and reduced together to yield a calibration product. Similarly the science pipeline is to be executed first on individual DCEs before multiple products are coadded to yield a 2-dimensional BCD, which Post-BCD pipeline picks up and extracts the 1-dimensional spectra. The Automated Processing Executive for SIRTF (APES) controls the orderly pipeline execution.

3.   The IRS Processing Pipelines

The IRS processing pipelines consist of stand-alone modules, each is communicated via wrapper scripts written in Perl. Each module performs a specific task, such as removing a detector electronic artifact, as well as calculating and propagating the uncertainty and updating pixel status mask files. The electronic and optical artifacts that the pipeline modules handle include baseline and dark current removal, analog-to-digital de-saturation, droop and row-droop effects removal, non-linearity correction, radhit detection, jail-bar pattern removal, stray-light or order cross-talk removal, and efficiency frame removal or flatfielding. Since the IRS science data is taken in a sample-up-the-ramp mode which creates a data cube, a slope image is calculated to reflect the total integration. Multiple such slope images of a given sky location and free of instrument artifacts are coadded to produce a high S/N BCD.

Further reduction of the BCD follows the curvature of the spectrum in both pixel and wavelength space in the 2-dimensional BCD image. The spectrum is Nyquist-sampled based on resolution of the instrument. The profile in the cross-dispersion direction is examined and an average profile generated for each spectral order. The spectrum extraction is done for each order based on the average profile and a wavelength-dependent extraction window. The extracted spectra of different orders are then stitched together using a set of tuning parameters, which are calibrated from reducing the IRS spectra of known astronomical sources. A 1-dimensional Post-BCD product is generated and archived.

Figure 2 shows a few examples of IRS BCD and Post-BCD pipelines. The nature of spectroscopy poses significant challenges on data reduction. A number of IRS calibrations, such as ensemble flatfield, wavelength, fringes, etc., are not suited for automated processing and have to be done offline. When automated pipelines finish the task, IRS scientists step in and close the loop of completing the calibration. Interactive tools are being developed to facilitate this task.

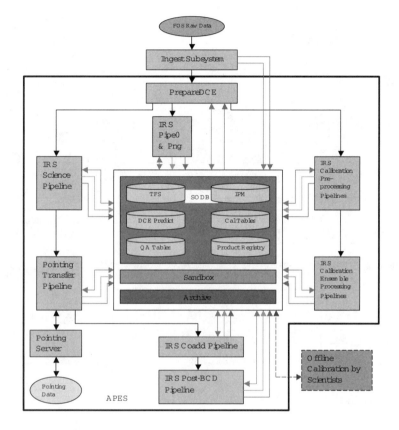

Figure 1. The architecture of the automated IRS data processing system. Several subsystems are involved in reducing an IRS DCE. The SODB plays a central role, from which each of the subsystem retrieves and loads information. The IRS pipelines use TFS to obtain version-controlled input configuration files, and call a Caltrans process to retrieve the best calibration files based on calibration table records. The QA subsystem, as a pipeline stage, loads selected ancillary data into the SODB. The Instrument Performance Monitoring (IPM) subsystem loads house-keeping data into the SODB. Both are used for monitoring purposes. The IRS pipeline0 & Png does minimal processing for DCEs, mostly engineering data. The automated pipeline processing is controlled and managed by APES.

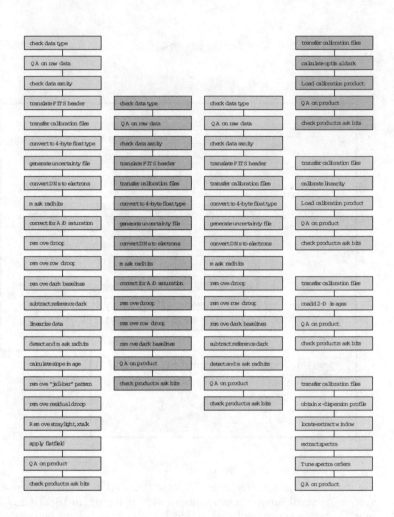

Figure 2. Examples of IRS BCD and Post-BCD processing pipelines. Shown here are IRS Science and Coadd (light blue), IRS Darkcal Pre- and Ensemble processing (light brown), IRS Lincal Pre- and Ensemble processing (light green), and IRS Post-BCD Science pipeline (yellow). Each pipeline processes from top down. IRS pipelines not shown here include Flatcal Pre-processing, Photocal Pre-processing, Pointing and Pipe0 & Png pipelines.

Astronomical Data Analysis Software and Systems XII
ASP Conference Series, Vol. 295, 2003
H. E. Payne, R. I. Jedrzejewski, and R. N. Hook, eds.

An Automatic Image Reduction Pipeline for the Advanced Camera for Surveys

John P. Blakeslee, Kenneth R. Anderson, G. R. Meurer, N. Benítez

Physics & Astronomy, Johns Hopkins University, Baltimore, MD 21218

D. Magee

UCO/Lick Observatory, University of California, Santa Cruz, CA 95064

Abstract. We have written an automatic image processing pipeline for the Advanced Camera for Surveys (ACS) Guaranteed Time Observation (GTO) program. The pipeline, known as Apsis, supports the different cameras available on the ACS instrument and is written in Python with a flexible object-oriented design that simplifies the incorporation of new pipeline modules. The processing steps include empirical determination of image offsets and rotation, cosmic ray rejection, image combination using the drizzle routine called via the STScI Pyraf package, object detection and photometry using SExtractor, and photometric redshift estimation in the event of multiple bandpasses. The products are encapsulated in XML markup for automated ingestion into the ACS Team archive.

1. Introduction and Basic Operation

The ACS science team was apportioned about 550 orbits of GTO time in exchange for its instrument development and calibration work. A robust and flexible astronomical data reduction and analysis pipeline was required for processing these data and other observations for which the science team is responsible. To fill this need, we developed a package called "Apsis" (ACS pipeline science investigation software), written in the Python programming language using a flexible, modular design. Apsis was used for processing the ACS early release observation (ERO) images of the Tadpole and Mice galaxies, the Cone Nebula, and M17 soon after ACS was installed on the Hubble Space Telescope. Since then, it has developed and been used extensively on Linux and Solaris platforms for processing WFC and HRC data from both science and calibration programs.

A given processing run starts with flat-fielded multi-extension FITS images that have been processed through the CALACS software at STScI (Hack 1999). The basic Apsis "observation object" consists of all the images of a given program field (or mosaic of adjacent fields). These are grouped into separate "associations" according to the different imaging/grism filters used or (sometimes) different epochs, and FITS tables are constructed similar to those used in STScI OPUS pipeline. Reading and manipulation of FITS images and tables are done with the aid of the PyFits and Numarray Python modules, and any

IRAF/STSDAS routines are called through Pyraf. Other external programs are accessed via system calls.

The observation object is then passed to the various python modules in succession, which have "methods" (python functions) for performing the following general tasks: image offset measurement corrected for distortion, sky estimation and subtraction, cosmic ray (CR) rejection and "drizzling," construction of error arrays and a multi-band "detection image," object detection and measurement, photometric calibration, and photo-z estimation. A running log keeps track of progress and records diagnostics. After completion, each module object is written to disk as a byte stream using the Python "pickling" utility; this allows for recovery of information in the event of failure and simplifies debugging. The modules also contain detailed methods for producing XML messages and markup of the data products (images and catalogs) for archiving purposes.

Although Apsis was designed primarily as an automated pipeline, it can be run by users as a standalone program, and provides a suite of command-line options for this purpose. These include switches for turning off various parts of the processing (e.g., sky subtraction, cataloging), specifying a particular input image as reference for the shifts, supplying an alternate distortion model, externally measured shifts, or sky values, lowering the CR rejection thresholds, changing the output image pixel scale, and several other options. The following sections provide a few details on the major processing steps.

2. Image Registration and Sky Subtraction

The `align` module determines the relative x, y shifts and rotations, as well as the sky levels, of the input images. SExtractor (Bertin & Arnout 1996) is run with a signal-to-noise threshold of 10 on each science extension of each image (there are two science extensions for WFC; one for HRC and SBC). The resultant catalogs are culled on the basis of object size and shape parameters, thereby rejecting the vast majority of cosmic rays and CCD artifacts as well as overly diffuse objects. If fewer than ten "good" sources remain, then SExtractor is rerun at lower thresholds. The x, y coordinates of each "good" source are corrected using the distortion model read from the IDCTAB FITS table specified in the image headers or on the command line. Sources from different extensions (different CCD chips) of the same image are placed on a common rectified frame using the IDCTAB parameters V2REF and V3REF.

We use the "Match" program (Richmond 2002) to derive shifts and rotations with respect to a reference image, by default the one having the most "good" sources. We modified Match to accept an input guessed transformation (derived from the headers) and to report more diagnostics for evaluating the success of the matching. In the event of failure, Match is rerun without an input guess, using the full triangle-matching search algorithm on the N brightest sources; this is repeated with larger N, and an N^6 hit in processor time, if necessary. All sources are used for tuning up the final transformation once it is found. We also evaluate the median x, y shifts for all matched sources, and we revert to these if the derived rotation is negligible.

This automatic, adaptive matching procedure works quite well in practice. Images taken at large offsets and in different visits can have header shift errors of $\sim 1''$ (~ 20 WFC pixels), but this is irrelevant for the triangle matching algorithm. Typical WFC GTO fields produce one-to-several hundred matched sources per exposure, and the resulting shift uncertainty is typically ~ 0.02 pix. Problems have only occurred for some images of blank fields taken with the HRC, which has an area 1/64 of the WFC. In this case Apsis defaults to the header shifts, although it is also possible to supply external shifts. Grism (G800L) images are by default aligned with direct images according to the headers.

The sky values and sigmas returned by SExtractor for each image extension are used as inputs to the STSDAS dither.sky task, which in turn uses the STSDAS gstatistics routine. However, experimentation indicated that the mean sky levels reported by SExtractor were more robust, although tended to be biased high in more crowded fields. For this reason, we adopt the SExtractor sky value when it is the lower estimate, and the mean of the two otherwise. The sky is then subtracted, with the option of averaging the values for different extensions of the same image. This step removes sky level differences for the image combination and CR rejection routines described in the following section.

3. Image Combination

The modules `combDither` and `pyblot` combine all exposures within each filter into a single geometrically corrected image while rejecting cosmic rays. This is done through the STSDAS Dither package drizzle-blot-drizzle cycle outlined by Gonzaga et al. (1998), although here coded in Python. First the images are "drizzled" to separate output images using the shifts and rotations supplied by the Apsis `align` module. These individually drizzled images are then median stacked using exposure time weighting and a 'minmax' clipping algorithm. The median image is then "blotted" back to each of the input image positions, rescaled in exposure time, and used as a template for CR rejection with the driz_cr task. The driz_cr parameters were optimized to achieve good CR rejection without harming the centers of any stars. In particular, this meant setting the derivative scale parameter to a value near unity.

A cosmic ray mask is produced for each science extension and is multiplied by the bad pixel mask that we produce from the data quality arrays using a call to Pydrizzle with the 'bits' parameter set to 8578 to include 'good', 'replaced', 'saturated,' and 'repaired' pixels (see Hack 1999). These combined CR/badpix masks are then used for the final drizzling of the input images in each filter to a single output image. We again use the shifts and rotations found by `align` and produce drizzled images in units of electrons. In so doing, it is necessary to divide the output pixel values by the number of science extensions, since the drizzle task does not recognize the different extensions as being part of the same image. The default drizzle pixfrac and scale parameters are unity but can be reset with flags on the Apsis command line. It is also possible to specify a non-standard higher order resolution-preserving kernel on the command line.

After the final images are produced, the image headers are thoroughly updated and corrected. This includes calculating new CD matrices from scratch based on the output pixel scale and image orientation, which is derived through spherical geometry from the PA_V3 header keyword of the reference image, the declination, and the detector orientation and location in the V2,V3 plane. The code also ensures that all of the output images have identical WCS information, as they should all be well aligned at this stage. At this writing, the WCS zero points are off by roughly $2''$ due to systematic pointing errors, but this is expected to improve with a recent FGS realignment. Eventually, we plan on-the-fly recalibration of the WCS zero points using online astrometric catalogs.

We produce an "RMS image" for each output science image. The RMS images have pixel values equal to the estimated error per pixel, based on the total read noise, signal level, Apsis cosmic ray rejection, and the effects of the multiple bias and dark frame subtractions. The actual root-mean-square pixel variation in the science image is of course lower due to the noise correlation induced by non-integer shifts and geometric correction. However, we verified that the RMS images reflect the pixel variation when images are stacked without shifting or correction. The RMS images are used in estimating photometric errors.

4. Object Detection, Photometry, and Redshift Estimation

A series of modules do the object photometry. The `combFilter` module produces a multi-band "detection image," which is the variance-weighted average of the science images in the different bandpasses. Images in specific filters (e.g., grism, polarizers) can be omitted from this average. This module also produces a detection weight image, which is a similarly weighted sum of the exposure maps from the drizzling process. The `detectionCatalog` and `filterCatalog` modules create parameter files and run SExtractor, first on the detection image alone, and then multiple times in "dual image mode." In dual mode, the detection image defines the object position and apertures, but the photometric measurements are done on the filter image with its associated RMS image.

The `colorCatalog` module derives the photometric zero points from the image header catalogs, sorts through the different SExtractor catalogs, and produces a single, calibrated multicolor catalog. It also uses simple logic for flagging apparently bad or anomalous magnitudes. Finally, the `photoz` module feeds the multicolor catalog to the Bayesian Photometric Redshift package (Benítez 2000), which is itself coded in Python. A final XML "run message" is written in the same format as the individual module messages. The images and XML catalogs can then be ingested into the ACS team data archive.

Acknowledgments. Apsis development was supported by NASA grant NAG5-7697. We are grateful to our ACS team colleagues for help and feedback. We thank Colin Cox, Warren Hack, and Richard Hook for helpful discussions.

References

Benítez, N. 2000, ApJ, 536, 571

Bertin, E. & Arnouts, S. 1996, A&AS, 117, 393

Gonzaga, S. et al. 1998, The Drizzling Cookbook, ISR WFPC2-98-04

Hack, W.J. 1999, CALACS Operation and Implementation, ISR ACS-99-03

Richmond, M. 2002, http://acd188a-005.rit.edu/match/

Astronomical Data Analysis Software and Systems XII
ASP Conference Series, Vol. 295, 2003
H. E. Payne, R. I. Jedrzejewski, and R. N. Hook, eds.

OPUS: A CORBA Pipeline for Java, Python, and Perl Applications

Walter Warren Miller III, Christopher Sontag, Jim Rose[2]

Space Telescope Science Institute, Baltimore, MD 21218

Abstract. With the introduction of the OPUS CORBA mode, a limited subset of OPUS Applications Programming Interface (OAPI) functionality was cast into CORBA IDL so that both OPUS applications and the Java-based OPUS pipeline managers were able to use the same CORBA infrastructure to access information on blackboards.

Exposing even more of the OAPI through CORBA interfaces benefits OPUS applications in similar ways. Those applications not developed in C++ could use CORBA to interact with OPUS facilities directly, providing that a CORBA binding exists for the programming language of choice. Other applications might benefit from running 'outside' of the traditional file system-based OPUS environment like the Java managers and, in particular, on platforms not supported by OPUS.

The enhancements to OPUS discussed in this paper have been exercised in both Java and Python, and the code for these examples are available on the web.

1. Introduction

While users always had the ability to provide external tasks written in any language, those tasks have a limited amount of flexibility to respond to the environment. With the advent of OPUS 4.2, users of the OPUS Pipeline Platform[1] now have the ability to write applications which are fully aware of the OPUS pipeline in any language which has a CORBA binding.

2. Background

The OPUS platform is a distributed pipeline system that allows multiple instances of multiple processes to run on multiple nodes over multiple paths. While OPUS was developed to support the telemetry processing for the HST instruments, it is a generic pipeline system, and is not tied to any particular processing environment, or to any particular mission. From this point of view the OPUS platform does not provide the mission specific applications themselves. Instead

---

[2]Astronomy Division, Computer Sciences Corp.

[1]http://www.stsci.edu/resources/software_hardware/opus

OPUS provides a fully distributed pipeline processing environment structured to help organize the applications, monitor the processing and control what is going on in the pipeline.

The basic architecture of the OPUS system is based on a blackboard model where processes do not communicate directly with one another, but simply read and write to a common blackboard. In the original implementation of OPUS, the blackboards are accessed through the (network) file system as a directory on a commonly accessible disk. In a cluster of workstations and larger machines, if the protections are set appropriately, any process can "see" any file in the blackboard directory: the "posting" of blackboard messages consists of either creating or renaming an empty file in that directory.

3.   The OPUS Application Programming Interface

The OPUS Application Programming Interface (OAPI[2]) is an object-oriented, C++ interface to the OPUS environment distributed for Solaris, Linux, and Tru64 platforms. With the OAPI, internal-polling OPUS pipeline applications can be developed that take full advantage of the capabilities and flexibility offered by OPUS. The OAPI contains classes for interacting with the OPUS blackboards and their contents, for reading an assortment of resource files, for message reporting, for event handling, and for exception handling. Its functionality can be extended to include additional or customized features not yet provided by the library through traditional object-oriented techniques like inheritance and composition.

The OAPI was designed to satisfy the needs of two groups of software developers. On the one hand, it serves the programmer who wants to develop OPUS-savvy processes without regard for the implementation details of the OPUS system. Ease of use is a primary consideration for such a developer. On the other hand, it must be easily maintainable, backwards compatible with previous versions of OPUS, and offer the flexibility to meet future requirements of OPUS pipelines with little impact on existing code. These goals demand a general, abstract approach to the architecture with strict isolation of interface from implementation—a methodology that is often at odds with ease of use. The library follows a middle-of-the-road tack by promoting flexibility and ease of use through run-time polymorphism.

The OAPI exposes a set of interfaces defined by a set of core abstract base classes. Where applicable, the base classes provide an implementation, but far more often, specialized classes are derived from these base classes that provide the actual functionality of OPUS. Access to these derived types is achieved through a pointer to the base class and is transparent to the client. Using the run-time polymorphic behavior of C++ class hierarchies in this way is a powerful tool that helps preserve a high degree of separation between implementation and interface. Separating implementation from interface allows the use of generic algorithms to process different implementations of an object through a common interface thereby reducing code duplication and development effort. In addition,

---

[2]http://www.stsci.edu/software/OPUS/oapi-how-to.pdf

it permits evolution of the OAPI with minimal impact on the clients of the library since they only reference the interface exposed by the base classes.

4.   Internal Pollers

An OPUS pipeline is defined by the set of applications that processes data or that performs tasks in a co-operative manner and the rules that determine when they should act and how their results should be interpreted. OPUS pipeline applications fall into two general classes: internal pollers and external pollers. Internal pollers are developed with explicit knowledge of the OPUS environment: they make direct calls into the OAPI library for initialization and for event handling, and must be linked against the OAPI library.

External pollers use a proxy application (xpoll) to communicate with OPUS and typically are wrapped by a shell script. xpoll interacts directly with OPUS and executes the external poller whenever work is to be performed by that process. xpoll communicates OPUS event data and receives process completion status through the external poller's environment. As long as a suitable shell script can be developed that meets the input requirements of the application, any application can be used in an OPUS pipeline. Both internal and external pollers share many of the same basic capabilities although internal pollers, by virtue of having direct access to the OAPI, are more flexible. The OPUS Sample Pipeline demonstrates both classes of applications (g2f is an internal poller; all of the other applications are external pollers).

Internal polling processes, like g2f, are programs written with knowledge of how the OPUS blackboard works. They are typically processes with some significant start-up overhead (e.g., database reading, etc.). The process is written to perform the start-up overhead and then enter a polling loop to wait for pipeline events. The process stays active as it polls for and processes events. Internal pollers are built using the OAPI to communicate with the OPUS system, and can respond to a reinitialization command.

5.   New Capabilities

With the introduction of the OPUS CORBA mode, a limited subset of OPUS Applications Programming Interface (OAPI) functionality was cast into CORBA IDL so that both OPUS applications and the Java managers were able to use the same CORBA infrastructure to access information on blackboards.

The primary motivation for doing so was to improve scalability, but moving to distributed object architecture also freed the managers from running strictly in the confines of an OPUS user environment. It also reduced the amount of duplicate code that otherwise would be required in a multi-programming language environment.

Exposing even more of the OAPI through CORBA interfaces benefits OPUS applications in similar ways. Those applications not developed in C++ could use CORBA to interact with OPUS as internal pollers providing that a CORBA binding exists for the programming language of choice. Other applications might benefit from running 'outside' of the traditional file system-based OPUS environment like the Java managers and, in particular, on platforms not supported by OPUS.

To help users get started with their own internal pollers in Python or Java, sample code has been included with the OPUS 4.2 distribution which demonstrates exactly how to set up your environment, build the tasks, and run the applications.

A more complete discussion of the design of the **opususer** class is presented on the web.[3]

6. Example

While there is not sufficient space to present a complete example, you can inspect the Python code on the web[4]. That example is written in Python (1.52 or higher) and runs on Solaris 5.7/8 using the free OmniORBpy CORBA ORB. All the code that is necessary to wrap the OPUS API is presented in this example. Full instructions on downloading the necessary libraries, building, installing and running the application are included on that web page.

The particular example illustrates how to access resources in the process resource file and how to construct the polling loop for normal applications. To develop your own applications you might need only to substitute your own **processDataset** method.

References

Miller, W. & Rose, J. 2001, The OPUS CORBA Blackboards and the New OPUS Java Managers, in ASP Conf. Ser., Vol. 238, Astronomical Data Analysis Software and Systems X, ed. F. R. Harnden, Jr., F. A. Primini, & H. E. Payne (San Francisco: ASP), 325

Rose, J. et al 1994, The OPUS Pipeline: A Partially Object-Oriented Pipeline System, in ASP Conf. Ser., Vol. 77, Astronomical Data Analysis Software and Systems IV, ed. R. A. Shaw, H. E. Payne, & J. J. E. Hayes (San Francisco: ASP), 429

Walter Warren Miller III 1999, OAPI: the OPUS Application Programming Interface, in ASP Conf. Ser., Vol. 172, Astronomical Data Analysis Software and Systems VIII, ed. D. M. Mehringer, R. L. Plante, & D. A. Roberts (San Francisco: ASP), 195

---

[3]http://www.ess.stsci.edu/gsd/dst/oapi/servers/oresource_java.html

[4]http://www.stsci.edu/software/OPUS/javafaq/opusfaq_pyint.html

Astronomical Data Analysis Software and Systems XII
ASP Conference Series, Vol. 295, 2003
H. E. Payne, R. I. Jedrzejewski, and R. N. Hook, eds.

The COBRA/CARMA Correlator Data Processing System

Stephen L. Scott[1], Rick Hobbs[1], Andrew D. Beard[1], Paul Daniel[1], David M. Mehringer[2], Raymond Plante[2], J. Colby Kraybill[3], Melvyn Wright[3], Erik Leitch[4], N. S. Amarnath[5], Marc W. Pound[5], Kevin P. Rauch[5], Peter J. Teuben[5]

Abstract. The Caltech Owens Valley Broadband Reprogrammable Array (COBRA) digital correlator is an FPGA based spectrometer with 16 MHz resolution and 4 GHz total bandwidth that will be commissioned on the Caltech Millimeter-wave Array in November, 2002. The Combined Array for Research in Millimeter-Wave Astronomy (CARMA) will join the Caltech array with the BIMA array on a new high elevation site in 2005. The COBRA hardware and computing architecture described here will be the basis for the two CARMA correlators. The COBRA architecture uses nine computers to provide the hardware interface and initial processing. Data is transported using CORBA to a tenth machine that implements the data processing pipeline as multiple processes passing data through shared memory.

1. Introduction

Spectrometers are the key instruments for millimeter-wave radio telescope arrays. The six antenna Caltech Millimeter-wave Array is currently commissioning a new spectrometer called the Caltech Owens Valley Broadband Reprogrammable Array (COBRA) that is based on FPGA technology. The wide bandwidth (4 GHz) makes COBRA well suited for observations of high redshift molecular lines and continuum emission. Of particular interest is the role that COBRA plays as the progenitor of spectrometers for a new millimeter-wave array.

---

[1]California Institute of Technology/Owens Valley Radio Observatory

[2]NCSA/University of Illinois

[3]University of California, Berkeley

[4]University of Chicago

[5]University of Maryland

2. CARMA

Radio interferometric arrays sample spatial scales dependent on antenna separation, but the antenna diameter provides a practical limit to short spacings. The use of multiple antenna sizes allows for retrieval of more spatial scales than arrays composed of antennas of a single diameter. The Combined Array for Research in Millimeter-Wave Astronomy (CARMA) will consist of 23 antennas ranging from 3.5 to 10.4 meters in diameter that will create a unique **millimeter-wave multi-scale synthesis imaging array**. The actual antenna details for CARMA are shown in Table 1.

Table 1.   CARMA Antennas

Number of antennas	Diameter(m)	Status	Organization
6	10.4	Exists at OVRO	Caltech
9	6.1	Exists at Hat Creek	BIMA
8	3.5	New	U. Chicago

CARMA is a collaboration of five universities, all of which are represented by the authors of this paper, and is scheduled for construction and operation in 2003–2005. CARMA will operate in three frequency bands, 27–36 GHz, 70–116 GHz, and 210–270 GHz. The new array will be located at an elevation of 7,000 to 8,000 feet and have a maximum baseline of 1.8 km and a resolution of 0.3 arc seconds. The CARMA correlators, based on the hardware and software of COBRA, expand the number of stations, bandwidth and resolution. The approach to software development for the new array is presented by Pound et al. (2003).

3. Architecture

The design of the computing system is based on the following principles:
- Computing components should run Linux without the need for realtime extensions.
- Processing should be broken into a series of discrete steps, each implemented by a separate process.
- The processing should be resilient to any time sharing system delays.
- It should be possible to tap into the data between any of the processing steps and display the data remotely.
- An industry standard, architecture neutral, data transport between computers should be used. CORBA is chosen for this.

The computing hardware architecture reflects the instrument hardware layout to a large degree and both are shown in Figure 1. There are two major types of instrument hardware components: the correlator crates containing digitizer and correlator boards, and the downconverter modules that convert segments of

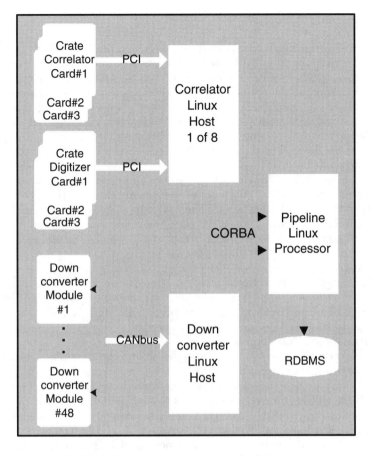

Figure 1. COBRA Computing Hardware Architecture

the IF band to the digitizer band. The total bandwidth of 4 GHz is broken into 8 bands, each with a width of 0.5 GHz.

The correlator crates are compact PCI (cPCI) backplanes containing digitizer and correlator cards that produce 6 antenna auto spectra and 15 baseline cross spectra for each band. Each band is mastered by a Linux/Intel cpu that handles configuration and accepts data from the hardware every 100 milliseconds. The net data rate into each crate cpu is approximately 110 KB/sec. The crates average the data to 500 msec samples and transmit it using CORBA events to the pipeline computer where data from all bands are combined.

The downconverter modules each contain a microprocessor (Philips XAC-3) that communicates using CANbus, an industrial field bus operating at 1 Mbps. All 48 of the downconverter modules communicate with a single Linux host over the CANbus, receiving configuration commands and sending the total power measurements that are needed to calibrate the spectra. The measurements are sent every 500 msec, synchronized to absolute time. The host aggregates this data and sends it to the pipeline computer using CORBA events.

4. Processing Pipeline

The processing pipeline is a dedicated computer that processes all of the COBRA data and writes the final calibrated visibilities to a relational database. Each step in the pipeline is implemented as a separate process that communicates with other processes using queues implemented on top of shared memory. This gives flexibility in modifying the pipeline and allows debugging processes to be inserted without modifying the running pipeline. The shared memory is very efficient, and the queues allow any processing delays to not result in the loss of critical data. The data in the queues between the processing steps can be remotely displayed using the Carma Data Viewer (Pound, Hobbs, & Scott 2001). The viewer is a Java tool that catches and graphs the data as it is sent via CORBA events. All of the processing steps are done on the 500 msec data samples until the final integration. The major pipeline steps are:

- Collection of data from the correlator and downconverter computers that were published using CORBA events and placement into pipeline queues. The input data rate is about 200 KB/sec.
- Passband gain correction using the auto spectra.
- Sideband gain correction, including atmospheric component.
- Calculation and application of system temperature and flux scaling.
- Data blanking (removal of data before integration).
- Apodization and decimation of the spectra.
- Atmospheric delay correction.
- Integration of the 500 msec samples up to the requested astronomical integration time, typically 10 to a few hundred seconds.

The same architecture (hardware, computing hardware, and software) used for COBRA will be applied to the CARMA wideband correlator (8 stations, 8 GHz bandwidth) and the CARMA spectral correlator (15 stations, 4 GHz bandwidth) scheduled for 2003 and 2004 respectively. The format, storage, and archiving of the correlator output data is described by Plante et al. (2003).

Acknowledgments. David Hawkins (Caltech/OVRO) is responsible for the design and implementation of the architecture, hardware, and firmware of the COBRA correlator.

References

Plante, R., Pound, M. W., Mehringer, D., Scott, S. L., Beard, A., Daniel, P., Hobbs, R., Kraybill, J. C., Wright, M., Leitch, E., Amarnath, N. S., Rauch, K. P., Teuben, P. J. 2003, this volume, 269

Pound, M. W., Amarnath, N. S., Rauch, K. P., Teuben, P. J., Kraybill, J. C., Wright, M., Beard, A., Daniel, P., Hobbs, R., Scott, S. L., Leitch, E., Mehringer, D., Plante, R. 2003, this volume, 377

Pound, M., Hobbs, R., Scott, S. 2001, in ASP Conf. Ser., Vol. 238, Astronomical Data Analysis Software and Systems X, ed. F. R. Harnden, Jr., F. A. Primini, & H. E. Payne (San Francisco: ASP), 82

Astronomical Data Analysis Software and Systems XII
ASP Conference Series, Vol. 295, 2003
H. E. Payne, R. I. Jedrzejewski, and R. N. Hook, eds.

CARMA Data Storage, Archiving, Pipeline Processing, and the Quest for a Data Format

Raymond Plante[1], Marc W. Pound[2], David M. Mehringer[1], Stephen L. Scott[3], Andy Beard[3], Paul Daniel[3], Rick Hobbs[3], J. Colby Kraybill[4], Melvyn Wright[4], Erik Leitch[5], N. S. Amarnath[2], Kevin P. Rauch[2], Peter J. Teuben[2]

Abstract. In 2005, the BIMA and OVRO mm-wave interferometers will be merged into a new array, the Combined Array for Research in Millimeter-wave Astronomy (CARMA). Each existing array has its own visibility data format, storage facility, and tradition of data analysis software. The choice for CARMA was to use one of a number of existing formats or devise a format that combined the best of each. Furthermore, it had to address three important considerations. First, the CARMA data format must satisfy the sometimes orthogonal needs of both astronomers and engineers. Second, forcing all users to adopt a single off-line reduction package is not practical; thus, multiple end-user formats are necessary. Finally, CARMA is on a strict schedule to first light; thus, any solution must meet the restrictions of an accelerated software development cycle and take advantage of code reuse as much as possible. We describe our solution in which the pipelined data passes through two forms: a low-level database-based format oriented toward engineers and a high-level dataset-based form oriented toward scientists.

The BIMA Data Archive at NCSA has been operating in production mode for a decade and will be reused for CARMA with enhanced search capabilities. The integrated BIMA Image Pipeline developed at NCSA will be used to produced calibrated visibility data and images for end-users. We describe the data flow from the CARMA telescope correlator to delivery to astronomers over the web and show current examples of pipeline-processed images of BIMA observations.

[1]NCSA/University of Illinois

[2]University of Maryland

[3]Caltech/OVRO

[4]University of California, Berkeley

[5]University of Chicago

1. Data Storage

The AIPS++ Measurement Set 2 (MS2) format will be the canonical format for astronomical data products. This will allow CARMA software components requiring high-level science-oriented access to take advantage of the existing functionality of the AIPS++ toolkit. An example of this would be automatic data quality evaluation.

In addition to the visibility data obtained by astronomical observing, the CARMA antennas also produce fast streams of telemetry data, called monitor points. These streams are sampled every half-second and the array as a whole will ultimately contain thousands of monitor points. The monitor data are important for tracking the health of the array, diagnosing problems, and assessing long-term trends. As such, they must be stored in a way that allows easy access and comparison among subsystems. A relational database is a natural solution.

The visibilities from the telescope are initially written as a "binary brick," and subsequently combined with the monitor data to create the MS2 (Figure 1).

2. Archiving

The CARMA Data Archive will be an extension of the BIMA Data Archive currently in use. Within the archive, data are organized in hierarchical collections that reflect how astronomers interact with their data. The broadest collection is a Project covering all data resulting from a single proposal and which can contain a number of different Experiments. Within each Experiment are a number of Trial collections. Data from each observing track will be in its own Trial collection. Processed data are also collected into their own trial collections. As with most archives, users can search and browse the collections through the web.

High level metadata describing the observational experiments are very important for driving the pipeline (see below). These ultimately come from the astronomer during the planning stage and will include science-related information such as the spectral lines of interest and target sensitivity. This information will be used to fill the Observational Programs database (see Figure 1). In addition to being used to schedule the telescope, the metadata will be packaged up with the science (MS2) datasets and shipped to the archive.

New features of the archive include the ability to request the data in any one of the three formats for off-line processing in the AIPS++, Miriad, or Mir packages. This conversion can take place on-the-fly. The converted version will be temporarily cached in the archive in case that format is desired again later. New searching capabilities will also be added to support the searching and downloading of historical engineering data.

3. Pipeline Processing

The CARMA Pipeline will be an extension of the existing BIMA Image Pipeline; Figure 2 illustrates its different components. Processing is triggered automatically whenever new data arrives in the archive. The pipeline analyzes the metadata associated with the collection to determine what needs to be done. This in-

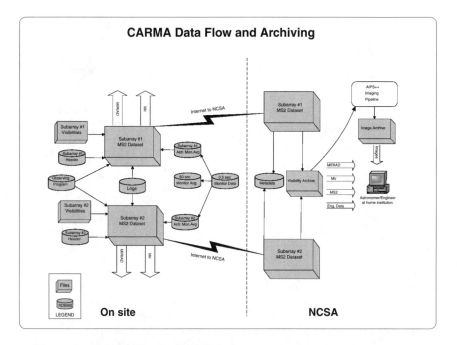

Figure 1.   *Left)* The 15 CARMA antennas may operate as one array or, as pictured above, two independent subarrays. For each subarray, visibilities are written out as a binary "brick" with header values stored in databases. Monitor points are stored in 3 databases: at the full half-second rate, in 1 minute averages, and averaged to the astronomical integration time. The relevant pieces are put together into an MS2 data file before shipment to the CARMA/NCSA archive, which happens in near real-time. *Right)* When the data arrive at NCSA, metadata are extracted for entry in the searchable archive. Visibility data are calibrated and imaged using the BIMA Imaging Pipeline (see Figure 2). The astronomer can download the unprocessed visibilities, the calibrated visibilities, and the processed images. The CARMA/NCSA archive will support MS2, MIRIAD, and Mir as export formats for visibilities as well as engineering tables of monitor data. Converters will also be available on-site to allow observers to inspect or analyze the data locally using the respective packages.

cludes special processing parameters and science-related information provided by the astronomer during the planning stage. After processing, the new products—the calibrated visibilities and deconvolved images—are sent back to the archive to be ingested and made available to astronomers. These new data can trigger additional processing; for example, after all requested observing tracks have been calibrated, new processing is triggered to image and deconvolve from all tracks into a single image cube.

The actual processing is done with AIPS++, enabled for parallel processing, using NCSA SGI and Linux clusters. Users not only have access to the processed

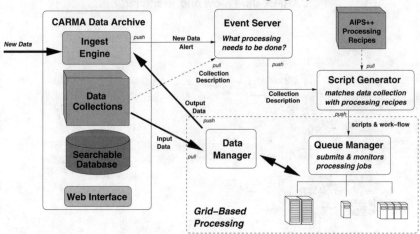

Figure 2.   When a new data collection arrives in the archive, a message is sent to the Event Server which figures out what processing needs to be done. This is done by retrieving and analyzing metadata about the collection. The metadata is forwarded to the script generator to prepare the scripts by drawing on "recipes" in a recipe library. The scripts and instructions on what order they should be run (i.e., "workflow") is sent to the Queue Manager. Through the Data Manager, it retrieves the input data from the archive and submits the scripts and data to the Grid for processing. In practice, serial processing (e.g., calibration) is done on different machines from the parallel parts (e.g., imaging). The resulting data products are then sent back to the archive to be ingested.

data, but also the AIPS++ (Glish) scripts used; this allows them to alter and redo the processing off-line.

The use of Grid-based computing technologies will open up interesting opportunities for distributed computing. For example, we plan to use the Teragrid—a national Grid of distributed tera-flop computing linked via high-speed backbone—to process the data. This will allow processing to be distributed between CalTech and NCSA. We can also use the Grid to set up partial mirrors of the archive at the other consortium sites as well as give users greater access to the Pipeline for reprocessing of data.

Part 8. Database Systems

Astronomical Data Analysis Software and Systems XII
ASP Conference Series, Vol. 295, 2003
H. E. Payne, R. I. Jedrzejewski, and R. N. Hook, eds.

Optimizing the Performance of ISO and XMM-Newton Data Archives

José Hernández, Christophe Arviset, John Dowson, Pedro Osuna and Aurèle Venet

ESA, Research and Scientific Support Department, Science Operations and Data Systems Division, Villafranca del Castillo, P.O. Box 50727, 28080 Madrid, Spain

Abstract. In this paper we try to give a quick overview of the techniques used in the development of the ISO and XMM-Newton Data Archives in order to optimize their performance.

1. IDA and XSA Quick Overview

1.1. ISO Data Archive

The ISO Data Archive[1] (IDA) has been developed at the European Space Agency ISO Data Centre at Villafranca, Spain. We believe that this archive has proven valid a new concept in the world of astronomical archives. Instead of the more commonly used HTML/cgi-bin based approach, the IDA was developed based on a "three-tiered architecture" (see Arviset 2003) and using the Java language on the Client and Middle tiers. This choice was not obvious in 1997 when the development of the archive started, however it has been very successful, according to the feedback received from archive users.

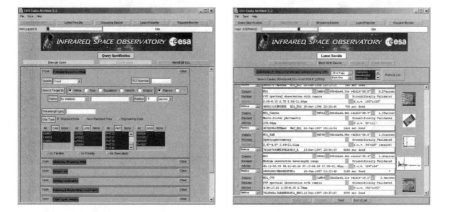

Figure 1. ISO Data Archive.

---

[1]http://www.iso.vilspa.esa.es/ida

The IDA main characteristics can be summarized as:

- Developed using Java, certified 100 % Pure Java.
- The first version of IDA was released on December 1998, current version is 5.2.
- The archive has been extensively used by the astronomical community:
  - Over 1300 registered users.
  - Archive data delivered 3 times to the external world.
  - Over 100.000 queries performed from outside.
  - Accessed from all sorts of platforms: Solaris, all Windows, Linux, Macintosh, Digital Unix, OSF, HP Unix, IRIX, AIX,...

1.2. XMM-Newton Science Archive

The XMM-Newton Science Archive[2] (XSA) has been developed at the European Space Agency XMM-Newton Science Operations Centre at Villafranca, Spain. Thanks to the choices made in the development of the ISO Data Archive, it was fairly easy to reuse its architecture and a great deal of its code. This led to a very short development time (less than a year), a more functionally rich system and a product that can now be more easily reused for other Data Archives.

The XSA archive has over 500 registered users. Some of the improvements made in its development were also applied to the IDA archive. Having a similar look and feel in the archives benefits both the end user and ESA. The archive user does not need to learn how to use a new interface and for ESA it helps in strengthening its corporate image among the scientific community.

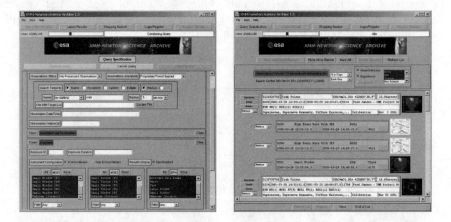

Figure 2.   XMM-Newton Science Archive.

---

[2]http://xmm.vilspa.esa.es/xsa

2. Performance Optimization Techniques Used

2.1. Optimizing the Applet Size

The ISO and XMM-Newton archives are accessed by the astronomers using a Java applet that gets downloaded to the user's computer and runs locally inside his browser. By using Java, one has access to powerful graphical capabilities and a very configurable and user friendly interface can be provided. However, Java applets can be very large in size leading to a bad user experience as he has to wait until the download is completed before starting the application. In order to minimize the size of the applet we have applied several techniques:

- **Build a thin client**. The client only takes care of gathering user input and presenting results. This, apart from other advantages, reduces the number of classes needed on the Client Tier.
- **Use obfuscation tools**. These tools reduce the size of the classes as they generate shorter symbol names. We used a commercial tool called Jshrink[3] and typically we get reductions in size of approximately 15%.
- **Use more than one jar file**. Only one is needed to start the application:
  - Expert functionality is downloaded on demand or in the background.
  - We use three jar/cab files of sizes 250, 75 and 175 Kbytes.
- **Use the standard Java 1.1 API** as much as possible. Don't write new classes when it can be done using the API.
- Even if the applet is Java 1.1 compliant, **compile it using Java.1.2** compilers as they generate more efficient byte code (smaller & faster).

2.2. Optimizing the Applet Execution

The portability of Java comes from the fact that the Java compilers do not generate machine dependent code but byte code that gets interpreted at runtime by the different Java Virtual Machines. This means that some performance is sacrificed for the sake of portability. However, the Java interpreters have become more and more efficient and the difference between the execution of Java byte code and machine code has narrowed.

In any case when one deals with applications distributed across the Internet, like our archives, the bottleneck is usually the network. Thus, great improvements can be expected when efforts are concentrated in improving the efficiency with which information is moved between the application layers.

These are the main techniques we have used in order to boost the application execution:

- Concerning the data transfer:
  - **Minimize the number of client-server interactions** by grouping them. Due to the overhead involved in creating a new connection it is more efficient to have a few big data interchanges than a lot of small ones.
  - **Persist client session information on the Middle Tier** to avoid unnecessary data interchanges.

---

[3]http://www.jshrink.com/

- **Embed initialization information in the client** jar files.
- **Compress all the data transferred** between the client and the server tiers, the standard Java API comes with classes that make the compression easy both on the client and the server. We are compressing all the serialized objects and obtaining reductions in size by a factor of four.
- Use the **transient modifier inside the Java classes** to avoid writing unnecessary data into the streams. Sometimes, overwriting the default serialization methods also helps.
- Concerning the application execution:
  - **Reduce the number of classes used to start up the application**. Then load the rest of the classes in the background or on demand if the user asks for extra functionality.
  - Use **Lightweight graphical components** instead of native ones. Note that this point conflicts one of the points mentioned before about using the standard Java API classes.
  - Use the **time the application is idle** to build the structures that will be needed later. For example when the application is started and before the user performs a search to the archive, we build the GUI elements that will be used to display the search results.
  - **Reduce the number of queries performed to the database** by grouping them and use cached statements when possible.
  - On the server tiers **use the latest Java Virtual Machines with Hotspot** turned on to improve the server performance.

2.3.   Conclusion

We believe that Java applets and applications can show a very good performance when a few rules are followed, it is advisable to consider performance issues early in the application design. Most of the performance benefits come from considering the network as the bottleneck.

Trying to optimize *a posteriori* by rewriting bits of the code is not a good idea, usually one ends up complicating the application code and introducing bugs that are difficult to spot and fix. Before tackling this sort of optimization it is better to make sure that it will produce a significant improvement.

References

Arviset, C. 2003, this volume, 47

Astronomical Data Analysis Software and Systems XII
ASP Conference Series, Vol. 295, 2003
H. E. Payne, R. I. Jedrzejewski, and R. N. Hook, eds.

ANDES: NOAO's Observatory Database System

D. Gasson, D. Bell, M. Hartman

National Optical Astronomy Observatory, 950 N. Cherry Ave. Tucson, AZ 85719

Abstract. ANDES (the Advanced NOAO Database Expert System) is NOAO's new observing proposal system. Recent improvements include the phase out of legacy components, such as our previous Access-based effort called ALPS++. New work focuses on pre and post-TAC procedures such as importation, scheduling, collection of observing reports on the mountain, and automatic compilation of various statistics. The ultimate goal is to provide an environment which allows a comprehensive understanding of the collection, evaluation, scheduling, execution and post-execution of proposals and programs.

1. Introduction

With the introduction of NOAO's new observing proposal system, ANDES (the Advanced NOAO Database Expert System), it has become easier to track a proposal from conception to execution–an approach that is often called end-to-end (e2e) in the jargon of the business sector. We give a brief description of some of the steps involved in this process at the NOAO, and explain our approach.

2. Proposal Import

Investigators can create a NOAO proposal in a number of ways, but they all boil down to the construction of a LaTeX file either through the use of a web form, e-mail template, or submission of an XML file. This LaTeX file is then parsed via a Perl script into a more structured format that is suitable for ingest into the database system (Bell, Barnes & Pilachowski 1998).

We require that every proposal be scrutinized by a person upon import to ensure the integrity of the data. In particular, it is crucial that investigator attributes such as name, e-mail, institution and address are carefully looked at since we maintain a master list of such information. Figure 1 demonstrates part of the web interface that allows our importers to do this. Highlighted cells represent a mismatch between the information we already have on file about a certain investigator, and the information which they have given us in the current proposal. It is up to the importer to decide what, if any, changes need to be made in such a situation. Run information is handled in an analogous manner.

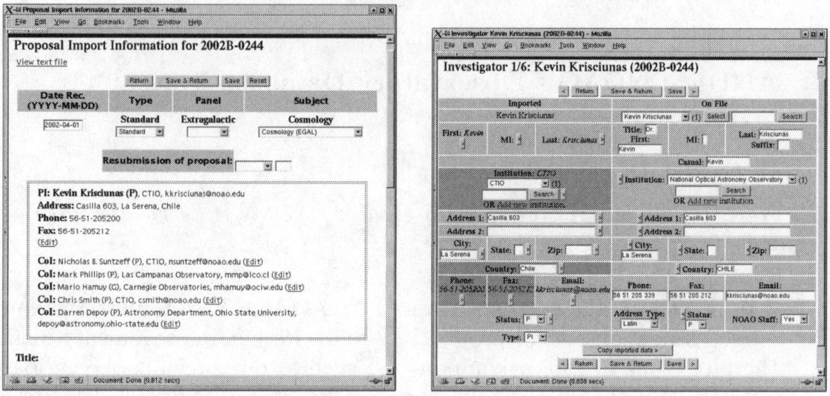

Figure 1.   *Left*. From this page, most proposal attributes are available for perusal by importers. In particular, it is required that each investigator and run is looked at in order to ensure mistakes and duplication are kept to a minimum. *Right*. If an investigator is already in our database (because they have proposed in previous semesters), that information is displayed in the "On File" column, and can be compared and updated to reflect any changes. At least the name and e-mail address must be defined before the page will allow editing of the next investigator.

3.   Time Allocation

Twice a year the NOAO's time allocation committees meet and decide how to apportion telescope resources for the coming semester. This process is discussed in more detail in Bell, Gasson & Hartman (2002) and Gasson & Bell (2003).

4.   Scheduling

Once proposals have been submitted, imported, and eventually graded and ranked by time allocation committees, NOAO schedulers can begin their job. In order to facilitate this process, we provide a simple, but effective, web interface (see Figure 2) for entry of scheduling information. We also dynamically generate a list of ranked proposals that uses color coding to draw attention to possible discrepancies. For instance, if a proposal has been scheduled in time that is brighter than requested, or in a month outside the optimal or acceptable date ranges specified on the proposal, the corresponding cell is colored. It is, again, entirely up to the scheduler to decide what, if anything, they will do to address these issues.

5.   Telescope Log Forms

Tracking exactly what happens at the telescope at observing time is an essential part of the night-to-night operation of the observatory. In conjunction with

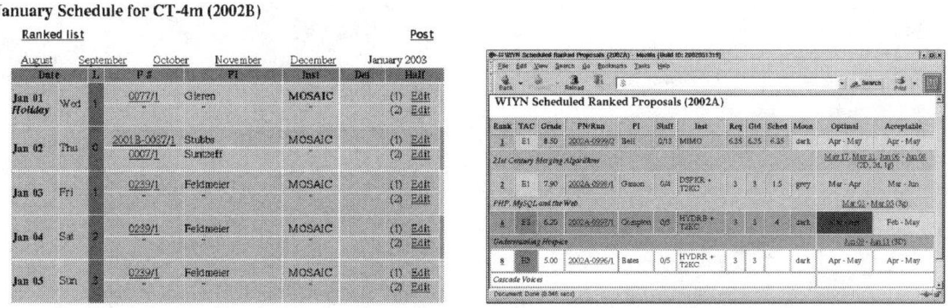

January Schedule for CT-4m (2002B)

Figure 2. *Left.* The schedule is edited on a month-by-month basis. Contiguous blocks of runs are color coded, and instrument changes are bolded. Clicking on a proposal number brings up more in-depth proposal information, including any relevant scheduling constraints or TAC comments. *Right.* The schedule checker compares what observers asked for to what they were actually scheduled. For instance, if a run has been scheduled for a time when the moon is brighter than was requested, or in a month outside the specified optimal or acceptable ranges, the cell is colored.

many other pieces of software on the mountain, authorized staff members can get an idea of the behaviour of the telescope from the point of view of the observer via the electronic observing/telescope log form (Figure 3).

At the end of each night, the observer fills out this form (identified by their proposal number), and specifies how much time has been lost to such things as weather and other technical problems. Support staff may then visit the log form viewer, fix mistakes (many of which are automatically flagged by the software), and view summary statistics over an arbitrary length of time.

6. Reports and Statistics

One difficulty associated with our move away from ALPS++ and Microsoft Access to ANDES has been creating paper reports. Many reports can be effectively moved to the web, and made more useful in the process (this is particularly true for some kinds of statistics which change often) but there are some for which it is either preferable or required to present them on paper. We employ a couple of strategies in this situation.

The first, and simplest, is to write a script which produces a comma-delimited file. This works well for data that is essentially tabular in nature, and likely to be further processed by support staff. An example would be many of the quarterly or annual reports the NSF requests.

The second solution, used in situations where more formatting is needed, is to programmatically fill in LaTeX templates. This requires a good deal more effort up front, but has proven to be quite effective. We often use this approach to create professional looking reports in near real time during the TAC process.

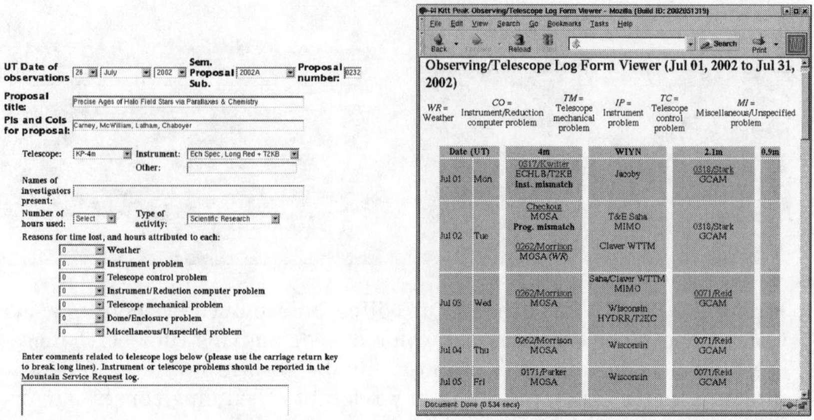

Figure 3.   *Left.* This page uses the current date and time to guess which program is likely to have taken place, and displays any relevant information (i.e., proposal number, investigators, title). This information can be overruled if it is found to be wrong due to changing conditions. *Right.* Observing statistics can be viewed by staff and used to form a picture of the behaviour of the telescope over a period of time. In addition, if there are any discrepancies between the content of the log, and what is expected (a different instrument was used than was recorded on the schedule, for instance), a note is displayed.

References

Bell, D. J., Barnes, J. & Pilachowski, C. 1998, in ASP Conf. Ser., Vol. 145, Astronomical Data Analysis Software and Systems VII, ed. R. Albrecht, R. N. Hook, & H. A. Bushouse (San Francisco: ASP), 288

Gasson, D. & Bell, D. 2003, in ASP Conf. Ser., Vol. 281, Astronomical Data Analysis Software and Systems XI, ed. D. A. Bohlender, D. Durand, & T. H. Handley (San Francisco: ASP), 457

Bell, D., Gasson, D., & Hartman, M. 2002, SPIE 2002, in press

Astronomical Data Analysis Software and Systems XII
ASP Conference Series, Vol. 295, 2003
H. E. Payne, R. I. Jedrzejewski, and R. N. Hook, eds.

Chandra Data Archive Download and Usage Database

Emily Blecksmith, Stéphane Paltani, Arnold Rots, Sherry Winkelman

Chandra X-Ray Center, Harvard-Smithsonian Center for Astrophysics,
60 Garden St., Cambridge, MA (USA)

Abstract. In order to support regular operations, the Chandra Data Archive Operations Group has developed a database that records and monitors the user activities that affect the archive servers. This database provides information on the number of users that are connected at a given time, what archive interfaces they use (we have several), and how much and what type of data is being downloaded.

The database consists of three tables populated by a set of four scripts that parse the archive server logs, the ftp logs and the login logs. User activity can be tracked through each of those logs, making information from a given connection easily accessible.

With this tool, the Archive Operations Group will be able to gather statistics and monitor trends, which will improve the accessibility of Chandra data.

1. Introduction

1.1. The Chandra X-Ray Observatory and Data Archive

The Chandra X-ray Observatory (CXO), a spacecraft launched in July 1999, carries an X-ray telescope with two main instruments: the Advanced CCD Imaging Spectrometer (ACIS) and the High Resolution Camera (HRC), supplemented with optional transmission gratings. The mission is operated by the Smithsonian Astrophysical Observatory at the Harvard-Smithsonian Center for Astrophysics in Cambridge, MA, under contract with NASA. The operation covers the entire institutional life cycle of the observations.

The Chandra Data Archive[1] (CDA) Group's fundamental tasks are the maintenance of the Chandra archive and archive servers and the distribution of the data products. These responsibilities can be broken into three major components: the database and database servers; the archive and archive servers and the interfaces for the ingest; search and retrieval of data (Rots et al. 2002).

1.2. The Chandra Data Archive Download and Usage Database

The Chandra Data Archive (CDA) Download and Usage Database is a comprehensive collection of all user activity on the Chandra Data Archive's search

---

[1]`http://cxc.harvard.edu/cda`

and retrieve (SR) servers. Users can connect to the archive and browse or retrieve data using a number of different interfaces: Chaser, a stand-alone Java application which provides the most retrieve/browse flexibility; WebChaser, a web-based version of Chaser; the Provisional Retrieval Interface (PRI), a single CGI script; the CDA FTP Staging site and the brand new CDA Anonymous FTP site.

The first three interfaces use the CDA servers to retrieve data products and either put them on the CDA FTP staging site or transmit them directly (Chaser only). In addition to staged products, the FTP staging site contains a number of pre-packaged distributions including special observations such as deep fields, the calibration database, ephemerides etc.

This database contains detailed information taken from various logs regarding user connections and activities. Three different logs are used to populate the database: the archive server activity log; the archive server login log and the FTP log. Four scripts parse the logs and populate the three tables in the database: 'SR_connections'; 'SR_usage' and 'downloads'.

The database can be used for a number of purposes, such as scheduled public statistics reports or specialized information for operational services. When unexpected failures and problems occur it is convenient to have all usage information in one place that can be displayed graphically.

2.   Why is this Database Useful?

Maintenance of server health is one of the primary concerns of the CDA Group at the CXC. Over time, it has become clear that in addition to monitoring internal server activities, outside users (individuals downloading Chandra data) must be tracked as well. The Chandra Data Archive Download and Usage Database consists of very detailed user information from several server logs. This database is useful in a number of different ways.

Because all information is in one place and can be easily queried, we have easy access to fundamental information. Answers to questions such as how many connections are made per day, how much data is transferred daily, monthly, yearly, which interface is used most often, which data set is most popular, etc, are readily available.

This database also enables us to monitor trends which will ultimately lead to better performance and easier, faster access to Chandra data. By tracking server errors users encounter and by observing typical user behavior, corrections and modifications to the system can be more easily and accurately made.

Finally, the download and usage database is helpful in diagnosing unexpected problems. Knowing who was connected and what was being done at the time of a server crash or other strange event can give us important clues as to what might have gone wrong.

3.   Population of the Database

All information in the database comes from three types of logs: the Archive Server Activity log, the Archive Server Login log, and the FTP log.

The activity log contains connect/disconnect times, user name, host name, user activity (retrieve or browse) and data requested. Entries concerning a retrieve or a browse have to be matched with the correct connection entry using the time, process id, user name and host that appears in both log entries. The data and activity information is then extracted from the 'procname' line. The information gleaned from this log populates the SR_connections and SR_usage tables. Here is an example of the activity log format:

```
10/01/02 17:12:52:644806 ConnectHandler, user guest, from
   host foo/000.000.00.000/foo-SunO, server pid:  89
10/01/02 17:12:52:653101 LangHandler, user guest, from host
   foo/000.000.00.000/foo-SunO, server pid:  89
dataset=flight
operation=retrieve
obsid=605
Server message:
10/01/02 17:12:52:760822 Message number:  5701 Severity:
   10 State:  2 Line:  1 Server sqlsao
Message String:  Changed database context to 'arcsrv'.
procname:  ret_primary, @prop_flag:  0, @arcusid:  2,
   @browse_flag:  0, @prop_num:  , @obsids:  605,
   @filetypes:  all, @acisfiletypes:  all
10/01/02 17:12:53:45234 DisconnectHandler, user guest, from
   host foo/000.000.00.000/foo-SunO, server pid:  89
```

The login log supplies the information to populate the 'downloads' table. Like the activity log, the login log contains connect/disconnect times along with user names. Unlike the activity log, the login log provides the download type (FTP or direct) and total byte size of the data transfer for connections made with Chaser and WebChaser. The download type gives important clues as to which interface was used. Because the login log provides times and names, entries can be fairly easily matched to entries in the activity log. An entry in the login log that corresponds with the above example might look like this:

```
Oct 1 17:12:52 2002:  User guest, from host
   foo/000.000.00.000/foo-SunO, server pid 89 just connected
Oct 1 17:12:57 2002:  User guest from
   foo/000.000.00.000-SunOS retrieved obsids 605 (ftp:  total
   410083938)
Oct 1 17:13:09 2002:  User guest, from host
   foo/000.000.00.000/foo-SunO, server pid 89 just disconnected
```

The FTP log is the final piece of the puzzle. It contains the information regarding data pickups for requests made through WebChaser, Chaser and the Provisional Retrieval Interface; it also contains information about data retrievals that is not in the other logs. Certain pre-packaged data, such as the calibration database and the Chandra deep field dataset are available on the CDA FTP Staging site and cannot be obtained through any of the above mentioned interfaces. Data transfers from the CDA Anonymous FTP site are also recorded in this log, but again cannot be connected to anything in the activity log or login log.

The records of data pickup that were requested through WebChaser, Chaser or the PRI can be matched back to information from the activity log and login log using the timestamp, host name, process id (pid) (for some records), and observation id (obsid) (again, just for some types of records). However, not all data requests are in fact picked up from the FTP site, so entries in the 'SR_usage' table will not always have a match in the FTP log.

In the current example, no obsid is mentioned in this particular type of tar file, but the pid is, and that in combination with the time and the host will be enough to match this line with entries in 'SR_connections' and 'SR_usage'.

```
Tue Oct 1 17:15:45 2002 171 foo 157304832
/export/ftp/ftphome/pub/srftp/000000/package_89_
   021001171545.tar a_ o a mozilla@ ftp 0 * c
```

4. Lessons Learned

During the rather lengthy development and implementation of this database, many difficulties and obstacles were encountered. Having to parse three different logs and match entries between all three is not easy. The example used above is very simple; most user activity is far more complex. Concocting algorithms to follow complex and sometimes inconsistent activities through three logs, all with different formats, is difficult and time-consuming.

For future missions we would recommend a more systematic approach, starting with the design of the various server log files. Log file requirements would need to address two particular issues: the type of information that should be recorded and the definition of a standard format. The tricky part is having enough foresight to conceive of a downloads and usage database before log file contents and formats are created. But our task would have been much easier if a proper requirements process had been followed from the beginning.

This work is supported by NASA contract NAS 8-39073 (CXC).

References

Rots, A. H., Winkelman, S. L., Paltani, S., & Deluca E. E. 2002, "Chandra Data Archive Operations", SPIE Conf. Ser. 4844: Observatory Operations to Optimize Scientific Returns III, in press

Astronomical Data Analysis Software and Systems XII
ASP Conference Series, Vol. 295, 2003
H. E. Payne, R. I. Jedrzejewski, and R. N. Hook, eds.

Autojoin: A Simple Rule Based Query Service for Complex Databases

Niall I. Gaffney, Lisa Gardner, Molly Brandt

Space Telescope Science Institute, 3700 San Martin Drive, Baltimore, MD 21218

Abstract. Most databases used today are no longer flat. While the power of using these more complex data stores is well known, construction of queries can be quite a complex task. Currently this often requires detailed knowledge of the database structure and schema. As we move towards a VO paradigm, users cannot be expected to know the structure of databases, but will need to query them. Databases will need to provide query engines to complete queries automatically given only what the user wants to have returned and any qualifications they place on the query.

For years StarView, a database query and data retrieval tool for the Space Telescope Science Institute, relied on a complex third party LISP-based program (QUICK) to construct valid SQL queries for the one database it could query. This limited our ability to support StarView as we could not easily add new rules to the system without completely rebuilding the query engine. Furthermore, QUICK did not have the ability to create SQL that would join tables in different databases (but hosted on the same server). Finally, the cost of upgrading to a new version of QUICK was prohibitively high.

Our solution was to develop a rather simple database table driven Perl CGI program which is able to take as its input a skeleton SQL program. This may come from a program or other web page. In the query only the SELECT and user qualified WHERE clause are specified; no FROM or WHERE clause join information is included. The service then returns a fully qualified and syntactically correct query for the host database SQL program that can be used to get the information the user needs. Thus, an additional layer of abstraction for dealing with databases is created, freeing the user from having to know how tables are related in the database.

In this paper we discuss the design and algorithm used to make Autojoin work as well as discuss how, when combined with a robust and searchable description of all the fields that can be publicly queried in the database, it allows users to tailor their questions to the database with ease and a high rate of success.

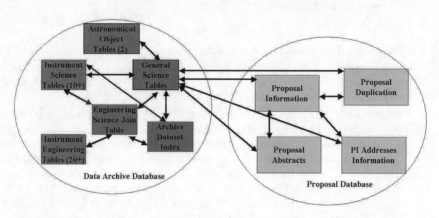

Figure 1.   A representation of the database schema at STScI.

1.   The STScI Database: The Task at Hand

At STScI, information about observed and planned observations is stored in several databases. These databases are rather large, and have many different rules for joining tables in one database, much less between separate databases. Different subsystems often map into the database schema differently, leading to complex intersystem data structures. Figure 1 gives a small example of the complexity of this system for a selection of tables from two of the STScI databases.

As illustrated in Figure 1, there are many different routes to join related information. To create a join from the Proposal Abstract to information in an Instrument Engineering table requires several interim join tables. Users cannot be expected to know this.

Laying out the database structure in this way reveals clear patterns in how the database works. When one looks at the keys that are used to join these tables, further patterns develop. It was clear from this exercise that a simple rule based system for creating arbitrary queries to the database could be constructed. We started by cataloging all the tables to be exposed to users. We then categorized these tables to group tables that join to other tables using the same keys. Finally we constructed rules for joining between different categories of tables. For some tables, interim join tables were required, and noted in the join rules.

2.   Autojoin: The Tables Used to Find Joins

With the categorization done, we created three tables to capture this information. The Table Categories table contains the list of all publically available tables and the databases that house them. For some databases at STScI a prefix for each table is designated to allow for a namespace differentiation of shared fields among different tables. For example two tables might have an RA field with prefixes one_ and two_. The field in table one would be called one_ra, while the other is two_ra. This prevents database field namespace conflicts in these complex databases while preserving shared field names for common fields. The last field sorts these tables into categories. Tables in the same category join with other tables the same way.

The Category Joins table lists all the possible joins between two table categories listed in the Table Categories table. Each join is assigned a join number. The rules for how to join these two tables are listed in the Join Methods table, where the join number from the Category Joins table indicated which rule to use for joining those tables. Examples of these tables follow.

Table 1.   Table Categories—public tables and their join categorization.

database_name	table_name	table_prefix	category
catalog	acs_a_data	aca_	hst-cal-exp
catalog	archive_data_set_all	ads_	hst-ads
catalog	science	sci_	hst-sci
proposal_db	abstract	NULL	hst-prop

Table 2.   Table Joins—possible joins between the different table categories.

category_1	category_2	join_number
hst-cal-exp	hst_sci	18
hst-ads	hst_sci	1
hst-prop	hst_sci	3

Table 3.   Join Methods–the stubbed out SQL for the where clause for each possible join number or the name of the join table to be used in the interim (as indicated by the leading #).

Join Number	Join Clause
1	$table1.${prefix}dataid = $table2.{$prefix}dataid AND $table1.ads_program_id not NULL
3	$table1.${prefix}proposalid = $table2.{$prefix}propid
18	#catelog.sci_inst_db_join

3.   Autojoin: The Algorithm

The autojoin algorithm takes these three tables and finds a path that uniquely joins each table. It is:

- Gather the list of tables to process from the initially supplied SELECT and WHERE statement
- Reorder input list sorted by their categories in Table Categories. This is done so that creating the join takes a minimum number of steps (similar table types will not join to a different type of table using an intermediate table except where needed).
- Create a new WHERE clause list and FROM list to store all the tables in the query and the new WHERE clause items as we discover them
- Loop through each pair of tables (i.e., 1st and 2nd, 2nd and 3rd)
- Swap in order if order in Category Joins is reversed
- Exit loop with an error if there is no entry in Category Joins for the two tables.
- Interpolate the join using Join Methods for that join number.
- Exit loop if both tables are the same or if new WHERE clause item appears in the new WHERE clause array.
- Add the new WHERE clause elements to the WHERE array and add the two tables to the from array.
- If dealing with an intermediate table (as identified by leading # in the Join Method entry):
  - If this intermediate table had already been used to join other tables in this query, join these tables to the other tables that used the intermediate table.
  - If this intermediate table had not already been used, join the intermediate table to the two current tables and add the intermediate table to table list if not already there and iterate until no join tables are needed and all join statements are determined.
- Create the FROM clause based on the table list.
- Create the WHERE clause based on the join lists and initial WHERE clause.
- Return a fully qualified query to the user to then be sent to the database (alternately do the query for the user and return the results).

This algorithm allows us to find joins simply and quickly and allows intermediate joins to tables as well. StarView uses this algorithm in a simple Perl CGI script. Its use has both improved the performance of the program and diminished the amount of support needed to update the system.

References

Kennedy, B. & Mayhew, B. 1999, in ASP Conf. Ser., Vol. 172, Astronomical Data Analysis Software and Systems VIII, ed. D. M. Mehringer, R. L. Plante, & D. A. Roberts (San Francisco: ASP), 383

Williams, J. 1994, in ASP Conf. Ser., Vol. 61, Astronomical Data Analysis Software and Systems III, ed. D. R. Crabtree, R. J. Hanisch, & J. Barnes (San Francisco: ASP), 96

Astronomical Data Analysis Software and Systems XII
ASP Conference Series, Vol. 295, 2003
H. E. Payne, R. I. Jedrzejewski, and R. N. Hook, eds.

The XMM-Newton SSC Database: Taking Advantage of a Full Object Data Model

L. Michel, C. Motch

CNRS, UMR 7550, Observatoire Astronomique de Strasbourg, Strasbourg, France

C. G. Page, M. G. Watson

X-ray Astronomy Group, Department of Physics and Astronomy, University of Leicester, Leicester LE1 7RH, UK

Abstract. One of the main responsibilities of the Science Survey Centre (SSC) of the XMM-Newton satellite, an X-ray observatory launched by the European Space Agency in 1999, is to carry out a systematic analysis of the entire scientific data stream. Products resulting from the pipeline processing are shipped to the guest observer and eventually enter the XMM-Newton archive. In addition, the SSC compiles a catalogue of X-Ray sources and provides an identification for $\sim 50,000$ new sources detected each year. In order to check product quality and to support the catalogue and source identification programmes, all SSC-generated products are stored in a database developed for that purpose. Because of the large number of transversal links, our data model was difficult to map into relational tables. It has therefore been designed with object oriented technology for both user interface and data repository, and based on an object-oriented DBMS called O2. The database is a powerful tool to browse and evaluate XMM-Newton data and to perform various kinds of scientific analysis. It provides on-line data views including relevant links between products and correlated entries extracted from many archival catalogues and also links to external databases. Besides browsing, the web-based user interface provides facilities to select data collections with any constraints on any keywords but also with constraints on correlated data patterns.

1. Database Overview

The SSC database contains all data products resulting from the pipeline processing of the photon-event lists and other raw data from the XMM-Newton spacecraft. The products from a typical observation include $\sim$100 FITS files and $\sim$400 other files (HTML, PDF, etc.), and occupy $\sim$400 MB. These data files are grouped by observations and contain both observational data (graphical products, tables, spectra, images and event lists) as well as extractions from astronomical archival catalogues generated by the cross-correlation (ACDS) with the archives at NED and at CDS in Strasbourg. They also include the catalogue of X-Ray sources compiled by the SSC. An overview of the pipeline structure can be found in Fyfe et al. (2001) and detailed product descriptions in Osborne (2000).

2.   The Common Data Model (CDM)

All data products and data containers (e.g., instrument exposures) are modeled with a hierarchy of classes, the Common Data Model (CDM). Classes contain atomic attributes (position, flux, ...) and references to related objects such as correlated sources. Class methods are in charge of both content update and content representation (see Figure 1).

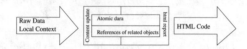

Figure 1.   CDM class.

Consistency between data and GUI is easily maintained since instances manage their own contents. Persistence is managed by O2C, the 4G language provided with O2. All DBMS features (transactions, caching, indexing, ...) rely on the O2 engine in a transparent way for the developer. Any transient object is automatically made persistent whenever it is referenced by another persistent object. The same code may work with either persistent or transient objects.

The Common Data Model uses the inheritance mechanism widely. Objects of different classes can be seen as instances of one super-class (e.g., sky object) when they are handled in collections (such as for queries). Thanks to the late binding mechanism, they are however considered as instances of their real class when they are accessed individually (e.g., to read their content).

All FITS headers are instantiated into the database (one attribute per keyword). Only FITS table extensions are exploded. Each table row is represented by one instance which belongs to a collection modeling that particular table. FITS file blobs as well as graphical and HTML products are stored on the external file system and referenced into the database using URLs.

Pipeline products include lists of entries extracted from various astronomical catalogues (part of cross-correlation products) and having positions matching those of EPIC X-ray sources, or for a subset of catalogues, being located in the observation's field of view. A single archival source may in some cases be correlated with several X-ray sources detected in one or more observations. This information is very relevant for astronomers and must enter the database. Archival sources are stored in specific collections where their uniqueness is ensured. Objects representing archival sources will own as many references to X-ray instances as they have correlated X-ray sources. This is a good example of an N to M relationship which is much simpler to manage with an OO database than with a relational system. There is no table join to deal with, just vectors for object references. Furthermore queries can easily include constraints on vectors patterns.

Ingested products are modeled by more than 300 specific classes. Managing the code of so many classes by hand is not realistic especially since the data formats may evolve during the mission. The data-loader deals with this task. Product compliance with data schema is checked at ingestion time and classes are updated or even created following predefined templates when required.

3. Graphical User Interface

Each HTML page is actually the HTML representation of one instance (see Figure 2). Atomic values are shown as such whereas related objects are represented by self-generated anchors. The database can be totally browsed by just following these links. All FITS keywords are listed and image and table FITS extensions can be displayed by the FITS previewer FIBRE (a Fortran90 CGI script which uses FITSIO and PGPLOT libraries).

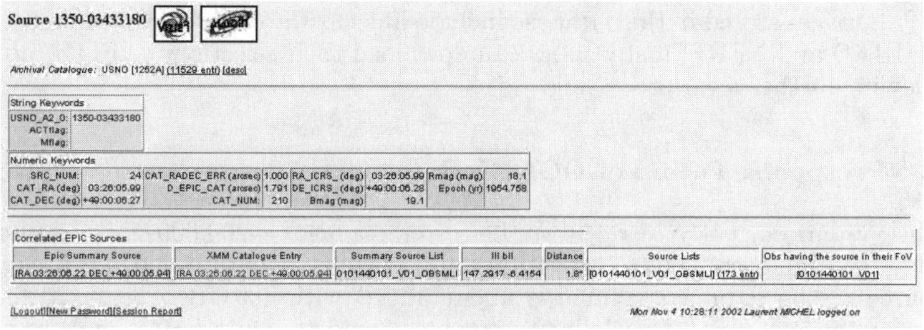

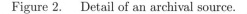

Figure 2. Detail of an archival source.

Users may set-up queries on the properties of X-ray sources, archival sources, observations and exposures of all instruments. Constraints may be put on any atomic attribute and on some related objects. In addition, one may also apply constraints on the correlation patterns between X-ray and archival entries. The number of constraints contained in queries is not limited. An example, in pseudo-code, of the type of query which can be handled is given below:

```
select X-ray sources
    having a hardness ratio 2 in the range of 0.5 to 1.0
    and detected in observations having a duration > 10000 sec
        done by "I. Newton" or by "G. Galileo"
    and correlated with USNO entries at less than 3".
        but not correlated with any SIMBAD or NED entry.
```

Query results are stored into the database and can be displayed (see Figure 3) again at any time. This feature makes the possibly long response time for very complex queries more acceptable. User selections are kept from one session to the next.

4. Interoperability

The system allows the field of view of the EPIC instruments and source positions to be overlaid on any external image using Aladin facilities (Bonnarel et al.

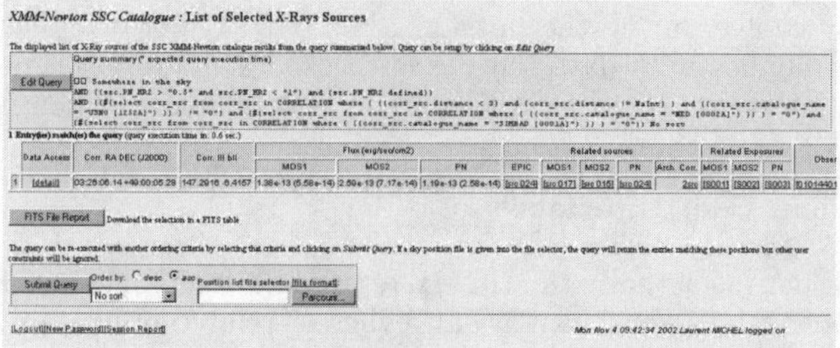

Figure 3.　Selection of X-Ray sources.

2001). Vizier may also be queried for any X-ray or archival source. In addition, HTML pages stored in the database include links forwarding real time queries to SIMBAD and NED. Finally, users can download their selections as FITS tables allowing further local processing.

5.　Prospects: Future of OODBMS

The system currently installed at Leicester manages ∼200,000 X-ray sources coming from over 2,000 observations and correlated with ∼400,000 archival sources. The database volume is about 30 GB with 400 GB of external files. Performance is good especially for complex queries. Only SSC members can currently use this database, but a version dedicated to the SSC XMM-Newton catalogue will soon be opened to the community. Although O2 matches our needs well, after a series of company take-overs, the product was withdrawn from the market in 2000 and is no longer under development. Software support continues from Oxymel, a company created by former O2 developers.

Since O2 has no future, we are actively seeking an alternative DBMS. Unfortunately object-oriented DBMS have failed to gain market share and we may have to move to a relational system. We have derived considerable benefit from transparent persistence, inheritance, abstract types and N-M relationships. These features can be implemented in relational systems with an object mapping layer provided we accept reduced flexibility and certainly more complex set-up.

References

Bonnarel, F., Fernique, P., Genova, F., Bienaymé, O., & Egret, D. 2001, in ASP Conf. Ser., Vol. 238, Astronomical Data Analysis Software and Systems X, ed. F. R. Harnden, Jr., F. A. Primini, & H. E. Payne (San Francisco: ASP), 74

Fyfe, D.J. et al. 2001, to appear in the Proceedings of the Symposium on 'New Visions of the X-ray Universe in the XMM-Newton and Chandra Era', 26-30 November 2001, ESTEC, The Netherlands

Osborne, J. 2000, SSC-LUX-SP-004, available at http://xmm.vilspa.esa.es/

Astronomical Data Analysis Software and Systems XII
ASP Conference Series, Vol. 295, 2003
H. E. Payne, R. I. Jedrzejewski, and R. N. Hook, eds.

Representations of DEIMOS Data Structures in FITS

Steven L. Allen, De A. Clarke, Robert I. Kibrick

UCO/Lick Observatory, University of California, Santa Cruz, CA 95064

Abstract. DEIMOS (the DEep Imaging Multi-Object Spectrograph) began producing scientific data from the Keck II telescope in 2002 June. The instrument is extremely configurable, and the form of the output data is highly variable. Filters and gratings may be swapped, gratings and mirrors tilt, readout modes and active amplifiers of the 8-CCD mosaic change, and numerous field-specific astrometric slitmasks may be inserted. For archival purposes and to enable fully-automated data reduction, FITS files from DEIMOS document the instrument state, all aspects of the slitmask design, and multiple world coordinate systems for the mosaic images. The FITS files are compatible with existing local conventions for mosaic image display systems and also with incipient FITS WCS standards.

1. Introduction

The DEIMOS mosaic detector contains 10 dual-amplifier CCDs in two arrays. The science array has 8 MIT/Lincoln Labs CCDs (2048 × 4096 15 μm pixels) each employing both amplifiers. Four of the science CCDs can receive direct images, and all 8 can receive spectra of celestial objects through slitlets cut into masks. The flexure compensation array has 2 UCO/Lick FCS CCDs (1200 × 600 15 μm pixels) each employing one amplifier. The FCS CCDs receive spots of arc-lamp light from fibers. They read continuously for a closed-loop compensation of flexure caused by rotation at the Nasmyth focal plane (Faber et al. 2002).

2. HDU Structure of DEIMOS FITS files

The analog signals from the pre-amplifiers of the 16 science CCDs travel to the digitizing video inputs via coaxial cables. Following the convention set by the NOAO mosaic (Tody & Valdes 1998), all of the digitized pixel values from one science readout go into a single FITS file. Subroutines from CFITSIO (Pence 1999) build the 140 Mbyte multi-HDU file in shared memory during a readout. The memory file is written to disk at the end of the readout. The PHDU contains a null image and keywords for about 400 variables describing the state of the instrument and telescope hardware. The pixels from each video input, along with keywords that document their provenance, are placed into a separate IMAGE extension HDU. Whenever an exposure is taken through a slitmask the data acquisition system appends FITS binary tables describing that mask.

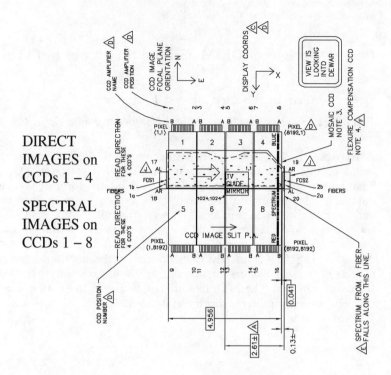

DIRECT IMAGES on CCDs 1 – 4

SPECTRAL IMAGES on CCDs 1 – 8

The resulting FITS file is archivally complete. It is viewable both by the IRAF ximtool using mscdisplay and by ds9 (Joye & Mandel 2000).

3. Using XML for the CCD Mosaic Problem of Numbers

In typical operation there are no changes to the identities of the CCDs, their locations in the mosaic focal plane, nor permutations of the coaxial cables. Nevertheless, it is trivial to reconfigure the hardware by permuting the cables, CCDs may be replaced and/or moved, and other mosaics may exist which have different configurations. Full documentation of the mosaic configuration by a general-purpose data acquisition system requires a schema that describes the configuration of the CCDs and their locations (world coordinates) in the focal plane. The schema describes the cabling in order to distinguish CCD amplifiers from video inputs. FITS writing software using this information should be as easy to reconfigure as the cables.

The syntax of XML and the many tools that manipulate it provided a convenient means of designing a general mosaic detector schema. The result is a set of entities describing CCD and amplifier types with their designed characteristics, and as-designed layout of different types of mosaics. Other entities describe names and peculiarities of individual CCDs, as-built names and locations of CCDs in mosaics, and wiring configurations. The XML data translate into C data structures used by the data acquisition system when writing FITS headers. Neglecting WCS information (see next section), there are 86 FITS keywords describing the mosaic in a 16-amplifier science readout.

4. World Coordinate Systems in IMAGE HDUs

Complete documentation of the provenance of each of the pixels in a multi-HDU FITS file, and correct viewing of the mosaic image, require a considerable amount of bookkeeping. DEIMOS images include three of the keywords defined for the NOAO mosaic, but the principal coordinate information is communicated via the standard FITS WCS keywords (Greisen & Calabretta 2002, Calabretta & Greisen 2002).

The real-time data acquisition system currently calculates the keyword values for 5 alternate, linear WCSs. The algorithm employs concatenation of numerous linear transformations which are components of each complete WCS. The components of the WCS start with the amplifier readout parameters, but many of the subsequent components are obtained from the XML schema describing the mosaic layout. A 16-amplifier DEIMOS FITS file contains approximately 1100 FITS keywords which document these WCSs in each of the image HDUs. Future addition of non-linear types of WCS will further increase this number.

Image The image WCS is a redundant reiteration of the default FITS array coordinates. It is the same for all images, and is equivalent to IRAF "logical".

Amplifier Each CCD pixel reads through an amplifier producing an array of digital values (`cpix`) in memory with a known WCS (`cpix2amp`). Transfer of pixel values to a FITS image array implicitly uses `cpix2fits` which inverts to `fits2cpix`. The amplifier WCS is the concatenation of `fits2cpix` and `cpix2amp`.

CCD The relation between amplifier pixels and CCD pixels (`amp2ccd`) is defined by the type of CCD in use. The CCD WCS is the concatenation of `fits2amp` and `amp2ccd`.

Pane & Detector Pane coordinates conform to longstanding pixel conventions at Lick; the observer uses them to define CCD readout windows. Detector coordinates conform to mosaic conventions at NOAO. The transformations `ccd2pane` and `ccd2ndet` are defined by the design of the mosaic in use and concatenated with the CCD WCS (`fits2ccd`).

slitmask, boresight, & other non-celestial The relation between CCD pixels and any other coordinate system is defined by applying astrometric techniques to direct images. These are concatenated with `fits2ccd`.

celestial The relation between FITS pixels in a direct image and celestial coordinates is defined by `fits2boresight` plus additional WCS keywords giving Euler angles of celestial orientation information from the telescope pointing.

spectral Defining a WCS for multi-slit spectra is beyond the current scope of FITS conventions. It will require the use of a locally-defined binary table.

5. Slitmask Schema for Design, Manufacturing, Observation and Archiving

The characteristics of DEIMOS slitmasks are described with seven normalized tables in a database. The observer creates mask designs using software that produces a FITS file containing binary tables. The tables in the FITS file are isomorphic with their counterparts in the relational database of all slitmasks. FITS serves as an expedient and self-documenting means of transporting subsets of the database.

The observer submits the FITS tables via WWW to request manufacture of the slitmask. Upon completion each slitmask receives a unique barcode which is added to the records in the database. When masks are loaded, DEIMOS scans barcodes, queries relevant data, writes records into FITS binary tables, and appends those to appropriate FITS image files. The tables are listed below.

ObjectCat Names of celestial objects and their astrometric properties

MaskDesign Name of a mask design plus its celestial pointing characteristics

DesiSlits Celestial coordinates of slitlets

SlitObjMap One slitlet may contain more than one object

MaskBlu "Blueprint" is "Design" corrected for distortion and refraction on its date of use

BluSlits Blueprint coordinates of slitlets on the metal of the mask

Mask Manufacturing data and barcode number for each particular mask

Further details of DEIMOS operation and data structures are available via http://deimos.ucolick.org/.

References

Calabretta, M. R., & Greisen, E. W. 2002, A&A, 395, 1077

Faber, S. M., et al. 2002, in SPIE Proc., Vol. 4841-186, in press

Greisen, E. W., & Calabretta, M. R. 2002, A&A, 395, 1061

Joye, W., & Mandel, E. 2000, in ASP Conf. Ser., Vol. 216, Astronomical Data Analysis Software and Systems IX, ed. N. Manset, C. Veillet, & D. Crabtree (San Francisco: ASP), 91

Pence, W. 1999, in ASP Conf. Ser., Vol. 172, Astronomical Data Analysis Software and Systems VIII, ed. D. M. Mehringer, R. L. Plante, & D. A. Roberts (San Francisco: ASP), 487

Tody, D., & Valdes, F. G. 1998, in SPIE Proc., Vol. 3355, 497

Astronomical Data Analysis Software and Systems XII
ASP Conference Series, Vol. 295, 2003
H. E. Payne, R. I. Jedrzejewski, and R. N. Hook, eds.

The SuperMacho+SuperNova Survey Database Design: Supporting Time Domain Analysis of GB to TB Astronomical Datasets

R. Hiriart and C. Smith

NOAO/CTIO, Casilla 603, La Serena, Chile

Andy Becker

Lucent Technologies, Bell Labs, 600 Mountain Ave., Murray Hill, NJ

C. Stubbs, A. Rest and G. Miknaitis

University of Washington, Dept. of Astronomy, Seattle, WA, USA

Gabe Prochter

Lawrence Livermore Nat. Lab., Livermore, CA 94550, USA

SuperMacho project and ESSENCE project collaborations

Abstract. Two large scale survey projects to discover transient events have recently been initiated at NOAO's Cerro Tololo Inter-American Observatory (CTIO) in Chile. The SuperMacho project seeks to detect and follow microlensing events toward the Large Magellanic Cloud (LMC) and the ESSENCE Supernova project seeks to detect and follow intermediate to high-redshift supernovae. Together, these projects (SM+SN) present challenging data management needs both due to the large size of the datasets and the kind of analysis to be performed on the data.

The database requirements of the SM+SN projects can be divided into three broad categories: support for the survey operation, storage and analysis of the data that comes from the image reduction and transient detection pipeline, and communication of the results to the project users and the astronomical community.

Current relational database technologies are being applied to address these requirements. The open source database PostgreSQL has been selected for the implementation of the system. This work presents the design of the database, along with some performance considerations that are necessary for the fast retrieval of information, thus allowing the development of data mining applications to take full advantage of the database.

1. Introduction

The combination of wide-field CCD detectors and increased computing power
has opened the opportunity for the study of astronomical events over large spatial scales **in the time domain**. Over the past few years, interest in such
studies has grown, as most recently demonstrated by the growing support for
the Large Synoptic Survey Telescope (LSST). At CTIO, we have recently begun
two large scale synoptic surveys which serve as precursors to LSST, exploring
the parameter space of managing large (GB to TB) datasets in **real-time** in
order to achieve the scientific goals of the projects. The SuperMacho project
is designed to study microlensing events due to MACHOs (MAssive Compact
Halo Objects) passing in front of the background of stars in the LMC. The goal
of this survey is to monitor millions of stars in the densest portions of the LMC
in order to detect $\approx$12 microlensing events per year over a five year period. The
ESSENCE project aims to constrain the equation of state of dark energy through
the study of intermediate redshift $(0.15 < z < 0.75)$ supernovae (SNe). In order
to accomplish this goal, this survey must discover $\approx$200 type Ia SNe distributed
evenly over the redshift range during the five year lifetime of the project.

   These two survey projects have many common data management requirements. Both are designed around an observing cadence of a half night every
other night during dark and grey time on the CTIO Blanco 4m telescope. The
observing period lasts for three months (October through December). Each
produces 10 to 15GB of data per half-night of observing (for a total of $\approx$25GB
per night). Both projects must process this data in near-real-time and automatically detect faint transient sources. These transients must be cataloged,
matched against previously known variable sources, and if new, classified and
announced to the astronomical community to allow for rapid follow-up on other
telescopes around the world. A modern database optimized for time-domain
science is necessary to support the combined SM+SN projects and manage the
millions of transient detections which are produced.

2. Database Schema

In general terms, the database requirements of the SM+SN projects are:
   - Support for the survey operations
   - Storage and analysis of the pipeline output data
   - Communication with users and the astronomical community

   As the observations take place, a considerable amount of information is
generated. This information includes: observation (coordinates, exposure time,
airmass, seeing sky conditions, etc.), area of sky covered, images produced, and
related calibration frames.

   The entity **observation** represents the action of pointing a given **opti-
cal_system** to a point in the sky, at a given time, and performing an astronomical observation of an **obs_object**. Since the SM+SN survey projects
have divided the sky into predetermined *fields*, it makes sense to attach to the
obs_object entity the attributes that define these fields. As a result of the
observation, an observation file (**obs_file**) or image is generated and stored in

a given physical location. Associated calibration frames may be taken before or after the **observation** to which they are linked.

The SM+SN pipeline reduces the images creating **reduced_images** entities, after applying cross-talk correction, WCS calibration, bias subtraction and flat fielding. The pipeline then proceeds through image subtraction and transient detection. A set of entities have been added to allow the definition of pipelines in the database. A **pipeline** is composed of individual **stages**. The execution of the pipeline at a given time is represented by the entity **pipeline_run**, which is configured by **pipeline_parameters** and a set of **stage_parameters**. The input of a **pipeline_run** is an image and the output is a set of **var_detections** and **abs_detections**, which represent the potential transient objects and absolute (non-transient) objects identified by the pipeline. This structure allows us to track the parameters that were used to generate any result stored in the database.

As a result of the transient analysis, a set of detections (**var_detections**) is generated for each processed image. These detections, including positions and all additional information produced by the analysis, are stored in the database, together with the relationships between the detections and the images, observations, and pipeline runs they come from. Because of the inherent precision of the observations and numerical analysis performed by the pipeline, two detections which were presumably generated by the same source at different epochs do not necessarily share the same exact spatial coordinates, although they are very close. As a result, the detections need to be aggregated into *clusters* (**diff_clusters** entity) around the same spatial coordinates before the extraction of lightcurves and object classification. A number of entities have been defined to take into account the different kinds of classifications for an object. As one object can be classified in different ways depending on the classifier, a **diff_classifier** entity along with a ternary relationships have been defined.

To effectively communicate the results of the transient analysis, a web site is being developed which integrates the PostgreSQL database through PHP, Perl, and Python. The delivery of data products to the community will eventually make use of XML-based technologies as these evolve to meet the needs of the surveys and the astronomical community.

3.   Performance Considerations

Because of the large sizes of some tables (for year 2001 SuperMacho observations, the size of the **var_detection** table is over 20 million tuples), it is necessary to define convenient access methods over these tables in order to get answers for queries in a practical time. Currently, PostgreSQL implements Hash, B-tree and R-tree indices into its database management system.

One critical query over the database was the search for detections in a box in the sky. An R-tree was created for this purpose, but because it is not possible to define R-trees over more than one column in the current PostgreSQL release, it was necessary to create an additional column in the **var_detection** table of type "box". This type is not part of the SQL standard, but is one of the object-oriented extensions of PostgreSQL. These boxes were initially generated as a function of the Full Width Half Maximum values of the detections, although we will probably redefine this definition to base the box on the astrometric uncertainty in the detection's position.

4. Data Mining Application: Cluster Analysis

The essential product of the pipeline analysis of the SM+SN is not a list of variable objects, but rather a list of individual (single-epoch) **detections**. Before validation and/or classification of the detections identified by the pipeline can begin, the detections must be grouped over multiple epochs into objects. For stationary objects this is done on the basis of the distances between detections.

To solve this *cluster analysis* problem, a state of the art clustering algorithm, OPTICS (Ankerst et al. 1999) has been implemented to be applied over the detections, creating additional entries and relationships in the database. This algorithm was selected because of its scalability with the number of detections as well as its ability to find subclusters in a given cluster of detections.

The OPTICS algorithm does not produce an explicit clustering for the data, but instead creates two additional attributes per detection: an order index and a *reachability distance*. Roughly speaking, the reachability distance is a measure of density at the location of a given detection, and it is the distance of a point to the set of its neighbors. Plotting the reachability distance for each one of the detections in the order generated by the algorithm, it is possible to reveal the clustering structure of the dataset.

5. Summary

Over the past ten years, the use of modern relational databases has become more common in astronomical contexts, due largely to the growing datasets and the complexity of the information astronomers are trying to track. The time-domain represents a new challenge in astronomical database design and use, especially in the face of the TB datasets of today and the PB datasets of tomorrow (e.g., LSST). Through support of the SuperMacho and ESSENCE projects, and based upon experience from previous surveys such as MACHO and the High-z SN searches, we have begun to explore the application of modern relational database technologies in support of time-domain astronomical research. While the details of the SM+SN database may be specific to the support of these projects, the general flow and large-scale structure of the database should be instructive for future time-domain database support, and many of the data mining tools and applications we are developing (clustering being but one example) will be applicable to future projects such as LSST.

References

Ankerst, M., Kriegel, H. P., & Sander, J. 1999. Proc. 1999 ACM-SIGMOD Int. Conf. Management of Data (SIGMOD'99), pp. 49–60

Part 9. Web Services and Publications

Astronomical Data Analysis Software and Systems XII
ASP Conference Series, Vol. 295, 2003
H. E. Payne, R. I. Jedrzejewski, and R. N. Hook, eds.

A Web-based Tool for SDSS and 2MASS Database Searches

Marci Hendrickson, Alan Uomoto, & David Golimowski

Johns Hopkins University, Baltimore, MD 21218

Abstract. We have developed a web site using HTML, Php, Python, and MySQL that extracts, processes, and displays data from the Sloan Digital Sky Survey (SDSS) and the Two-Micron All-Sky Survey (2MASS). The goal is to locate brown dwarf candidates in the SDSS database by looking at color cuts; however, this site could also be useful for targeted searches of other databases as well.

MySQL databases are created from broad searches of SDSS and 2MASS data. Broad queries on the SDSS and 2MASS database servers are run weekly so that observers have the most up-to-date information from which to select candidates for observation. Observers can look at detailed information about specific objects including finding charts, images, and available spectra. In addition, updates from previous observations can be added by any collaborators; this format makes observational collaboration simple. Observers can also restrict the database search, just before or during an observing run, to select objects of special interest.

1. Introduction

By far the most common objects in the galaxy are low mass stars and brown dwarfs. Only 32 of the coolest brown dwarfs (spectral class T) are known, but hundreds are needed to measure the space distribution, kinematics, and spectral type distribution of these objects.

2. Combining SDSS and 2MASS Photometry

The prototype uses EDR (Early Data Release) SDSS data as well as Second Incremental Data Release 2MASS data.

The coolest brown dwarfs require both SDSS and 2MASS photometry for selection. In the 2MASS catalog (JHK_s photometry), the rare T dwarfs have the same colors as much more common M dwarfs and are hard to find for that reason (Hawley et al. 2002). Also, T dwarfs are sometimes detected by SDSS only in the z-band, and so are hard to distinguish from cosmic rays and high redshift quasars. Fortunately, T dwarfs occupy a sparsely populated region in the $i-J$, $z-J$ color space and can be selected with these color cuts: $i-J > 3.5$ and $z-J > 2.2$.

Red stellar objects are selected from the SDSS database with sdssQT, an SQL-based query tool for the SDSS science database. Photometry and astrom-

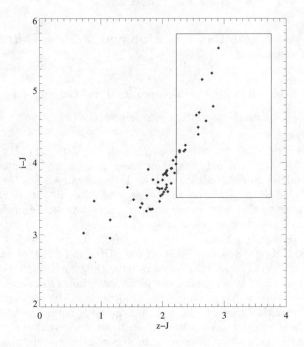

Figure 1.   Color-color plot of candidates, using both SDSS (ugirz) and 2MASS (JHK$_s$) photometry. The box indicates the location of probable T dwarfs.

etry for the selected objects are loaded into a MySQL SDSS subset database using Python. This list is then used as input to Gator, a 2MASS database interface, which finds 2MASS objects within five arc seconds of the SDSS subset objects. These are loaded into a MySQL 2MASS subset database.

Brown dwarfs are nearby so we need a relatively large search radius to catch high proper motion objects. Multiple hits (binaries or cosmic rays) are resolved with a visual inspection of the SDSS images.

Automated weekly updates are run: (i) a query is performed on the SDSS database, (ii) a script is run which appropriately formats the data, (iii) a query is performed on the 2MASS data using Gator, and (iv) a second script is run to format the data and insert it into the database.

Our color criteria for selecting objects from SDSS are: (i) objects detected in r, i, and z, r$-$i > 2 and i$-$z > 1.5, (ii) objects detected only in i and z, i$-$z > 1.75, and (iii) objects detected only in z, i$-$z > 2.

3.   The Web Site – http://annabel-lee.pha.jhu.edu/bd/

Php is used to call MySQL and find matches in 2MASS and SDSS databases. Using Php and HTML, the matches are loaded onto the front page of the web

Selected Candidate

Candidate number
568775004390264

u	g	r	i	z	J	H	K_s
23.20	23.37	22.32	20.18	17.74	14.940	13.851	13.195

r-i	i-z	i-J	z-J	z-K_s	J-H	J-K_s	H-K_s
2.14	2.44	5.24	2.8	4.545	1.089	1.745	0.656

Atlas

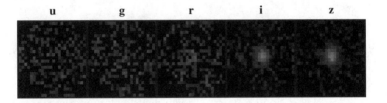

Spectrum

No SDSS spectra for this object

Notes

Possible T dwarf (MH 10/02)

Add Notes

568775004390264

Remove Candidate

568775004390264

Figure 2.   A screen shot showing a likely T dwarf candidate

site. Included is all the color information, as well as a link to the rest of the data available for each object.

When the link is clicked, the rest of the information on the object is displayed. This includes the atlas images, a finding chart, spectra when available, and any notes left regarding the object. There is also an option to add notes, as well as to delete the object if it is not of interest. While this does not delete the object from the database, is does prevent it from being viewed from the main page. An observer can view the list of objects that have been deleted, and can restore them.

Each of these pages are created dynamically using Php. The candidate number, a unique value in the database, is passed from one page to the next, and the data are pulled from the database after the selection is made.

Color-color plots are created using IDL. An observer can look at the plots to determine whether the query run was appropriate.

Users can also select objects based on colors or positions, to customize the main page just before an observing run, making it easier to locate objects of special interest.

4.   Future Work

Follow-up spectra will be taken using DIS (Double Imaging Spectrograph) on the Apache Point 3.5 meter telescope. At that time, we will be able to ascertain whether we indeed have found a unique brown dwarf color-color space, and will be able to see what adjustments need to be made on the target selection.

References

Hawley, S. L. et al. 2002, AJ, 123, 3409

Astronomical Data Analysis Software and Systems XII
ASP Conference Series, Vol. 295, 2003
H. E. Payne, R. I. Jedrzejewski, and R. N. Hook, eds.

ADS Web Services for the Discovery and Linking of Bibliographic Records

Alberto Accomazzi, Günther Eichhorn, Carolyn S. Grant,
Michael J. Kurtz, and Stephen S. Murray

*Harvard-Smithsonian Center for Astrophysics, 60 Garden Street,
Cambridge, MA 02138*

Abstract. The NASA Astrophysics Data System (ADS) currently provides free access to over 2.9 million records in four bibliographic databases through a sophisticated search interface. An increasingly larger number of publishers and institutions are using the ADS to verify the existence and availability of references published in the scientific literature. To facilitate the exchange of metadata necessary to establish these links, the ADS is developing prototype Web Services based on emerging industry standards such as SOAP as part of a collaboration with the major NASA Astrophysics Data Centers. In this paper we discuss possible approaches to the implementation of SOAP services and present three different prototypes developed by the ADS group as our contribution to this effort. We conclude with a brief discussion of the issues still confronting data providers and software developers as we embrace these new technologies.

1. Introduction

In the past few years, the Simple Object Access Protocol (SOAP) has emerged as one of the main industry-supported protocols for the implementation of web services. SOAP is an XML-based, platform and language independent protocol that can use HTTP as its transport mechanism. As such, it has become one of the standard ways of exchanging structured data and metadata among web-based services.

There are several SOAP libraries currently available that provide bindings for a variety of programming languages, greatly simplifying the deployment of SOAP clients and servers. These libraries can take care of all aspects related to data serialization so that users can simply write code that passes objects and data structures between clients and servers, without worrying about how such objects are represented in the underlying protocol. As an alternative, most libraries also allow developers to override the default methods used to format and exchange messages between clients and servers. When writing a service that uses SOAP to return data to a client request, the developer can choose three different alternatives:

1. The service returns an object reference to the client. The client then invokes methods on the object to retrieve data from the remote SOAP server. While this may seem the most desirable paradigm (after all the

O in SOAP stands for Object), no standard mechanism exists today for the serialization of objects and methods, nor for the management of state information necessary for this implementation to work. This is still an area where SOAP has not (yet?) delivered the promise of cross-language, object-oriented, distributed computing. Even if the technical issues concerning the serialization of objects between server and client are resolved, the necessity of a round-trip between the two for each method call would present a prohibitive performance barrier for many distributed applications.

2. The service returns an XML document representing a serialization of the query results according to a published schema. The document is embedded in the usual XML-based SOAP envelope used by the client-server protocol. This way of serializing data in a SOAP response (also called "Literal XML Encoding") can be used to override the default data encoding, giving the developer total control of how the data being returned is formatted. However, with this freedom comes the burden of forcing the client to deal with the parsing and validation of the incoming data stream, something that by default is handled transparently by the SOAP protocol.

3. The service returns a pure data structure, that is then transparently serialized by the SOAP library as an XML-based message according to the standard SOAP encoding. The data structure is then unpacked once it reaches the client and can be readily used by the application.

2. ADS SOAP Services Implementation

The promise of interoperability among platforms and languages and the availability of public-domain implementations for this protocol have contributed to the adoption of SOAP by astronomical data providers, among others. The ADS group, in the context of its collaboration with other NASA Data Centers, has started developing prototype SOAP services that can be used to query its search engine and other interfaces used to establish links to its data holdings.

The prototype services we present here provide a SOAP interface to existing functionality that ADS has so far made available via the traditional HTML/HTTP/CGI user interfaces (Accomazzi et al. 1997) as well as through customized client-server interfaces (Eichhorn et al. 1996). We tackled these services first since they are the ones that most of our collaborators use on a daily basis and because they expose the ADS search engine interface and our data holdings in a natural way. To simplify access to these services, we have implemented them following the approach described in point 3 above: the SOAP servers return data structures that can be readily used by the client interfaces. We felt that at this point this implementation is the one which offers the minimum buy-in cost from a user perspective, and is the one that highlights the "S" for "Simple" in SOAP.

We have also attempted to minimize the complexity of the data structures returned by the SOAP servers by adopting a simple representation for the bibliographic elements in our records. While this may fall short of the level of detail desired by some of our users, it greatly simplifies the amount of post-processing

```
#!/bin/env perl
# ADS Reference resolution client via SOAP services
# Usage: refresolver-client.pl refstring [...]

use SOAP::Lite;
use XML::Simple;

my $response = SOAP::Lite
    -> uri('http://ads.harvard.edu/RefResolver')
    -> proxy('http://ads.harvard.edu/ws/bibserver')
    -> resolve(@ARGV);

print XMLout($response->result, noattr => 1);

$ refresolver-client.pl 'Accomazzi, A., et al. 2000, A&AS, 143, 85'
<opt>
  <anon>
    <input>Accomazzi, A., et al. 2000, A&amp;AS, 143, 85</input>
    <bibcode>2000A&amp;AS..143...85A</bibcode>
    <status>Ok</status>
    <url>http://adsabs.harvard.edu/cgi-bin/bib_query?2000A%26AS..143...85A</url>
  </anon>
</opt>
```

Figure 1.   Sample PERL SOAP client script for reference resolution. The script uses the public domain PERL library *SOAP::Lite* to send a list of freetext references given on the command line to the SOAP server for identification with ADS records. The server sends back a data structure that is accessible via the variable returned by `$response->result`. In the *SOAP::Lite* implementation, this corresponds to a reference to an array of hash references, which we serialize as an XML document via a call to `XMLout`, available from the *XML::Simple* PERL module.

that client applications need to perform in order to create links to the ADS services. The following SOAP services have been implemented so far:

- **Bibcode Verification:** a service that verifies the existence of bibliographic records and returns their canonical bibcodes and URLs suitable for linking.
- **Reference Resolution:** a service that requests the identification of freetext reference strings with their corresponding bibliographic records in ADS.
- **Abstract Query:** a service that returns a list of records in the ADS abstract databases matching the input search parameters.

A sample PERL SOAP client for reference resolution and an example of its usage is shown in Figure 1.

3. Discussion

The services described in this paper offer new access methods to the existing ADS query interfaces. In this sense, they do not provide new functionalities but rather make the existing functionality available through technology that is becoming an industry standard. While this may encourage the deployment of distributed agents that take advantage of these services, much work still remains to be done by the ADS and the other astronomical data centers before we can all take advantage of these technologies in a seamless way. Some of the issues we have identified as needing resolution are listed below.

- Publication of interface specifications for web services using standards such as WSDL. These specifications can help implementors in creating clients capable of properly accessing the many web services being deployed.
- Agreement on a common set of XML Schemas that can be adopted by the astronomical data centers. Being able to attach semantic meaning to a dataset representation by making use of a common set of schemas would tremendously increase the level of interoperability between data providers.
- Standardization of protocols and client/server responses. Even assuming most of the data centers settle on a single protocol such as SOAP, there are still issues that need to be resolved. Should there be services returning objects rather than datasets? Should stateful information be included in the messages exchanged by clients and servers?

4. Conclusions

We have implemented the SOAP prototypes described in this paper in response to the suggestions and requests from other NASA Astrophysics Data Centers. Their deployment and the deployment of similar services by other data providers allows interested parties to test how usefully they can be integrated in distributed applications. Currently, access to these SOAP services is available upon request. For more information on how to register to gain access to them, please visit the following url: `http://ads.harvard.edu/pubs/ws`.

We hope that the availability of these interfaces will provide us with feedback about their usefulness and suggestions about how they can be improved. To this end, we solicit any and all comments from any potential users.

Acknowledgments. The ADS is funded by NASA Grant NCC5-189.

References

Accomazzi, A., Eichhorn, G., Kurtz, M. J., Grant, C. S., & Murray, S. S. 1997, in ASP Conf. Ser., Vol. 125, Astronomical Data Analysis Software and Systems VI, ed. G. Hunt & H. E. Payne (San Francisco: ASP), 357

Eichhorn, G., Accomazzi, A., Grant, C. S., Kurtz, M. J., & Murray, S. S. 1996, in ASP Conf. Ser., Vol. 101, Astronomical Data Analysis Software and Systems V, ed. G. H. Jacoby & J. Barnes (San Francisco: ASP), 569

Astronomical Data Analysis Software and Systems XII
ASP Conference Series, Vol. 295, 2003
H. E. Payne, R. I. Jedrzejewski, and R. N. Hook, eds.

Web Services in AIPS++

Boyd Waters, John Benson, Tim Cornwell

*National Radio Astronomy Observatory, PO Box 0, Socorro, NM
87801-0387*

Jason Ye

Brown University, Box 4087, Providence, RI 02912

Melissa Douthit

*Computer Science Department, California State University, San
Marcos, CA 92096*

Abstract. The ease of distributed computing in AIPS++ has traditionally obviated the need for standard networking components, such as
those found in Java, Python, or Perl. However, Glish is able to "wrap"
arbitrary commands, enabling us to link powerful, Java-based toolkits to
Glish's event-based, client-server processing model. We have used this
technique to implement a SOAP[1]-based Cone Search[2] web service for
the Virtual Observatory. Integration of Java with AIPS++ leveraged
industry-standard toolkits, and simplified the code.

1. Motivation and Initial Design

The NRAO on-line data archive is part of NRAO's "End-to-End" Project (Cornwell, this conference). It is implemented as a series of Glish scripts, which implement queries to the AIPS++ Table System.[3] The actual data files are stored
on our multi-terabyte Storage-Area Network (SAN).

We wished to provide archive data via a web browser, which meant that we
needed to implement a web server process that could interact with the AIPS++
Table system.

With the addition of a "business logic" layer between our user form and
the "raw" tables, we were able to re-use a TCP/IP table-data socket server
that Wes Young had developed for use by his VLA Calibrator Flux applet.[4]
The applet opens a socket and talks to a stand-alone, C++ program; this C++

---

[1] http://www.w3.org/2000/xp/Group/

[2] http://www.us-vo.org/metadata/conesearch/

[3] http://aips2.nrao.edu/docs/notes/199/199.html

[4] http://aips2.nrao.edu/vla/calflux.html

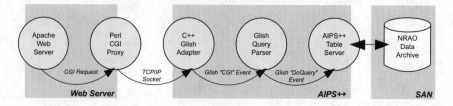

Figure 1.   Initial Deployment: Receiving an Archive Query Request.
A TCP/IP client/server pair, implemented in Perl and C++, implements the adapter between a web server and AIPS++. (Circles represent processes; grey boxes correspond to host computer boundaries.)

program acts as a stand-alone, "table data server" (called `atabd`) for the applet.
A slight modification of Wes' `atabd` could accept web form data from a Perl
CGI script over a TCP/IP connection, and return an HTML string that was in
turn presented to the web browser.

2.   A Web Services-Based Re-Implementation

The ability to browse the on-line NRAO database is a great boon to our data
analysts, but real utility will be realized when this data can be aggregated
with other astronomical data sources and manipulated by our image-processing
systems.

A first step was to map our catalog information, our meta-data, onto the
VOTable format, with particular attention to the proper attribution of Unified
Column Descriptors[5] to each column. Once this mapping was understood, we
used a nice set of Glish XML tools,[6] written by Ray Plante at NCSA, to emit a
VOTable directly from our AIPS++/Glish scripts.

Once we had simple XML output capability, we considered XML input;
we wished to receive archive query requests from other computer processes.
Clearly, we needed a SOAP framework; SOAP is exactly an XML messaging
system primarily based upon HTTP. Writing our own SOAP framework in
Glish, based on Ray's XML toolset, was possible. But why do so, when the
entire computer industry is providing these tools for us?

3.   Java/AIPS++ Interoperability Issues

For this experiment, we decided to focus on Java tools, as the rapid-development
aspects of Java were a nice match to our team's expertise, and a nice complement
to Glish.

---

[5]http://cdsweb.u-strasbg.fr/doc/UCD.htx

[6]Code is available in the AIPS++ distribution under the `code/trial/implement/XML` directory.

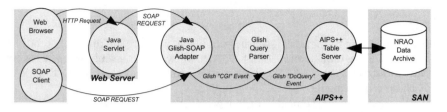

Figure 2.   Java Implementation. The Glish adapter handles SOAP
clients directly; traditional Web browser clients are handled by an
HTTP adapter servlet. (Circles represent processes; grey boxes correspond to host computer boundaries.)

We were able to replace the C++ socket-server implementation with a Java
command-line program wrapped with the Glish `shell` function.[7] The `shell`
function logs any Unix command onto the Glish Event bus by mapping the `stdin`
and `stdout` streams: Java raises an event to the Glish/AIPS++ system simply
by printing to `stdout`, and receives event values from AIPS++ by accepting
data on `stdin`. Since XML messages are simply string values, this approach
works well enough.[8]

Re-implementing the server in Java gave us Java as the socket client, and
the socket server. It was theoretically possible to replace the simple socket
messaging scheme with Java RMI, but the complexity of Java RMI deployment
stymied our efforts. Currently, we use the same SOAP messaging scheme to
talk between the web service front-end and the Java/Glish back-end that we use
for other services. Therefore, the Glish "back-end" became our SOAP server:
SOAP is the default, and traditional, HTML web servers are a special front-end!

3.1.   Life-Cycle Management: Who Owns the Process?

We had intended to re-engineer the C++ server at some point; as written,
it cannot handle more than one client. This is because the C++ server is
launched from an AIPS++/Glish process; AIPS++ controls the lifecycle of the
process. We were not able to create a process that `forks` upon `accepting` a
socket connection, as such a system confused the parent AIPS++ process.

Upon implementing the web front-end, as well as the Glish socket adapter
in Java, we had Java on both ends of a socket connection. It would seem that we
could do away with this socket approach entirely, and have a monolithic system
that integrated the web facade and the Glish query server. But life-cycle issues
are still there: the web server (or web service framework) is parent to one of
the processes, and AIPS++ is parent to the other. In order to keep our system
manageable, we kept the "front-end"/"back-end" split.

---

[7] `http://aips2.nrao.edu/docs/reference/Glish/node60.html`

[8] However, shell clients are limited to a single output event (`stdout`) and a single input event
(`stdin`). Some dispatch code, written in Glish, is used to parse event values as they come in,
effectively multiplexing the events into and out of the `stdin/out` stream events.

4. Java Tools

Since we had our framework essentially in place, we were looking for a relatively lightweight Java implementation of SOAP; we wanted the minimum necessary to instantiate and send a SOAP Message. We found that the GLUE Toolkit[9] to suit these requirements.

We used Apache Tomcat[10] for our web server front-end.

5. Future Work

The remote procedure call approaches discussed here are very similar to what Glish already does very well: optimized, socket-based distributed computing (Schiebel 2000). A much better approach would be to implement the Glish messaging protocol, SOS, in 100% pure Java.

We also wish to implement web services clients that leverage the visualization and astronomical-processing capabilities of AIPS++.

References

Schiebel, D. R. 2000, in ASP Conf. Ser., Vol. 216, Astronomical Data Analysis Software and Systems IX, ed. N. Manset, C. Veillet, & D. Crabtree (San Francisco: ASP), 39

---

[9]http://www.themindelectric.com/

[10]http://jakarta.apache.org/tomcat/index.html

Astronomical Data Analysis Software and Systems XII
ASP Conference Series, Vol. 295, 2003
H. E. Payne, R. I. Jedrzejewski, and R. N. Hook, eds.

Turning Besançon Observatory On-line Facilities into the VO: Galactic Model Simulation, Binary Star, Molecular Collisional and TNO Databases

B. Debray

Observatoire de Besançon, BP 1615, 25010 Besançon Cedex, France

M.-L. Dubernet-Tuckey

LERMA, Observatoire de Paris-Meudon, 92195 Meudon Cedex, France and Université de Franche-Comté, 25030 Besançon Cedex, France

A. Grosjean, E. Oblak, J.-M. Petit, C. Reylé, A.C. Robin

Observatoire de Besançon

Abstract. For several years, the Besançon Observatory has been developing scientific facilities that are, or will be in the near future, accessible on-line through the World-Wide Web, namely the Besançon model of stellar population synthesis of the Galaxy, and three databases: the BDB Double and Multiple Star database, the BASECOL Molecular Collisional Excitation database and a database of discovery and recovery observations of TNOs. We summarize here the scientific objectives of these facilities and the characteristics of the information exchange protocols implemented so far. Next we describe how we envisage turning these facilities into the Virtual Observatory grid and what are the expectations and needs of VO standards given the specificities of these facilities.

1. Galactic Model of Stellar Population Synthesis

The Besançon model of population synthesis of the Galaxy[1] is based on a semi-empirical approach, where physical constraints and current knowledge of the formation and evolution scenario of the Galaxy are used as a first approximation for the population synthesis. The new revised version (Robin et al. 2002a) includes several important updates of the current knowledge for stellar populations and galactic evolution, such as: (*i*) new parameters for the thin disc, due to significant improvements after Hipparcos: potential, velocity ellipsoid and local luminosity function; (*ii*) the disc is warped and flared in the external part following new constraints from near-infrared star counts; (*iii*) the overall parameters of the thick disc and spheroid (density law, local density and Initial Mass Function) have been adjusted to most recent surveys; and (*iv*) a triaxial outer bulge has been included.

---

[1] http://www.obs-besancon.fr/model/

The model has been accessible over the World-Wide Web since 1996. Parameters for the simulation are passed through web forms and the result is retrieved through ftp. In the framework of the VO, the Galaxy model can be useful to complement observational data to interpolate stellar statistics at new wavelengths or at directions where no data are available yet. We are also implementing a Bayesian classification tool to apply to observational data, based on probabilities computed by the galactic model assuming given observational parameters (Robin et al. 2002b).

2.   Double and Multiple Star Database

The BDB database[2] for double and multiple stars has been developed since 1995 to provide the astronomical community through the Internet, with numerical and image data specific to each category of binaries (observational categories at first), raising in particular the difficulties of the identification of the components (Oblak et al. 2002).

To fulfill these goals, the database presents the following functionalities: (*i*) it incorporates catalogues from all observational categories; (*ii*) it is interfaced (or will be in the near future) to other more specialized binary star databases such as Cracow (eclipsing binaries), SIDONIE (visual) and SB9 (spectroscopic); (*iii*) a specific Java tool has been developed to compare numerical data from several catalogues with Digitized Sky Survey and CCD images (from a European Network) of visual binaries; and (*iv*) the database will provide some tools specific to double stars such as ephemeris for eclipsing binaries. The database can be queried through web forms and mail-supplied lists of stars.

3.   Ro-Vibrational Collisional Excitation Database

The objective is to build a database concerning molecular ro-vibrational transitions induced by collisions with atoms or molecules, which will provide all or some of the following items: rate coefficients as a function of temperature and fitted functions, total cross sections as a function of energy, potential energy surface used in the calculations, full reference on the PES and on the methods used in the calculations of cross sections, codes to deal with some of the data.

The idea is to have a dynamical database that allows the user to read, transform or create more data (if allowed by the available codes). We are currently calculating the collisional excitation rates of H_2O by H_2; some of the results are already published (Dubernet & Grosjean 2002) and we intend to start the database with our own results on the $H_2O + H_2$ system. The fitted coefficients and functions of the collisional rates will be available as well as the Fortran code used to rebuild the collisional rates. The cross-section (tables and graphs) will be available in order for a user to check the completeness of the data and to complete the data if necessary.

A bibliographic database on ro-vibrational excitation processes has been built. It contains about 400 references from physical and chemical journals,

---

[2]http://bdb.obs-besancon.fr/

with specific keywords added to all references. It gives the possibility to choose the molecules and atoms in collision, the origin of the data (theoretical, experimental), the type of processes (rotational excitation, vibrational excitation, etc.), the type of data (probabilities, cross-sections, collisional rates, etc.) and the usual information (author, year since 1974). The database can be updated automatically via a web page. All the papers providing data relevant to astrophysical use will be linked to files containing the traceability and validation of the data, as well as fits or links of/to the data.

The databases[3] have three main goals: exploitation of observational data, in particular data that will be provided by HERSCHEL/ALMA or existing data from SWAS/ISO, modeling of cometary, planetary and interstellar media, and maximum of information given to theoreticians wishing to do calculations.

4. Trans-Neptunian Object Database

Thanks to our experience in discovery and follow-up of TNOs with the CFH12k (Petit et al. 2001), Besançon Observatory is actively participating in the definition of the strategy of the Ultra-Wide component of the CFHT Legacy Survey, aimed at discovering all TNOs around the ecliptic down to magnitude $m_R = 23.2$. In collaboration with CADC and Department of Physics and Astronomy of the University of British Columbia, we will prepare the observations and data processing and will participate in the additional observations required to determine the orbital parameters of the detected objects.

The outcome of this programme will be an orbital database of more than 1000 TNOs, all discovered in a well characterized survey. In addition, all the TNOs discovered in this survey will be followed to the third opposition, to avoid follow-up bias which is impossible to model. For each discovered TNO, the database will contain: (i) the field coordinates and size, with "filling factor" for a mosaic camera, (ii) the exposure time, (iii) the efficiency curve versus magnitude of discovery observations, together with range of rate of motion of validity, (iv) all astrometric measurements, at discovery and recoveries, (v) the estimated orbit, and (vi) for objects not yet with three oppositions, the full history of recovery attempts, in particular, the failing observations with circumstances.

5. Turning into the VO: Some Considerations

One of the basic concepts of the Virtual Observatory is to use recent technology to enable access to data spread worldwide, keeping them where the relevant scientific expertise resides. In this framework, the Besançon Observatory will make available experimental or simulated data as well as scientific added value to the astronomical community more efficiently through the different facilities described above which have been accessed so far through the World-Wide Web. This makes necessary to broaden the operation methods implemented so far (web pages and forms, HTML or flat files output, http or ftp retrieval); this implies definition of metadata, broader query modes, extraction of large amount of data,

---

[3]http://basecol.obs-besancon.fr/

on-the-fly analysis tools, etc. Some particular milestones of this process have been laid, namely: (*i*) XML formatted output of the data of the BDB database, with interoperability in mind (Debray 2002); while initial developments were done following the Astrores DTD, full final implementation will use the VOTables format (Ochsenbein et al. 2002); (*ii*) planned implementation of the bibcode (Schmitz et al. 1995) within the bibliographic database of the BASECOL facility; it aims mainly at allowing both direct access to the bibliographic services such as ADS, and external retrieval of the keywords added in BASECOL used to classify the compiled references.

To implement VO concepts and standards in the future, we need them to comprehensively account for the scientific and technical requirements of our facilities, for instance, the definition of unambiguous metadata for the description of both services and data. Some requirements are already addressed by present definitions of *Unified Column Descriptors* (UCDs, see Derrière et al. 2002); more specific metadata are however needed for, e.g., the observational log of transneptunian objects or the parameters of simulated stellar populations.

On the other hand, our facilities (the Galactic simulation model mainly, but not exclusively) require that emerging protocols properly consider that a request issued by a remote service (web server, remote program) may require a long computing time before the output is sent back; simple http requests do not properly handle this case. Lastly, the VO will likely increase significantly the access rate to our services; replications via mirror sites have to be envisaged.

References

Robin, A. C. , Reylé, C., Derrière, S., & Picaud, S. 2002a, A&A, submitted

Robin, A. C., Reylé, C., Picaud, S., & Debray, B. 2002b, in Toward an International Virtual Observatory, ESO Astrophysics Symposia, ed. K.M. Górski & P. J. Quinn (Berlin: Springer-Verlag), in press

Oblak, E., Debray, B., Lastennet, E., & Kundera, T. 2002, in SF2A 2002: Semaine de l'Astrophysique Française, EDP-Sciences, ed. F. Combes & D. Barret, in press

Dubernet, M.-L., Grosjean, A. 2002, A&A, 390, 793

Petit, J.-M., et al. 2001, BAAS, 33, 1030

Debray, B. 2002, in Toward an International Virtual Observatory, Scientific Motivation, ESO Astrophysics Symposia, ed. K.M. Górski & P. J. Quinn (Berlin: Springer-Verlag), in press

Ochsenbein, F., et al. 2002, in Toward an International Virtual Observatory, ESO Astrophysics Symposia, ed. K.M. Górski & P. J. Quinn (Berlin: Springer-Verlag), in press

Schmitz, M., et al. 1995, Vistas Astron. 39, 272

Derrière, S., Ochsenbein, F., & Ortiz, P. 2002, in Toward an International Virtual Observatory, ESO Astrophysics Symposia, ed. K.M. Górski & P.J. Quinn (Berlin: Springer-Verlag), in press

Astronomical Data Analysis Software and Systems XII
ASP Conference Series, Vol. 295, 2003
H. E. Payne, R. I. Jedrzejewski, and R. N. Hook, eds.

Manuscript Preparation, Submission and Features of the Electronic IBVS

András Holl

Konkoly Observatory, H-1525 P.O.Box 67, Budapest, Hungary

Abstract. IBVS is a small journal in the field of variable star research, which is fully electronic now. The HTML version of the journal features object database links and reference links. The necessary markup is provided by the authors, using the macros implemented in the LaTeX style file. We are testing a web-based manuscript submission tool, which would enable authors to submit data files, draw or upload simple figures, and enter plain ASCII or LaTeX text. The text is typeset on the server. The submitted manuscript can be previewed, and links tested by the authors themselves. The markup has been designed to facilitate automatic information exchange between the journal and databases. A short description is given on the other features of the electronic IBVS.

1. The IBVS

The Information Bulletin on Variable Stars (IBVS) is a small journal covering variable star research. It is published by Konkoly Observatory on behalf of the Commissions 27 and 42 of the IAU. The Bulletin, started in 1961, now publishes 150–200 short papers annually.

The main characteristics of the Bulletin are the narrow field, the rapid publication cycle and the small editorial staff. In the past decade IBVS has grown from a bulletin to a peer-reviewed journal.

2. The Electronic IBVS

The electronic version of IBVS[1] was created in 1994, with printable (PostScript) issues on the web and anonymous ftp (alongside with LaTeX sources). Shortly afterwards archive issues started to become on-line, both in image (PostScript) and OCR-ed text form (Holl 1998). Printable issues were published on CD-ROMs as well (Holl & Sterken 2000; 2001). The web site offers simple ToC and full text search capability.

Rapid publication of manuscripts is a must at IBVS. Peer review takes time, editorial resources are limited, so manuscripts should be technically well prepared. The papers published in the journal are (mostly) typeset by the authors in LaTeX, using the specific style file. The work-flow is another critical

---

[1]http://www.konkoly.hu/IBVS/IBVS.html

factor: the tasks of maintaining the web-pages, moving the files around, indexing, backup, etc., are helped by a set of small shell scripts.

The HTML version of the bulletin was created with the help of the CDS, Strasbourg, in 1999. HTML pages are generated on-the-fly. The system was built on a prototype created by F. Ochsenbein (1999), and uses CGI programs, awk scripts and `cgiprint` (LaTeX-to-HTML conversion, Ochsenbein 1999). Link generation is aided by the GLU system (Fernique 1998).

The HTML version of the IBVS has—besides trivial e-mail and URL links— object and reference links, which are produced in a completely different way. Object links point to the SIMBAD database, and are created from the markup inserted by the author. The original idea was using a specific LaTeX tag (preferably inserted by the author) marking up the object name resolvable by SIMBAD. Maintaining hashing tables at CDS makes it possible now to use otherwise non-resolvable names. In the course of years we started to use those object tags to build object indexes for the printed volumes of the journal. The situation became more complicated allowing large tables with thousands of object links. Object tags proliferated—now we have six different tags of the genre.

Reference links are created by processing the source text, recognizing information needed for bibcode creation: author initial, year, journal, volume and page. The reference syntax at IBVS is not very strict; we do not require standard journal abbreviations, for instance. Automatic reference resolution is far from being complete; some references are not resolved automatically. To supplement this, the LaTeX style file allows the author to insert bibcodes explicitly.

Besides the links to those services from the journal, ADS and SIMBAD have links to IBVS, too. The script which uploads issues to the IBVS web and ftp server sends e-mail messages with the ADS tagged format bibliographic descriptions to both ADS and SIMBAD. There are plans for future improvements of the HTML version of the IBVS. We intend to enable linking with other astronomical services like Aladin and VizieR.

Papers in the journal are often accompanied by extensive tabular or graphical data available only electronically. IBVS allows linking for LaTeX format tables, plain ASCII data files, and figures. Moreover, electronic-only tables might contain further database, local data file or figure links, which makes it possible to store and deliver large amounts of auxiliary data.

3.   Challenges

A fair percentage of the authors at IBVS has problems with LaTeX (and with PostScript). Sometimes even experienced professionals get confused with the usage of special markup for links (it would be desirable for astronomical journals to standardize such markup to some degree). Furthermore, object name syntax in SIMBAD link markup or reference syntax often contains errors too, and authors do mistype or mix up bibliographic data. Again, IBVS has only limited capacities for correcting these.

A further problem might be the preparation of PostScript figures. Some authors have difficulty in supplying PostScript, others (mainly using commercial PC-based graphical packages) produce non-standard PostScript.

It would be desirable to let the authors check how their paper would look with the links, and having them check those links. (The same line of argument has led to the idea of the authors typesetting their own papers.) A manuscript preparation tool could free the authors from (some of) the burden of LATEX typesetting, and let them do what should really be their task: preparing semantically better manuscripts. Such a tool could reconcile the conflict between rich markup and user-friendly manuscript preparation.

4.   Web-based Manuscript Preparation and Submission Tool

There is a newly invented article-style at IBVS which makes the development of a manuscript preparation tool easier. The Editors of the journal have introduced special, form-like styles for simple papers reporting merely observational data. Incidentally, the authors who benefit most from this are largely the same who have problems with manuscript preparation.

The manuscript checking and submission tool is a set of HTML pages and CGI programs. The first page allows the submitting author to enter their name and addresses and chose an identifier/password pair for the submission. The submitted manuscript can be over-written in a subsequent session using the same identifier and password.

The first publicly available version allows submission of manuscripts without figures. It is for papers on observations of minima of variables, mainly eclipsing binaries, which commonly appear in IBVS. Browsers can not be used as editors, so authors are advised to compose their papers locally with an editor of their choice, and then copy the content to the appropriate HTML form fields using cut-and-paste technique. Both LATEX markup and plain ASCII text can be used (the editors can add some necessary markup if needed).

Having filled in the form, the submitting author can proceed to preview, where links can be tested. Finally, the manuscript can be submitted. It will be typeset by the server side CGI program in LATEX. This technique allows syntactical checking to some degree. Incomplete manuscripts are rejected with an error message.

Another version of the tool is under development. This would allow the submitting author to upload a data file, upload a PostScript figure or to have it drawn by the server from the uploaded data file.

It would be entirely possible, of course, to have the server save the submitted manuscript, or parts of it (tables) in XML. The tool could be used for link testing only—authors could test the links they get from their manuscript, do the typesetting in LATEX, and submit the manuscript by ftp.

Acknowledgments.   The author is grateful for the Ambassade de France en Hongrie for a travel grant, and the CDS, Strasbourg, for their help in creating the HTML version of IBVS.

References

Fernique, P., Ochsenbein, F., & Wenger, M. 1998, in ASP Conf. Ser., Vol. 145, Astronomical Data Analysis Software and Systems VII, ed. R. Albrecht, R. N. Hook, & H. A. Bushouse (San Francisco: ASP), 466

Holl, A. 1998, in ASP Conf. Ser., Vol. 145, Astronomical Data Analysis Software and Systems VII, ed. R. Albrecht, R. N. Hook, & H. A. Bushouse (San Francisco: ASP), 474

Holl, A. & Sterken, C. (eds.) 2000, IBVS CD-ROM, Konkoly Observatory

Holl, A. & Sterken, C. (eds.) 2001, IBVS CD-ROM Vol. II., Konkoly Observatory

Ochsenbein, F. 1999, personal communication

Astronomical Data Analysis Software and Systems XII
ASP Conference Series, Vol. 295, 2003
H. E. Payne, R. I. Jedrzejewski, and R. N. Hook, eds.

Web Services and Their Use in Starlink Software

Mark Taylor, Roy Platon, Alan Chipperfield, Peter Draper, Brian McIlwrath, David Giaretta

Starlink Project, UK

Abstract. Web Services are gaining great popularity in the Grid community, and with good reason. The Starlink project is adopting Web Services as the method of interapplication communication. This is being done natively in new Java-based applications while older applications are being wrapped to provide Web Service interfaces. We are in this way providing interoperability between the generations of software in a heterogeneous, distributed manner and allowing the software to be usable in a distributed environment such as the GRID.

1. Introduction

Starlink applications have until now used a dedicated messaging system. This gives a closely coupled command interface to applications. In addition, data is accessed via the NDF data access layer. Figure 1 illustrates the overall architecture of a typical application.

As part of a new phase of developments we are starting to use Web Services as our messaging system. This not only bases our work on Open Standards, allowing us greater opportunities for interoperability, but also gives us access to a variety of tools. It allows us to work naturally in a distributed environment, and in particular positions the applications to play a natural role in the Virtual Observatory.

2. New Application Architecture

The new architecture, shown in Figure 2, must allow us to work transparently with old as well as new applications. Clients communicate with a server (for example a TOMCAT/AXIS or embedded server) via SOAP messages, usually over HTTP. The server then redirects the messages to either a JNI interface for a non-Java application, OR to a native Java application.

Data access is via the network enabled NDF data access layer for the older, non-Java applications and via the new HDX layer (Giaretta et al. 2003) for the pure-Java application. Data access could include appropriate authentication and authorisation, for example using GLOBUS-type certificates and fitting in to the Open Grid Services Architecture[1] (OGSA).

---

[1]http://www.globus.org/ogsa

Figure 1.   Starlink classic application architecture.

When defining interfaces to existing applications a number of options are available. These are not mutually exclusive, but too many interfaces can cause maintenance problems. The simplest choices include (a) complete command lines as a single string and (b) making each parameter separately available. Option (a) is simpler but less easy to use and to validate. However it may provide an easier transition for pipeline processing systems such as ORAC-DR.[2] Option (b) on the other hand is better suited to an application which is being run effectively interactively with user input.

3.   Web Services Approach

Based on our investigations at the time of writing, a number of problems and advantages have been identified. Problems:
- Robustness: if the server and application are part of the same JVM then a fatal exception in the latter can kill the former.
- Interactivity: the loss of close coupling between the command interface and the application makes interactive work difficult.
- Interface definitions: any plans for replacing "classic applications" by pure Java ones will require the older interfaces to be supported, although they can be extended. Web Service interfaces to non-Java applications should therefore be chosen carefully.
- Error handling: requires special care.
- Image display: While display via X is possible, it is an extra complication.

Advantages:
- Distributable: tasks can be distributed to appropriate servers for example co-located with the data or to use available CPU power.
- Replaceable components: applications can be transparently replaced, as long as the interfaces are replaced by single or multiple new components.
- Available infrastructure software: UDDI servers to advertise information, SOAP servers.

---

[2]http://www.jach.hawaii.edu/JACpublic/UKIRT/software/oracdr/

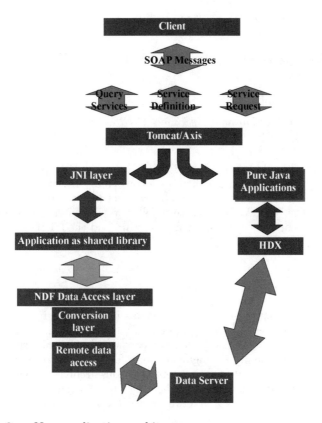

Figure 2.   New application architecture.

- Compatibility with GRID: OGSA is built on Web Services. Publishing astronomical applications as Web Services is the first step in making these available via OGSA.
- Flexible command interface implementation: SOAP-enabled clients can be produced in a variety of languages using easily available support libraries, e.g., Java, Perl, Python, etc.

4.   Conclusions

Use of Web Services as a new messaging system will allow Starlink applications increased flexibility. Old and new applications will be able to interoperate easily and the software will be suitable to use in the Virtual Observatory.

References

Giaretta, D., Taylor, M., Draper, P., Gray, N., & McIlwrath, B. 2003, this volume, 221

Astronomical Data Analysis Software and Systems XII
ASP Conference Series, Vol. 295, 2003
H. E. Payne, R. I. Jedrzejewski, and R. N. Hook, eds.

A Collaborative Extension to the Solar Web Tool

Romain Linsolas, Isabelle Scholl & Eric Legay

Institut d'Astrophysique Spatiale - CNRS, Bât 121 - Université Paris-Sud, F-91405 Orsay Cedex, France

Abstract. The Solar Web Project is a tool that permits the consultation of distributed and heterogeneous solar observations databases. It is currently based on a 3-tiered architecture. Its main evolution is to adapt the Solar Web server to a collaborative model. Two solutions are considered: the peer-to-peer architecture and the GRID model.

1. Introduction

The number of archives of solar observations is continuously growing and the location of their storage is getting more and more scattered. Consequently, the number of existing tools or web sites for consulting these observation catalogs (i.e., metadata) is equally in augmentation. The interest of a single program capable of accessing distributed and heterogeneous archives is therefore obvious. The Solar Web Project, developed by the MEDOC IAS team, is designed to come up to these expectations, as a first step toward a Virtual Solar Observatory.

2. The Current State of the Solar Web Architecture

2.1. Principles

The architecture of the current version of Solar Web[1] (Scholl, Linsolas & Legay 2001) is based on the 3-tiered model. Clients are connected to a single server that provides them with results obtained by querying archives. Since they are heterogeneous and distributed, the Solar Web server acquired the capabilities to access distant SQL databases, FTP server (where files are stored) and web-based portals, built on PHP or CGI scripts (see Figure 1, left).

2.2. Query Processing

Solar Web uses XML for communication between clients and server, as well as for the description of accessible databases (i.e., metadata). The processing of an XML query by the server can be broken down into four steps (see Figure 1):

1. The server receives an XML query from the client. This query is parsed by the *QueryProcessor* module, which creates a subquery for each database involved. This operation is performed using an XML document describing

---

[1] http://www.medoc-ias.u-psud.fr/archive/solar_web

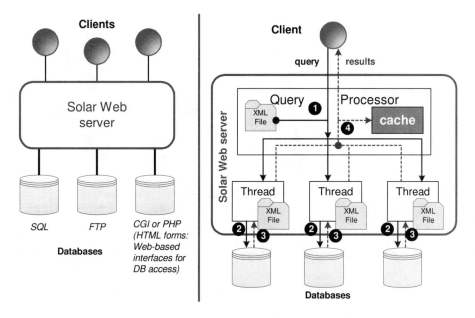

Figure 1.   Current Solar Web Architecture (left) and Query Processing (right).

each accessible database. Subqueries are sent to threads dedicated in each databases access (one thread per accessible database).

2. Each thread translates an XML subquery into an query understandable by the database (e.g., a SQL query). This is made using an XML document, which describes the structure of the corresponding database.

3. The reverse processing, i.e., the translation from the database query language into the XML language, is accomplished by these threads. The XML document is also used here by the thread that receives results from database.

4. The last step of the query processing consists in merging the results obtained from accessed databases, and, if needed, in processing them (e.g., sort). Final results are then sent to the client through the server cache.

2.3. Characteristics

The centralized architecture of the Solar Web tool can have a significant impact on security, performance, and flexibility of the policy management.

First of all, since there is only one instance of the server, it may be overloaded. The outcome is that the query processing will be slowed down, especially if the number of connected clients is important. Secondly, the presence of only one server is a single point of failure from a reliability point of view. Thirdly, some data centers would prefer to have an instance of a Solar Web server at their disposal, instead of letting a distant server access directly their databases.

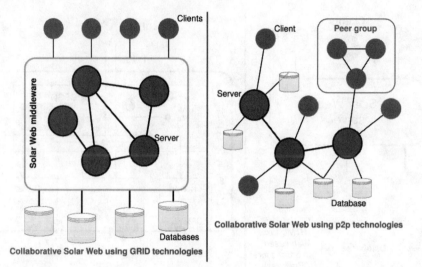

Figure 2.   Future Architectures for Solar Web: GRID (left) vs. Peer-to-Peer (right).

3.   Future Version of Solar Web

3.1.   Objectives

Characteristics previously described can be seen as drawbacks, especially its oneness and encourage us to improve the current version of the Solar Web system. The main evolution consists in moving to a distributed architecture. Two solutions are currently under consideration:

1. One solution is to create collaborative servers, where all instances of the Solar Web server are networked together. The purpose is to distribute to all servers a query sent by one client. This architecture is inspired by GRID technologies (OGSA[2]).
2. Another solution is built on top of the peer-to-peer networks technology. It consists in redesigning the network level by using JXTA infrastructure.[3] This solution can easily provide new features such as the dynamic creation of groups of users around their domain of interest.

3.2.   GRID Solution

According to Foster & Iamnitchi (2002), GRID consists of "sharing environments implemented via the deployment of a persistent, standard-based service infrastructure that supports the creation of, and resource—computers, storage space, sensors, software applications, and data—sharing within distributed computing." The concept of the GRID can be applied to Solar Web servers in order

---

[2]Open GRID Services Architecture

[3]Sun's peer-to-peer technology: http://www.jxta.org/

to create a network of servers, also called middleware. Clients are connected to this middleware which will provide them with different kinds of services, from data providing to remote data processing.

The GRID solution brings reliability to the Solar Web, thanks to the multiplicity of servers and therefore to the absence of a single point of failure. GRID also improves the system's performances by allowing collaborative works between servers.

3.3. Peer-to-Peer Solution

Peer-to-peer terminology refers to networks where members (also called peers) may act as client and server. As a server, it offers services such as data providers, while it takes advantage of these services as a client. The Sun's JXTA project is a platform designed for the development of applications based on this kind of technology. It provides basic mechanisms for communications, security and resources discovery for such applications.

The JXTA platform can be used for the evolution of Solar Web, as a foundation for servers and clients' applications. The Sun's platform takes care of security and communications (composed of XML and binary messages), as well as connection processing (which also includes resources and servers discovery). The creation and distribution of subqueries are based on the same mechanism as for the current Solar Web architecture. The main difference, due to the scattering of servers, is that servers have to communicate to update their metadata: since they describe the databases accessible by a server, they must be up-to-date.

Peer-to-peer technologies may also be exploited to introduce new capabilities to clients, such as the creation of users groups. These groups are built to suit to user expectations. They can be compared to collaborative workspaces that allow distributed work on data, or even discussions between scientists.

4. Conclusion

These possible evolutions for Solar Web architecture will improve the reliability and the performance of the system. Nevertheless, the principle of Solar Web (based on the use of XML files for database descriptions) will remain similar to the current implementation. In conclusion, the next version of the Solar Web tool is designed to be a powerful tool to access distributed and heterogeneous archives of solar observations. It will also provide an environment to introduce collaborative works.

References

Scholl, I., Linsolas, R., & Legay, E. 2001, in ASP Conf. Ser., Vol. 281, Astronomical Data Analysis Software and Systems XI, ed. D. A. Bohlender, D. Durand, & T. H. Handley (San Francisco: ASP), 307

Foster, I. & Iamnitchi, A. 2002, On Death, Taxes, and the Convergence of Peer-to-Peer and Grid Computing, draft

Astronomical Data Analysis Software and Systems XII
ASP Conference Series, Vol. 295, 2003
H. E. Payne, R. I. Jedrzejewski, and R. N. Hook, eds.

ADASS XII Meeting Web Site

Carolyn Liou,[1,2] Steve Hulbert[1]

Abstract. We present the architecture, design, and implementation details of the ADASS XII web site. The web site was implemented in Zope, a high-performance application server, web server, and content management system rolled into one. Zope includes a robust, scalable object database, web services architecture, and powerful programming capabilities. The web site was built to conform to HTML, CSS, and accessibility standards as adopted by the W3C. This dynamic web site also taps into a back-end Sybase database while requiring a minimal amount of coding. We offer this site as a prototype web site suitable for reuse in supporting future ADASS meetings.

1. Sitemap

The ADASS sitemap was an integral part of the web development. The sitemap was created in the beginning to organize the constantly flowing and changing information of web sites. As developers began to construct each page of the ADASS site, the sitemap assisted them in building a navigation scheme that can easily and effectively display differing types of content. The sitemap helped developers align user-friendly navigation with effective content management.

2. Design

The design of the ADASS web site promotes usability and aesthetic harmony. At the top, the heading is composed of the ADASS title and logo. STScI graphic artists designed the logo more then a year ago. The logo places an image of a crab on the Crab Nebula. The left-sided navigation bar sits below the heading. The navigation bar uses colors that match the colors on the logo. The rest of web site remains white to convey clarity and simplicity.

3. Implementation

The ADASS site was built using Zope, a dynamic content management application. Given the nature of the conference, all collected information was divided into events, people, and instructions categories:

---

[1]Space Telescope Science Institute, 3700 San Martin Drive, Baltimore, MD 21218

[2]University of Maryland

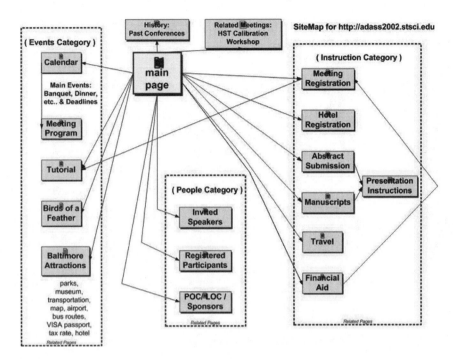

Figure 1.   Sitemap of ADASS web site.

- The events category stored data that was relevant to the four-day conference such as the meeting program, calendar, BoF, and city attractions.
- The people category stored information on invited speakers, participants, and the organizing committees.
- The last category instructed users on conference, hotel, financial aid registration, travel options, and instructions for abstract submissions.

Each category folder contains the HTML pages that are retrieved by Zope to display. The navigation items are stored in Zope's tiny tables and are linked to the corresponding HTML page.

The ADASS developers use a Sybase connection to display a listing of registered participants and oral abstracts. Zope's built-in database connections have the ability to initiate SQL queries and display the query results.

4.   Zope Standards

The ADASS web site was developed using Zope, a web building application that includes a built-in server, management interface, scripting language support, and relational database integration. The web-based server allows users to access and save files in Zope via the Internet. The content management tool allows users to organize information into a hierarchy of folders. One of the advantages of Zope is that it allows information from different folders to be retrieved and

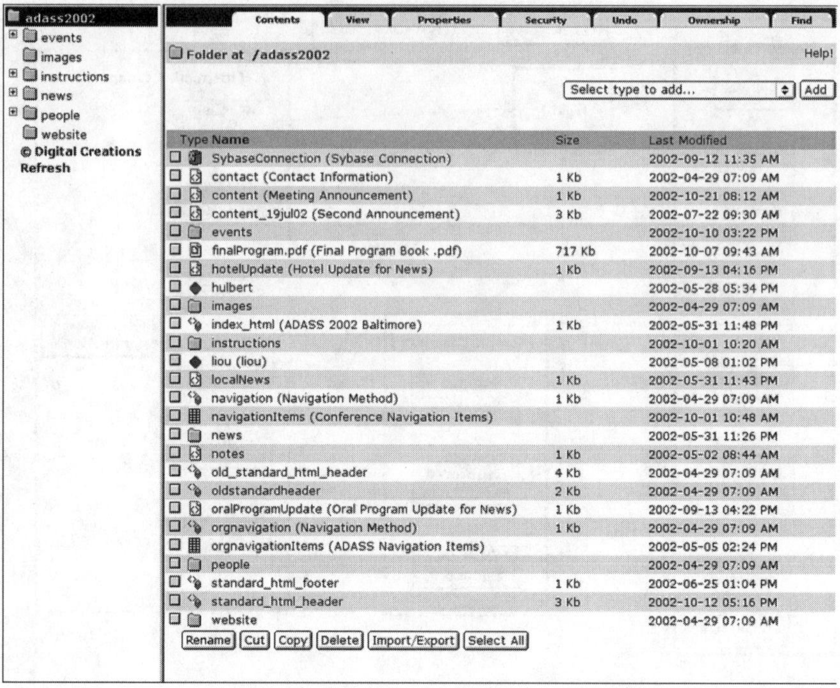

Figure 2.   Glimpse into Zope.

displayed on the same web page. For example, the ADASS page that displays Baltimore Attractions is retrieving information from three different sources:

- The heading lives in the root folder object `standard_html_header`.
- The navigation information lives in both the `navigationItems` object and the `index_html` object.
- The content on Baltimore Attractions is stored in objects in the subfolder `/events/attractions/content`.

Zope's unique management environment allows users to manage the site's data, logic, and presentation right on the Web browser. Zope also offers powerful built-in tools such as a search engine, database connectivity, security, and site management tools. Zope supports a diverse range of standard including SQL, ODOC, XML, DTML, FTP, HTTP, CGI, and more.

5.   Accessibility

The ADASS web site conforms to the specifications for HTML 4.01 Transitional, Cascading Style Sheet, and Level A of the Web Content Accessibility Guidelines 1.0. One of the primary goals for the ADASS web site is to promote accessibility and to make Web content more available to all users. Following these guidelines allows the ADASS users to find information on the Web more quickly.

Future ADASS Conferences

Place Title Here

Place Date Here

Figure 3. The ADASS web site serves as a prototype for future conferences.

6. Prototype

The ADASS web site is designed as a prototype for future ADASS conferences. The unique Zope content management application divides web content from the site design. This division allows developers to easily locate and change content.

Acknowledgments. This web site was created by the Information Services Team of the Computing and Information Services Division of Space Telescope Science Institute.

References

Latteier, A., & Pelletier, M. 2002, The Zope Book (Indianapolis: New Riders)

Part 10. Enabling Technologies

Astronomical Data Analysis Software and Systems XII
ASP Conference Series, Vol. 295, 2003
H. E. Payne, R. I. Jedrzejewski, and R. N. Hook, eds.

Mirage: A Tool for Interactive Pattern Recognition from Multimedia Data

Tin Kam Ho

Bell Laboratories, Lucent Technologies

Abstract. Many data mining queries in astronomy involve the identification of objects that are similar or discernible in different aspects such as spectral shapes and features, light curves, morphology, positions, or other derived attributes. Analyses must go beyond conventional clustering algorithms that stop at computing a single proximity structure according to a specific criterion. We describe Mirage, a software tool designed for interactive exploration of the correlation of multiple partitional or hierarchical cluster structures arising in different contexts. The tool shows points, point classes, traversals of proximity structures in one, two, or higher dimensional projections, in linked views of various types or over an image background. It supports highly flexible layouts of plots, simple clustering procedures, intuitive graphical querying, and includes a command interpreter for further extensions. Mirage has found uses in many scientific and engineering contexts.

1. Introduction

An important class of questions in astronomical data analysis involve comparing objects simultaneously from different perspectives: positions in a specific coordinate system, image features, spectra, time variability, or other derived measures such as kinematic properties. Are the objects similar in spectral features in one band also similar in another band? Do objects with similar morphological features show similar patterns in their light curves? Are there unexpected correlations between the parameters suggesting a systematic error? Questions like these are routinely asked to confirm a classification, to discover new regularities, or to validate a data processing design. Common to all these questions is a need to correlate data from different representations. Mirage is a software tool designed to facilitate exploration of such correlations.

2. Analysis of Point Proximity

Mirage takes as input a data matrix, where a row represents an object and a column represents an attribute of the object. There are no limits on the number of rows or columns other than those imposed by machine capacity. One can define feature vectors that consist of arbitrary subsets of the attributes. A feature vector represents a set of measurements that are on a common scale and can be interpreted as a group, such as a spectrum. Instances of the same feature

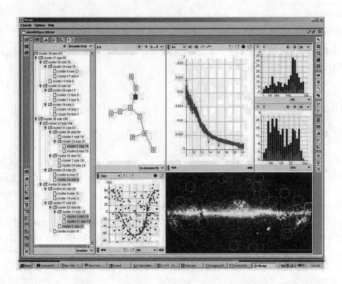

Figure 1.   A screenshot showing a variety of views. A cluster is selected on the graph and tracked in other views.

vector are expected to be comparable by the same metric for cluster analysis.
Mirage takes the results of a cluster analysis in the form of a data structure
summarizing information about inter-point proximity. These data structures are
correlated with simple one, two, or multi-dimensional projections of the data via
linked displays that include histograms, scatter plots, parallel coordinate plots,
tables, trees, and graphs (Figure 1). Users can highlight or color points from an
arbitrary display and see the highlights or colors echoed in other displays. In
addition, points can have attributes that describe their positions on an image
background that is also linked to the displays. A page layout tool allows one to
tile a view pane arbitrarily and open an arbitrary display in any tile. The tool
keeps all displays neatly organized in a set of pages.

    With this setup, one can track points that are in close proximity in different
feature spaces that can be as simple as a single attribute or a 100-dimensional
space of flux measurements. A user can append all available descriptions of the
objects to the data matrix as columns. Some columns can be position angles,
color estimates, flux within specific wavebands, where other groups of columns
can be a spectrum, a set of morphological features extracted from an image,
or luminosity estimates at various times. The selection operations and echoing
mechanisms enable many kinds of proximity related queries in data mining.

3.   Cluster Analysis from Multiple Perspectives

The design of Mirage is motivated by the need to study correlations of proximity relationships between points from different perspectives. In images, one
or two dimensional projections (histograms or scatter plots), points falling in
a neighborhood are easy to find by visual inspection. The parallel coordinate

plot can be used to find points that are close in projections on the individual dimensions. But detailed studies of proximity relationships in high-dimensional spaces require the aid of automatic cluster analysis.

A k-means procedure is provided that can be applied to an arbitrary feature space that the user defines. The results are returned as a minimum spanning tree (MST) connecting the centers of the resultant clusters. The MST is then embedded in a two-dimensional display by a graph layout algorithm and is linked with other views. Paths for leaf-to-leaf traversal are provided. User can walk along any path and see the corresponding points highlighted in other views. These paths represent the dominant directions of variations in the corresponding feature space, and the entire MST outlines a skeleton of the data distribution in that space. One can also compute a hierarchical cluster structure from an arbitrary feature space, and inspect the cluster tree in several standard traversals (e.g., depth-first, breadth-first). The walk is echoed in all other views.

Here cluster analysis is used as a way to compress the data and summarize their proximity relationships. One can initiate the k-means procedure with different numbers of desired clusters for a multi-resolution study. Computation of clusters is restricted to the chosen feature space where the metric (e.g., the Euclidean distance) is meaningful because the group of attributes are on a common scale. Thus one avoids the difficulty of finding a global metric that takes into account all attributes that can be on mixed scales. Cluster structures computed from each feature space can be correlated by walking on one structure and checking the echo on other structures. Histograms are treated as a special cluster structure where the clusters are points in each bin. One can walk along the array of bins and see the corresponding points highlighted in other views. This provides a convenient way for sensitivity analysis between spaces of arbitrary dimensions.

Since the data matrix can have arbitrary columns, it is easy to use Mirage along with other dimensionality reduction techniques such as projection to principal components or non-metric multidimensional scaling. One can simply compute the projected coordinates by an external procedure and merge them with the data set as new columns. The separation of computation and graphics simplifies the code and also allows for arbitrary coupling with those techniques.

4. Software Features

Mirage is written in Java with heavy use of the Swing library. The software is organized around an interpreter that takes commands from either the graphical interface or as textual input from a prompt. Commands can also be packaged in a script to be loaded at run time, or executed off-line for a preparatory analysis. A few features are emphasized in the design:

1. allow different treatments for different subspace projections,
2. facilitate traversals of partitional or hierarchical cluster structures,
3. provide easy-to-use user interfaces and data formats, and
4. support potential extensions by new commands.

Each graphical display includes a canvas and a control panel. Attributes, vectors, or cluster structures can be selected via the list boxes on the control panel. The control panel can be removed once all display-specific choices are made, and re-inserted when needed. Split panes with movable dividers are used extensively to provide maximum flexibility in screen utilization.

Communication of selections between displays is done via passing points represented as Java objects to a console, and forcing a repaint. The repaint manager figures out which display is visible and calls the display-specific update method which looks up the selections from the console. Color tags are stored in a field of the point objects and used when a color plot is requested. By default all plots are monochrome for highlights to show up easily and to minimize visual clutter.

5. Usage Scenarios

In addition to proximity queries in a data mining context, Mirage can also be used in several other scenarios as follows.

Analysis of simulations. Simulations involving a parameter sweep can be studied in Mirage by tracking samples with neighboring input parameter values in the space of output features. One can also gain insights on the inverse model by finding points close in the output space and tracking the corresponding input values via the broadcasting mechanism.

Comparison of observation and theoretical prediction. One can construct a data matrix by appending the observations to the predictions, with a flag distinguishing between the two sets. Each set can then be selected using the flag and colored differently for comparison in all views.

Examination and verification of existing classification. The user can code the classes numerically and then open a histogram on the class code, and walk on the bins to examine in other views the attributes of points belonging to each class. Alternatively each class can be painted a different color for simultaneous comparison.

We have used Mirage in a large variety of contexts involving both observation or simulation data. Examples include analysis of optical fiber designs, testing for robustness of optical devices, monitoring network traffic, making diagnosis of wireless communication systems, inspecting spectral classes in the IRAS point source catalog, and checking for systematics in the data pipeline of the Deep Lens Survey. These exemplify many potential usages in astronomy driven by science or engineering goals.

Acknowledgments. I thank L. Cowsar, J.A. Tyson, D. Wittman, V. Margoniner, and A. Becker for motivations of the project, suggestions of many features, and trials of the early prototypes, A. Jain and G. Nagy for perspectives in pattern recognition, and W. Cleveland and D. Temple Lang for discussions on statistical graphics.

References

Inselberg, A., & Dimsdale, B. 1994, SIAM J. of Appl. Math., 54, 559.

Ho, T. K. 2002, Proc. 16th Int'l. Conf. on Pattern Recognition, II.4p.

Astronomical Data Analysis Software and Systems XII
ASP Conference Series, Vol. 295, 2003
H. E. Payne, R. I. Jedrzejewski, and R. N. Hook, eds.

Montage: An On-Demand Image Mosaic Service for the NVO

G. B. Berriman, J. C. Good

Infrared Processing and Analysis Center, California Institute of Technology, Pasadena, CA 91125

D. Curkendall, J. Jacob, D. S. Katz

Jet Propulsion Laboratory, California Institute of Technology, Pasadena, CA 91109

T. A. Prince

Division of Physics, Mathematics and Astronomy, California Institute of Technology, Pasadena, CA 91125

R. Williams

Center for Advanced Computing Research, California Institute of Technology, Pasadena, CA 91125

Abstract. Montage will deliver a generalized toolkit for generating on-demand, science-grade custom astronomical image mosaics. "Science-grade" in this context requires that terrestrial and instrumental features are removed from images in a way that can be described quantitatively. "Custom" refers to user-specified parameters of projection, coordinates, size, rotation and spatial sampling, and whether the drizzle algorithm should be invoked. The greatest value of Montage will be its ability to analyze images at multiple wavelengths, by delivering them on a common projection, coordinate system and spatial sampling and thereby allowing analysis as if they were part of the same multi-wavelength image. Montage will be deployed as a compute-intensive service through existing portals. It will be integrated into the emerging NVO architecture, and run operationally on the Teragrid, where it will process the 2MASS, DPOSS and SDSS image collections. The software will also be portable and publicly available.

1. Introduction: What Is Montage?

Montage is an astronomical image mosaic service. It will deliver science-grade custom image mosaics according to input specifications of size, WCS projection, coordinate system, image rotation, spatial sampling, and background removal. Science grade in this context has two definitions: Montage will preserve the astrometric and photometric accuracy of the input images, and it will perform background rectification on the input images in such a fashion that its impact on the photometric quality of the data can be described quantitatively.

The principal science goal of Montage is to extend the mosaicking capabilities available to astronomers by supporting the production of multi-wavelength images. That is, images from diverse sources over many wavelengths can be combined into mosaics having common coordinates, WCS projection, spatial sampling, size and image rotation. Such mosaics are requisite for analysis tasks such as multi-wavelength source extraction and band-merging. The SIRTF Wide Area Infrared Experiment (SWIRE) has adopted Montage to support analysis of multi-wavelength images of deep SIRTF (infrared) images, and ground based optical and radio images.

2.   Schedules and Platforms

The Montage software will be publicly available through the project website at `http://montage.ipac.caltech.edu`. Montage will be designed and developed as a portable software package written in ANSI C, and supported under current plans on Solaris 2.7 and 2.8, Linux 6.x and 7.x and AIX. It will be delivered incrementally at roughly six monthly intervals between February 2003 and January 2005. Early deliveries will emphasize delivery of astrometrically and photometrically accurate, science grade mosaics, while later ones will emphasize speed and throughput. On final delivery, Montage will achieve a throughput of 30 square degrees (e.g., thirty 1 degree × 1 degree mosaics, or one 5.4 degrees × 5.4 degrees mosaic, etc.) per minute on a 1024×400MHz R12K Processor Origin 3000 or machine equivalent with sustained bandwidth to disk of 160 MB/sec.

In August 2003, Montage will be deployed as an operational service through the National Virtual Observatory (NVO; `http://www.us-vo.org`. Users will then order mosaics through existing astronomy portals, with the calculations performed on the Distributed Terascale Facility (`http://www.teragrid.org`), a high performance computational grid provided by the NSF Partnership for Advanced Computational Infrastructure. When fully deployed, the Teragrid will provide aggregate computational power on the order of 10 teraflops, aggregate disk cache on the order of 800 TB and archival storage capacity of 6 petabytes.

3.   Design of Montage

Montage is designed as a portable toolkit that performs the tasks needed to compute image mosaics in stand-alone modules, controlled by simple executives or scripts. Montage performs the following steps in computing an image mosaic: re-projection of input images to a common spatial scale, coordinate system and World Coordinate System (WCS) projection; modeling of background radiation in images to achieve common flux scales and background levels; rectification of images to a common flux scale and background level (if requested); and co-addition of re-projected, background-corrected images into a final mosaic.

The most complex parts of Montage are the image reprojection and the background modeling and rectification. These are described separately below.

3.1.   Image Reprojection

Image reprojection involves the redistribution of information from a set of input pixels to a set of output pixels. For astronomical data, the input pixels represent the total energy received from an area on the sky. It is critical to preserve this information when redistributed into output pixels. And, it is important to preserve the positional (astrometric) accuracy of the energy distribution, so common techniques such as adding all the energy from an input pixel to the "nearest" output pixel are inadequate.

Instead, we must redistribute input pixel energy to the output based on the exact overlap of these pixels, possibly even with a weighting function across the pixels based on the point spread function for the original instrument. The goal is to create an output image which is as close as possible to that which would have been created if the sky had been observed using an instrument with the output image's pixel pattern. We are also committed to building a system which handles all astronomical projections and coordinate systems equally well.

The most common approach to determining pixel overlap is to project the input pixel into the output pixel Cartesian space, but Montage will instead project both input and output pixels onto the celestial sphere. Since all such "forward" projections are well defined, the rest of the problem reduces to calculating the area of overlap of two convex polygons on a sphere (with no further consideration of the projections involved). The issue of handling reprojections therefore becomes a problem of classical spherical trigonometry. General algorithms exist for determining the overlap of polygons in Cartesian space (O'Rourke 1998). We have modified this approach for use in spherical coordinates to determine the intersection polygon on the sphere (a convex hull) and applied Girard's Theorem to calculate the polygon's area.

The result is that for any two overlapping pixels, we can determine the area of the sky from the input pixel that contributes energy to the output pixel. This provides not only a mechanism for accurately distributing input energy to output pixels but, as we shall see, a natural weighting mechanism when combining overlapping images. Our approach implicitly assumes that the polygon defining a single pixel can be approximated by the set of great circle segments connecting the pixel's corners. Since even the largest pixels in any realistic image are on the order of a degree across, the non-linearities along a pixel edge are insignificant. Furthermore, the only effect of this assumption would be on the astrometric accuracy of the energy location information and would amount to a very small fraction (typically less that 0.01) of the size of a pixel. Total energy is still conserved. Finally, this design easily supports parallel processing because each image can be processed independently of the others.

3.2.   Background Modeling and Rectification

If several images are to be combined into a mosaic, they must all be projected onto a common coordinate system (see above) and then any discrepancies in brightness or background must be removed. Our assumption is that the input images are all calibrated to an absolute energy scale (i.e., brightnesses are absolute and should not be modified) and that any discrepancies between the images are due to variations in their background levels that are terrestrial or instrumental in origin.

The Montage background matching algorithm is based on the assumption that terrestrial and instrumental backgrounds can be described by simple functions or surfaces (e.g., slopes and offsets). Stated more generally, we assume that the "non-sky" background has very little energy in any but the lowest spatial frequencies. If this not the case, it is unlikely that any generalized background matching algorithm will be able distinguish between "sky" and rapidly varying "background"; background removal will then require an approach that depends on detailed knowledge of an individual data set.

Given a set of overlapping images, characterization of the overlap differences is key to determining how each image should be adjusted before combining them. We take the approach of considering each image individually with respect to its neighbors. Specifically, we determine the areas of overlap between each image and its neighbors and use the complete set of overlap pixels in a least-squares fit to determine how each image should be adjusted (e.g., what gradient and offset should be added) to bring it "best" in line with its neighbors. In practice, we only adjust the image by half this amount, since all the neighbors are also being analyzed and adjusted and we want to avoid ringing in the algorithm. After doing this for all the images, we iterate (currently for a fixed number of times though we may later introduce convergence criteria). The final effect is to have subtracted a low-frequency (currently a gradient/offset) background from each image in such a way that the cumulative image-to-image differences are minimized. To speed the computation (and minimize memory usage), we approximate the gradient and offset values by a planar surface fit to the overlap area difference images rather than perform a least squares fit.

4. Conclusions

The Montage image mosaic service will deliver science grade astronomical image mosaics. These science grade images will preserve the photometric and astrometric accuracy of the input images, and rectify the images for terrestrial background emission. Montage will be deployed on the Distributed Terascale Facility, but the code will be portable and available for download. We invite comments and participation from the community, especially for testing and validation. Interested parties should contact the project at montage@ipac.caltech.edu.

Acknowledgments. We wish to thank Dr. Ewa Deelman, Dr. Reagan Moore and Ms. Leesa Brieger for technical guidance and assistance in our efforts to run Montage on parallel processors. Montage is supported by the NASA Earth Sciences Technology Office Computing Technologies program, under Cooperative Agreement Notice NCC 5-6261.

References

O' Rourke, J. 1998, in Computational Geometry, (Cambridge University Press), 220.

Astronomical Data Analysis Software and Systems XII
ASP Conference Series, Vol. 295, 2003
H. E. Payne, R. I. Jedrzejewski, and R. N. Hook, eds.

Efficient Distribution of Computational Load on a Beowulf-Like Cluster

Luca Fini, Marcel Carbillet

INAF—Osservatorio Astrofisico di Arcetri, Firenze, I-50125, Italy

Abstract. The CAOS Application Builder is a Graphical Programming Environment which allows the building of complex simulation applications by putting together elementary blocks. The resulting simulation programs are often very heavy in computational needs and could be profitably run on Beowulf-like clusters, provided the computational load can be efficiently distributed on the CPUs. In the paper we describe a project to provide the CAOS Application Builder with software tools which allow the user to optimize the distribution of blocks on a multi-CPU machine and show a few preliminary results.

1. Introduction

CAOS and AIRY are two sets of tools designed to allow the building of complex simulation programs specifically targeted to adaptive optics (CAOS) and interferometric image restoration (AIRY).

Each package consists essentially of a number of modules which can be assembled together in a simulation program (Carbillet 2001, Correia 2002).

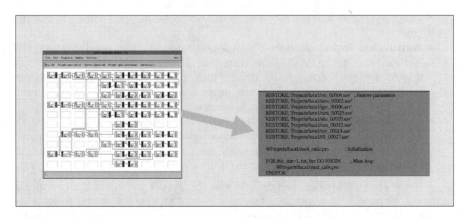

Figure 1. The CAOS Application Builder generates program code

A module is actually a single routine and the simulation program is usually built by assembling a sequence of calls to proper modules and wrapping everything within an iteration loop. In order to simplify the design of application programs by hiding the actual code of the simulation algorithms, the packages are provided with the Application Builder[1] (Fini 2001), a Graphic Programming Environment where application programs can be assembled in a graphical manner and the actual simulation code is generated automatically (see Figure 1).

The CAOS/AIRY systems and the Application Builder have been developed under IDL and are currently targeted to IDL programs, although the same techniques could be applied to other programming environments as well.

Simulation programs are typically very CPU intensive, thus the ability to run production simulations on a high performance parallel machines is quite appealing.

Unfortunately most current programs (and notably both CAOS and AIRY) have been designed for scalar machines and should be rewritten, at least partially, to exploit the capabilities of parallel architectures and, moreover, programming for parallelism is not usually an easy task.

2. Common Parallelization Strategies

Parallelizing programs is in principle a simple job: the program is subdivided into partially independent tasks which can be executed concurrently on various CPUs. The actual improvement in performance, however, depends critically on how the program is divided into tasks and on the architecture of the parallel machine and its actual performance. To divide a program into tasks one can follow essentially three strategies:

- **Parallelize core algorithms**. This is done by identifying the "core" of the program, i.e., the portions of code where it spends most of the running time and implementing a parallel version of that part of the program (D'Amore 2003). This approach is well suited whenever the program actually contains a few and well identified cores, which is not always the case.
- **Subdivide input domain**. Simulation programs are usually structured as iterations on the input domain space. It is sometimes possible to identify one of the space dimensions along which iterations are independent from each other and then subdivide the input along that dimension so that each CPU of a parallel machine operates on a subset of the input domain.
- **Parallelize the program as a whole**, i.e., analyze the program's structure and redesign it carefully to identify concurrent tasks in some optimal way. This approach is a very general one, and is substantially independent of the architecture of the program, but is also the most complex.

All the three strategies, alone or even used together, can yield improvements in execution time, but in any case the need for data exchange among tasks must be carefully considered. On most parallel machines, and notably on Beowulf clusters, task-to-task data communication is performed through a comparatively

---

[1]Due to historical reasons the name "CAOS Application Builder" is often used, but the tool can be used for assembling AIRY related programs too.

slow channel so that the related overhead can easily spoil the time improvement gained with parallelization.

3. Parallelization Made Easy

The third parallelization strategy quoted above is the most general, but also the most challenging in that the complexity of the program structure may notably be increased when the code is redesigned for parallelism. Moreover parallel programming skills are pretty unusual in the common curricula of physicists or engineers who are the main users of the CAOS system.

The aim of this work is thus to exploit the automatic code generation capabilities of the Application Builder to implement a code generator which can automatically produce source code optimized for a target Beowulf architecture.

What is most important is that all the essential tools to analyze the structure of the program and to generate the equivalent code are already there because they are also needed for the scalar version of the Application Builder.

4. How Do We Proceed?

In order to allow the Application Builder to generate optimized parallel code, it must be augmented with three tools:

- Code Profiler. It is essentially a modification of the Application Builder code generator which includes calls to profiling routines in the program's code. During a sample run of the program, data on execution time and on the amount of data exchanged between modules are gathered and stored in a profile table.
- Enhanced code generator. Based on profile table data, linear programming techniques are used to subdivide modules into tasks in an optimal manner, so that the code is suitable to be executed on a grid of computers. The code generator also includes calls to proper data exchange routines based on the the standard MPI library for task-to-task communication.
- Cluster Evaluation Tool. A simple tool which characterizes the performances of a given Beowulf cluster in order to guide the optimization of the task allocation process.

A simulation program life cycle can thus be as follows: a) build the graphic representation of the simulation program by using the Application Builder just as before (or open an existing simulation program); b) select the profiling option and run a sample version of the program on a sensible but small subset of the input data using any scalar machine; c) evaluate the cluster characteristics by using the suitable tool (or get the same info from a previously stored table); d) let the Application Builder generate code for your target grid of computers. e) run the parallel version of the program to your satisfaction.

5. Conclusion

By exploiting the code generation capabilities of an existing Graphic Programming Environment it is possible to implement a system which is capable of generating code optimized for running on parallel system of the Beowulf class.

Most of the code needed is already part of the existing CAOS Application Builder and we have presented the architecture of the tools to be added to it for the purpose of parallel code generation. The coding is currently on the way and will yield a beta version in the near future.

More information about the CAOS and the AIRY packages can be found at:

`http://www.arcetri.astro.it/caos`

References

Carbillet, M., Fini, L., Femenía, B., Riccardi, A., Esposito, S., Viard, E., Delplanke, F. & Hubin, N. 2001, in ASP Conf. Ser., Vol. 238, Astronomical Data Analysis Software and Systems X, ed. F. R. Harnden, Jr., F. A. Primini, & H. E. Payne (San Francisco: ASP), 349

Correia, S., Carbillet, M., Boccacci, P., Bertero, M., Fini, L. 2002, A&A, 387, 733.

D'Amore, L., Guarracino, M.R., Laccetti, G. 2003, "On the Parallelization of a Commercial PSE for Scientific Computation", to appear in "Proceedings of IEEE International Conference on Parallel and Distributed Processing", Genova, Italy.

Fini, L., Carbillet, M., & Riccardi, A. 2001, in ASP Conf. Ser., Vol. 238, Astronomical Data Analysis Software and Systems X, ed. F. R. Harnden, Jr., F. A. Primini, & H. E. Payne (San Francisco: ASP), 253

Astronomical Data Analysis Software and Systems XII
ASP Conference Series, Vol. 295, 2003
H. E. Payne, R. I. Jedrzejewski, and R. N. Hook, eds.

Mac OS X for Astronomy

Francesco Pierfederici, Norbert Pirzkal, Richard N. Hook

ESO/ST-ECF Karl-Schwarzschild-Str. 2 D-85748 Garching Germany

Abstract. Mac OS X is the new Unix based version of the Macintosh operating system. It combines a high performance DisplayPDF user interface with a standard BSD UNIX subsystem and provides users with simultaneous access to a broad range of applications which were not previously available on a single system such as Microsoft Office and Adobe Photoshop, as well as legacy X11-based scientific tools and packages like IRAF, SuperMongo, MIDAS, etc. The combination of a modern GUI layered on top of a familiar UNIX environment paves the way for new, more flexible and powerful astronomical tools to be developed while assuring compatibility with already existing, older programs. In this paper, we outline the strengths of the Mac OS X platform in a scientific environment, astronomy in particular, and point to the numerous astronomical software packages available for this platform; most notably the Scisoft collection which we have compiled.

1. Introduction

With their new UNIX based operating system, PowerPC based computers from Apple have become the latest computer platform to become attractive for astronomy. Using more than one operating system has become the norm in astronomy today where UNIX is used to get the work done (thanks to its robustness and value as a number crunching machine), and Windows applications are used to communicate results with others (and read administrative e-mails containing MS Word attachments). This has meant having to use more than one computer or running Windows under emulation under Linux. Neither of these two solutions is particularly efficient. While being a bona fide BSD UNIX operating system, Mac OS X manages to bridge an important gap by allowing users to use standard Unix applications such as IRAF, SuperMongo, and LaTeX side by side with "industry standard" applications such as MS Word, MS Powerpoint, and Adobe Photoshop. At the same time, Mac OS X offers ease of installation, use and configuration, making it an ideal operating system for both personal workstations and laptops.

2. Scisoft

Scisoft is a project within the European Southern Observatory (ESO) to provide a collection of astronomical software utilities, mostly public domain tools devel-

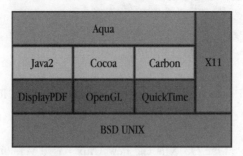

Figure 1.   Mac OS X has a layered structure based on standard BSD
UNIX. Modern services like DisplayPDF are build on top of the low
level UNIX layer. At the very top there is a modern and graphically
rich user interface (Aqua).

oped outside ESO, in a uniform way at all four ESO sites and to external users.
Major data-analysis packages (e.g., IRAF/STSDAS, ESO-MIDAS and IDL) are
included as well as many smaller utilities (http://www.eso.org/scisoft).

Noting the popularity of the other versions of Scisoft and the growing acceptance of Apple computers in astronomical environments, we, at the Space
Telescope European Coordinating Facility (ST-ECF), decided to come up with
something similar for Mac OS X. The outcome of this project is the first public
preview release of Scisoft for Mac OS X. Most major Scisoft software packages
have been successfully ported to the Macintosh. While the majority of them
still require X11, a couple of notable exceptions (GNUPlot and PGPlot) now
have a native Aqua interface. Interestingly enough, a Mac OS X native port
results in increased functionality being gained for free. The obvious example is
the ability to produce PDF output natively. The Mac version of Scisoft comes
with a user friendly and hands-free installer. No special pre/post installation
setup is required, other than installing X11.

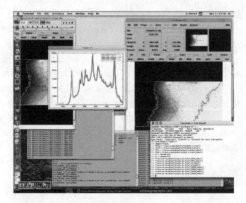

Figure 2.   X11 based IRAF and DS9 running side by side with the
Aqua version of GNUPlot on Mac OS X.

Future versions of Scisoft for Mac OS X will, resources permitting, feature more Aqua ports of astronomical packages which will not require the X11 environment. In addition, the Fink project is bringing the full world of UNIX Open Source software to Mac OS X (http://fink.sf.net).

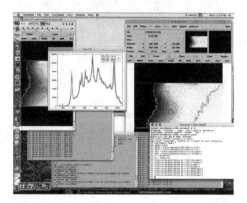

Figure 3.   Aqua in action: double buffering of on-screen graphics, per-pixel transparency and alpha channel, full anti-aliasing on top of hardware accelerated DisplayPDF provide a responsive and rich User Interface.

3.   Advanced Graphics

Mac OS X is based on hardware accelerated DisplayPDF (Quartz). This means a quick and responsive User Interface together with a device-independent and resolution-independent rendering of anti-aliased text, raster and vector graphics. Quartz technologies offer, thanks to the PDF engine, a tight integration with print services (what you see really is what you get). In particular, every Mac OS X application that is able to print can generate PDF output. Other features include: automatic color management (via ColorSync), system-wide support for all the major font formats (TrueType, Type 1 and OpenType), system-wide support for Roman and non Roman languages, use of industry standard PCI and AGP video cards, out-of-the-box support for all the major input/output devices, hardware accelerated OpenGL, compatibility with X11 applications (with use of XFree86), and cut and paste from between Aqua and X11 applications.

4.   Productivity

Perhaps the biggest advantages of modern Macs are the ease of installation, use, customization and administration of their OS and the high quality of their hardware. This offers, finally, something surprisingly close to a hassle-free operating system, most of the time.

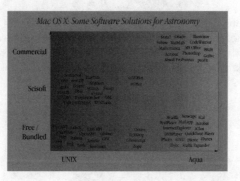

Figure 4.   Thousands of applications are already available for Mac OS X, ranging from free Open Source tools to commercial packages. The Fink project and Scisoft for Mac OS X are among the most active groups porting legacy UNIX software to the Mac.

5.   Closing Remarks

The Scisoft for Mac OS X[1] home page, at the time of writing (end of October 2002), includes the following software packages: cFITSIO 2.420, DS9 2.1, eclipse 4.3.0, GNUplot 3.8h.0, ggobi, gsl 1.0, IRAF 2.12.1 with TABLES/STSDAS 3.0, etc., ESO-Midas 02SEPpl0.9, netCDF 3.5.0, pgplot 5.2.2, Python 2.2.1 with Numeric, PIL, etc., SExtractor 2.2.2, Tiny Tim 6.0, slalib 1.6, SWarp 1.36, WeightWatcher 1.3, WCSTools 3.1.2, X11IRAF 1.3, and XEphem 3.5.2.

---

[1]http://www.stecf.org/macosxscisoft/

Astronomical Data Analysis Software and Systems XII
ASP Conference Series, Vol. 295, 2003
H. E. Payne, R. I. Jedrzejewski, and R. N. Hook, eds.

The Fasti Project

C. Baffa, V. Biliotti, A. Checcucci, S. Gennari, E. Giani, F. Lisi

INAF—Osservatorio Astrofisico di Arcetri, Largo E. Fermi 5, Firenze, Italy

V. Gavrioussev, M. Sozzi

IRA-CNR, Sezione di Firenze, Largo E. Fermi 5, Firenze, Italy

G. Marcucci

Dipartimento di Astronomia, Università di Firenze, Italy

Abstract.   Fasti is a controller architecture originally developed for fast infrared astronomical array detectors, and intended to be powerful and extendible. It is suitable to be used with both DRO and CCD detectors and it is also well suited for very fast optical detectors, as those used in Adaptive Optics. In the framework of the LBT project, a L^3CCD version is in development. More information can be found at
http://www.arcetri.astro.it/irlab/fasti.

1.   Fasti general description

Fasti is an innovative design for infrared and fast optical detectors and is mainly implemented as software. All circuit logic is built using programmable chips, the sequence generator is a specialized microprocessor build in a PGA (Programmable Gate Array), all the system is controlled by a Linux embedded controller, the waveforms are described by an ad hoc assembler.

Fasti is meant to be a light electronic system, and is designed to be modular, flexible, extendible and to avoid obsolescence as much as possible. It is divided into modules with clear-cut boundaries. Fasti is seen as a network device, giving very few constraints to the controlling architecture. Fasti can hold up to four completely different waveforms, so is capable of controlling the detector in radically different operation modes.

The first uses of Fasti will be the replacement of the Nics (Nics is the Infrared Camera Spectrometer developed by Arcetri Infrared Group for the TNG, the Italian National Telescope Galileo, see Baffa et al. 2001) electronics and the fast LBT (Large Binocular Telescope) wavefront sensor optical detectors control (Esposito et al. (2002), Foppiani et al. (2002)).

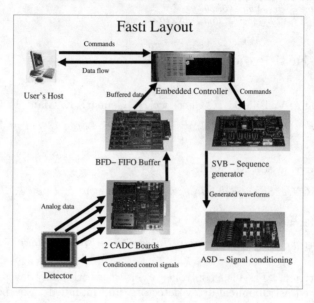

Figure 1.   Fasti general structure. Board images are relative to Nics version

2.   Fasti components

Fasti is designed as modules, its structure can be seen in Figure 1. Fasti building blocks are:

- The embedded computer system, acting as a global controller.
- The internal serial bus for general setup and control.
- The parallel input interface (now a commercial board).
- SVB - the flexible waveform generator.
- CADC - the analog signals conditioning and conversion board.
- BDF - the FIFO and multiplexer board.
- ASD - the digital signal conditioning board.

We describe briefly the main modules.

2.1.   The Waveform Generator

The flexible waveform generator is a custom part of which we had already built the prototype. It is based on a specialized micro-controller, where the waveform definition is built by means of a program in a pseudo assembler language, greatly simplifying the definition of new waveforms. We had already developed all the support software for waveform design and testing. This part, named SVB, can generate not only the standard waveforms to read the full array, but also arbitrary sub-array scan patterns. It can be reprogrammed in seconds, and hold up to four different clocking schemes, which can be selected on a per-integration basis. The SVB is implemented in programmable chips, but, being a conceptual design, can be easily transferred to newer devices.

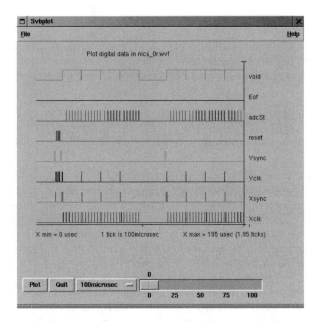

Figure 2.   Plotsv output of a simplified Hawaii IR detector clock sequence

2.2. The Global Controller

Inside Fasti there is a central controller for startup, general housekeeping, global control of operations (start integrations for example), data collection, formatting and buffering, or for data preprocessing when needed. In the present design all this is realized with a diskless embedded computer, using an Intel or Alpha family CPU and few commercial boards. The parallel digital acquisition board and the fast Ethernet interface are hosted here.

2.3. The Conversion Subsystem

This part has been custom developed. This section mainly consists of a small number (4 for NICMOS3 and Hawaii) of analog to digital converters and some glue logic. We will use high quality 16 bit converters for the Nics version, and very fast, lower resolution (12 or 14 bits), converters for the Adaptive Optics version.

2.4.   The Analog Interfaces

This part consists mainly of the bias level generation, of digital clocks level shifting and of detector output conditioning. For the Infrared version this part inherits the Nics design, and for L^{3}CCD uses a Marconi commercial board.

3.   Fasti ancillary software

Fasti has some support software to ease its use and integration in a particular application.

- Svbasm. To develop specific waveforms, we designed an ad hoc assembler, and we wrote a cross assembler program. It has integer and floating point capabilities and has been written using the GNU bison parser generator.
- Emusvb. To check the correctness of assembled waveforms, we wrote a software emulator of the sequence generator board. It is implemented as a *state machine*, and is accurate enough to reproduce the internal checksum of the board during waveforms output.
- Plotsvb. To graphically verify the waveforms generated, we developed a specialized interactive plotting program which emulates the output of a logic analyzer. It is written in perl_tk and permits plotting and panning of the multiple waveforms generated. An example can be seen in Figure 2
- Ftest. To test single components of Fasti, or to execute low level operations, we developed a text menu application which gives both a fine grain control on the machine and the ability to execute higher level tasks as a series of integrations.

References

Baffa, C., Comoretto, G., Gennari, S., Lisi, F., Oliva, E., Biliotti, V., Checcucci, A., G., Gavrioussev, V., Giani, E., Ghinassi, F., Hunt, L. K., Maiolino, R., Mannucci, F., Marcucci, G., Sozzi, M., Stefanini, P., Testi, L. 2001, A&A, 378, 722

Baffa, C. 2001, IV Convegno Nazionale di Astronomia Infrarossa, Ciprini, S. ed., Perugia, Italy

Esposito, S., Riccardi, A., Storm, J., Accardo, M., Baffa, C., Biliotti, V., Foppiani, I., Puglisi, A., Ragazzoni, R., Ranfagni, P., Stefanini, P., Salinari, P., Seifert, W., Storm, J. 2002, SPIE Conference AS06, Wizinowich, P. L. Ed., in press

Foppiani, I., Baffa, C., Biliotti, V., Bregoli, G., Cosentino, G, Giani, E., Esposito, S., Marano, B., Salinari, P. 2002, SPIE Conference AS06, Wizinowich, P.L. Ed., in press

Part 11. Outreach and Education

Astronomical Data Analysis Software and Systems XII
ASP Conference Series, Vol. 295, 2003
H. E. Payne, R. I. Jedrzejewski, and R. N. Hook, eds.

AstroVirgil: A Chandra Data Analysis Tool for the General Public

Steve McDonald

Silicon Spaceships and University of Massachusetts Boston

Srikanth Buddha

University of Massachusetts Boston

Abstract.   This paper reviews AstroVirgil, a user friendly program for the analysis of Chandra event files. AstroVirgil integrates photon filtering and visualization into a single GIU based tool. Photons can be filtered using custom GUI panels based on spatial position (in multiple coordinate systems), photon energy level (using multiple measures) or time of arrival. Filtered photons can be displayed as images, spectrums or lightcurves. This paper also reviews some of the performance and memory consequences of performing non-disk file based processing.

AstroVirgil is a GPLed pure Java program. It is built on top of JSky, a collection of reusable Java components developed at ESO and first described at ADASS'99. AstroVirgil is available from: www.SiliconSpaceships.com.

1.   A Step Back

The web is full of scientific data sets that are used to discover the nature of the universe. Our goal is to empower non-scientists so they can also use this data as a vehicle for exploration. This paper reviews AstroVigil. It is an X-ray analysis tool designed for high school students and amateur astronomers. It is not intended for scientists; they already have their own tools. Instead it is intended to make the Chandra archive usable and relevant to the general public.

Before discussing the details of AstroVirgil, we need to step back and consider the earlier days of astronomy. By the year 1611, astronomical research using a telescope was open to a large number of people. Since the only resources a would-be astronomer needed was glass and grit, they were only limited by their talent and their time. Those with an interest in astronomy could contribute to the field and join the quest for knowledge or at least closely follow the field as it advanced.

But those welcoming conditions never last. Over time, resources become the limiting factor. Doing significant work requires larger and more expensive telescopes. Those without funding are left out of the game. No matter how great their interest or talent, the work done by researchers becomes more remote and the unfunded general public become more alienated. We are now in a world where orbital telescopes are very important, but most people don't live in a country that can launch one. And for citizens of the developing nations, orbital telescopes and their data simply aren't relevant. The forefront of a field even as well loved as astronomy becomes more and more distant.

Can this change? Over the last 20 years, the processing power in the average home or classroom has gone from nothing to astonishing. During this same time, scientific instruments have left the analog world and been swept up by the digital revolution. Archives of these digital data sets have made their way onto the world wide web where they are available and free to anyone. Are we still in a world where resources present a huge barrier? The very best data and vast computational resources are plentiful. Is it possible to return to the days of 1611 when people were only limited by their talent and their time? If we build an X-ray analysis tool for the masses, will they come? We have built it, so soon we will find out if they care.

2.　AstroVirgil Overview

AstroVirgil is a X-ray analysis tool designed for people who aren't astronomers such as students or amateur astronomers. It is for those with an interest in high energy astronomy, but a limited background. It was built on top of JSky, an open source pure Java application from ESO. AstroVirgil was built with the help of several graduate students at the University of Massachusetts Boston. More information on the program, as well as screen shots and download information, is available at www.SiliconSpaceships.com.

AstroVirgil is not intended to replace any existing Chandra tools. It lacks an awful lot of important features. It currently does not support: forward folding, PSF, ARF, RDF, CALDB, HRC, HETG, LEGT or scripting. If you are fluent in Chandra-speak, you can see there are many very important things missing. It is hoped that even with these limitations amateurs can still work on projects they find interesting.

2.1.　Memory Based Processing

Existing X-ray data analysis tools such as CIAO or funtools typically operate by reading in a FITS event file, performing some operation and writing out a FITS file. This approach works well with both their command line interface and their scripting interface. However, AstroVirgil needs to be a much more novice user friendly program. Therefore, it implements a Graphical User Interface. The user controls factors such as the coordinate system and display parameters via menus and buttons. To see what the possible options are the user need not refer to a manual, but just looks at what the menus have to offer.

Typically, Chandra event files are under 100 MB. Most are small enough that can comfortably be loaded into RAM where they can be manipulated more quickly. Files of this size can contain data on roughly a million individual photons. Responding to the user's request to filter and display this many photons takes less than a second. For those Chandra files that are too large to fit in memory, AstroVirgil won't work. Since it is a tool for amateurs, it is not required to handle all Chandra data. AstroVirgil need only solve the simpler problems needed to engage the amateur community.

2.2. Photon Filtering

When using the Advanced CCD Imaging Spectrometer (ACIS), the sky position, approximate energy and time of arrival for each photon is recorded in the FITS event file. From this data cube, AstroVirgil can create either an image, a spectrum or a light curve. AstroVirgil also supports filtering of photons based on sky position, energy level or time of arrival. This provides the user with an amount of flexibility not possible with data from optical or radio telescopes. Detectors in lower energy astronomy do not register every photon. Instead, they integrate photons over time until a detectable signal has been accumulated. To answer specific questions, the choice of which photon to integrate is made before the observation by placing filters or prisms in front of the sensor. The Chandra X-ray Telescope need not employ filters. That is done during data analysis.

With AstroVirgil, the user can create a spatial filter by drawing a polygon on the image. Photons can either be excluded because they are inside or outside the polygon. Once the spatial filter has been created, spectra and light curves can be created that only use a subset of the photons in the original observation.

With AstroVirgil, the user can create an energy filter by selecting the region of interest by clicking on the graph of the spectrum. The images and light curves then display only the photons in the defined energy range.

With AstroVirgil, the user can filter photons based on their time of arrival. The user selects the desired time by picking points on a graph of the light curve. Then, the image and spectrum displays only use the photons with the right arrival times based on their time stamps.

These filters can be combined in many ways. Images can be made from just the hard or just the soft photons. Spectra can be made from just the photons when the source is brightest. Lightcurves can be created from just a small region of the image. Since all of these filters are created by clicking on images and graphs, the user need not understand the internal representation of information. Analysis tools for scientists expect the user to understand the units energy is expressed in, how Chandra keeps track of time and its spatial coordinate systems. While this does not present a challenge for astronomers, it does present barriers for beginners. By eliminating these barriers, we reduce what the user needs to learn. If the things to learn can be reduced enough, a threshold will be crossed and X-ray astronomy will be available to new communities.

3. Science with AstroVirgil

By filtering photons and analyzing images, spectra and lightcurves users can gain an understanding of astronomical objects. For many reasonably bright sources, the user may measure its temperature. For non-point sources the user can explore whether they are isothermal and if there are variations in heavy element ratios. For sources that show a variable light curve, the user can see if the image or spectrum vary over the same intervals.

The user can ask these questions and others for any non-grating ACIS observation in the Chandra archive. In the near future, we hope to support grating observations by reading Chandra 'pha2' files.

A group of students at Somerville High School is currently working on Science Fair projects using AstroVirgil and Chandra data. With help from scientists at the Harvard-Smithsonian Center for Astrophysics, these students will measure the rate of cooling of supernova remnants, survey the X-ray sources near the galactic center and compute the geometry of eclipsing X-ray binary star systems.

4. Future Plans

AstroVirgil is currently available on the web at www.SiliconSpaceships.com. It is downloaded by someone every day. We will continue to change and extend AstroVirgil based on suggestions from astronomers and users. Over time, we hope it will become a much more complete and powerful tool.

The Chandra Calibration Database (CALDB) is large, consuming roughly 1 GB of disk space. Even if this were made available to amateurs, it is doubtful they would want to give up that much disk space. We hope to develop a 10 MB mini-calibration database that contains information of the frequency-based varying response of the telescope at a coarse resolution.

Much interesting work can be done with grating observations. In the near future, we plan to extend AstroVirgil so it can read and display the processed pha2 files available from the archive. We have no plans to display grating observations based on event files.

We welcome suggestions for extending AstroVirgil or including other data sets that might engage students and the amateur community.

Acknowledgments.   The AstroVirgil prototype was developed as part of a software engineering class at the University of Massachusetts Boston. The development team was lead by Srikanth Buddha and included Tim Hok, Hua Tang, Tetsya Abe and Naveen Yeruva.

Astronomical Data Analysis Software and Systems XII
ASP Conference Series, Vol. 295, 2003
H. E. Payne, R. I. Jedrzejewski, and R. N. Hook, eds.

NBodyLab: A Testbed for Undergraduates Utilizing a Web Interface to NEMO and MD-GRAPE2 Hardware

Vicki Johnson

Interconnect Technologies Corporation, Claremont, CA

Peter Teuben

Astronomy Department, University of Maryland, College Park, MD

Bryan Penprase

Physics Department, Pomona College, Claremont, CA

Abstract. An N-body simulation testbed called NBodyLab was developed at Pomona College as a teaching tool for undergraduates. The testbed runs under Linux and provides a web interface to selected back-end NEMO modeling and analysis tools, and several integration methods which can optionally use an MD-GRAPE2 supercomputer card in the server to accelerate calculation of particle-particle forces. The testbed provides a framework for using and experimenting with the main components of N-body simulations: data models and transformations, numerical integration of the equations of motion, analysis and visualization products, and acceleration techniques (in this case, special purpose hardware). The testbed can be used by students with no knowledge of programming or Unix, freeing such students and their instructor to spend more time on scientific experimentation. The advanced student can extend the testbed software and/or more quickly transition to the use of more advanced Unix-based toolsets such as NEMO, Starlab and model builders such as GalactICS. Cosmology students at Pomona College used the testbed to study collisions of galaxies with different speeds, masses, densities, collision angles, angular momentum, etc., attempting to simulate, for example, the Tadpole Galaxy and the Antenna Galaxies. The testbed framework is available as open-source to assist other researchers and educators. Recommendations are made for testbed enhancements.

1. Introduction and Motivations

NBodyLab[1] is a web-based N-body simulation testbed for undergraduate astronomy students. It was developed for the Astronomical Computing Initiative at Pomona College and used initially to support the curriculum for a course in

---

[1]http://www.nbodylab.com

cosmology. Students can use the testbed to simulate stellar dynamics: dynamics of single galaxies (relaxation, scattering and collapse); interacting galaxies (collisions and mergers); and to explore interesting structures like tidal tails.

At Pomona, a liberal arts college, students work primarily with Microsoft products and some students, even physics seniors, are unfamiliar with Unix and/or programming. NBodyLab runs server-side, under Linux, and supports a CGI-based web interface for ease of use by students with little background in computing. Its open-source framework was designed to enable students with programming ability to learn scientific computing and refine the software components. NEMO programs provide commonly used data models and analysis functions. NEMO is a widely used, advanced stellar dynamics toolbox that runs under Unix. Students with astrophysics knowledge can add additional data models and analysis programs from NEMO, or write their own, and they are encouraged to master NEMO natively under Unix. A menu of data sets is also offered, including, for example, disk-halo-bulge models of Andromeda and the Milky Way, produced by the package GalactICS (Kuijken & Dubinski 1995). To accelerate the particle-particle force calculations, a desktop supercomputer card, the MD-GRAPE2, may optionally be used.

2.   Input Data Parameter Selection

Using a web interface, the user can select the number of galaxies to be modeled, and for each, the model type, number of particles for a model, scale factor and type, rotation about axes, shift, and addition of velocity addition and spin. Models include, from NEMO, Plummer, baredisk, exponential disk, homogeneous sphere, polytrope and spiral. Scale factor choices include scaling mass and velocities, positions, or positions and velocities while retaining the virial ratio.

3.   Model Generation and Data Selection

If a model is selected, the appropriate NEMO program is called. Prebuilt datasets, not generated from NEMO programs, include combined and separate disk, bulge and halo components of Milky Way and Andromeda models, produced by the galactICS model builder.

The model and/or datasets are transformed, if requested, and stacked into one data file in preparation for the numerical integration.

4.   N-body Evolution and MD-GRAPE2

The user inputs integration options for the type of integrator, number of iterations, output increment, $\Delta-t$, and the softening factor.

The force exerted on each of the N particles by all of the other N-1 particles is computed for each time step, from Newton's law of gravitation. By Newton's second law of motion, the force calculation has yielded the acceleration for each particle. Two first-order differential equations involving acceleration and velocity must be solved, using numerical integration, to estimate new positions and velocities of each particle for the next time step. Integration options include NEMO's `hackcode1`, 2nd order leapfrog, 2nd, 4th and 6th order symplectic, 4th order Runge-Kutta, and others. Except for `hackcode1`, all may run optionally with the MD-GRAPE2.

The MD-GRAPE2 is designed specifically to accelerate force calculations between a list of particles. The MD-GRAPE2 (molecular dynamics-gravity pipeline) card runs at 64 GFlops, peak, has a PCI interface, and can provide the computational power of, roughly, a 24 node Beowulf cluster for direct summation of forces. The MD-GRAPE board has memory for five hundred thousand particle positions. The card is manufactured in Japan, costs less then $20,000, and can also be used for forces used in molecular dynamics simulations.

5. Analyses, Displays and Viewers

The user specifies the plot observation plane, plot axes range, and whether the following should be produced: animated GIF, image and velocity maps, radial profiles, slit spectrogram simulation, and debugging information. These analyses products and displays are presented on the resulting web pages and are produced by corresponding NEMO programs.

An ASCII dataset is produced by the initial and final states. A binary-only Windows OpenGL viewer supplied by the MD-GRAPE2 vendor allows the user to visualize, rotate and scale the results in three-space.

6. Examples of Student Exercises

Examples of student exercises include:

- *Single galaxy* – How does a Plummer model evolve with time? What are the central mass distributions and velocity dispersions? Experiment with an exponential disk: what does its rotation curve look like? Comment on the effects of the addition of angular momentum.
- *Dynamics of two galaxies* – Make two Plummer spheres interact by colliding and merging. How does the new equilibrium configuration compare in shape and size to the original? Try glancing blows where the spheres are sent at various impact parameters and constant velocity. Try to create a polar ring galaxy by dropping a compact dense galaxy normal to a disk galaxy in a path perpendicular to the disk.

7. Future Plans

Due to limitations in time and budget, many desirable features were not implemented, including a scheduler to handle concurrent requests for the MD-GRAPE2, better error handling, more data modeling capabilities, a simple open-source OpenGL visualizer, instructions and translations for using `partiview` (Teuben et al. 2001), a popular viewer, more efficient and accurate integration methods, and a library of student experiments. Pomona College has recently upgraded its telescopes (14 inch and one meter) and future research projects could relate observational data to simulations.

8. Acknowledgments

Technical assistance from Dr. Bruce Elmegreen, IBM, RIKEN (the Japanese Institute of Physical and Chemical Research), and the Peta Computing Institute is gratefully acknowledged. NBodyLab was developed by Interconnect Technologies Corporation through a grant to Dr. Bryan Penprase of Pomona College from the Fletcher Jones Foundation.

References

Kuijken, K. & Dubinski, J., 1995, MNRAS, 277, 1341

Narumi, T. et al. 1999, Molecular Simulation, 21, 401

Stein, L., 1998, Guide to Programming with CGI.pm (New York: Wiley)

Teuben, P. J. 1994, in ASP Conf. Ser., Vol. 77, Astronomical Data Analysis Software and Systems IV, ed. R. A. Shaw, H. E. Payne, & J. J. E. Hayes (San Francisco: ASP), 398

Teuben, P. J. et al. 2001, in ASP Conf. Ser., Vol. 238, Astronomical Data Analysis Software and Systems X, ed. F. R. Harnden, Jr., F. A. Primini, & H. E. Payne (San Francisco: ASP), 499

Astronomical Data Analysis Software and Systems XII
ASP Conference Series, Vol. 295, 2003
H. E. Payne, R. I. Jedrzejewski, and R. N. Hook, eds.

Astronomical Web Sites

Anthony J. Ferro

Steward Observatory/NICMOS Project, University of Arizona, Tucson, AZ 85721

Abstract. This BoF was an informal get-together to discuss the trials and tribulations involved in creating and running a web site associated with the wacky world of astronomy.

1. Open Forum Discussion

Twenty to thirty people attended the session. Some of the discussion topics were:

- Types of Web Sites: internal (inventory, control systems); group (collaboration); professional (services, preprints).
- Development Tools: various editors (vi, Bluefish, Composer) as well as environments (Zope).
- Platforms: operating system (Linux, Unix, Microsoft); server (Apache, AOLserver).
- Hardware: bandwidth and compute power.
- Network Relations: isolating web servers from the rest of an internal network; supporting efficient protocols; warning network administrators when large number of hits is expected (e.g., when a press release occurs).
- Web Security: the server, CGI scripts and problems of popularity.
- Services: new realm of potential problems and solutions.

The offering of web services and generation and use of XML were not discussed much, other than their impact on the general running of a web site. These topics were well covered in the tutorial and other presentations.

Astronomical Data Analysis Software and Systems XII
ASP Conference Series, Vol. 295, 2003
H. E. Payne, R. I. Jedrzejewski, and R. N. Hook, eds.

Teaching Scientific Computing with N-Body Simulations

Vicki Johnson

Interconnect Technologies Corporation, Claremont, CA

Peter Teuben

Astronomy Department, University of Maryland, College Park, MD

Abstract. The classic N-body problem can be used to teach many dimensions of scientific computing. The BoF participants were invited to discuss approaches and motivations.

1. Birds-of-a-Feather Discussion Topics

Many undergraduate students are not learning how to program, how to use Unix, or the basic principles of scientific computing and numerical estimation. The classic N-body problem can be used to illustrate many dimensions of scientific computing, The BoF participants were invited to discuss how to use the classic N-body problem to introduce students to modeling, algorithms, the development of simple programs to implement basic algorithms, the Unix environment and open source tools, tradeoffs between efficiency and accuracy, numerical analysis, visualization and animation, scalability, and supercomputing (e.g., GRAPE cards) and parallel programming, and interdisciplinary uses of N-body simulations, such as in computational biology and astrophysics.

The group generally agreed that the N-body problem is a good teaching tool. As you progress with the N-body problem, opportunities to teach yourself naturally arise—how to improve accuracy, deal with long run times and lots of output, visualizing the results, etc. The consensus was that the N-body problem lends itself well to a simple Java implementation, which would be a good starting point for young students. An appealing approach is to make the motions in N-body simulations fun to play with, by tweaking parameters for spin, rotation and scaling. Above the level of equations, give students a game-like feel for motions that could be almost a tactile experience. Wolfram's work shows both complexity and fun can arise from simple examples. For more information, see `http://www.nbodylab.com/adass2002-bof.html`.

Part 12. Software Development and Testing

Astronomical Data Analysis Software and Systems XII
ASP Conference Series, Vol. 295, 2003
H. E. Payne, R. I. Jedrzejewski, and R. N. Hook, eds.

Source Code Management and Software Distribution using Open Source Technologies

Martin Bly

Rutherford Appleton Laboratory, Chilton, Didcot, Oxfordshire OX11 0QX, United Kingdom

Alasdair Allan

School of Physics, University of Exeter, Stocker Road, Exeter EX4 4QL, United Kingdom

Tim Jenness

Joint Astronomy Centre, 660 N. A'ohōkū Place, University Park, Hilo, HI 96720

Abstract. The Starlink Software Collection (USSC) runs on three different platforms and contains approximately 130 separate software items, totaling over 6 million lines of code. Distribution of such large software systems and installation at multiple remote sites has always been problematic due to the complex web of inter-dependencies such systems invariably generate.

The rise of the Open Source movement has brought standard tools into common use to cope with such large and complex tasks. The RedHat Package Manager (RPM) software is one such which is available for many platforms. We have shown it is possible to automate the distribution and installation of the Starlink Software using RPM. We anticipate that this will vastly simplify installation and package management for Systems Administrators who must support the USSC in production data processing environments.

1. Introduction

The Starlink Software Collection[1] (Bly et al. 2003) is a large collection of software packages comprising subroutine libraries, applications packages and utilities for astronomical data reduction and analysis. The whole collection is governed by a set of interdependencies which not only complicates the process of building the software but also which packages depend on which others at runtime.

Each package has its own `makefile` which contains the rules defining how and in what order the components should be built, and their dependencies on other packages. However, none of the packages are able to trigger the building

---

[1] http://www.starlink.ac.uk/

of another package — this is traditionally done by a master `makefile` which builds the packages in the correct order.

The master `makefile` is maintained by the Software Manager but has two disadvantages — it does not express the package dependencies at run-time, and contains only a simple ordered-list of packages to build — making it difficult to slot a new package into a suitable place in the build sequence. A new approach to managing the build and installation dependencies was needed. We have investigated 'wrapping' the USSC using the RedHat Package Manager (RPM) system (Bailey, 1997) and have shown it is possible to automate the building and distribution and simplify the installation and maintenance of the USSC for Systems Administrators and users.

2.   Why Choose the RPM System

The RedHat Package Manager[2] is becoming ubiquitous in the Linux world, having been adopted by most of the major distributions. It is also supported on may other Unix systems including those supported by Starlink. The RPM system has several advantageous features:

Tracking mechanism – it keeps track of installed packages and package version numbers, and all files associated with each package.

Dependency and dependents checking – RPM checks dependencies of the packages it is processing and warns of conflicts and unfulfilled dependencies, and checks for packages that are dependent on those being processed.

Query capabilities – it has a full suite of query capabilities that provide information about the package, its dependencies and status.

Relocation – RPM can install packages in locations other than the one they were intended to go (provided the set is re-locatable).

Adaptability – the RPM system works with existing build systems, and can easily be used to provide a wrapping for existing package build systems, from the simple to the most complex of systems.

Ease of use – installation of patches and updates can be automated.

Open-Source – the RPM package is open-source and runs on many operating systems.

3.   Wrapping the Starlink Packages

Each Starlink package has its own makefile and documents which conform to a standard template, although the makefile and documents may have slight variations from the standard. This makes them suitable for processing to provide RPM with the information it requires.

---

[2]http://www.rpm.org/

```
[ast]
group=Starlink/Libraries
version=1.5.8
suns=sun210,sun211
requires=htx
buildrequires=sla,ems,chr,sae
fixup=STARBIN/ast_dev
summary=AST - A Library for Handling World Coordinate\
Systems in Astronomy
abstract=The AST library provides a comprehensive range\
of facilities for attaching world coordinate systems to\
astronomical data, for retrieving and interpreting that\
information and for generating graphical output based on it.
```

Figure 1.   A typical **depend.ini** dependency file expressing build and installation dependencies.

RPM requires a 'spec' file for a package, to define the various dependencies. These can be generated by hand or automatically by processing a master dependency list. A template dependency file **depend.ini** was created by hand listing the software group, version, and list of SUNs (Starlink User Notes — the documents) and then a Perl script is used to extract summary and abstract information from the package documents. The **buildrequires** and **fixup** lines are then added by hand examination of the **makefile** to see which files are edited and in what way at installation time. **Buildrequires** expresses the additional packages required at build time and **fixup** expresses files that have to be changed at installation.

A dependency file may contain details of more than one package — the abstract extraction script **getabst.pl** processes all the package entries. Where the document listed in the **depend.ini** file does not have the appropriate LATEX keywords, the keys are left blank. Since this is demonstrating the concept, the system depends on an existing Starlink installation with source files from which it extracts its data.

Once a dependency file is ready, the RPM 'spec' file(s) can be generated. This is the file that controls what RPM does when building and manipulating the package. A Perl script **mkspec.pl** has been produced to interpret the dependency file and generate 'spec' files based on a template for all packages listed in the dependency file.

Existing Starlink installations do not have the source packaged in a single tarball though the makefiles can provide them via the **export_source** target which generates a compressed tarball of the appropriate files. The master **makefile** can generate tarballs for all the packages.

The next step is to create a set of links for each package from an existing USSC installation to the standard location for RPM build directories. A Perl script **mklinks.pl** does this for all the packages in the dependency file, creating links from **/usr/src/redhat/SOURCES** to the source files. Since the default location is `/usr`, one has to be `root` for this and the remaining steps. Once the links are in place, the 'spec' files are copied to the `/usr/src/redhat/SPECS` directory and the `rpm` program can take over to build the RPMs, both source and installation sets.

4.   Results

The resulting RPM files are re-locatable so you don't have to install the packages in the default location (`/star`). Using the `--relocate` command line switch one can instead direct the package to any chosen path — since the normal location is `/star`, one has to be careful where there is an existing (non-RPM) USSC installation. Most packages are easily re-locatable and do not require special tricks to be detailed in the `depend.ini` file. However, some packages do have complex installation requirements and these need to be carefully expressed. The whole collection can be processed to build RPM sets and installations made based on them.

4.1.   Problems

RPM itself requires access to the standard RPM database of dependencies needed to track all the files. This is owned by `root` so general users cannot create and install packages using the standard RPM distribution. At the time this work was undertaken, the facilities in RPM to allow alternative databases didn't work, however a distribution that can use a database elsewhere should be possible.

This work is proof of concept. The technology for extracting dependencies and details from the existing build systems is rather basic, and some Starlink packages are under regular development which tends to change the dependencies. Stable packages such as libraries are easier to deal with. Nevertheless we have demonstrated that RPM can be adapted to deal with an alien software management system.

References

Bailey, E. 1997, "Maximum RPM", Sams, ISBN: 0672311054

Bly, M. J., Giaretta, D. L., Taylor, M. B., & Currie, M. J. 2003, this volume, 445

Astronomical Data Analysis Software and Systems XII
ASP Conference Series, Vol. 295, 2003
H. E. Payne, R. I. Jedrzejewski, and R. N. Hook, eds.

CARMA Software Development

Marc W. Pound[1], N. S. Amarnath[1], Kevin P. Rauch[1], Peter J. Teuben[1], Stephen L. Scott[2], Rick Hobbs[2], Andrew D. Beard[2], Paul Daniel[2], David M. Mehringer[3], Raymond Plante[3], J. Colby Kraybill[4], Melvyn Wright[4], Erik Leitch[5]

Abstract. CARMA (Combined Array for Research in Millimeter-Wave Astronomy) will combine the existing BIMA and OVRO mm interferometers into a single array at a new high altitude site ($\sim$ 8000 ft). A third array, the Sunyaev-Zeldovich Array (SZA), will be built in the next two years and co-located with the CARMA interferometer. The SZA antennas will be available at times for cross-correlation with the CARMA antennas. This combination of heterogeneous antennas and their subsystems bring up new challenges not only in hardware, but also in software and in remote collaborations.

The two existing arrays have their own mature operations software, developed over the last decade, and the SZA software will be partially based on the DASI system currently at the South Pole. For CARMA, the situation is not as simple as choosing one over the other. It is further complicated by the fact that the software developers are dispersed among five institutions and three time zones. Such multi-institution development requires frequent communication, local oversight, and reliable code management tools.

Timeline has forced us to carefully balance reusing existing software, with perhaps wrappers to a new more object oriented approach, and rewriting from scratch. New hardware, such as the correlator, has already resulted in new software, but we anticipate re-using a fair fraction of the existing telescope software.

This paper summarizes our ideas on how we plan to do this, as well as outline what we call the CARMA Software Toolkit and associated Software Engineering aspects.

---

[1]University of Maryland

[2]California Institute of Technology/Owens Valley Radio Observatory

[3]NCSA/University of Illinois

[4]University of California, Berkeley

[5]University of Chicago

1.   Introduction

Two preceding papers by Scott et al. (2003) and Plante et al. (2003) describe the COBRA/CARMA correlator and the need for a new CARMA native data format. The software required to control the CARMA array will be gradually phased in to co-exist with the current array control systems, which will be used as testbeds for the CARMA software.

BIMA uses one central computer, running Solaris (Hoffman et al. 1996; Welch et al. 1996; Yu 2001) controlling all antennas, and is currently starting to use Antenna Computers (AC) running Linux. Antenna Computers are housed in the antennas themselves and are intended to take over some of the functionality of the central computer (e.g., drive system control). OVRO has already been using AC's (microVax), with a VaxStation running VMS as the central control computer. Although the SZA is a newly built array, some of the existing software from the DASI system will be reused.

CARMA will be run by a central Array Control Computer (ACC), running Linux, and each antenna will have a diskless AC running real-time Linux. The ACs will be booted from flash ROM and use NFS to access system disks. All off-line software will be running Linux and Solaris, but MacOS X and Windows will most likely be used for monitoring purposes.

2.   Software Reuse: Carma Software Toolkit

We identified four types of software components we will use for CARMA:

- **In-house** — the software we design ourselves, using CVS for version control, and for which we will have our own build system. We still expect some of the software in this category to be reusable from the original arrays.
- **Friendly** — written by colleagues or collaborating groups, and over which we have some control in terms of code development. Their build system is however not integrated into ours and we limit ourselves to using stable releases. Examples: MIRIAD, AIPS++.
- **Alien** — imported directly from other Open Source projects, but over which we have no direct control and whose build system will have to be understood by ours. Examples: pgplot, cfitsio, USNO ephemeris.
- **Commercial** — either in source code form, or binary only. Unlike the previous three, the distribution of this type will have to be controlled and cannot be open. Examples: ORBacus, IDL.

Together these components will make up the *Carma Software Toolkit* (CST).

3.   Basic Tools

Source code management will be done using CVS. We will use CVS dead-end branches to create releases that will be used by observers to control the array. Feature enhancements, as well as coding experiments, are also encouraged to occur via branching, though meant to be merged back to the mainline development. Lastly, CVS has also proven to be a very useful backup tool.

C++ will be our main language for development, using the GNU compiler, though compilation using at least one other compiler and one other architecture is done to improve portability. The build system is configured using *autoconf* (a GNU toolkit), and a set of hierarchical makefiles. Documentation is extracted automatically from the source code via the *doxygen* tool.

4. Hardware Interfaces

On the hardware side, CARMA Interface Control Documents (ICDs) are intended to be the definitive documents governing the mechanical and electrical interfaces between various subsystems. Although some of the information will inevitably be included in documentation for the subsystems themselves, the ICDs are the governing document in the case of any discrepancies. The ICDs are stored in a linked system diagram, making it easy to traverse the CARMA system and see the interrelation of components, all the while having detailed documentation immediately available.

For software ICDs, we have followed a similar approach. Where a software system is strongly tied to hardware, we will create direct links from the hardware system diagram to the doxygen-generated high-level software API. For pure software ICDs, we will use a parallel package tree, also generated by doxygen. Documentation updates will be part of the nightly build.

Some subsystems have large autonomous software components: e.g., gpib, canbus, and cobra.

5. Software Engineering

We use a classical approach of writing requirements, design and implementation. Our work will be very distributed, across five locations and three timezones, aided by CVS for source code control. Nightly builds will keep track of the stability of the system. Due to the distributed development environment, off-site a number of hardware components need to be emulated. This will also simplify writing observing checkers. All workers meet during weekly tele-conferences and regular (twice a year) face-to-face meetings.

6. Work Packages

After analysis and prioritization of CARMA's high-level computing requirements, we have divided the work into 42 Work Packages, about half of which have a strong tie to hardware. Examples of work packages are Master Clock, Atmospheric Delay Correction, Monitoring, and Atomic Commands. Each package has been assigned to one or more institutions and a lead developer identified. The lead developer is principally responsible for design, implementation, and testing of the work package, as well as biweekly status reports to the CARMA Project Manager. In addition, each institution has a Work Package Manager (who is also one of the developers), whose job it is to keep an eye on local milestones and identify any scheduling problems that may arise.

References

Hoffman, W., Hudson, J., Sharpe, R. K., Grossman, A. W., Morgan, J. A., & Teuben, P. J. 1996, in ASP Conf. Ser., Vol. 101, Astronomical Data Analysis Software and Systems V, ed. G. H. Jacoby & J. Barnes (San Francisco: ASP), 436.

Plante, R., Pound, M. W., Mehringer, D., Scott, S. L., Beard, A., Daniel, P., Hobbs, R., Kraybill, J. C., Wright, M., Leitch, E., Amarnath, N. S., Rauch, K. P., & Teuben, P. J. 2003, this volume, 269

Scott, S. L., Hobbs, R., Beard, A., Daniel, P., Mehringer, D., Plante, R., Kraybill, J. C., Wright, M., Leitch, E., Amarnath, N. S., Pound, M. W., Rauch, K. P., & Teuben, P. J. 2003, this volume, 265

Welch, W. J. et al. 1996, PASP, 108, 93

Yu, T. 2001, in ASP Conf. Ser., Vol. 238, Astronomical Data Analysis Software and Systems X, ed. F. R. Harnden, Jr., F. A. Primini, & H. E. Payne (San Francisco: ASP), 495

Astronomical Data Analysis Software and Systems XII
ASP Conference Series, Vol. 295, 2003
H. E. Payne, R. I. Jedrzejewski, and R. N. Hook, eds.

Refactoring DIRT

N. S. Amarnath, Marc W. Pound and Mark G. Wolfire

Astronomy Department, University of Maryland, College Park, MD 20742, Email: amar@astro.umd.edu

Abstract. The Dust InfraRed ToolBox (DIRT - a part of the Web Infrared ToolShed, or WITS, located at http://dustem.astro.umd.edu) is a Java applet for modeling astrophysical processes in circumstellar shells around young and evolved stars. DIRT has been used by the astrophysics community for about 4 years. DIRT uses results from a number of numerical models of astrophysical processes, and has an AWT based user interface. DIRT has been refactored to decouple data representation from plotting and curve fitting. This makes it easier to add new kinds of astrophysical models, use the plotter in other applications, migrate the user interface to Swing components, and modify the user interface to add functionality (for example, SIRTF tools).

DIRT is now an extension of two generic libraries, one of which manages data representation and caching, and the second of which manages plotting and curve fitting. This project is an example of refactoring with no impact on user interface, so the existing user community was not affected.

1. Rationale for Refactoring

DIRT is a powerful tool for searching pre-calculated models to fit observed data. DIRT provides access to over 500,000 models, parameterized over a large set of physical parameters and dust types. DIRT has been used by the astronomy community since 1999. For a more complete description of DIRT and its user interface, refer to Pound et al. (2000).

DIRT had a user interface that was closely coupled to the data representation, both on disk and in memory. Essentially, DIRT did not use a Model-View-Controller (MVC) pattern.

At the present time, DIRT is being extended to

- support missions such as SIRTF by providing instrument based models,
- support models for disk shaped dust regions around young and evolved stars.

Such extensions are less effort to implement if data storage is decoupled from data representation in memory, and the user interface makes minimal assumptions about data representation and manipulation.

2.   DIRT - Application Structure & Modifications

DIRT is an application that is made up of

1. model files, containing pre-calculated data from parameterized models,
2. a directory tree containing the model files, where each level in the tree represents a specific parameter, and a value of that parameter is represented by a node at that level,
3. Perl scripts for retrieving model data from the disk,
4. a Java applet using the Perl script that provides an AWT-based interface for plotting and fitting.

The model data files store data as ASCII columns of numbers with human readable column headers. A model may have multiple data files, each with its own columns and rows.

Before refactoring, model data was represented within the user interface using Database and Record objects. The Database object (a Java class), is a set of records, where each record is a row in the model data file represented by the Database object. Each plot window was associated with an array of database objects, representing the model data of interest for a set of plots. A column within a Database object was accessed by name, and these column names were explicitly used within the user interface. Database objects were associated with specific files by name. Datasets for plotting were selected using an class Filter object, and the chosen datasets were mapped to plot axes using a Mapper. Adding model data files, adding new types of models, and modifying the user interface required significant development effort with this design.

In order to simplify future upgrades, we decided to decouple the user interface and data representations and move to a more MVC compliant design for the application. However, any redesign (refactoring) had to be accomplished without affecting DIRT's user community. This implied that anything directly visible to the user had to remain unchanged, and behavioral changes to the user interface had to be minimal. Since our resources were limited, we also had to pick redesign options that would minimize the effort required to make the necessary code changes. These constraints meant that we could only change the representation of model data and the interface to data storage. To simplify the process of change, we decided to change only the Java code, and leave the Perl scripts mostly intact.

We decoupled data storage representations from the user interface by replacing the Database and Record classes by ModelMap, Model and ModelData classes. ModelMap is an ordered collection of Model objects. Each Model object is a collection of ModelData objects, which represent the data in one model file. Data in a ModelData object are read from the disk file and parsed using a description of the model data file contained in a schema, or Schema object. Information about the nature of the model, for example, the number of model parameters and the structure of the directory tree, are managed by an object of type ModelInfo. In this design, a ModelMap object now contains all models of interest to the user. Data from all data files associated with a specific model are managed by the associated Model object. Filter was slightly modified to filter datasets out of ModelMap objects, and Mapper changed to manage mapping and scaling of data to plot axes, which was formerly handled by Database.

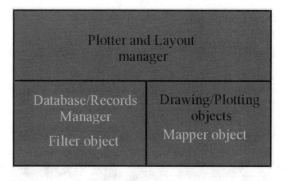

Unreconstructed DIRT – Shows structure of
DIRT prior to refactoring.

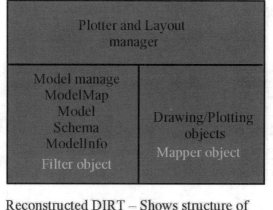

Reconstructed DIRT – Shows structure of
DIRT after refactoring.

Figure 1. A block diagram showing changes to DIRT.

Figure 1 provides a picture of the modifications to DIRT - grayed out objects
represent classes that were modified, or eliminated.

3. The New, Refactored DIRT

As a result of our refactoring, we can now add new model types and instrument
based model data without changing any code. The process of designing the
addition of SIRTF based model data was considerably accelerated - in fact,
apart from the additional model data files, it involved the addition of just three
text files.

In addition, source code was greatly simplified, making it more readable and
comprehensible. For example, referring to Figure 2, which describes a routine

for displaying the details of a point on a plot, the refactored code on the right is more understandable.

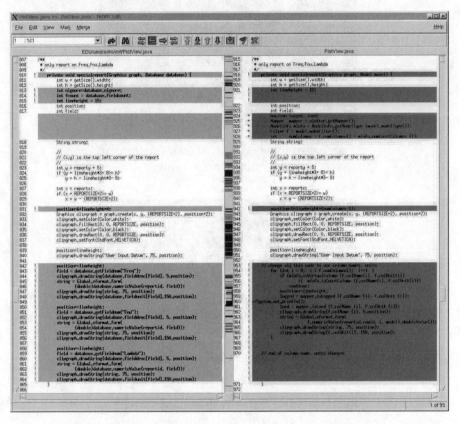

Figure 2. Sample difference in source code between the original version, on the left, and the refactored version on the right.

The Java applet in DIRT is now composed of 3 packages, one for plotting and fitting numeric data, a second for managing data in memory, and a set of DIRT-specific classes.

Acknowledgments. Refactoring of DIRT was supported by NASA Applied Information Systems Research Program (AISRP) grant NAG 5-10751.

References

Pound, M. W., Wolfire, M., Mundy, L., Teuben, P. J., Lord, S., 2000, in ASP Conf. Ser., Vol. 216, Astronomical Data Analysis Software and Systems IX, ed. N. Manset, C. Veillet, & D. Crabtree (San Francisco: ASP), 628

Astronomical Data Analysis Software and Systems XII
ASP Conference Series, Vol. 295, 2003
H. E. Payne, R. I. Jedrzejewski, and R. N. Hook, eds.

Systems Integration Testing of OPUS and the new DADS

Lisa E. Sherbert, Lauretta Nagel

Space Telescope Science Institute, Baltimore, MD 21218

Abstract. The Data Archive and Distribution System (DADS) will be entering the IDR (Ingest Distribution Redesign) era soon and more major functions will be shifting from the VMS platforms to various Unix platforms. As the first phase, Distribution, is delivered to testing, interfaces with OPUS and OTFR (On The Fly Reprocessing) will change. We will give a current overview of the OPUS/DADS/OTFR system and identify interface changes that will impact the operators and archive users.

1. Introduction

We illustrate the back-end HST ground systems and the types of data that flow through them, from Goddard Space Flight Center (GSFC) through various pipelines and into the data archive at the Space Telescope Science Institute (STScI). Recent changes to the platforms and software will be highlighted in SMALL CAPS. The OPUS/DADS/OTFR super-system is a mixture of platforms connected by NFS cross-mounted disks, email, and socket connections. The whole super-system is moving towards a Unix-based platform and away from the VMS platforms, making tracking of the various states interesting and the system performance definition difficult. Testing relies on stable environments, attempts to validate the system against its requirements, and then benchmarks the system performance. Here we document the current testing environment.

2. Data Flow Overview

PACOR-A at Goddard Space Flight Center now flows the HST science and engineering data to STScI. STScI picks up the engineering data and runs it through the engineering data pipeline system (EDPS), from whence it is archived. The system now runs on Unix/Solaris instead of VMS.

STScI receives the science telemetry data in the form of POD files and runs them through the data receipt pipeline. The data receipt pipeline puts the POD files into the pre-archive science pipeline. The pre-archive science pipeline reforms and calibrates the data and sends the POD files and the raw data to DADS to be archived. The headers of the raw and calibrated data are used to populate the HST archive catalog via the DADS/Ingest software. The DADS/Ingest subsystem also archives the files directly to storage media and catalogs the file locations. The storage media used in this case is Magneto-Optical (MO) platters stored in jukeboxes. The software that runs the jukeboxes lives on a Solaris Unix machine and it interfaces with both DADS/Ingest and DADS/Distribution.

Non-HST and non-FUSE data are input into MAST with CDs as the storage media. The MAST software manages user distribution requests for this data. The StarView and MAST interfaces are used to peruse the science catalog and to request HST and FUSE data. The DADS/Distribution software manages these user requests.

The Distribution software is moving off the VMS operating system onto Unix. It will now communicate with StarView and MAST via port connections instead of via email files. Distribution will make OTFR requests through IPC connections: putting a message on a shared file system which both pieces of software have access to.

The changes that will impact the end users are:

- Users can now receive data on CD or DVD.
- StarView can now generate requests for non-HST/FUSE data from MAST.
- Users may browse the archive anonymously (MAST and HST/FUSE).
- Users may be more specific about exactly what files they want returned to them by specifying the extension of interest.

3. Physical Block Overview

3.1. OPUS

Subsystem PACOR-A

- Operating System: Tru64 Unix
- Input: telemetry from HST
- Output: POD data
- Function: get POD files from GSFC to STScI
- Interfaces: PACOR-A

Subsystem SCIENCE

- Operating System: Tru64 Unix (with a VAX/VMS leftover)
- Input: POD data
- Output: Raw and calibrated data in form of FITS files (GEIS for WF2)
- Function: Change pod files into calibrated observation sets
- Interfaces: STSDAS/PyRAF software; 4 databases; Holding Tank pipeline, which converts WF2 (and FOC) to VMS GEIS

Subsystem EDPS

- Operating System: SOLARIS Unix
- Input: gzipped FOF files and PASS data, such as mission schedules
- Output: Jitter, astrometry, and engineering data
- Function: Processes engineering telemetry into observation logs (jitter files), instrument save files, breathing/thermal files, and astrometry (FGS science data); and processes PASS products.
- Interfaces: PASS, GSFC (CCS system), 3 databases

Subsystem OTFR

- Operating System: Tru64 Unix

- Input: specific output file requests
- Output: Raw and calibrated data, email about request success
- Function: Replaced OTFC - Reprocesses archived pod files through the SCIENCE pipeline. Automatic for ACS, NIC, STIS, WF2
- Interfaces: OPUS Science pipeline, DADS/Distribution

3.2. DADS

Subsystem INGEST

- OS VAX/VMS
- Input: Receives data over NFS-mounted disks.
- Output: Success/Failure response files over NFS-mounted disks.
- Function: Checks that it is a valid dataset, repairs keywords; Strips out information from the headers for the archive catalog; Writes data to permanent media and logs the location of the files in the housekeeping catalog.
- Interfaces: Sends OSTDB requests to catalog the header keywords in the database; Sends IPC messages to the InstallationServer (NSA); operator command line interface

Subsystem DISTRIBUTION

- OS: SOLARIS 2.8
- Input: Starview and MAST requests VIA PORT CONNECTIONS; AutoBulk requests from a directory.
- Output: Deploys data to portable media: Tape, CD, DVD; Ships data to user: NET, HOST
- Function: Validates the request (is the data proprietary or restricted?), then retrieves from permanent media and ships the data.
- Interfaces: Submits an IPC message to AcquireServer (NSA); Transfers the data via NFS-mounted disks from NSA and OTFR; REQUESTS OTFR PROCESSING THRU IPC MESSAGES

Subsystem NSA

- OS: Solaris 2.7
- Input: IPC messages pick up requests for installation/acquisition to MO platters in the jukebox
- Output: JDBC to update the database as platter/data relations; Java client/server messages help monitor the request status; Transfers files back and forth through NFS-mounted disks
- Function: Store the data on permanent media and retrieve it as requested.
- Interfaces: COTS product called Bakbone to run the jukebox; Database; Ingest, Distribution

Subsystem Archive Database (dadsops, mastops)

- OS: N/A
- Input: OSTDB JDBC requests to store header keywords and indexing information
- Output: OSTDB JDBC requests to provide StarView and MAST web pages with the above; Provides Distribution with platter/file correlations; Provides the Notification Tool (PROMPT) and AutoBulk Distribution with receipt dates and catalog information

- Function: Track location and science information of the files archived.
- Interfaces: Ingest, NSA, Distribution, AutoBulk Distribution, StarView, MAST, OTFR, PROMPT.

Subsystem MAST
- OS: Solaris 2.7
- Input: Accepts requests from the MAST web page
- Output: Transmits the data to the desired location.
- Function: Validates the request, then retrieves from permanent media and ships the data.
- Interfaces: the Solaris machine running the CD jukebox; COTS product called KPAR to run the jukebox; Database

Subsystem MAST CDs
- OS: Solaris 2.7
- Input: pick up requests for installation/acquisition to CDs in the jukebox
- Output: OSTDB to update the database as platter/CD relations; Transfers files back and forth through NFS-mounted disks
- Function: Store the data on permanent media and retrieve it as requested.
- Interfaces: COTS product called KPAR to run the jukebox; Database; MAST

Subsystem Observer Interfaces: StarView (Java GUI Application) AND MAST (Web Page)
- Input: User ID, Archive Password, Address (electronic or snail)
- Output: submit a request to DADS VIA PORT CONNECTION OR pull the data over from MAST as a tar file.
- Function: allow browsing of the MAST (including DADS) databases; allow user to indicate which datasets to retrieve and any special parameters:
  - Calibrated
  - UnCalibrated
  - DataQuality
  - JitterFiles
  - BestReferenceFiles
  - UsedReferenceFiles
  - Media Shipment: Tapes, CDs, DVDs
  - ANONYMOUS ARCHIVE USERIDS
  - EXTENSIONSONLY:<INSERT HERE> (will work even with OTFR)

4. Conclusion

We have presented an overview of the flow of HST data into OPUS science processing and engineering processing systems and from there into the Data Archive and Distribution System. The types of operating systems and recent changes to the software have been highlighted.

Acknowledgments. The authors would like to thank the members of the Data Systems Branch (and those matrixed into it) for their help in describing parts of this complicated system.

Part 13. Algorithms

Astronomical Data Analysis Software and Systems XII
ASP Conference Series, Vol. 295, 2003
H. E. Payne, R. I. Jedrzejewski, and R. N. Hook, eds.

Pointing Refinement of SIRTF Images

F. Masci, D. Makovoz, M. Moshir, D. Shupe and John W. Fowler

SIRTF Science Center, California Institute of Technology, Pasadena, CA 91125, Email: fmasci@ipac.caltech.edu

Abstract. The soon-to-be-launched Space Infrared Telescope Facility (SIRTF) should produce image data with an a-posteriori pointing knowledge of $1.4''$ (1σ radial) with a goal of $1.2''$ in the International Celestial Reference System (ICRS). To perform robust image coaddition, mosaic generation, extraction and position determination of faint sources, the pointing will need to be refined to better than a few-tenths of an arcsecond. This paper summarizes the pointing-refinement algorithm and presents the results of testing on simulated data.

1. Introduction

One of the goals of astronomical image data acquisition is to infer the pointing in an absolute coordinate system as accurately as possible, in this case the celestial reference system. Instabilities in telescope pointing and tracking however, can prevent us from achieving this goal. SIRTF for instance, is expected to provide pointing and control of at least $5''$ absolute accuracy with $0.3''$ stability over 200 sec (1σ radial). In the ICRS, the star-tracker assembly provides an a-posteriori pointing knowledge of $1.4''$. The end-to-end pointing accuracy is a function of the inherent star-tracker accuracy, the spacecraft control system, how well the star-tracker bore-sight is known in the focal plane array (instrument) frame, and variations in the latter due to thermo-mechanical deflections. The SIRTF observatory will have a data flow rate of $> 10,000$ science images per day. This will require an automated, self-consistent means of refining the celestial pointing as robustly as possible.

The conventional method to refine the pointing is to make comparisons of astrometric sources with positions known to better than a few percent of the observed positional errors. The primary motivation for pointing refinement is to enable robust coaddition of image frames in a common reference frame so that source extraction and position determination to faint flux levels can be performed. Moreover, refinement in an absolute (celestial) reference frame will enable robust cross-identification of extracted sources with other catalogs.

For these purposes, we have developed the *"pointingrefine"* stand-alone software package with a goal to generate science products with sub-arcsecond pointing accuracy in the ICRS. The software can refine the pointings and orientations of SIRTF images in either a "relative" sense where pointings become fixed relative to a single image of a mosaic, or, in an "absolute" sense (in the ICRS) when absolute point source information is known.

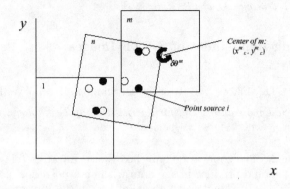

Figure 1.   A simple three image mosaic.

2.   Software Summary

As part of routine pipeline operations at the SIRTF Science Center (SSC), all input images are pre-processed for instrument artifact removal and pointing data attached to raw FITS images. Following this, point source extraction is performed on individual frames for input into *pointingrefine*. The software expects point source lists adhering to the format produced by the SSC source extractor. The *pointingrefine* software performs the following:

1. Reads source extraction tables, FITS images from input lists and if absolute refinement is desired, a list of absolute point source positions;
2. Point source position and flux matching is performed between all possible image pairs in the input list. This includes absolute point sources if available;
3. Transform correlated point source positions and uncertainties to a Cartesian fiducial (mosaic) reference frame;
4. Set up global minimization equations involving relative offsets between all correlated point source positions;
5. Solve a linear matrix equation for translational and rotational offsets in the mosaic reference frame for each input image and compute the full error-covariance matrix;
6. Apply these offsets to the pointing centers (x_c, y_c) of all images. Transform to RA, Dec to obtain refined celestial pointings and orientations;
7. Results output: Write new refined pointing keywords to FITS headers and to a table file with diagnostic information.

3.   Algorithm

A brief outline of the refinement algorithm (primarily steps 4, 5, and 6 above) is as follows. Consider the simple three image mosaic in Figure 1. Image "1" defines the "fiducial" reference frame. The circles represent point sources detected from each overlapping image pair transformed into the fiducial frame. The filled circles are sources extracted from image n and the open circles are sources extracted from either image 1 or m. The correlated source pairs are slightly offset from each other to mimic the presence of pointing uncertainty in each raw input image. The Cartesian coordinates of a correlated point source <u>common</u> to an image pair are related by:

$$x_i^m \to \tilde{x}_i^n = x_i^m - (y_i^m - y_c^m)\delta\theta^m + \delta X^m$$

$$y_i^m \to \tilde{y}_i^n = y_i^m - (x_i^m - x_c^m)\delta\theta^m + \delta Y^m,$$

(1)

where $\delta\theta^m$, δX^m, δY^m are rotational and Cartesian offsets respectively in the fiducial mosaic frame. We have made the approximation $\sin \delta\theta \approx \delta\theta$ ($\cos \delta\theta \approx 1$) since uncertainties in measured position angles are expected to be small ($\lesssim 20''$).

We define a cost function L, representing the sum of the squares of the "corrected" differences of all correlated point source positions in all overlapping image pairs (m,n):

$$L = \sum_{m,n} \sum_i \left\{ \frac{1}{\Delta x_i^{m,n}} [\tilde{x}_i^n - \tilde{x}_i^m]^2 + \frac{1}{\Delta y_i^{m,n}} [\tilde{y}_i^n - \tilde{y}_i^m]^2 \right\}, \qquad (2)$$

where

$$\Delta x_i^{m,n} = \sigma^2(x_i^m) + \sigma^2(x_i^n) \qquad (3)$$
$$\Delta y_i^{m,n} = \sigma^2(y_i^m) + \sigma^2(y_i^n)$$

and the σ^2 represent variances in extracted point source positions. The function L (Equation 2) is minimized with respect to the Cartesian offsets ($\delta\theta^m$, δX^m, δY^m) for an image m which contains point sources in common with all other images n. At the global minimum of L, the following conditions hold:

$$\frac{\partial L}{\partial \delta\theta^m} = 0; \quad \frac{\partial L}{\partial \delta X^m} = 0; \quad \frac{\partial L}{\partial \delta Y^m} = 0. \qquad (4)$$

Evaluating these partial derivatives leads to a set of three simultaneous equations for each image in our mosaic. In general, for N correlated images, we will have $3(N-1)$ simultaneous equations in $3(N-1)$ unknowns. It is "$N-1$" because we exclude the reference image frame, which by definition has the constraint $\delta\theta^m = \delta X^m = \delta Y^m = 0$. The $3(N-1)$ system of equations can be solved using linear sparse matrix methods since a large number of the matrix elements will be zero. We use the UMFPACK[1] library, which is adapted for solving large unsymmetric matrix systems.

When absolute astrometric references are available, the "fiducial" reference image (mosaic) frame is treated like a single input image, which contains the *absolute* point source positions. When the input images become refined relative to this fiducial image, they in reality become *absolutely* refined (in the ICRS). The presence of absolute point sources also reduces the effect of "random walks" in offset uncertainties with distance if a single input image were chosen as the

---

[1]http://www.cise.ufl.edu/research/sparse/umfpack/

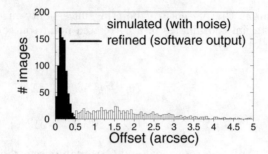

Figure 2.   Distribution of radial offsets between "true" (noiseless) and simulated pointings (with noise) - *broad histogram*, and between true and refined pointings - *narrow histogram*.

reference instead. Once Cartesian offsets ($\delta\theta^m$, δX^m, δY^m) in the reference (mosaic) frame are computed, the pointing centers (x_c, y_c) are corrected (by use of Equation 1) and transformed back to the sky to yield refined pointings. Image orientations are refined in a similar manner, but in this case, we need to transform at least two fiducial points per image to uniquely determine the orientation.

4.   Simulations

The Infrared Array Camera (IRAC) on SIRTF will perform simultaneous imaging at four bands spanning the range $\approx 3.6\mu m$ to $8\mu m$. Each array consists of 256×256 $1.2''$ pixels. We simulated a mosaic of 800 IRAC ($3.6\mu m$) "truth" images (i.e., *with no* pointing error) with each image containing randomly distributed point sources. Input image overlap coverage was $\sim 50\%$. A second set of 800 images was simulated with random errors added to the pointing keywords of image headers. The errors were drawn from a Gaussian distribution with mean radial error $\langle\delta\rangle \approx 1.4''$. An absolute point source list was also simulated by extracting the brightest sources with smallest centroiding errors from each "truth" image. The average number of "absolutes" per input image was 10. The SSC point source extractor was then used to extract ≈ 50 point sources from each input image (with pointing error).

Figure 2 shows the results of our simulation where we compare the distributions of radial offsets relative to "truth" pointings before and after refinement. The refinement is better than 85% for almost every image. The main limitation is full knowledge of the Point Response Function (PRF) to reduce centroiding errors in source extractions. However, we expect extraction centroids better than $0.1''$ with better sampled PRFs. This will give us the sub-arcsecond absolute pointing accuracy sought in SIRTF's imaging detectors.

Acknowledgments.   This work was carried out at the SIRTF Science Center, with funding from NASA under contract to the California Institute of Technology and the Jet Propulsion Laboratory.

Astronomical Data Analysis Software and Systems XII
ASP Conference Series, Vol. 295, 2003
H. E. Payne, R. I. Jedrzejewski, and R. N. Hook, eds.

A Theoretical Photometric and Astrometric Performance Model for Point Spread Function CCD Stellar Photometry

Kenneth J. Mighell

National Optical Astronomy Observatory, 950 North Cherry Avenue, Tucson, AZ 85719, Email: mighell@noao.edu

Abstract. Using a simple 2-D Gaussian Point Spread Function (PSF) on a constant (flat) sky background, I derive a theoretical photometric and astrometric performance model for analytical and digital PSF-fitting stellar photometry. The theoretical model makes excellent predictions for the photometric and astrometric performance of over-sampled and under-sampled CCD stellar observations even with cameras with pixels that have large *intra*-pixel quantum efficiency variations. The performance model accurately predicts the photometric and astrometric performance of realistic space-based observations from segmented-mirror telescope concepts like the Next Generation Space Telescope with the MATPHOT algorithm for digital PSF CCD stellar photometry which I presented last year at ADASS XI. The key PSF-based parameter of the theoretical performance model is the effective background area which is defined to be the reciprocal of the volume integral of the square of the (normalized) PSF; a critically-sampled PSF has an effective background area of 4π (≈ 12.57) pixels. A bright star with a million photons can theoretically simultaneously achieve a signal-to-noise ratio of 1000 with a (relative) astrometric error of a *milli*pixel. The photometric performance is maximized when either the effective background area or the effective-background-level measurement error is minimized. Real-world considerations, like the use of poor CCD flat fields to calibrate the observations, can and do cause many existing space-based and ground-based CCD imagers to fail to live up to their theoretical performance limits. Future optical and infrared imaging instruments can be designed and operated to avoid the limitations of some existing space-based and ground-based cameras. This work is supported by grants from the Office of Space Science of the National Aeronautics and Space Administration (NASA).

1. Photometry

1.1. Bright Star Limit

Let us assume that the variance of the noise associated with the ith pixel of an observation of a bright star is due only to stellar photon noise,

$$\sigma_i^2 \equiv S_E \Phi(x_i, y_i),$$

where Φ is the normalized *sampled* Point Spread Function (PSF). All other noise sources (for example, the background sky, instrumental readout noise, etc.) are assumed, in this case, to be negligibly small. The variance of the stellar intensity measurement of bright *over-sampled* stars is thus

$$\sigma^2_{S_E:\,\text{bright}} \approx \left[\sum_{i=1}^{N} \frac{1}{\sigma_i^2} \left(\frac{\partial}{\partial S_E} S_E \Phi(x_i, y_i) \right)^2 \right]^{-1} \equiv \left[\sum_{i=1}^{N} \frac{1}{S_E \Phi(x_i, y_i)} \Phi^2(x_i, y_i) \right]^{-1}$$

$$= \left[\frac{1}{S_E} \sum_{i=1}^{N} \Phi(x_i, y_i) \right]^{-1} \approx S_E \left[\int_{-\infty}^{+\infty} \int_{-\infty}^{+\infty} \phi(x, y)\, dx\, dy \right]^{-1} \equiv S_E \,,$$

as expected from photon statistics with a normalized unsampled PSF (ϕ).

1.2.   Faint Star Limit

Let us assume that we can replace the measurement error associated with the ith pixel of an observation of a faint star with an average *constant* rms value of

$$\sigma^2_{\text{rms}} \equiv \frac{1}{N} \sum_{i=1}^{N} \sigma_i^{-2} \approx B_E + \sigma^2_{\text{RON}},$$

where B_E is the constant background level in electrons per pixel (e$^-$/px) and σ^2_{RON} is the square of the rms readout noise (e$^-$/px). Using this approximation, we find that the variance of the stellar intensity measurement of faint *over-sampled* stars is

$$\sigma^2_{S_E:\,\text{faint}} \approx \left[\sum_{i=1}^{N} \frac{1}{\sigma_i^2} \left(\frac{\partial}{\partial S_E} S_E \Phi(x_i, y_i) \right)^2 \right]^{-1} \equiv \left[\sum_{i=1}^{N} \frac{1}{\sigma^2_{\text{rms}}} \Phi^2(x_i, y_i) \right]^{-1}$$

$$= \sigma^2_{\text{rms}} \left[\sum_{i=1}^{N} \Phi^2(x_i, y_i) \right]^{-1} \approx \sigma^2_{\text{rms}} \left[\int_{-\infty}^{+\infty} \int_{-\infty}^{+\infty} \phi^2(x, y)\, dx\, dy \right]^{-1} \equiv \sigma^2_{\text{rms}}\, \beta \,,$$

where the constant β is the "effective background area" defined as the *reciprocal* of the volume integral of the *square* of the normalized unsampled PSF (ϕ). The effective background area for a normalized Gaussian PSF with a standard deviation of S_σ px is $\beta = 4\pi S_\sigma^2$ px^2; the value for a critically-sampled normalized Gaussian is, by definition, 4π (≈ 12.57) px^2. King (1983) identifies β as the "equivalent-noise area" and notes that numerical integration of a realistic ground-based stellar profile gives an equivalent area of $30.8 S_\sigma^2$ px^2 instead of the value of $4\pi S_\sigma^2$ px^2 for a Gaussian profile.

1.3.   Photometic Performance Model

A simple performance model for photometry can be created by combining the bright and faint star limits developed above. The total variance of the stellar intensity measurement of over-sampled stars is thus

$$\sigma^2_{S_E} \approx \sigma^2_{S_E:\,\text{bright}} + \sigma^2_{S_E:\,\text{faint}} = S_E + \sigma^2_{\text{rms}}\, \beta \approx S_E + \beta \left[B_E + \sigma^2_{\text{RON}} \right] \,.$$

The term in brackets in the last equation can physically be thought of as the "effective background level".

An important, but frequently ignored, noise source is the uncertainty of the measurement of the effective background level (σ_B). If the "sky" background is assumed to be flat, then the lower limit for measurement error of the effective background level is

$$\sigma_B \lesssim \frac{\sqrt{B_E + \sigma_{RON}^2}}{\sqrt{N}} .$$

In order to have a more realistic performance model for photometry, this noise source must be added as the <u>square</u> of $\beta\sigma_B$ because it is a systematic error:

$$\sigma_{S_E} \approx \sqrt{S_E + \beta \left[B_E + \sigma_{RON}^2\right] + (\beta\sigma_B)^2} \quad e^- .$$

Photometric performance will be maximized when either the effective background area (β) or the effective-background-level measurement error (σ_B) is minimized.

We now have the basis for a simple, yet realistic, photometric performance model for PSF-fitting algorithms. An upper limit for the theoretical signal-to-noise ratio of a PSF-fitting algorithm is

$$\boxed{SNR \lesssim \frac{S_E}{\sqrt{S_E + \beta \left[B_E + \sigma_{RON}^2\right] + (\beta\sigma_B)^2}} .}$$

2. Astrometry

2.1. Bright Star Limit

Let us again assume that the variance of the noise associated with the ith pixel of an observation of a bright star is due only to stellar photon noise. The variance of the stellar x position measurement, S_X, of bright *over-sampled* stars with a normalized *unsampled* Gaussian PSF at the ith pixel is

$$\phi_i \equiv \phi(x_i, y_i; S_X, S_Y, S_\sigma) \equiv \frac{1}{2\pi S_\sigma^2} \exp\left(-\frac{(x - S_X)^2 + (y - S_Y)^2}{2S_\sigma^2}\right) ,$$

is

$$\sigma_{S_X:\text{bright}}^2 \approx \left[\sum_{i=1}^{N} \frac{1}{\sigma_i^2} \left(\frac{\partial}{\partial S_X} S_E \phi_i\right)^2\right]^{-1} \equiv \left[\sum_{i=1}^{N} \frac{1}{S_E \phi_i} \left(S_E \phi_i \frac{S_X - x_i}{S_\sigma^2}\right)^2\right]^{-1}$$

$$\approx \left[\frac{S_E}{S_\sigma^4} \int_{-\infty}^{+\infty}\int_{-\infty}^{+\infty} \phi(x, y)(S_X - x)^2 \, dx \, dy\right]^{-1} = \frac{S_\sigma^4}{S_E} \left[S_\sigma^2\right]^{-1} \equiv \frac{1}{S_E}\left(\frac{\beta}{4\pi}\right) ,$$

where β is the effective background area as defined above. By symmetry, the variance of the stellar y position measurement of bright over-sampled stars is the same.

2.2. Faint Star Limit

Let us again assume that noise contribution from the star is negligibly small and that can replace σ_i^2 with with an average *constant* rms value of σ_{rms}^2. Using this approximation, we find that the variance of the stellar x position measurement of faint *over-sampled* stars with a normalized *unsampled* Gaussian PSF is

$$\sigma_{S_X:\,\text{faint}}^2 \approx \left[\sum_{i=1}^N \frac{1}{\sigma_i^2} \left(\frac{\partial}{\partial S_X} S_E \phi_i \right)^2 \right]^{-1} \equiv \left[\sum_{i=1}^N \frac{1}{\sigma_{\text{rms}}^2} \left(S_E \phi_i \frac{S_X - x_i}{S_\sigma^2} \right)^2 \right]^{-1}$$

$$\approx \sigma_{\text{rms}}^2 \left[\frac{S_E^2}{S_\sigma^4} \int_{-\infty}^{+\infty} \int_{-\infty}^{+\infty} \phi^2(x,y)(S_X - x)^2 \, dx \, dy \right]^{-1} = \sigma_{\text{rms}}^2 \frac{S_\sigma^4}{S_E^2} \left[\frac{1}{8\pi} \right]^{-1}$$

$$\equiv \sigma_{\text{rms}}^2 \frac{\beta^2}{2\pi S_E^2} \equiv 8\pi \, \sigma_{\text{rms}}^2 \left(\sigma_{S_X:\,\text{bright}}^2 \right)^2 .$$

By symmetry, the variance of the stellar y position measurement of faint over-sampled stars is the same.

2.3. Astrometric Performance Model

We can now create a simple performance model for astrometry by combining the bright and faint star limits developed above. The expected lower limit of the rms measurement error of the stellar x position of a PSF-fitting algorithm is

$$\sigma_{S_X}$$
$$\approx \sqrt{\sigma_{S_X:\,\text{bright}}^2 + \sigma_{S_X:\,\text{faint}}^2}$$
$$\gtrsim \sqrt{\left[\left(\frac{\beta}{4\pi} \right) \frac{1}{S_E} \right] \left[1 + \left(\frac{\beta}{4\pi} \right) \frac{8\pi}{S_E} (B_E + \sigma_{\text{RON}}^2) \right]} \text{ px} .$$

By symmetry, the expected lower limit of the variance of the measured y coordinate of the stellar position of a PSF-fitting algorithm is the same.

Acknowledgments. This work is supported by grants awarded by the Office of Space Science of the National Aeronautics and Space Administration (NASA) from the Applied Information Systems Research Program (AISRP) and the Long-Term Space Astrophysics (LTSA) program.

References

King, I. R. 1983, PASP, 95, 163

Astronomical Data Analysis Software and Systems XII
ASP Conference Series, Vol. 295, 2003
H. E. Payne, R. I. Jedrzejewski, and R. N. Hook, eds.

Adaptive Optics Software on the CfAO Web Page

Andreas Quirrenbach, Vesa Junkkarinen, Rainer Köhler

University of California, San Diego, Center for Astrophysics and Space Sciences, Mail Code 0424, La Jolla, CA 92093-0424, USA

Abstract. The Center for Adaptive Optics maintains a web site, which serves as a repository for software and tools related to adaptive optics. We describe the purpose and structure of this web site, and give brief descriptions of the currently available software packages. In the future, the CfAO web page can evolve into a complete data reduction toolbox for adaptive optics observations.

1. Purpose and Structure of the CfAO Software Web Server

The Center for Adaptive Optics (CfAO) is a Science and Technology Center, funded by the National Science Foundation. It was established in November 1999 with the mission "to advance and disseminate the technology of adaptive optics in service to science, health care, industry, and education". The activities of the CfAO cover a broad range of research topics related to adaptive optics; they also include programs to distribute know-how and tools for adaptive optics to the scientific community. (One of these programs is an annual summer school series on adaptive optics for astronomy and vision science.)

Among the goals of the CfAO is the distribution of software for adaptive optics, with the intention to prevent duplication of efforts by CfAO members and others, and to give researchers in adaptive optics a place to distribute their software. One of the CfAO member institutions, the University of California, San Diego, hosts and maintains a web server[1], from which a number of software packages can be downloaded. The software on this site comes from the scientists and institutions affiliated with the CfAO, and from other scientists and institutions interested in sharing AO software with the astronomical and general scientific community. The philosophy is not to initiate a coherent software development effort, but rather to gather independently developed packages, and to make them accessible at one site. Therefore no attempts have been made to homogenize the programming languages used, or the platforms on which the programs run. All software packages have been tested and documented by the respective author(s); in many cases we have carried out additional testing, and added brief user guides or instructions. The software and its associated documentation is placed in directories accessible by anonymous ftp. Web pages provide convenient links to the directories and/or files for downloading.

---

[1]http://babcock.ucsd.edu/cfao_ucsd/software.html

2. Available Packages

The main criterion for the inclusion of software on the CfAO web page has been their utility for a broad range of users of adaptive optics systems, with a bias towards packages that CfAO scientists are using for their own research. The following eight packages are currently available for download from the CfAO web site:

- **A++** This complex package is a tool to generate wavefront reconstruction matrices for adaptive optics systems, which are used to calculate the deformable mirror commands from the wavefront sensor data. **A++** was originally written by Walter Wild, and modified by the University of Chicago AO group. **A++** has an extensive user manual. Many astronomical AO systems with Shack-Hartmann wavefront sensors currently in operation use versions of Walter Wild's reconstruction matrix.

- **AO Simulation Package** This software, written by François Rigaut, simulates an adaptive optics system. The user sets the parameters of the AO system and telescope. The software calculates the closed-loop performance of the telescope and AO system and simulates the observation of a star using a phase screen model for the Earth's atmosphere.

- **AOTOOLS** This set of scripts written by Eric Steinbring simplifies the reduction of near-infrared data acquired with an adaptive optics system. (Most current astronomical AO systems are equipped with near-infrared focal plane instruments.) The package consists of IRAF cl scripts that need both IRAF and STSDAS. It installs as an external IRAF package with help files.

- **idac** This is a large package of software for adaptive optics data reduction using blind deconvolution. The software has been written and documented by Stuart Jefferies, Julian Christou, Keith Hege, and Matt Cheselka (see Jefferies & Christou 1993; Christou et al. 1995). Blind deconvolution is a technique that allows the point spread function to be determined by the analysis of multiple images of a single science field, which may or may not contain point sources. Blind deconvolution has the advantage that many separate telescope pointings to acquire observations of a calibration point source for PSF estimation are not required. Blind deconvolution is in many cases preferable to separate PSF star observations due to the time-variable nature of the atmosphere and PSF.

- **Rainer's Binary/Speckle Package** This is a software package written by Rainer Köhler to reduce speckle data on binary and triple stars (Köhler et al. 2000). Speckle methods take advantage of short exposures to "freeze" the atmospheric seeing, and the binary information is preserved in speckles, or bright regions. Each image consists of a large number of speckles, and considerable analysis must be done to extract scientifically useful measurements from the raw images. The package works completely in the Fourier domain; it has also been used with great success for adaptive optics observations of binary stars.

- **StarFinder** This software package, written by Emiliano Diolaiti and colleagues at Bologna Observatory, carries out some of the fundamental tasks in the analysis of adaptive optics data (Diolaiti et al. 2000). It provides both point spread function estimation and, by using the PSF, astrometry and photometry in crowded stellar fields. Bright stars are used for an initial estimate of the point spread function. The PSF estimate and the set of detected faint stars are then iteratively improved until the entire field is analyzed.

- **Strehl Code/FitStars** This software, contributed by Theo ten Brummelaar, is used to analyze an adaptive optics observation of a point source to estimate the Strehl ratio. The Strehl ratio is the ratio of the peak intensity actually observed to the peak intensity that would be observed if the telescope were operating at the diffraction limit. The Strehl ratio is the most common figure of merit for the performance of an AO system. The package also contains utilities for photometry, astrometry, and PSF fitting of binary star images (ten Brummelaar et al. 2000).

- **Virtual_Telescope** This is an IDL program (with supporting files) written by Eric Steinbring for the simulation of observations, and to predict their signal-to-noise ratio. This tool is designed to simulate a telescope along with its instruments. An artificial field is generated that is deep enough to test even the capabilities of the James Webb Space Telescope (JWST). The telescope itself, its point spread function, and backgrounds for ground or space observations are then simulated.

The first two of these packages (**A++** and the **AO Simulation Package**) are primarily meant to be used by designers and operators of adaptive optics systems. The other packages are more related to observing preparation and data reduction, and address the needs of astronomers who use AO systems for their observing projects.

3. Outlook

In addition to the software packages described above, the CfAO web page contains a few introductory articles on adaptive optics, and links to additional tools that can help to prepare proposals or observing projects. It is also planned to make a number of test data sets available, which can be used to investigate the effects of anisoplanatism in reduced images, and to cross-compare different data reduction and deconvolution algorithms. On a longer time scale, the CfAO web site could evolve into a complete modular AO data analysis toolbox (Quirrenbach 1999). This would require contributions from a larger group of AO users, and a more systematic approach to algorithm development, interface definitions, coding, and documentation. For the near future, the main purpose of the CfAO web page will remain the provision of access to an increasing number of useful software packages and tools, for anyone interested in designing or using adaptive optics systems. With this function, the services provided by the CfAO web page are complementary to those of the large observatories, which provide complete data reduction pipelines and data analysis packages, but with no specific emphasis on adaptive optics.

Acknowledgments. We are grateful to all those who have contributed their software and data reduction tools to our web site. This work has been supported by the National Science Foundation Science and Technology Center for Adaptive Optics, managed by the University of California at Santa Cruz under cooperative agreement No. AST-98-76783.

References

Christou, J.C., Hege, E.K., & Jefferies, S.M. 1995, Proc. SPIE 2256, 134

Diolaiti, E., Bedinelli, O., Bonaccini, D., Close, L., Currie, D., & Parmeggiani, G. 2000,A&AS, 147, 335

Jefferies, S.M. & Christou, J.C. 1993, ApJ, 415, 862

Köhler, R., Kunkel, M., Leinert, C., & Zinnecker, H. 2000, A&A, 356, 541

Quirrenbach, A. 1999, in Proceedings of ESO/OSA Topical Meeting on Astronomy with Adaptive Optics, Ed. Bonaccini, D., European Southern Observatory conference and workshop proceedings, 56, 361

ten Brummelaar, T., Mason, B.D., McAlister, H.A., Roberts, L.C., Turner, N.H., Hartkopf, W.I., & Bagnuolo, W.G. 2000, AJ, 119, 2403

Astronomical Data Analysis Software and Systems XII
ASP Conference Series, Vol. 295, 2003
H. E. Payne, R. I. Jedrzejewski, and R. N. Hook, eds.

Representations of Spectral Coordinates in FITS

Eric W. Greisen[1]

*National Radio Astronomy Observatory, P. O. Box O, Socorro, NM
87801 USA; Email:* egreisen@nrao.edu

Francisco G. Valdes[2]

*National Optical Astronomy Observatories, P. O. Box 26732, Tucson,
AZ 85719 USA; Email:* valdes@noao.edu

Mark R. Calabretta[3]

*Australia Telescope National Facility, P. O. Box 76, Epping, NSW 1710
Australia; Email:* Mark.Calabretta@atnf.csiro.au

Steven L. Allen[4]

*UCO/Lick Observatory, University of California, Santa Cruz, CA
95064 USA; Email:* sla@ucolick.org

Abstract. In Paper I, Greisen & Calabretta (2003) describe a generalized method for specifying the coordinates of FITS data samples. Following that general method, Calabretta & Greisen (2003) in Paper II describe detailed conventions for defining celestial coordinates as they are projected onto a two-dimensional plane. The present paper extends the discussion to the spectral coordinates of wavelength, frequency, and velocity. World coordinate functions are defined for spectral axes sampled evenly in wavelength, frequency, or velocity, evenly in the logarithm of wavelength or frequency, as projected by ideal dispersing elements, and as specified by a lookup table. Papers I and II have been accepted into the FITS standard by the North American, Japanese and European FITS Committees; we expect the present work to be accepted as well. The full text of the proposed standards can be found at http://www.aoc.nrao.edu/~egreisen.

---

[1]The National Radio Astronomy Observatory is a facility of the (U.S.) National Science Foundation operated under cooperative agreement by Associated Universities, Inc.

[2]The National Optical Astronomy Observatory is a facility of the (U.S.) National Science Foundation operated under cooperative agreement by Associated Universities for Research in Astronomy, Inc.

[3]The Australia Telescope is funded by the Commonwealth of Australia for operation as a National Facility managed by CSIRO.

[4]UCO/Lick Observatory is operated by the University of California.

1. Introduction

Greisen & Calabretta (2003, "Paper I") describes the computation of the world or physical coordinates as a multi-step process. The vector of pixel offsets from the reference point is multiplied by a linear transformation matrix and then scaled to physical units. Mathematically, this is given by

$$x_i = s_i \, q_i = s_i \sum_{j=1}^{N} m_{ij} \, (p_j - r_j) \,, \tag{1}$$

where p_j are pixel coordinates, r_j are pixel coordinates of the reference point given by CRPIX j, m_{ij} is a linear transformation matrix given either by PC i_j or CD i_j, N is the dimensionality of the WCS representation given by WCSAXES, and s_i is a scaling given either by CDELT i or by 1.0. The final step in the computation is the conversion of these linear relative coordinates into the actual physical coordinates. The conventions to be applied to ideal spectral axes are described in "Paper III" (Greisen et al. 2003) and summarized here. A later work (Calabretta, et al. 2003, "Paper IV") will address the corrections needed to convert real astronomical data into the ideal axes assumed in the celestial coordinates (Calabretta & Greisen 2003, "Paper II") and present manuscripts.

2. Basic Coordinates

The basic "spectral" coordinates are frequency, wavelength, and Doppler relativistic velocity. There are several other coordinates which are proportional to one of these, including wavenumber, energy, and "radio" and "optical" conventional velocities. Let us consider the case in which an axis is linearly sampled in spectral variable X, but is to be expressed in terms of variable S. We may restrict X to the basic types since all others are linearly proportional to one of them. Let us also introduce an intermediate variable P which is the basic variable associated with S. The relationship between X and S is then $S(X) = S(P(X))$ with inverse $X(S) = X(P(S))$. The statement that an axis is linearly sampled in X simply means that

$$X = X_{\rm r} + w \frac{{\rm d}X}{{\rm d}w} \tag{2}$$

where w is the intermediate value x_i for the spectral axis and ${\rm d}X/{\rm d}w$ is a constant. Since, to first order and very near the reference point, the axis is linear in S, i.e., $S \approx S_{\rm r} + w$, we may determine the derivative by

$$\frac{{\rm d}X}{{\rm d}w} = \left.\frac{{\rm d}P}{{\rm d}S}\right|_{\rm r} \Big/ \left.\frac{{\rm d}P}{{\rm d}X}\right|_{\rm r} \,. \tag{3}$$

A three-step algorithm chain is then indicated:
1. Compute once $X_{\rm r} = X(P(S_{\rm r}))$ and ${\rm d}X/{\rm d}w$ using Equation (3) and then compute X at w using Equation (2).
2. Compute P from X using the set of non-linear relationships between the basic spectral coordinates..
3. Compute S from P using the set of linear relationships between the basic and secondary spectral coordinates.

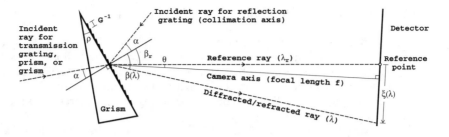

Figure 1.   Geometry of gratings, prisms, and grisms. This simplified representation omits the collimation and focusing optics. Dashed lines mark ray paths in the plane of the figure – the "dispersion plane". The normal to the grating/exit prism face and the normal to the detector plane are each projected onto the dispersion plane, and angles α, β, and θ are measured with respect to these projected normals. Usually the incident ray for a prism or grism is perpendicular to the entry face so that α is equal to the prism angle, ρ. Angle β is wavelength-dependent, and consequently so is the offset ξ in the dispersion direction on the detector. The intermediate spectral world coordinate, w, is proportional to ξ. Reference wavelength λ_r follows the reference ray defined by β_r and illuminates the reference point at $w = \xi = 0$. The normal to the detector plane is shown tilted by angle θ from the reference ray though typically this angle is zero. The grating spacing G^{-1} is indicated.

Dispersion coordinates for UV, optical, and IR spectra at $\lambda > 200$ nm are commonly given as wavelengths in air rather than in vacuum. The relationship between these is given by $\lambda = n(\lambda_a)\lambda_a$ and causes a relative difference of around 0.03%. The conversion between wavelengths in air and wavelengths in vacuum adds another step in the chain described above.

Paper III presents a full set of codes to be used in keyword CTYPE*ia* for spectral coordinate types and for the non-linear algorithms involved, including air wavelengths. Keywords RESTFRQ*a* and RESTWAV*a* are reserved to give the line rest frequency (in Hz) or wavelength (in m) needed for the conversion between frequency/wavelength and velocity.

3.   Dispersed Spectra: -GRI Non-linear Algorithm

One common form of spectral data is produced by imaging the light from a disperser, such as a prism, grating, or grism, as illustrated in Figure 1. Paper III presents the full mathematics by which the wavelength λ and the spacing at the detector $\xi(\lambda)$ may be related. The basic grism equation is given by

$$\lambda = \frac{(n_r - n_r'\lambda_r)\sin\alpha + \sin\beta}{Gm/\cos\epsilon - n_r'\sin\alpha}.\tag{4}$$

Despite numerous approximations made in the development of the mathematics, it is found that suitable parameters provide good fits to a variety of spectrometers in use at the KPNO.

4. Coordinates by Table Lookup: -TAB Algorithm

There are numerous instances in which a physical coordinate is well defined at each pixel along an image axis, but the relationship of the coordinate values between pixels cannot be described by a simple functional form. Observations of the same object made at an arbitrary set of frequencies or times are the simplest examples. In addition, the calibration of some spectrographs is represented best by a list of wavelengths for each pixel on the spectral axis.

Fully separable, one-dimensional axes of this type may be represented by an algorithm, -TAB, defined in Paper III. A FITS binary table containing only one row is used. The coordinates are given by a vector of values in a single cell, optionally accompanied by a second indexing vector in a second cell within the row. The parameters required by -TAB are the table extension name, the table version number, the table level number, the column name for the coordinate vector, and the column name for the optional indexing vector. The character-valued generic keyword PS i_j is introduced to provide the three character-valued parameters of this algorithm. The coordinate value is found by first evaluating Equation (1) and adding the reference value. The result is used as a value to be looked up in the vector of values found in the indexing vector cell. The corresponding position in the vector of values in the coordinate vector cell then provides the actual coordinate. If the indexing vector is omitted, the value found with Equation (1) is used as a direct index for the coordinate vector.

The -TAB algorithm described above is then generalized to cases in which the coordinates on N axes are dependent on each other, but the indexing vectors are independent. In this case, the values of the coordinates are contained in one column of the (one-row) table as an array of dimensions $(N, K_1, K_2, \ldots, K_N)$, where K_i is the number of indexing values on axis i. The indexing vector for axis i, if present, will occupy a separate column and will contain K_i values in a one-dimensional array. An additional parameter is required for each of the N coordinates to give the axis number i within the coordinate array.

5. Summary

Paper I has defined a general framework to describe world coordinates in the FITS format; Paper II has extended that framework to describe ideal celestial coordinate representations. Paper III, summarized here, extends the discussion to ideal spectral coordinates and introduces a general table lookup algorithm. All three papers are well on their way to becoming part of the IAU FITS Standard.

References

Calabretta, M. R. et al. 2003, Representations of distortions in FITS world coordinate systems, in preparation, ("Paper IV")

Calabretta, M. R. & Greisen, E. W. 2003, A&A, accepted ("Paper II")

Greisen, E. W. & Calabretta, M. R. 2003, A&A, accepted ("Paper I")

Greisen, E. W., Valdes, F. G., Calabretta, M. R., & Allen, S. A. 2003, A&A, in preparation ("Paper III")

Astronomical Data Analysis Software and Systems XII
ASP Conference Series, Vol. 295, 2003
H. E. Payne, R. I. Jedrzejewski, and R. N. Hook, eds.

Restoration of Digitized Astronomical Plates with the Pixon Method

Peter R. Hiltner, Peter Kroll

Sonneberg Observatory, Sternwartestr. 32, D-96515 Sonneberg

Rico Nestler, Karl-Heinz Franke

Technical University of Ilmenau, Faculty of Computer Science and Automation, Computer Graphics Program, POB 100565, D-98684 Ilmenau, Email: rico.nestler@tu-ilmenau.de

Abstract. We report applications of the Pixon Restoration Method to digitized plates of the Sonneberg Plate Archive – the world's 2nd largest. Results so far obtained show that the severe astigmatism/coma distortion present in the outer parts of the wide field images can be almost completely removed. Object definition (FHWM) of point sources and S/N also improve by factors of 2 to 7, depending on the object strength and location, background etc. We briefly address implications for the inclusion of digitized archives in the virtual observatory context.

1. Introduction

Sonneberg Observatory in the Thuringian forest is blessed with a night sky which is still almost free of light-pollution. It has been collecting photographic images of selected sky areas since about 1930 and since the 1950s this has been supplemented by imaging of the whole northern sky, in a systematic manner known as "Sky Patrol". The main purpose up to now has been the detection and study of variable stars. In order to transform this rich collection of photographic images into a form which is useful and accessible to the astronomical community, digitization of the plates was begun several years ago.

Many different telescopes, cameras and photographic emulsions have been used over the years to collect these data, each of them with its own peculiarities and shortcomings. In particular, we are dealing with wide angle astrophotography for which there is no comparison in the era of CCDs. The field size is about 4.3° for the Schmidt plates, 11° for astrograph plates, and 27° for the Sky Patrol plates. The latter, on which we shall concentrate here, suffer from severe astigmatism affecting more than 75% of the plate area. It is therefore obvious that the processing of the digitized data should include steps beyond the basic reduction of dark current subtraction and flat-fielding.

We report here on our attempts to roll back part of the image degradation that occurs between infalling starlight and the digitized plate, using the Pixon image deconvolution method, first described by Pina & Puetter (1993) and then further developed by others (e.g., Eke 2001).

407

2.   Astronomical Aims

The information contained in the $\approx 275,000$ plates of our plate archive, collected over more than 70 years, is surely not yet fully exploited, although C. Hoffmeister and his co-workers have discovered over 10,000 variable stars on these plates, including very important objects such as HZ Her, FG Sge and BL Lac.

We are convinced that the data currently buried in our and the other existing archives deserve to be excavated and treated using modern methods of mass image processing. Since each plate of the Sky Patrol contains information on some 100,000 stars, such an effort would extend current surveys back by about 50 years down to the plate limits of $13^m - 14^m$. Not only are many more variable stars likely to be detected by an automated search, but topical questions such as the existence of sun-like cycles in stars, or simply the long term behaviour of "normal" stars, could also be attacked on a broad basis (Kroll 1999). To do this, we have to push the detection threshold and photometry to the limits.

3.   Restoration

Image restoration in general is an inverse problem, where the blurry and distorted data is related to an undistorted image through an imaging model that describes all the degradations influencing the true underlying image. Our model includes the local blurring process, the nonlinearity of the photographic emulsion, the characteristics of the image scanner and a model for the noise. The scanner signal fluctuations are modelled as additive, plate specific, signal dependent, gaussian noise. The solution sought is considered to be the best explanation of the data. In image restoration, especially in the presence of noise, there is a set of solutions rather than a unique solution. Small fluctuations in the data due to noise lead to large-scale fluctuations in the solution set. This discrepancy between the number of degrees of freedom used in the restoration and the corrupted information in the data is usually called an "ill-posed problem". In addition to the data, further constraints must be imposed by "regularization".

The idea of regularization is to take all a-priori-information into account to select and weight the solutions in the set. This prior information is combined with the data and defines a best solution by trying to achieve smoothness and yet remain faithful to the data. The pixon method is an efficient way to regularize inverse problems. "Pixons" instead of image pixels are used to obtain the "simplest" solution that explains the data through the imaging model. Details of the theoretical basis and some practical implementations can be found in Pina & Puetter (1993), Puetter (1994) and Puetter (1996).

We use a fuzzy pixon basis to represent our solution E. In this "correlation" approach adjacent pixons share some of each other's signal instead of having hard boundaries. The unblurred image is described as the local convolution of a so called "pseudo-image" E^P containing the signal with a scale-dependent symmetric 2d-Gaussian pixon-kernel. The distribution of the local pixon sizes represents the model-part, P, of the image description. The goal of the restoration process is to determine a combined image-model-*pair*, in a nonlinear iterative manner. That task can be interpreted in terms of a Bayesian estimation scheme in which the solution sought maximizes the joint probability $p(E^P, P, \Omega, S^M)$:

$$E_{\vec{x}} = \sum_{\vec{y}} \hat{E}^P_{\vec{y}} \cdot \hat{P}(\delta_{\vec{x}})_{\vec{y}-\vec{x}} \quad : \quad \hat{E}^P, \hat{P} \rightarrow \max_{E^P,P,\Omega} \left\{ \underbrace{p(E^P, P, \Omega | S^M)}_{\text{Maximum-A-Posteriori}} \propto \underbrace{p(S^M | E^P, P, \Omega)}_{\text{Likelihood}} \cdot \underbrace{p(E^P, P, \Omega)}_{\text{Prior}} \right\}$$

where

E represents the solution set $E : E_{\vec{x}} | \vec{x} \in N^2$

S^M represents the data set $S^M : S^M_{\vec{x}} | \vec{x} \in N^2$

Ω represents the set of regularization parameters $\Omega : \Omega_{\vec{x}} | \vec{x} \in N^2$

The image-model-pair is calculated in a modified version of the scheme introduced in Pina & Puetter (1993). Instead of calculating a pixon width distribution approximately, our procedure estimates a Bayesian model. Therefore a regularization is needed to weight the influences of the likelihood and prior terms on the solution. In addition, some ideas from other researchers in the field of pixon restoration are used, adapted and refined, such as a specific weight of the signal distribution with respect to the current distribution of pixon sizes (Eke 2001). The calculation of the cost functions and their derivatives is done mainly by FFT-convolutions, thus preserving the $n * log(n)$ scaling of the algorithm.

4. Results

The example to be discussed here comes from a Sky Patrol plate, exposed for 20 minutes close to the zenith on a very clear night in August 2000. The emulsion used was a Foma Astro Blue film without filter, sensitive to a wavelength range of about 420 – 520 nm. The example is based on a $1° \times 1°$ (294×294 pixel) section centered on M31 and also including M110. On the plate this section is located in the extreme corner with strongly astigmatic star images. For a larger field, north-west of κ Cas and closer to the optical axis and hence markedly less astigmatic, we only give some statistical results.

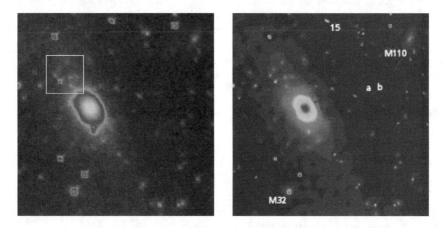

Figure 1. M31 field. North is at the top and west to the right. The original (dark current and flatfield corrected) is to the left and the restored form on the right.

Statistical Results: The automatic identifications of stars was based on the "find" procedure in the IDL Astronomy Library[1]. On the M31 field "find" found 38 (36) stars on the restored (original) image, for which the median FWHM is 1.8 (5.4) pixels and the median S/N-ratio is 15.9 (6.1). The corresponding figures for the κ Cas field are 747 (606) stars, 1.8 (3.4) pixel and 10.5 (3.0) for S/N respectively.

Individual Stars: Close doubles are well separated in the restored image. A limiting case is the pair marked "15". Here the original profile of the pair can hardly be distinguished from that of a single luminous star, whereas the restored profile shows a shoulder and has the maximum displaced by 1 pixel, indicating the distinction between the $9.^m6$ star PPM43223 and its $11.^m2$ NE companion.

The non-stellarity of M32 appears more pronounced in the restored image than in the original data. If the excess of the FWHM of M32 over the median of the sample stars is expressed in units of the mean absolute deviation from the median, this excess is 1.5 times larger in the restored image than in the original data although the M32-FWHM itself is a factor of 3.5 smaller. The galaxy shape of M110 also comes out much more clearly in the restored image. Finally, there are a number of stars which can only be evaluated photometrically in the restored image, e.g., the "boxed" group on the NE ridge of M31, and it shows some real stars (e.g., "a", "b"), which one would not have guessed the existence of from the original.

5. Further Prospects

We identify the following tasks for future work: to implement semi-automatic extraction of a PSF valid for a particular plate region, and to reduce the run time (e.g., tiling, parallelizing). We also note that restoration near the edge, and also more centrally, stops at a FWHM of ≈ 2 pixels, very close to the minimum allowed by the sampling theorem. The connection between sampling and the pixon method seems worth exploring further. Finally, astrometry and photometry with the restored image have to be tested more thoroughly.

We consider it essential to make digitized plate archives—the work of generations of observers—accessible in the virtual observatories to come. From our results we conclude that somewhere in the query chain a web-based (pixon) deconvolution tool should be available.

References

Eke, V. 2001, MNRAS, 324, 108

Kroll, P. 1999, in Treasure Hunting in Astronomical Plate Archives, eds. Kroll P., la Dous C., Bräuer H.-J. (Frankfurt am Main: Deutsch), 97

Puetter, R. 1996, in Digital Image Recovery and Synthesis III, SPIE., 2827, 12

Puetter, R. 1994, in Digital Image Recovery and Synthesis III, SPIE., 2302, 112

Pina, R., & Puetter, R. 1993, PASP, 105, 630

---

[1]http://idlastro.gsfc.nasa.gov

Astronomical Data Analysis Software and Systems XII
ASP Conference Series, Vol. 295, 2003
H. E. Payne, R. I. Jedrzejewski, and R. N. Hook, eds.

Desmearing Solar System Objects in Chandra Data

R. Hain, J. McDowell, A. Rots, K. Glotfelty, S. Wolk

Harvard-Smithsonian Center for Astrophysics, 60 Garden St., Cambridge, MA 02138

Abstract. Observations by the Chandra X-Ray Observatory are made in a coordinate frame that is essentially fixed. Most objects observed with Chandra, such as supernova remnants, quasars, or pulsars, are at infinity for all practical purposes and the observations produce sharp, focused images. However, the motion of objects observed within the solar system, such as planets or comets, will cause the object's image to appear blurred when viewed in a fixed frame. This effect is similar to the blur which would be seen if a fixed camera were to take a photograph of a fast moving car.

To reconstruct the image, the CXC CIAO tool sso_freeze corrects for this effect. An origin is chosen at the center of the object, and moves along with the object as it moves with respect to inertial space. The positions of the source photons are then recalculated with respect to this moving origin. The image formed from the recalculated photons now shows a clear object, such as a disk for a planet. As an effect of this processing, fixed X-ray sources become smeared in the image. The effect is similar to moving the camera to follow the fast moving car in the earlier example. The car becomes clearly focused, and the scene around the car is blurred. Images which demonstrate the effect of sso_freeze are shown for Jupiter and Comet C/1999 S4 Linear.

1. Introduction

Data from the Chandra X-Ray Observatory are assigned positions in the International Celestial Reference System (ICRS) World Coordinate System. The motion of most of the distant targets observed by Chandra are negligible in this reference frame. However, certain objects, such as those within the solar system, can move with respect to the ICRS frame during the observation interval. As a result, the image of the observed object is spread across the observed region and blurred. This effect is similar to that seen when an optical camera is used to take a picture of a fast moving object, such as a race car. Just as the car's image would be blurred in the picture, local objects appear blurred in the Chandra image.

In order to resolve the local object cleanly, without any blurring, photons from the object need to be displayed in an alternate World Coordinate System—one which moves with the object, as opposed to being fixed to distant points. At the top of Figure 1, the ICRS reference frame is shown as a coordinate system

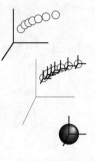

Figure 1. Fixed and Moving Reference Frames

with heavy lines. An example of the motion possible by a solar system object is shown as a series of circles extending up and to the right.

To redisplay the image without any blur, an instantaneous coordinate system with an origin at the center of the solar system object is defined. This is illustrated in the center image of the figure, where a new coordinate system is attached to each image of the object. Finally, data from the observation are redisplayed in the new, object centered coordinate system. The result is shown in the bottom portion of Figure 1, where a discernible object is seen instead of the previous blurred images.

In the actual implementation for Chandra data, a new object-centered coordinate system is defined for each new photon timetag (unlike the example in the figure where the time steps are much coarser). An effect of this processing is that non-solar system object X-ray sources are also displayed in the new, moving coordinate system. This has the effect of sometimes blurring what would otherwise be X-ray point sources. The origin of the object-centered reference frame is defined as the instantaneous ephemeris of the solar system object.

2. Jupiter Example

An example showing Chandra data for an observation of Jupiter both before and after processing with sso_freeze is shown in Figure 2. The image on the left shows the photons from a Jupiter observation in SKY (X,Y) coordinates, which are based on the ICRS world coordinate system. Near the center of the image are two lines, starting in the left half of the image and continuing slightly downward and to the right. These are X-ray emissions from Jupiter's poles, and trace the upper and lower bounds of the disc of Jupiter as it travels across the field of view during this observation.

The image on the right shows the same data in Object Centered coordinates (OCX,OCY). Jupiter is clearly visible as a disc, and the strong X-ray emissions near the polar regions show up as brighter regions. Since the entire image is

Figure 2. Jupiter in ICRS and Object Centered coordinates

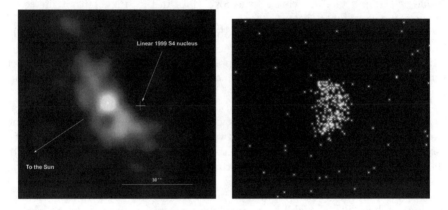

Figure 3. Comet 1999/S4 Linear and Venus in X-rays

displayed in Object Centered coordinates (not just the disc of Jupiter), note that the clean rectangle of the left image has been smeared a little in the right image. If a strong X-ray source were present in this observation, it would been seen as a clean point source in the left image, but it would appear to be smeared left to right in the image on the right. Since only background data seem to be present, the random nature of the events does not appear to be any different in either coordinate system.

Two other images produced with data processed by sso_freeze are shown in Figure 3. On the left, a Chandra X-ray image of Comet C/1999 S4 (LINEAR) (Lisse et al. 2001) shows X-rays from oxygen and nitrogen ions, which are produced by ions in the solar wind colliding with with gas in the comet. On the right is the first X-ray image ever made of Venus (Dennerl et al. 2002). The X-rays seen in the half crescent come from that part of Venus' atmosphere at an altitude of 120 to 140 kilometers illuminated by the Sun. They are produced by fluorescent radiation from oxygen and other atoms.

3. Code Highlights

There are three sets of input files required by sso_freeze. The events files provide the SKY (X,Y) coordinates for the observation, the spacecraft ephemeris files specify the Chandra ephemeris parameters, and the 'sso' ephemeris files specify the solar system object ephemeris parameters.

Both the Chandra ephemeris data and the solar system object ephemeris data are interpolated to the exact time of the current event record. Each time a new event record is read, if the timetag increases, ephemeris data are reinterpolated.

Coordinate transformation information is read from the input file to convert SKY (X,Y) coordinates to the ICRS world coordinate system. This coordinate transformation information for the first file is stored, so that subsequent input files can use this data to reproject SKY coordinates into the same reference frame as the first file, allowing all the SKY data in the single output file to be in the same coordinate system.

The vector from Chandra to the object is calculated, and the vector elements are used to compute the Chandracentric RA and Dec of the object. This data, updated for each new ephemeris position, is used to define the new object centered coordinate frame, and the SKY coordinates are then reprojected in this frame.

If several observations are made of an object which are significantly separated in time, the change in distance between the object and Chandra due to the respective relative motion between the two may cause the object to appear to be larger or smaller in later observations. To normalize the data so that the size of the object appears constant, an option to output linear coordinates (kilometers) can be selected.

Future plans for sso_freeze include incorporating the tool into pipeline processing, and adding the ability to produce exposure maps which are also in object centered coordinates. This project is supported by the Chandra X-ray Center under NASA contract NAS8-39073.

References

Lisse, C.M. et al. 2001, "Charge Exchange-Induced X-Ray Emission from Comet C/1999 S4 (LINEAR)", Science, 292, 1343

Dennerl, K. et al. 2002, "Discovery of X-rays from Venus with Chandra", A&A, 386, 319

Astronomical Data Analysis Software and Systems XII
ASP Conference Series, Vol. 295, 2003
H. E. Payne, R. I. Jedrzejewski, and R. N. Hook, eds.

Merging of Spectral Orders from Fiber Echelle Spectrographs

Petr Škoda

Astronomical Institute of the Academy of Sciences of the Czech Republic

Herman Hensberge

Royal Observatory of Belgium

Abstract.   We review the data reduction of two fiber-based echelle spectrographs (HEROS and FEROS) with emphasis on the similarity of the inconsistencies between the overlap of spectral orders before merging.

The literature on echelle data reduction shows that such inconsistencies are commonly observed and usually handled by rather heuristic interactive procedures.

For both instruments it seems to be the calibration unit that introduces the bulk of the problem through errors in the flat field. We discuss strategies to treat the problem and to remove the inconsistencies before merging the spectral orders with minimal use of interactive, subjective algorithms.

1.   Introduction

Merging spectral orders from echelle spectra is known to be non-trivial. Some manuals of echelle spectroscopy even advise against trying it. Authors who do the merging usually report problems and try to solve the order inconsistencies by some heuristic interactive method (Churchill 1994; Hall et al. 1994; Erspamer & North 2002). Recently, De Cuyper & Hensberge (2003) commented on a study of calibration flat-fields taken with the FEROS fiber-fed echelle spectrograph at ESO and pointed out several effects influencing the merging. In this contribution, we present the results of an extended analysis including special calibration flat-fields, dome flat-fields and science exposures of bright objects. The results obtained from FEROS were compared, where possible, to red-channel exposures made with HEROS at Ondřejov observatory.

2.   Spectrographs

A detailed description of both instruments can be found on web pages of FEROS[1] and HEROS[2] respectively. FEROS is a 2-fiber spectrograph covering a wide spectral region (3600–9000 Å) in 39 spectral orders. It is particularly suited to distinguish effects that are related to blazed spectral orders from optical projection effects since the bluest spectral orders are much narrower than the size of the detector while the reddest orders are covered over a bit less than their free spectral range. FEROS operates in a temperature and humidity controlled room. HEROS is a one-fiber instrument developed earlier by the same team in Heidelberg, as a compact echelle spectrograph that has been used at several telescopes. Since August 2000 it has been connected for more than two years to the 2m telescope of Ondřejov observatory. The light from the telescope Cassegrain focus is fed by the 10m long fiber to the echelle grating and then, after the beam-splitter, it goes to two independent channels: blue (3600–5600 Å in 70 orders) and red (5800–8400 Å in 32 orders).

2.1.   Experiences with FEROS

The projection of the spectral orders on the detector over an observing run of 4 nights was stable in the wavelength direction at the level of 0.1 pixel (except for an explained, and meanwhile removed oscillation, due to short-term temperature fluctuations of 1 K in the FEROS room) and in the spatial (cross-order) direction at the level of 0.5 pixel (Figure 1).

However, the position of the blaze profile in wavelength changed by of the order of 10 pixels (i.e., 10^{-4} of the wavelength) in a highly correlated way with the changes in spatial direction (Figure 1). These slow temporal changes apply as well to calibration unit flat-fields as to dome flat-fields or scientific exposures. Such changes, if not taken into account when flat-fielding a science frame, lead to inconsistencies at the level of several percent of the flux in the overlap of spectral orders. The data suggest a very similar shift of the blaze function over all orders in the case of FEROS, leading to larger overlap mismatch in the narrower orders in the blue spectral region i.e., with larger gradients in the blaze function.

2.2.   Experiences with HEROS

Temporal changes in the blaze profile are detected on shorter time-scales, which is presumably related to the fact that the spectrograph is operating in the dome and not in a controlled room. The changes vary smoothly over subsequent orders, but cannot be represented by a simple small shift in wavelength of the blaze function. This may be related to the fact that the blaze profiles produced by HEROS are not so near to the theoretical predictions than in the case of FEROS: the blaze profiles of different spectral orders are almost identical when expressed in the coordinate

---

[1]http://www.ls.eso.org/lasilla/Telescopes/2p2T/E1p5M/FEROS/index.html

[2]http://www.lsw.uni-heidelberg.de/projects/instrumentation/Heros

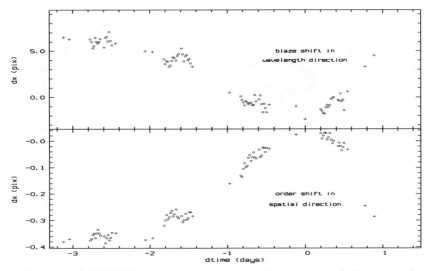

Figure 1. FEROS — time evolution of the position of the spectral orders in cross-order direction (lower part) and the shift of the blaze function along the spectral order (upper part) during an observing run. Flat-field images (+) and science frames (o) are indicated with different symbols.

$$\frac{\nu}{2\pi} = \frac{m}{2}\left(\frac{\lambda_b(m)}{\lambda} - 1\right)$$

where m refers to the spectral order, λ to the wavelength and $\lambda_b(m)$ to λ in order m at the peak of the blaze intensity. De Cuyper & Hensberge (2003) discuss the similar case for FEROS, but the shape and the width do not scale accurately in the same way for HEROS.

Since flat-fields are commonly taken with each science exposure at Ondřejov (because of the fast low-frequency temporal changes of the calibration images), efforts to address the order merging problems were directed to the study of the unblazed science frames rather than considering the calibration images and the science frames separately, as in the FEROS case.

In order to visualize the lack of consistency in the order overlap regions more clearly, we present figures where the global wavelength dependency of instrument and object is removed from the separate orders. This step, the normalization of the merged spectrum, comes last in a real data reduction chain.

Figure 2 shows the separate spectral orders and the level of inconsistency in the regions of spectral order overlap. Overplotted is a correction function with identical shape (in pixel space) in all 32 spectral orders, but smoothly varying amplitude. Dividing by this function reduces the inconsistencies in the overlap of spectral orders to well below the 1% level.

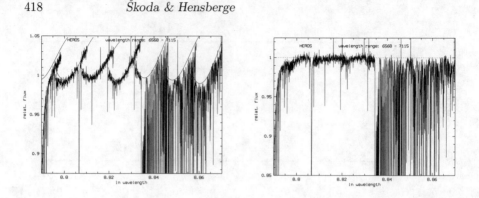

Figure 2.   HEROS — seven spectral orders starting from the long-
ward wing of Hα before (left panel) and after (right panel) correction

3. Conclusion

Analysis of data obtained by the fiber echelle spectrographs FEROS at ESO, La
Silla, Chile and HEROS at Ondřejov, Czech Republic, identifies the high sensitivity of the shape and position of the blaze function as the primary source of
order overlap inconsistencies. Since changes in the blaze function are very consistent over many spectral orders, and highly correlated with positional changes in
the projection of orders on the detector, a robust empirical model can be developed. However, on a longer term, the origin of these effects should be understood
such that action can be taken to stabilize the blaze function sufficiently.

If sufficient attention is paid to understand the calibration unit, in order
not to introduce spurious low-frequency patterns in the flat-fielded science data,
merging spectral orders becomes a trivial exercise.

Acknowledgments.   Part of this research is done in the framework of the
IUAP P5/36 project financed by the Belgian Federal DWTC/SSTC and project
K2043105 of the Academy of Sciences of the Czech Republic.

References

Churchill, C. W. 1994, Lick Obs. Techn. Rep., 74, 1

De Cuyper J. P. & Hensberge, H. 2003, in ASP Conf. Ser., Vol. 281, Astronomical
        Data Analysis Software and Systems XI, ed. D. A. Bohlender, D. Durand,
        & T. H. Handley (San Francisco: ASP), 324

Erspamer, D. & North, P. 2002, A&A, 383, 227

Hall, J. C., Fultoni, E. E., Huenemoerder, D. P., Welty, A. D. & Neff, J. E. 1994,
        PASP, 106, 315

Astronomical Data Analysis Software and Systems XII
ASP Conference Series, Vol. 295, 2003
H. E. Payne, R. I. Jedrzejewski, and R. N. Hook, eds.

Automated Object Classification with ClassX

A. A. Suchkov, R. J. Hanisch, R. L. White, M. Postman, & M. E. Donahue

Space Telescope Science Institute

T. A. McGlynn, L. Angelini, M.F. Corcoran, S.A. Drake, W.D. Pence, N. White, & E.L. Winter

Goddard Space Flight Center

F. Genova, F. Ochsenbein, P. Fernique, & S. Derriere

Centre de Données astronomiques de Strasbourg

Abstract. ClassX is a project aimed at creating an automated system to classify X-ray sources and is envisaged as a prototype of the Virtual Observatory. As a system, ClassX creates a pipeline by integrating a network of classifiers with an engine that searches and retrieves multi-wavelength counterparts for a given target from the worldwide data storage media. At the start of the project we identified a number of issues that needed to be addressed to make the implementation of such a system possible. The most fundamental are: (a) classification methods and algorithms, (b) selection and definition of classes (object types), and (c) identification of source counterparts across multi-wavelength data. Their relevance to the project objectives will be seen in the results below as we discuss ClassX classifiers.

1. Classifiers

We apply machine learning methods to generate classifiers from 'training' data sets, each set being a particular sample of objects with pre-assigned class names that have measured X-ray fluxes and, wherever possible, data from other wavelength bands. In this paper, a classifier is represented by a set of oblique decision trees (DT) induced by a DT generation system OC1. An X-ray source is input into a classifier as a set of X-ray fluxes and possibly data from the optical, infrared, radio, etc. The discussion below includes some results obtained with classifiers trained on the data from the ROSAT WGA, GSC2, and 2MASS catalogs.

1.1. Classifier Metrics

In order to quantify the quality and efficiency of classifiers, we have introduced a variety of metrics. They include the classifier's preference, P_{ij}, which is the probability that a class i object will be classified as class j (Figure 1); its affinity,

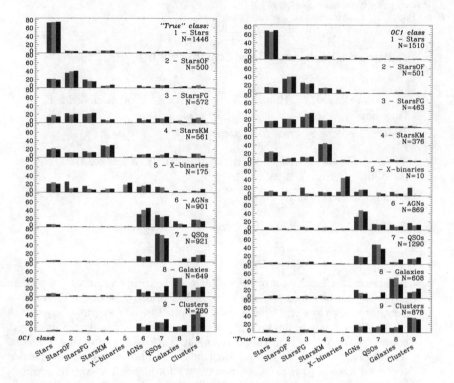

Figure 1.   Preference, P_{ij}, (left) and affinity, A_{ij}, (right) for three classifiers trained using (a) X-ray magnitudes, (b) GSC2 magnitudes, and (c) both GSC2 and X-ray magnitudes along with coordinates and GSC2 "extended" vs. "point" source parameter. Notice that the OC1 classifiers separate stellar objects from non-stellar ones quite reliably. At the same time, a confusion between different types of stars or, say, QSO and AGN should be expected because of original misclassification and significant overlap of the respective object types in the parameter space.

A_{ij}, which is the probability that an object classified as class i does in fact belong to class j (Figure 1), and the power, S_i, which is the ratio of the probability that an object classified as class i is indeed class i to the probability that a randomly selected object belongs to class i. Additional useful characteristics are completeness, $C_i = P_{ii}$, and reliability, $R_i = A_{ii}$.

1.2.   Classifier Networks

Using different sets of training parameters (attributes), we get different classifiers for the same list of class names (e.g., Figure 1). We integrate them into a network, in which each classifier makes its own class assignment and is optimized for handling different tasks or different object types. We envision that, having a set of X-ray sources, a user would generally select a certain classifier to make, for instance, the most complete list of candidate QSOs, but a different classifier would be used to make a most reliable list of such candidates. Additional classifiers would be selected to make similar lists for other object types. Figure 1 suggests that one would prefer the xray_gsc2 classifier to pick up cluster candidates, while AGNs call for the xray_only classifier.

2. Training Set Deficiencies

A classifier is adversely impacted by source misclassification, counterpart misidentification, data bias, etc. As the training data improve, so do the classifiers. In Figure 2, about 50% of class "Stars" sources (stars without spectral classification) come from the LMC/SMC region. This introduces a coordinate bias that affects classifiers generated from those data. Certain metrics of a classifier can be improved if stars from the LMC/SMC region are dropped from the respective training sets.

3. Validating Pre-assigned Classes with ClassX

An X-ray source in a training set may have an inappropriate class name or incorrect optical or other counterpart. Candidates with these deficiencies can be identified as a classifier is applied to the training data. In Figure 2, an OC1 classifier is seen to noticeably enhance the contrast between "extended" and "point" sources for StarsKM, QSOs, and Clusters, suggesting that the sources contributing to that enhancement were probably misclassified in the training set. They can further be examined and then reclassified if warranted, which would improve the training set itself.

4. Counterpart Search Strategies with ClassX

Classifiers trained using optical counterparts proved to be much better if a counterpart is selected as a brightest objects within 30 arcsec as opposed, for instance, to a nearest object within 30 arcsec or a brightest object within 60 arcsec. Thus, classifier validation in ClassX offers a way to find the best strategies to search for multi-wavelength counterparts.

5. Class Ambiguity in ClassX

A class is rarely a clear-cut notion. One person's QSO is another's AGN or galaxy. The overlap of object properties that often results in confusion in the object type assignement is an essential issue for any classification system. With ClassX, one can isolate sources with a greater degree of class name ambiguity and look into why their classification in the training set differs from the OC1 classification (see Figure 2).

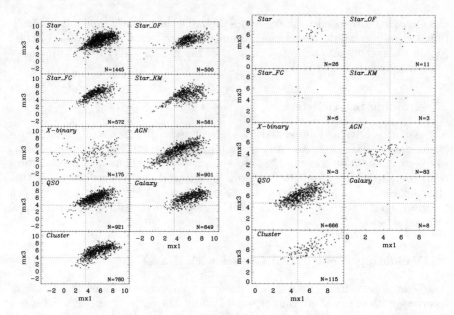

Figure 2.   X-ray soft versus hard magnitudes for classes from the WGA catalog (left) and the OC1 classifier (right). On the right, only the WGA class QSO is shown. Most of the brightest and the faintest WGA QSOs have been classified by the OC1 classifier as AGN and Cluster, respectively, which partly reflects the class name ambiguity for these sources.

6.   ClassX Outputs

A network classifier outputs the class name and the probability that the source belongs to the assigned class. It also outputs the probabilities that the source belongs, in fact, to other classes in the class name list. This is useful, for instance, for assessing how close the source association is with various classes in parameter space.

Astronomical Data Analysis Software and Systems XII
ASP Conference Series, Vol. 295, 2003
H. E. Payne, R. I. Jedrzejewski, and R. N. Hook, eds.

FLY: a Tree Code for Adaptive Mesh Refinement

U. Becciani, V. Antonuccio-Delogu, A. Costa

INAF – Astrophysical Observatory of Catania

D. Ferro

Department of Physics and Astronomy – University of Catania

Abstract. FLY[1] is a public domain parallel treecode, which makes heavy use of the one-sided communication paradigm to handle the management of the tree structure. It implements the equations for cosmological evolution and can be run for different cosmological models. This paper shows an example of the integration of a tree N-body code with an adaptive mesh, following the PARAMESH scheme. This new implementation will allow the FLY output, and more generally any binary output, to be used with any hydrodynamics code that adopts the PARAMESH data structure, to study compressible flow problems.

1. Introduction

We have developed a powerful N-body code to evolve three-dimensional self-gravitating collisionless systems with a large number of particles ($N \geq 10^7$). FLY (**F**ast **L**evel-based N-bod**Y** code) is a fully parallel code based on a tree algorithm. It adopts periodic boundary conditions implemented by means of the Ewald summation technique. FLY is based on the one-sided communication paradigm to share data among the processors that access remote private data with any synchronism. The code was originally developed on a CRAY T3E system using the logically SHared MEMory access routines (*SHMEM*) and it was ported to SGI ORIGIN systems and IBM SP, on the latter making use of the Low-Level Application Programming Interface routines (*LAPI*). This paper shows an example of integration of a tree code with an adaptive mesh scheme. PARAMESH is a package of Fortran 90 subroutines using *SHMEM* and *MPI* libraries, designed to provide an application developer with an easy route to extend an existing serial code which uses a logically cartesian structured mesh into a parallel code with an adaptive mesh refinement. The computational domain is hierarchically subdivided into sub-blocks following a 3D tree data-structure. The use of *SHMEM* and the tree data-structure eases the integration with FLY, which adopts the same data structure and the same parallel communication library. This implementation of FLY with PARAMESH integrates the output of FLY

---

[1]http://www.ct.astro.it/fly/

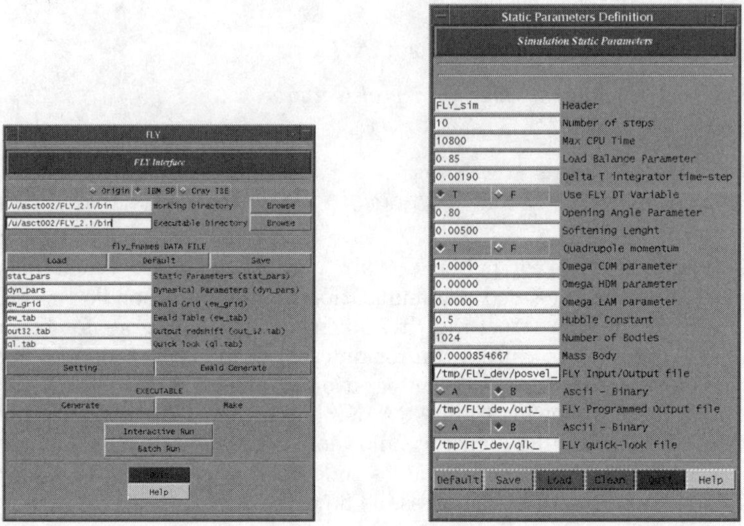

Figure 1.   Main FLY window and the window where the static parameter file is set.

with an adaptive mesh, having the same data structure as PARAMESH. The adaptive mesh structure can be read by FLY or generated from it, and contains the potential field of each data block of the mesh, following the PARAMESH scheme.

2.   FLY Main Features

FLY is a dynamically load balanced code based on four main characteristics: it adopts a simple domain decomposition, a grouping strategy and a data buffering that minimize data communication. The domain decomposition is based on a fixed distribution of particles among the processors: the same number of particles is assigned to each processor. The data structures of both particles and tree are subdivided among the PEs to ensure a good initial distribution of the load and to avoid any bottleneck while accessing remote data. FLY uses a grouping strategy with the aim of computing a component of the force to be applied to all particles inside a *grouping cell* and to reduce the number of remote access to build the global force on each particle. With the data buffering, FLY uses the free RAM portion of each PE to allocate dynamically the tree and the bodies data structures in order to cache remote elements.

All these features allow FLY to run very large cosmological simulations on parallel systems with high performances: more than 20×10^4 particles per second were computed using 16 PEs on an IBM SP Power4 1300 MHz at Cineca.

3. From the Tree to the Adaptive Mesh

FLY is a pure gravitational tree N-body code performing LSS cosmological simulations using dark matter particles. Some codes include hydrodynamical effects, star formation as well as dark matter particles. However, due to the global code performances, the N-body number of particles that can be simulated is not very high. This obviously reduces the resolution of the formed structures.

The design of an interface between FLY and pure hydrodynamical codes allows us to have a high performance code running large simulations, with its data output (the potential field) integrated into the data structures of another code, running a gas evolution with the adaptive mesh refinement technique. The FLY output of the mesh is data input to the hydrodynamical code.

The mesh generated by FLY is identical to the PARAMESH structured mesh blocks. FLY creates the PARAMESH blocks at the minimum refinement level. Each block is geometrically mapped onto a tree cell. For each block all the sub-cells are computed: the *unk* variable being the potential field.

The computation is based on the tree structure, each block sub-cell is a virtual body and the unk variable is computed with the tree interaction (Barnes-Hut method). FLY can also decide that the block must be refined, depending on the mass density in each block, but it can also externally read all the blocks, at the refinement level given by the user. The FLY block of PARAMESH is the following:

```
TYPE BLOCK
  INTEGER(KIND=4)   :: lrefine_block
  INTEGER(KIND=4)   :: nodetype
  REAL(KIND=4), DIMENSION(ndim):: coord_block
  REAL(KIND=4) :: size
  REAL(KIND=4), DIMENSION(ndim) :: bnd_box_min
  REAL(KIND=4), DIMENSION(ndim) :: bnd_box_max
  REAL(KIND=4), DIMENSION(nxb+nguard,nyb+nguard,nzb+nguard):: unk
END TYPE BLOCK
```

FLY block can be used with any hydrodynamical code that adopts the PARA-MESH data structure, to study compressible flow.

4. FLY User-friendly Interface

FLY has a graphical Tcl/Tk interface that help the user to create all the parameter files, excluding the initial condition file. The main window sets the working directory, the executable directory and will create directories if they don not exist. Figure 1 shows the main window and the window used to set the static parameter file. If this file exists, it is loaded with the values of the existing file. Other files are created using similar windows.

In the main window the user can click on the *Generate* button and insert data to create the fly_h.F module, the makefiles in the directory *src* and the script file that can be submitted to the system queue. The *Make* button executes the makefile and creates the executable program.

Figure 2.   Monitor of Astrocomp job status

In the main window it is also possible to click on the buttons *Interactive Run* and *Batch Run* to submit the FLY job.

5. FLY in the Web

Astrocomp is a portal which creates a repository of easily usable computational codes and a common data base available to the entire international community. The Astrocomp server is based on a PHP-MYSQL environment. Registered users have free time on HPC systems included in Astrocomp and can run all the Astrophysical codes of the portal. FLY is included in this portal[2], where the users can run FLY directly on the IBM SP Power3 a 24 processor based system at the INAF OACT, on IBM SP Power4 a 512 processor based system and on the SGI Origin 3000 a 64 processor based system at the Cineca. The user can create parameter files with initial conditions and can submit a job on each system without knowing the commands of the selected system (Figure 2).

6. Conclusion

This new implementation of FLY is the first step towards the integration of this tree N-body code with hydrodynamical codes. The choice of an adaptive mesh refinement such as PARAMESH allows us to design a new interface aimed at *mixed* applications: a code running hydrodynamical simulations that receives data from FLY, evolving an N-body simulation at the same time. This kind of relationship could also be further enhanced using grid computing facilities.

References

Becciani, U. & Antonuccio, V. 2001, Comp. Phys. Comm. 54, 136

Barnes, J. & Hut, P. 1986, Nature 324, 446

MacNiece, P. et al. 2000, Comp. Phys. Comm. 126, 330

Di Matteo, P. et al 2003, this volume, 17

---

[2]http://www.astrocomp.it

Astronomical Data Analysis Software and Systems XII
ASP Conference Series, Vol. 295, 2003
H. E. Payne, R. I. Jedrzejewski, and R. N. Hook, eds.

Novel Approaches to Semi-supervised and Unsupervised Learning

David Bazell

Eureka Scientific, Inc., 6509 Evensong Mews, Columbia, MD 21044

David J. Miller

Department of Electrical Engineering, Pennsylvania State University, University Park, PA 16802

Kirk Bourne

Institute for Science and Technology at Raytheon, NASA/GSFC, Code 630, Greenbelt, MD 20771

Abstract. We discuss a novel approach to the exploration, understanding, and classification of astronomical data. We are exploring the use of unlabeled data for supervised classification and for semi-supervised clustering. Current automated classification methods rely heavily on supervised learning algorithms that require training data sets containing large amounts of previously classified, or labeled, data. While unlabeled data are often cheap and plentiful, using a human to classify the data is tedious, time consuming, and expensive. We are examining methods whereby supervised classification techniques can use cheaply available, large volumes of unlabeled data to substantially improve their ability to classify objects.

1. Introduction

Machine learning falls into two broad categories. One is called supervised learning, the other unsupervised learning. An area of research that has had only mild activity over the past decade attempts to combine supervised and unsupervised learning (Miller & Uyar 1997; Nigam et al. 2000). The hope is to develop powerful new classification algorithms that combine the strengths of the two methods while minimizing their shortcomings. We are investigating one approach to this problem and applying it to astronomical data.

Examples of supervised learning algorithms include neural networks, decision trees, and mixture models. Neural networks consist of a set of individual cross-linked processing units connected by weights. Training samples are fed into the network which produces an output representing one of several possible classes. Each training sample has an associated target class, i.e., the correct class for that sample. The algorithm compares the network output and the target values and changes the connection weights in order to make the network and target outputs match. Iterating this procedure trains the network.

Decision trees consist of a large number of nodes at which decisions are made regarding which path to follow down the tree. The decisions are typically whether a certain feature value is greater than or less than a threshold value at a node. Training samples are passed down the tree. The number of nodes and the threshold values at the nodes are changed during training in order to make the class value at a terminal leaf node match the desired target value. This results in a tree structure wherein new examples trickle down through the tree and end up on a terminal leaf node corresponding to the class predicted by the decision tree.

The technique we are examining is based on using mixture models to describe the probability densities from which features are drawn. A mixture model is a representation of the target function as a linear combination of probability densities. In our case the target function is an unknown function describing the features of our data. The parameters for each of the component probability densities (e.g., mean, standard deviation, and component amplitude) are fit by maximum likelihood using the Expectation Maximization algorithm described briefly below.

While supervised learning algorithms can do very well given an adequate training data set, they have a number of drawbacks. Typically they require a large training data set. Generation of a training data set can be very costly. Furthermore, it is generally not possible to add incrementally to the training data while training the classifier. If the training data are changed in any way, the entire training data set must be used to retrain the classifier.

By contrast, unsupervised learning algorithms often attempt to find groups or clusters in data. There are several approaches to clustering algorithms. For example, one might attempt to find clusters or groups of data points with all data within a cluster being similar to each other. Another approach would be to find groups where the emphasis is on the groups being distinct, rather than the points within the group being similar. These two extremes can be accomplished by minimizing different forms of the objective function.

Some of the drawbacks of unsupervised learning include not being able to guide the cluster generation, and finding too many or too few clusters. From a scientific standpoint we often have an idea of what we would like to see in terms of clustering. Thus, the ability to guide clustering algorithms or to incorporate limits on the number of clusters allowed would be very useful.

Looked at the problem another way, the traditional distinction between supervised and unsupervised learning is the use of labeled vs. unlabeled data. Our project relies on statistical learning to combine labeled and unlabeled data in new ways. We are developing new methods that allow us to train classifiers with a small amount of labeled data, and boost performance by adding unlabeled data. This allows us to benefit from the vast quantities of unlabeled astronomical data, and to modify our training by adding in new labeled data when it becomes available.

2. How do we do it?

The key point of this approach—and I hope you remember this if you remember nothing else from this paper—is that unlabeled data provide information about the joint probability distribution of features. For example, if we perform a search on-line for documents discussing "open source" we will find that both "Linux" and "Gnu" also commonly show up (try it using Google). This suggests that Linux, Gnu, and open source are all related in some way. In this example open source, Linux and Gnu are all features. Given enough documents, we can find a reasonable estimate of the joint probability distribution of the features. That is, we can find an expression that tells us the probability of finding two or more features with specific values in a given document. We don't know what these documents are (white papers, theses, manuals), because they're unlabeled. Joint probability distributions help us use unlabeled data effectively.

If features are generated by a two component Gaussian mixture model, we can recover the model parameters using unlabeled data alone. However, we need class labels to determine classes. Some labeled data are needed to actually classify rather than cluster the data.

We assume that our training data form two disjoint sets. One set, χ_l, consists of the labeled data (x_i, c_i) where x_i is a feature vector and c_i is a class label. The other set, χ_u consists of the unlabeled data (x_j). We assume the features are generated from a conditional probability density $f(x|\theta)$, where the density parameters are contained in the parameter vector θ. The class labels are assumed to be generated from the conditional probability density $P(c|m, x)$, where m denotes the mixture model component.

The best classifier is then found by using the maximum a posteriori (MAP) rule, which maximizes the total posterior probability of the model.

The map rule depends upon both $f(x|\theta)$ and $P(c|m, x)$, which gives us the critical point in this procedure: *Even though $f(x|\theta)$ is independent of class labels, improving $f(x|\theta)$ can improve classification.*

3. Expectation Maximization

The expectation maximization (EM) algorithm is used to iteratively refine estimates of model parameters when using incomplete data. EM can be used to estimate the values of missing parameters such as class labels. The basic algorithm can be described as follows. Assume an initial set of parameter values: $\theta = \{\mu_i, \sigma_i, \alpha_i\}$.

E-Step Use current parameter estimates, θ, to find the "best" values of class membership, i.e., best probabilistic labels.

M-Step Refine the parameters θ by using the map rule to maximize the total likelihood.

The steps are iterated until the change in parameter values falls below some predefined threshold.

4. Status and Applications

In testing our approach we are attempting classification of large data sets using limited labeled data. We are currently using a data set called ESOLV that has been used previously when testing neural networks (Storrie-Lombardi et al. 1992) and decision trees (Owens, Griffiths, & Ratnatunga 1996). This data set contains galaxy morphology parameters for over 5000 galaxies of a range of morphological types. We are trying to classify these data into five morphologial classes. Using about 100 labeled samples we achieve a test set error of around 50%. Using standard backpropagation neural networks or decision trees and training using about 1700 samples we get a test set error of about 35% to 38%.

Another interesting feature of this model is the ability to identify "interesting" objects based on class conditional probabilities. After classification of the data set has been completed we can examine the class membership probabilities associated with each of the objects.

While not specifically designed for this task, our method does have a limited ability to do class discovery. Class discovery means identifying objects that are not well categorized by existing classes. This can obviously be very useful when examining large data sets. A method that can put known objects into existing classes and create new classes when needed will help researchers direct future observations and analysis to some interesting areas.

Acknowledgments.   This work is being funded by a contract from the NASA/Applied Information Systems Research Program.

References

Miller, D.J. & Uyar, H.S.   1997, Advances in Neural Information Processing Systems, 9, 571

Nigam, K., McCallum, A.K., Thrun, S. & Mitchel, T.   2000, Machine Learning, 39, 103

Owens, E.A., Griffiths, R.E., & Ratnatunga, K.U. 1996, MNRAS, 281, 1530

Storrie-Lombardi, M.C., Lahav, O., Sodré, Jr., L., & Storrie-Lombardi, L.J 1992, MNRAS, 259, 8p

Astronomical Data Analysis Software and Systems XII
ASP Conference Series, Vol. 295, 2003
H. E. Payne, R. I. Jedrzejewski, and R. N. Hook, eds.

Predictive Mining of Time Series Data in Astronomy

Eric Perlman, Akshay Java

Joint Center for Astrophysics, University of Maryland, Baltimore County, 1000 Hilltop Circle, Baltimore, MD 21250

Abstract. We discuss the development of a Java toolbox for astronomical time series data. Rather than using methods conventional in astronomy (e.g., power spectrum and cross-correlation analysis) we employ rule discovery techniques commonly used in analyzing stock-market data. By clustering patterns found within the data, rule discovery allows one to build predictive models, allowing one to forecast when a given event might occur or whether the occurrence of one event will trigger a second. We have tested the toolbox and accompanying display tool on datasets (representing several classes of objects) from the RXTE All Sky Monitor. We use these datasets to illustrate the methods and functionality of the toolbox. We also discuss issues that can come up in data analysis as well as the possible future development of the package.

1. Introduction

Many types of variable objects exist in the universe, including stars with predictable behavior (e.g., Cepheids), objects with behavior that is inherently unpredictable (e.g, AGN), and objects with both predictable and irregular variability patterns (e.g., X-ray binaries). Constant monitoring of variable objects has been a continuing interest in astronomy, beginning with 16th century astronomer David Fabricius, and extending through history to Herschel, Leavitt and others. Today, monitoring is done by a wide variety of techniques, observers and instruments, from dedicated amateurs, to professional astronomers interested in intensive monitoring of individual objects, to all-sky monitors such as the RXTE ASM and BATSE aboard CGRO.

Despite being a new tool, all-sky monitors have already made important, if not decisive contributions to solving some of astronomy's most persistent mysteries, such as the cosmological origin of gamma-ray bursts and linking emission regions in AGN. With major initiatives such as the Large-Area Synoptic Survey Telescope (LSST) and Supernova Acceleration Probe (SNAP), all-sky monitors are poised to become a major discovery tool in astronomy. To maximize the utility of large monitoring programs, it is important to devise ways of handling large amounts of data in real time and find not only variability but also predictive patterns among these large data streams. It was with these goals in mind that we undertook this project.

431

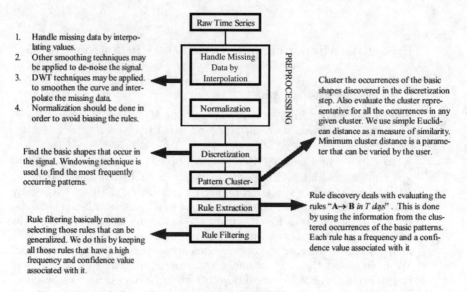

Figure 1.   A flow chart describing the basic rule discovery algorithm.

2. Clustering and Rule Discovery

The need to understand time series data is not unique to astronomy: time series data exists in a wide variety of fields including geology and atmospheric science as well as many business applications. The common problem is how to efficiently find patterns in the data. Fourier transform and power spectrum methods, commonly used in astronomy research, are well suited for finding patterns with well-determined periodicities (e.g., see Scargle 1997). However, they may be less helpful for objects with irregular behavior, and are not optimized to serve as predictive tools. Our approach was to employ clustering and rule discovery, which are optimized for finding patterns that do not rely on a regular periodicity.

We first attempt to represent the dataset as a collection of patterns, by sliding a window through the time series to get subsequences. We then cluster these points using the greedy clustering algorithm explained in Das, Gunopulos & Mannila (1997). Once a good fit is achieved, these clusters can then be considered as the basic shapes of the time series, with the entire series composed of superpositions and/or combinations of these basic shapes. The next and main step of the process is to find interesting probabilistic rules between the clusters in the two time series. These rules are of the form: "If a cluster A occurs in time series 1 then we can say with confidence c that B will occur in time series 2 within time T". Figure 1 displays a flow chart of the basic algorithm used in predictive time series analysis.

3. Data Analysis Structure and Usage

Two goals are possible with this approach, each requiring a slightly different analysis tree: (1) to schedule a telescope more intelligently to observe objects

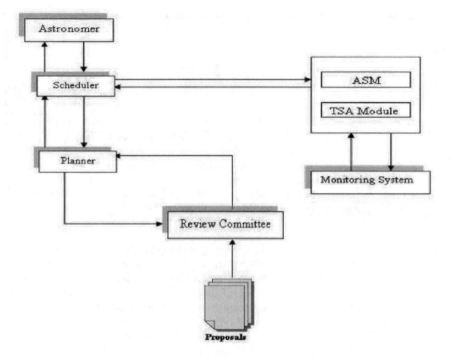

Figure 2. Flow charts for the possible use of this algorithm in scheduling a telescope.

when they are at their brightest or most interesting stage, or (2) as an analysis tool to find patterns within a (possibly multivariate) time series (see Figure 2).

Within the time-series analysis (TSA) module, the user can control three main parameters: the window size, the minimum cluster distance and the time period for prediction. The TSA module analyzes the time series data and performs trend prediction and rule discovery on both real time and historical data. This output can either be used directly for data analysis for a paper or to forecast both the activity level of an object and the ability of the telescope or satellite to perform the desired observations. All of these factors could be considered in the light of the constraints imposed by individual investigators as well as the review committee. The goal of such a process would be to maximize the scientific usefulness of all the observations. If, for example, a given observation required that a source be above a certain flux level, such a program might have a better chance of ensuring that this was so during the observations.

4. Results, Limitations and Future Work

To test and validate the toolbox, we used RXTE ASM datasets for various objects, spanning several different object classes. In Figure 3, we show one particularly interesting dataset, from SMC X-1. SMC X-1 shows interesting periodic behavior on several different timescales: a long time-period behavior

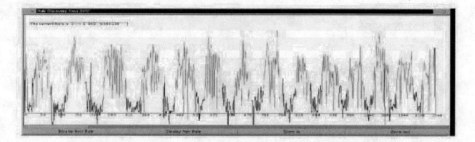

Figure 3.   A screenshot of the Java GUI application that is used to display the rules generated. Each color represents an occurrence of a basic pattern. As each rule is cicked on, the GUI shows the rule's frequency and associated confidence values.

as well as short time-scale variations superposed upon the long-period behavior, but occurring only when the object is bright (see e.g., Kahabka & Li 1999). The toolkit was found to be particularly effective for predicting short-period rules. Longer-period rules can be found by varying the window size, although possibly at the expense of losing short time-scale rules as the window size becomes larger than the rules in question. We can also find longer-period rules with smoothing techniques.

The current implementation of the toolkit consist of a rule inference engine, programmed in C and a visualizer, programmed in Java. The current toolkit has several limitations. First, the current toolkit can analyze only a single time series at any time. This obviously gives it limited functionality, as many objects are studied with multiple instruments. Second, it has limited ability to deal with missing data. In addition, one could envision multiple processing options, including the incorporation of dynamic time warping techniques, which could be particularly useful to spot quasi-periodic oscillations.

References

Agarwal, R., Inmielinski, T., Swami, A. 1993, in Proc. ACM SIGMOD, 207

Das, G., Gunopulos, D., & Mannila, H. 1997, Principles of Data Mining and Knowledge Discovery (Springer), 88

Hetland, M. L. 2002, in Data Mining in Time Series Databases, ed. M. Last, A. Kandel and H. Bunke (World Scientific), in press.

Kahabka, P. & Li, X-D. 1999, A&A, 345, 117

Scargle, J. D. 1997, in Astronomical Time Series, ed. D. Maoz, A. Steinberg & E. M. Leibowitz (Dordrecht: Kluwer), 1

Astronomical Data Analysis Software and Systems XII
ASP Conference Series, Vol. 295, 2003
H. E. Payne, R. I. Jedrzejewski, and R. N. Hook, eds.

Undistorting FUSE Using Wavelets

Paul Barrett

Space Telescope Science Institute, 3700 San Martin Drive, Baltimore, MD 21218

Abstract. This paper describes a method for determining the geometric distortion of the *FUSE* detectors using data from the in-orbit stimulation lamp exposures. A wavelet approach is used to smooth the image, while enhancing the shape of the shadows cast by the QE and plasma grids suspended above the detectors. By tracing pixel-by-pixel the horizontal and vertical shadows and by using interpolation for the regions between them, a two-dimensional map of the geometric distortion can be created.

1. Geometrical Distortions in the FUSE Detectors

The Far Ultraviolet Spectroscopic Explorer (*FUSE*) employs two microchannel plate (MCP), double-delay line detectors on which up to six individual spectra are simultaneously projected. Segment 1A of detector 1 is shown in Figure 1. The horizontal and vertical lines are shadows cast by the quantum efficiency (QE) and plasma grid wires suspended above the detector and illuminated by an on-board stimulation or "stim" lamp. In addition to the large scale distortions caused by the detector electronics, the distortion map clearly shows an ~ 85 pixel periodic distortion running vertically across the detector, which is due to the differential non-linearity (DNL) of the detector electronics.

2. Wavelets

The fundamental idea behind wavelets is to analyze according to scale (see e.g., Chui 1992). Wavelets are functions that satisfy certain mathematical requirements and are used in representing data or other functions. This idea is not new. Approximation using superposition of functions has existed since the early 1800's, when Joseph Fourier discovered that he could superpose sines and cosines to represent other functions. However, in wavelet analysis, the scale that one uses in looking at data plays a special role. Wavelet algorithms process data at different scales or resolutions. If we look at a signal with a large "window," we would notice gross features. Similarly, if we look at a signal with a small "window," we would notice small discontinuities. The result in wavelet analysis is to "see the forest and the trees."

For many decades, scientists have wanted more appropriate functions to approximate choppy signals than the the sines and cosines that comprise the bases of Fourier analysis. By their definition, these functions are non-local (and

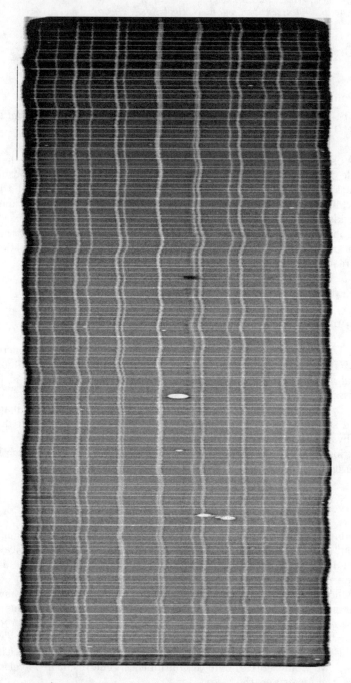

Figure 1.   A negative rotated image of detector 1A showing the vertical distortion. The image is a sum of 28 stimulation lamp exposures
and is compressed from its original size of 16384×1024 pixels.

stretch out to infinity), and therefore do a very poor job in approximating sharp spikes. With wavelet analysis, we can use approximating functions that are contained neatly in finite domains and hence, well-suited for approximating data with sharp discontinuities. The wavelet analysis procedure is to adopt a wavelet prototype function, called an "analyzing wavelet" or "mother wavelet." The original signal or function can be represented in terms of a wavelet expansion (using coefficients in a linear combination of the wavelet functions), data operations can be performed using just the corresponding wavelet coefficients.

3. Method

A wavelet approach was chosen for determining the two dimensional geometric distortions, because wavelet methods are typically quite efficient, which is important when dealing with large images, such as those produced by *FUSE*. Our approach is similar to that of Starck & Murtagh (1994) and uses a B-spline of degree 3 (B_3-spline) for our "mother wavelet." The B_3-spline leads to a convolution with a 5×5 kernel in two-dimensions.

At the smallest wavelet scale, the image mostly contains noise, and a B_3-spline does a good job at producing a smoothed image without degrading the resolution. The B_3-spline at the next larger scale is a good approximation to the cross-section of the grid wire shadows, which results in the shadow minimum being well localized in the low signal-to-noise data. Once the shadow's minimum is known, it is easy to trace the grid wire from one end to the other. The distortion is then just the difference in position of the measured minimum and the true minimum, which we approximate by assuming the grid wires are straight.

In the case where two wires are close together and their shadows start to merge (see Figure 1), we use a modified B_3-spline. We pad either end of the kernel with one or more zeros to bias the wavelet in that direction. This modified wavelet enhances one side of the shadow in relation to the other and enables us to bias our trace toward one wire or the other.

4. Results

Figure 2 shows segment 1A after correcting for the geometric distortion. The corrected image is nearly perfectly rectangular and the grid wires are evenly spaced. We have also aligned the six spectra across the two segments of each detector and removed the large scale wavelength distortions.

Some notable features of the wavelet method outlined here are: 1) the sensitivity to distortions on scales of < 10 pixels, 2) the sub-pixel accuracy of the distortion map after smoothing is applied, and 3) the ability to deconvolve and trace two wires whose shadows are nearly merged.

References

Chui, C. K. 1992, An Introduction to Wavelets (Boston: Academic Press)

Stark, J.-L. & Murtagh, F. 1994, A&A, 288, 342

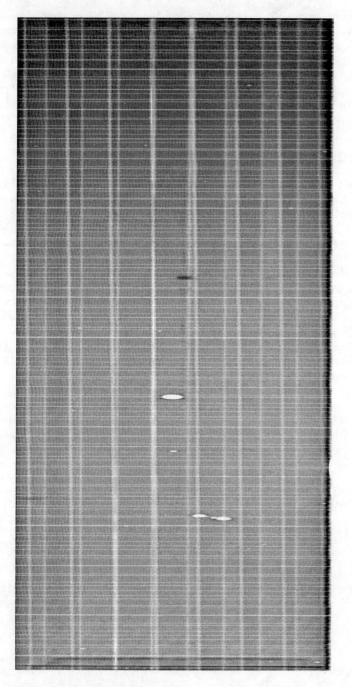

Figure 2.   A negative rotated image of detector 1A after removing the geometric distortion. See the caption of Figure 1.

Astronomical Data Analysis Software and Systems XII
ASP Conference Series, Vol. 295, 2003
H. E. Payne, R. I. Jedrzejewski, and R. N. Hook, eds.

Projecting 3-D Simulations Into Pseudo Observations

Alex Antunes, John Wallin

School of Computational Sciences, George Mason University, Fairfax, VA 22030

Abstract. We present methods for converting particle method three-dimensional simulations into observationally verifiable projected column densities, channel maps, fluxes, and velocity contours. Such projections are suitable for direct comparison with radio data (such as produced by AIPS), X-ray observations (e.g., ximage), optical, and IR. Whereas modeling usually involves N-body, mesh, SPH, or LPR calculations upon an idealized 3-D space, our observational data is always limited to a single line of sight projection, observing only one 'plane' of the object, emission from which may or may not include extinction. For models to have any validity, we must be able to generate pseudo-observational data from the model, to compare with actual observations. This connects our modeling with the real universe we see; herein we discuss the methods for creating such projections.

1. Introduction

Pseudo observations provide a connection between data and modeling. In N-body simulations, we model bulk gas, heated gas, and stars as individual particles in three-dimensional space. We can run time forward or backward from 'now' to study evolution.

Yet from Earth, we see flat images. Therefore we must convert our three-dimensional simulations to two-dimensional surface densities in order to compare directly with observational results.

This is about pinning down the crime scene—getting our simulations to match observations. From that, we can then make theories. Is a given feature dynamically created or evolutionary (e.g., did existing stuff move to that position, or did new stuff get formed there due to the collision)? Is it stable, will it be long-lived?

The goal here is to replicate nature. We make assumptions based on what we see ('most gas is near the radio-visible gas'), we run a model using that assumption, then we create results thinking "I'll plot all the gas as if it were radio-visible, because gas congregates, right?" In some cases, modeling can point out conceptual flaws (e.g., a dark matter halo is required for stability; sims verify this), in other cases our model will simply regurgitate our expectations. So the feedback between data and mode is complex, and validation via pseudo observations is therefore crucial.

Nature $\Rightarrow$
View from 1 location + limited wavelength range + instrument limitations $\Rightarrow$
Theoretical model $\Rightarrow$ Guess at evolutionary history $\Rightarrow$
Input to computer model $\Rightarrow$ Series of individual time frames $\Rightarrow$
3-D+time movie

2.   Pseudo-Observations

2.1.   Data Space

In the real world, radio observations show cool bulk gas (abundances and velocities with no extinction) and basic kinematics (inc. rotation curve). Optical
and near-IR observations show hotter gas, extinction (dust). Broadband optical shows hot and massive short-lived O/B stars (recent star formation) and
stellar populations and evolution. X-ray data show very hot regions—typically
due to singularly active objects that, at our N-body resolution of $10^5 - 10^7$
stars/computational point, are not sim-resolvable. But they do help show very
hot gas regions as well.

   In N-body Simulation Space, we have collisionless point-like particles, which
we call 'stars.' Each represents a lot of stars. We also have gas blobs that represent local gas, with a somewhat unified temperature and group velocity. Each
blob interacts with nearby blobs in a smooth way (hence the term Smoothed
Particle Hydrodynamics). Some of the gas forms into stars, changing the overall particle total metallicity (and removing some of the gas), and also injecting
energy (as supernovae) into the region.

   This high level of abstraction has to be mapped to the real world observations in order to obtain meaningful results. Our short list of criteria includes being able to create a 2-D projection of the data set, creating surface brightnesses
or density contours (hopefully with extinction), and allowing per-component
tagging to create false color images similar to the processing done to real data.

   Our code (**mass99**) is an N-body code with SPH, LPR, and various evolution and solid codes. Other packages (TreeSPH and its kin, NEMO's N-body,
etc.) do similar work. The basic approach is to simulate a galaxy with a lesser
number of collisionless particles and some sort of gas surrogate. The higher
the number of particles, N, the more accurate the simulation. The more (and
more accurate) the physics included, the better the simulation. The better the
simulation, the longer it takes to run on a supercomputer.

2.2.   Analysis Space

To create a pseudo-observation, we must:

1. Run a 3-D simulation using an N-body tree, a mesh, SPH blobules, LPR
    gridless grid, or whatever method is in our code.
2. Choose a data frame (time slice) that matches 'now.'
3. Project the 3-D data along the Earth-directed line of sight.
4. Sum up the surface brightness or fluxes or surface density or volumetric
    average or contour value for our given quantity. Some sums are extincted
    across the volume, others are surface summations only, others are accu-
    mulated totals.

5. Optionally, degrade by the appropriate interstellar medium, telescope response, or atmospheric observation. Or, if our observation data analysis already removed these effects, skip this.
6. Repeat for all wavelengths that we have data. This means make column densities, velocity contours, and channel maps for radio data, fluxes and direct image projections for *HST* and *CHANDRA* work (optical and X-ray), et cetera.
7. Display our assumptions. For example, our sim false color images assume star formation produces blue/white stars, and older stars are redder, and all gas is radio-visible or distributed where the radio-visible gas is.

Reduction items must therefore include projected particle/gas data as well as binned and/or averaged contours and/or surface densities, z-buffer sorted and with any extinction applied. Radial binning and radial profiles, phase plots, and velocity slices are also needed. Any data should be 'sliceable' as observational techniques typically 'catch' only a specific type or temperature of particle. All of this is best handled at the data digestion stage, before creating the pseudo-observation. First select the possible data, then filter and massage that to get the associated physically related output.

3. Keyframing Techniques

The issue of how to match a simulation to an observation runs into an interesting limitation, as finding the slice of time that corresponds to 'now' is a necessary step in creating the pseudo-observation. High performance computing is almost becoming i/o limited, creating more data than we can effectively manage. As data sets go from 10^8 to 10^9 in size, individual data frames of several gigabytes are common. So we deliberately degrade data, analyze during runtime to save on storage, and use Disney-esque keyframing to pre-focus on times of interest.

- Half a million star+gas particles = 720MB
- Projected subset of data = 500MB
- FITS datafile of above subset = 100MB
- Contour plot of data = under 1MB

Keyframing lets us do on-the-fly reduction. To create a simulation matching observations, we first do a small sim (10k particles) and create a movie. This lets us define keyframes—significant points of interaction crucial to defining the system. For example, we mark six frames (of 60+ run) that define the evolution best, from approach through merging and departure: six unevenly spaced frames that define the system.

We can then do a large scale (million-particle) simulation. At each keyframe, we first create intermediate data products using the many saved output files since the last keyframe. This includes a movie, radial velocity evolution, etc. Having created this, we can delete the massive intermediate output files and simply keep our bracketing keyframes.

After the run, we need only transfer the keyframes and the pre-reduced products to our workstation for analysis. This saves time and trouble: only 7GB of files are needed, not 150GB. And, our initial guess at reduced files are already created.

If we need to investigate sim results other than at the keyframes or in the pre-reduced set, we simply rerun the sim from the nearest keyframe (rather than from time zero).

4. Codes Available

Our own N-body+kitchensink code, **mass99**, includes the **reduce99** package for creating useful scientific output from the fairly abstract simulation space. **reduce99** handles projections of entire or per-component elements, with various summations to create surface densities, volumetric averages, and contours (as well as simple movie-making).

Nemo is a large set of tools that can handle individual frames (snapshots), plot angular momentum, and create conservation plots. Nemo is both flexible and extensible. Tipsy is a good freeware 4-D data analysis package, with a GUI that includes the ability to move around your simulation data space.

Other packages include AstroMD, NVisF (N-body Visualization Framework, formerly NVision), and Partiview (also used within Nemo). In addition, packages like IRAF, MIDAS, IDL, Geomview, QDP, plplot, gnuplot, and other raw plotting tools and scripts are often useful.

It is useful to be able to create pseudo-observations, as they can be directly loaded into your favorite data analysis (not modeling) package to cross-compare with real (observational) data. For example, a pseudo-radio contour of a 10^9 particle simulation imported into AIPS allows direct numerical comparison with the actual observation.

5. Conclusion

For our current work, we study AM0644-741 as our sample case. It is a wonderful example of a Lindsay-Shapley Ring, a beautiful off-axis collision for which we have a good orientation angle for viewing. We see an outer ring of presumed star formation and an older interior, a possible double ring, uneven star formation, blobby gas, a break, a possible ejecta or jet (or tidal feature).

A lot of people do 3-D visualization. Ironically, we want lossy 2-D visualizations of our perfect 4-Dimensional N-body+SPH simulations. Our goal is to just be handed a file and not know if it is an observation or a simulation. This is the antithesis of data mining. The key is to use our simulations to recreate observations. Only then can 'forensic data mining' have meaning. We welcome feedback and suggestions on further tools to support this. All work will go up at http://science.gmu.edu/~aantunes/.

References

Antunes, A. & Wallin, J. 2001, AAS, 199, 8706A

Borne, K. 1988, ApJ, 330, 38

Higdon, J. & Wallin, J. 1997, ApJ, 474, 686

Part 14. Data Analysis Software and Systems

Astronomical Data Analysis Software and Systems XII
ASP Conference Series, Vol. 295, 2003
H. E. Payne, R. I. Jedrzejewski, and R. N. Hook, eds.

Starlink Software Developments

Martin Bly, David Giaretta, Malcolm Currie

Starlink, Space Science and Technology Department, Rutherford Appleton Laboratory, Chilton, Didcot, Oxon, OX11 0QX, UK

Mark Taylor

Astrophysics group, H. H. Wills Physics Laboratory, Tyndall Avenue, Bristol University, Bristol, BS8 1TL, UK

Abstract. Some current and upcoming software developments from Starlink were demonstrated. These included invoking traditional Starlink applications via web services, the current version of the ORAC-DR reduction pipeline, and some new Java-based tools including Treeview, an interactive explorer of hierarchical data structures.

1. Introduction

Starlink is continuing to serve UK astronomers in a era of change; as well as supporting our established range of reduction and analysis software we are providing new tools and ways of controlling existing applications which fit in with the grid/virtual observatory paradigm while remaining compatible with existing data and ways of working. Key technologies for this work are Java, XML and SOAP.

This paper summarises new features of some existing packages and describes some new Java-based tools. Control of existing applications via web services is presented in a separate paper (Taylor et al. 2003) and not covered further here.

Up to date details of all Starlink software, including information for obtaining it, can be found at the Starlink web site.[1]

2. New Features of Existing Software

A number of packages were on display with major new facilities, including the following:

CCDPACK — CCD data reduction package

- Graphical display and interactive registration are greatly improved.
- Integrated support for reduction and registration of frames from mosaic cameras has been added.

---

[1]http://www.starlink.ac.uk/

GAIA — multi-purpose interactive image display and analysis tool

- Multi-extension FITS files can be displayed.
- Linear polarization maps can be displayed.
- Positions can be recorded from an image.

KAPPA — generic analysis and display package

- After many years, version 1.0 is finally released!
- All tasks now use the Starlink NDF structure instead of the old IM-AGE format.
- All applications are now WCS-aware.
- All graphics are now produced using native PGPLOT.
- Graphics applications are no longer restricted to 8-bit displays.

ORAC-DR — general purpose automatic data reduction pipeline

- More instruments are supported (Cavanagh et al. 2003).
- Data error handling is more accurate.
- A graphical front end is provided.

POLPACK — polarimetry data reduction package

- Support is now provided for spectro-polarimetry data.

Additionally a new package DATACUBE, consisting of A-tasks, shell scripts and a cookbook for IFU data reduction, has been introduced.

3. New Tools

New Starlink software development is being done using Java. We are developing an array data access layer called HDX/NDX (Giaretta et al. 2003) which permits network-transparent and (largely) portable access to data stored in a variety of forms. In this way the application software does not need to worry about the source (local or remote) or the format (FITS, NDF, XML) of a data array.

New tools written using this framework, demonstrated at the conference, are described in the following sections. All are undergoing active development and will offer new facilities in the near future.

3.1. Treeview

Treeview is an interactive graphical browser for hierarchical structures which knows about astronomical data formats. It resembles Windows Explorer in representing a hierarchical structure as a tree of nodes which the user may expand or collapse, but as well as displaying directory trees containing files, it can look inside files to display their structure in a hierarchical fashion to whatever depth makes sense. The GUI has a single window with two panels: one displays the tree-like hierarchical structure being browsed, and the other offers a variety of views of a selected node according to what kind of object it is. For instance you might open up a directory containing a number of FITS files, open one FITS file to find that it contains a BINTABLE and four IMAGE extensions, select one of the images, and then examine its header cards or WCS

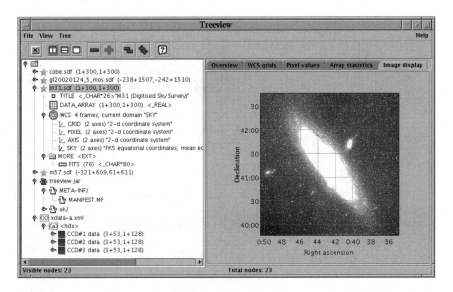

Figure 1.   Treeview displaying various files in a directory.

information, or view it as an image or a table of pixel values. Operation is extremely intuitive.

Treeview understands many kinds of structure, and more are being added. The current list includes file systems, Starlink NDF and HDS files, FITS files, zip/jar archives, XML documents, AST FrameSets, and Starlink NDX and HDX structures. More are being added; in particular VOTable support will be available very soon.

It is easy to add new node types and new views of existing ones, and explicit support for users to extend functionality by local provision of class libraries is planned in the near future.

The various data views which Treeview can provide of a selected node are confined to a single window and intended to be useful for a quick look. More detailed analysis of data, for instance line fitting of spectra or photometry on images is best delegated to external applications. For nodes of a suitable type, Treeview allows invocation of external applications to do this; currently SPLAT (Section 3.2) for spectra and SoG (Section 3.3) for images. Communication between the applications is done via SOAP, serialising data array references using NDX. This permits very flexible deployment of resources; for instance the machine running Treeview, the machine running the data analysis application and the machine hosting the data might all be geographically separated.

Treeview itself is written entirely in Java, but for WCS-related tasks and display of Starlink HDS/NDF files it uses some platform-specific shared library code (JNI wraps of the Starlink AST and HDS libraries respectively). These are currently available for Linux, Solaris and Tru64 Unix, while Windows versions should be available shortly. However, if these libraries are not detected at runtime, Treeview will run happily with some features unavailable. This means that it can run anywhere that a J2SE1.4 Java Runtime Environment is installed,

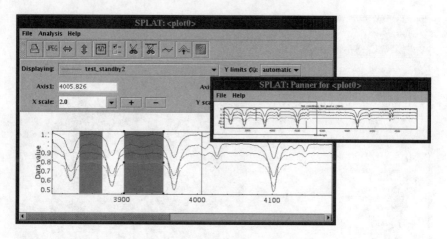

Figure 2.   The SPLAT spectral analysis tool.

which makes it highly portable. Installation is simply a case of unpacking a single tar or zip archive.

3.2. SPLAT

SPLAT (SPectraL Analysis Tool) is an interactive Java application for display, comparison and analysis of astronomical spectra. Spectra can be viewed singly, together or as an animated sequence; the display is highly configurable and publication quality plots can be produced. Facilities are provided for fitting spectral lines using a variety of profile models, fitting background levels using polynomials, and doing spectrum arithmetic. The program can be controlled from the command line, or using sockets or via SOAP messages.

3.3. SoG

SoG ("Son of Gaia") is an extension of JSkycat which can display NDX images, and is planned in due course to provide toolkits interfacing with other software. By taking advantage of grid technologies it will be able to provide similar functionality to the existing Gaia tool, while offering platform independence and network transparency.

References

Cavanagh, B., Hirst, P., Currie, M. J., Jenness, T., Economou, F., Ryder, S. & Todd, S. P. 2003, this volume, 237

Giaretta, D. L., Taylor, M. B., Draper, P. W., Gray, N. G. & McIlwrath B. K. 2003, this volume, 221

Taylor, M. B., Platon, R. T., Chipperfield, A. J., Draper, P. W. & Giaretta, D. L. 2003, this volume, 325

Astronomical Data Analysis Software and Systems XII
ASP Conference Series, Vol. 295, 2003
H. E. Payne, R. I. Jedrzejewski, and R. N. Hook, eds.

The Cosmo.Lab Project: Developing AstroMD, an Object Oriented, Open Source Visualization and Pre-analysis Tool for Astrophysical Data

C. Gheller, M. Melotti and L. Calori[1]

CINECA - Interuniversitary Center for High Performance Computing, Bologna, Italy

U. Becciani and D. Ferro[2]

Astrophysical Observatory of Catania, Italy

Abstract. The Cosmo.Lab project, financed by the European Community, has the object of developing AstroMD, a tool of visualization and analysis of astrophysical data. AstroMD responds to the requirements proposed by several research fields: data coming from cosmological simulations, from observational catalogues and extended objects like radiosources or clusters of galaxies. AstroMD exploits also the most advanced visualization technology, based on virtual reality, in order to build a leading edge instrument for scientific research. However it is a scalable software which can be used also on PCs or workstations. It is open-source and freely downloadable from the web site `http://cosmolab.cineca.it`.

1. Introduction

Today both astrophysical observation and simulations produce many gigabytes of data which have to be efficiently visualized and analyzed. Visualization is the most intuitive approach to data and basic information can be obtained just "at a glance." Then the possibility of moving inside the data allows the scientist to focus on regions of interest and to perform quantitative calculations. Therefore image processing tools are of fundamental importance in astronomy.

AstroMD is a new data visualization and analysis software specifically designed to deal with astrophysical data; it can powerfully handle large datasets allowing both their graphical representation and analysis, corresponding to the requirements proposed by several research fields. This new tool is tested on the dataset of the VIRMOS (observational galaxy catalogue) project, on data coming from observations of extragalactic radio sources and those obtained from cosmological simulations. Although these fields do not cover all the requirements of astronomy, they pose many typical problems that we expect to be solved by AstroMD. The solution to these problems was implemented following the suggestions and the indications of the research groups involved in the project and of a User Interest group.

Astrophysical data have peculiarities that make them different from data coming from any other kind of simulation or experiment, therefore they require

449

a specific treatment. For example, cosmological simulations consider both baryonic matter (described by fluid-dynamics) and dark matter (described by N-body algorithms). Further components, like stars or different chemical species, can be introduced and followed in a specific way. These different species require different types of visualization: dark matter needs particle position or velocity rendering while baryons require mesh based visualization. Furthermore particle associated quantities, like mass density or gravitational potential, require their calculation and visualization on a mesh. Then simulated structures have a fully three-dimensional distribution. Therefore it is necessary to have a clear 3-D representation, efficient and fast tools of navigation, selection, zoom and the possibility of improving the resolution and the accuracy in specific user-selected regions. Moreover evolution can dramatically change the properties of the simulated objects and the information that can be retrieved, therefore it is important to efficiently control sequences of time-frames. AstroMD will satisfy all these requirements.

2.   The Software

In order to build a widely used product it was chosen to use a low cost software portable on a number of different platforms, the open source Visualization Toolkit[1] (VTK) by Kitware (Schroeder et al. 1999), available for nearly every Unix-based platform (e.g., Linux or IRIX) and PC's (Windows 2000 and Windows XP). The design and implementation of the library is that visualization and analysis built-in functionalities are controlled by a specific Graphic User Interface (Antonuccio et al. 2002), written in Incr Tcl/Tk[2] that supports the object-oriented programming structure. This allows to extend easily the software. AstroMD objects can represent readers, that allow the user to read data from a file or from a database, filters, that allow the user to manipulate data, and viewers, to visualize the results. VTK supports a wide variety of visualization algorithms and supports stereographic rendering and can be used for virtual reality visualization. Furthermore, being easily extensible, the system allows ad hoc implementation of specific modules.

Efficient manipulation and analysis tools, like smoothing of the particle masses on a mesh or calculation of the power spectrum and correlation functions, are parts of the basic functionalities. AstroMD has also stereographic rendering capabilities, which makes it usable for immersive visualization, presently implemented at the Virtual Theatre of CINECA.[3] The display of data gives the illusion of a surrounding medium into which the user is immersed. The result is that the user has the impression of traveling through a computer-based multidimensional model which could be directly hand-manipulated. In this sense, the virtual reality is a progressive lowering of the barrier which separates users from their data (Earnshaw & Watson 1993).

---

[1]http://public.kitware.com/VTK/

[2]http://incrtcl.sourceforge.net/itcl/

[3]http://cosmolab.cineca.it

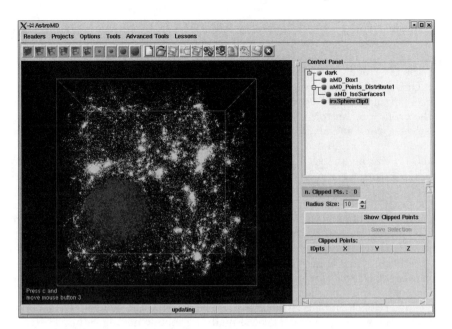

Figure 1.   The main GUI of AstroMD.

3.   AstroMD Functionalities

AstroMD allows the user to treat both particles (unstructured data) and continuous fields discretely represented over a computational mesh (structured data). The input data formats presently accepted by AstroMD are the common unformatted C standard (raw format), the TIPSY[4] and the FITS[5] formats. ASCII files can be also read.

Data are visualized with respect to a box which describes the analyzed region. A cubic or spherical sub-region can be selected interactively inside the parent box with a different spatial resolution, in order to focus on the most interesting regions. Data inside the sampler can be analyzed with the embedded tools or can be saved in specific files for an off-line analysis. Boxes can be translated, rotated, zoomed in and out with respect to selected positions. Colours and luminosities can be chosen by the user. Images of different evolutionary stages can be combined in order to obtain a dynamic view of the behaviour of the system. The opacity of the particles can be increased, so that low density regions are more easily detectable, or decreased, so that the details of the high density regions substructures are shown. Different particles species (e.g., dark matter and baryons) can be visualized at the same time using different colours. Other particles related to continuous quantities, like density fields, can be calculated as typical grid based fields and visualized as isosurfaces or volumes.

---

[4]http://www-hpcc.astro.washington.edu-/tools/tipsy/tipsy.html

[5]http://heasarc.gsfc.nasa.gov/docs/heasarc/fits.html

Scalar fields can be visualized by isosurfaces or by volume rendering. The value of the isosurface can be selected on the user interface (Antonuccio et al. 2002). The volume rendering can be calculated using both the texture mapping and the ray tracing technique.

Different time frames can be shown in a sequence. A single image or sequences of images can be saved in bitmap or jpeg format to prepare an animation of the evolution. AstroMD includes also a randomizer tool that allows the user to select a random subset of data, with no systematic errors in the selection procedure.

Data can be analyzed by various tools. First of all, the Power Spectrum, which expresses the weight of each of the Fourier components of the mass distribution. The Power Spectrum is a powerful measure of the statistical properties of the distribution (Antonuccio et al. 2002). Then the Correlation Function, that indicates the probability to find a particle at a distance r from any other particle, and is usually used to analyze the clustering properties of a sample of discrete objects (particle, galaxies, galaxy clusters, etc). It has been implemented using the Peebles and Hauser estimator (Pons-Borderia & Martinez 1999), that is preferable at large scale, for samples with non uniform density. The Minkowski Functionals, which provide a tool to characterize the large-scale distribution in the Universe (Schmalzing et al. 1996). They describe the geometry, the curvature and the topology of a point set. Finally, a group finder algorithm, known as Friends-of-Friends,[6] which allows to identify clusters in a particle distribution. A particle belongs to a FoF group if it is within some linking length of any other particle in the group.

New functionalities are being developed to allow AstroMD to handle observational data and to interact with databases allowing the user to submit query to extract and/or insert data in database tables.

Finally special attention is devoted to the implementation of didactic tools (like html pages related to data and catalogues and objects therein), to make AstroMD also a valuable instrument for teaching and disseminating astronomy.

References

Antonuccio-Delogu, V., Becciani, U., & Ferro, D. 2002, Comp. Phys. Comms., submitted

Earnshaw, R. A. & Watson, D. 1993, Animation and Scientific Visualization (San Diego: Academic Press)

Pons-Borderia, M. J. et al. 1999, ApJ, 523, 480

Schmalzing, J., Kerscher, M., & Buchert, T. 1996, Minkowski Functionals in Cosmology (Amsterdam: IOP Press), 281

Schroeder, W., Ken, M., & Lorensen B. 1999, The Visualization Toolkit. An Object-Oriented Approach to 3-D Graphics (Upper Saddle River, NJ: Prentice Hall)

---

[6]http://www-hpcc.astro.washington.edu/tools/fof.html

Astronomical Data Analysis Software and Systems XII
ASP Conference Series, Vol. 295, 2003
H. E. Payne, R. I. Jedrzejewski, and R. N. Hook, eds.

New STScI Data Analysis Applications

Warren Hack, Ivo Busko, Robert Jedrzejewski

Space Telescope Science Institute, 3800 San Martin Dr., Baltimore, MD 21218

Abstract. Tools exist within the STSDAS package for visualizing and analyzing spectra and for removing cosmic rays and distortion from sets of images. However, using these tools can sometimes be a complex experience. PyDrizzle and Specview have been developed at STScI to simplify the tasks of working with images and spectra, respectively. The Python task PyDrizzle automates the use of the *drizzle* and *blot* tasks from the dither package in STSDAS. The demonstration illustrated some of the most recently added capabilities to PyDrizzle that allow it to be used as a basis for removing cosmic rays and distortion from ACS data. Specview, on the other hand, provides easy simultaneous display and analysis of multiple 1-D spectrograms of the same astronomical source taken with different instruments. Its visualization and powerful spectral model fitting capabilities were demonstrated. Both tasks can be obtained online from STScI.

1. PyDrizzle

This package of tasks makes it easy for a user to dither-combine and/or remove geometric distortion from either dithered or single images. The tasks use the IRAF tasks *drizzle* and *blot* from the STSDAS **dither** package which implements the Drizzle algorithm (Fruchter & Hook 2002) to remove distortion and combine images. It consists of the tasks:

- **pydrizzle**
  Automates the use of both *drizzle* and *blot* by calculating all the necessary parameters, creating the appropriate distortion coefficients tables, and keeping track of all the inputs and outputs.
- **buildasn**
  Generates association tables for user-specified sets of images to be processed by PyDrizzle.
- **xytosky**
  Computes the distortion corrected RA/Dec based on the X/Y pixel position from a distorted image.

All these tasks have both a Python command line interface as well as an IRAF parameter-driven interface suitable for use with PyRAF's graphical EPAR. Pipeline use only requires the name of the input association table or exposure as input while all other parameters can be determined automatically or use conservative default values. This allows the task to be run, in most cases, with only one simple command and almost no parameters compared to the many required parameters for the *drizzle* or *blot* tasks themselves.

The task *pydrizzle* provides the user with the ability to:

- process ACS, WFPC2, and eventually STIS and NICMOS, images,
- modify computed parameters with values updated using external programs,
- keep track and modify intermediate file products, such as the static mask image,
- keep track of offsets from nominal shifts and rotations,
- compute distortion-corrected RA/Dec positions for any object from any input image,
- *drizzle* each input observation to a separate output, and
- *blot* separate outputs to separate inputs.

These capabilities allow PyDrizzle to maintain all the bookkeeping necessary for performing more advanced processing such as cosmic-ray rejection using the techniques from the Dither Handbook. PyDrizzle can also serve as the basis for a library of functions usable by any Python task for astronomical reductions. The *xytosky* task demonstrates how the methods from PyDrizzle can be developed into a separate task for use on data from any supported instrument.

A lot of work still needs to be done to expand the range of additional tasks derived from the PyDrizzle methods and classes, such as a *skytoxy* task, with an emphasis on making them generally applicable to any astronomical dataset. However, the current software still represents a dramatic step forward in the ease of use of advanced image processing, specifically processing provided by the tasks in the STSDAS *dither* package.

1.1. Status

PyDrizzle Version 3.0 was released with STSDAS Version 3.0. The latest version, starting with *Version 3.3e (7-Nov-2002)*, can be downloaded from the PyDrizzle WWW pages.[1]

A serious effort to provide documentation for PyDrizzle has been undertaken, starting with built-in help, IRAF-style help files in STSDAS and a user's guide for PyDrizzle. As a starting place, a preliminary draft of the first chapter of a user's guide can be downloaded from the WWW site, with the full version being posted as soon as it gets completed.

2. Specview

Specview is a spectral visualization tool that has been designed to provide easy simultaneous display and analysis of multiple 1-D spectrograms of the same astronomical source taken with different instruments.

Currently, Specview fully supports a variety of FITS file formats:

- HST STIS 1-D extracted spectra,
- HST STIS 2-D rectified spectra,
- HST GHRS,

---

[1]http://stsdas.stsci.edu/pydrizzle/

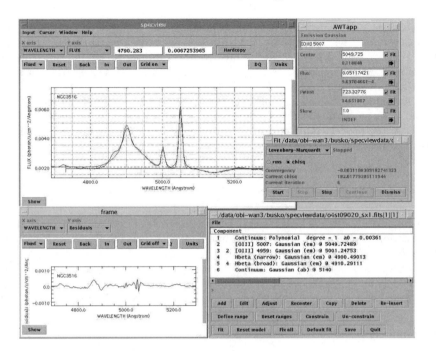

Figure 1.   Specview in action.

- HST FOS,
- ACS grism 1-D spectra extracted by aXe,
- IUE MXHI echelle,
- IUE MXLO first order,
- SDSS 1-D extracted spectra,
- FUSE,
- STScI Archive preview FITS files,
- generic FITS binary table reader, and
- generic text-based format that can be used to input almost anything, including SED data.

Specview provides a number of interactive tools to enable the user to explore the internal structure of complex spectroscopic files, such as STIS and IUE echelle data. It provides interactive tools for zooming and panning into the data, and for selecting particular data arrays within a file. There are also interactive tools for browsing the FITS headers, and for customizing the plots, such as a physical units selector, log scaling, a color and plot style editor, and plot annotation. Plots can be sent to a hardcopy device or a file. Most of these features can be accessed from buttons or menus shown in Figure 1.

Specview features a powerful spectral model fitting engine which allows the user to: build spectral models, maintain spectral models using interactive tools, and fit data using non-linear chi-square minimization. Models are built from spectral components selectable from a library. Choices include functions such as blackbody, power laws, recombination continuum, bremsstrahlung, accretion disk, a variety of Gaussian types, Lorentz, Voigt, etc. Components can be edited in a variety of ways, and also be constrained to each other using physical criteria. Users with minimal proficiency in Java coding can add their own functions to the library as well. Models can be saved to disk at any time and brought back later for further use.

A "quick measurement tool" is in the works to provide point-and-click functionality to measure spectral line properties without the need to invoke the full power of the model fitting engine. Also in the works is a data processing engine that will provide spectrum arithmetic, splicing, rebinning, and Fourier filtering capabilities.

2.1. Status

Specview is a standalone application written in Java. It can be downloaded and installed as independent software, or it can be bundled with other Java applications. Specview is currently bundled with the StarView archive data browser as its main spectral preview tool.

Specview has been tested under a variety of systems: Solaris, Linux, Windows 98/NT/XP. A MacOS X port will occur in the near future.

The software can be downloaded from the Specview WWW pages.[2]

References

Fruchter, A. S. & Hook R. N. 2002, PASP, 114, 144

---

[2]http://specview.stsci.edu

Astronomical Data Analysis Software and Systems XII
ASP Conference Series, Vol. 295, 2003
H. E. Payne, R. I. Jedrzejewski, and R. N. Hook, eds.

Synchronous Observations by Ground Based Optical and X-ray Space Born Telescopes

A. Pozanenko, A. Chernenko

Space Research Institute, Moscow, Russia

G. Beskin, V. Plokhotnichenko

Special Astrophysical Observatory, Karachay-Cherkessia republic, Russia

S. Bondar

State Technical Research Center "Kosmoten," Russia

V. Rumyantsev

Crimean Astrophysical Observatory, Crimea, Ukraine

Abstract. Simultaneous multiwavelength observations are critically important for understanding physical and astronomical properties of many celestial phenomena. We consider simultaneous X- and γ-ray/optical observations of cosmic Gamma-Ray Bursts. An important task of optical transient observation requires continuous wide field telescope surveys. Based on available observations we discuss criteria for development of optical wide-field camera and present the automatic telescope that is being developed for the purpose of simultaneous optical observations of GRB counterparts.

1. Gamma-Ray Burst Afterglow and Optical Prompt Emission

Gamma-Ray Burst (GRB) phenomenon has been studied in γ-rays since 1967 (first publication in 1971) by space born wide field γ-ray detectors. More than 4000 events have been registered. Technology development, onboard GRB source position calculation, rapid information downlink to tracking station and the Internet, allow looking for GRB events worldwide with large optic telescopes. Since discovery of the first optical counterpart of GRB970228 (Guarnieri et al. 1997), more than 30 GRBs optical afterglows were found, and the cosmological nature of the phenomenon is proved. The typical brightness of a detected Optical Transient (OT) is about 18 mag and large telescope response time is about one day. However, response time is decreasing as more telescopes join the GRB Coordinates Network (Barthelmy et al. 1994).

Search for prompt optic emission has lead to creation of a new generation of optical telescopes—fast response wide field cameras, which can be automatically pointed to a GRB error box having been alerted by γ-ray telescopes via the network. However, in only one case was prompt optical emission successfully registered by robotic telescope: GRB990123. ROTSE was alerted via network, started observation 22 s after GRB trigger, and recorded optical emission with a maximum brightness about 8.5 mag (Akerloff et al. 1999).

2. Usefulness of Classical Approach

Even if an alert is generated, transmitted, accepted and responded to in near real time, the alerted system could not effectively record prompt emission if time delay after burst trigger is greater than duration of the burst. And the typical duration of bursts is 10 s. Indeed the necessary time to generate alert depends on brightness of the burst and its time profile in γ-ray domain: e.g., according to current trigger algorithms a slow rise burst will generate alert later than a fast rise burst; some bursts were found only in post flight analysis. Accuracy of GRB source position calculation also depends on brightness and duration of the burst; sometimes ground analysis is necessary to reduce an error-box, which also delays the start of ground based observation.

The class of short bursts and Soft Gamma-Ray Repeaters with specific duration of about 0.1 s cannot be observed by alerted system in real-time. No afterglow from short burst has been detected till now (Hurley et al. 2002). Also the optical emission preceding the burst onset (which is discussed in GRB models (Mezaros et al. 2001, Beloborodov 2001) cannot be detected by alert-based system at all. Now the detection of a prompt emission and possible optical precursor as well as variability investigation of the optical emission is a crucial point in understanding of physics of γ-ray bursts.

3. Requirements for Observation of Prompt Emission

Synchronicity. To effectively observe prompt optical emission one needs to monitor simultaneously the same area of the sky by space-born γ-ray observatories and an optical observatory. While GRB monitors do so regularly (at present the HETE-2 and IPN collaboration, consisting of Konus-Wind, Ulysses, HEND/Mars Odyssey, and GRS/Mars Odyssey, is operating in space), as far as the authors know, no one optical system is continuously monitoring the sky synchronously with space labs.

Independence. Monitoring should be independent, to avoid the need for any alerted transmission in real-time. The full data reduction and correlation with space labs could be done after observation, which additionally decreases the uptime requirements and cost of telecommunication channels.

Time scale. As opposed to the case of afterglow observations, the time resolution for prompt emission search should be near equal or better than the duration of the event. Though time scale of the optical emission may significantly differ from that of the γ-ray emission, one may estimate the specific duration of prompt emission from the only one detected, GRB990123, as 20 s. However, prompt emission duration may be different for different events. On the other hand, variability measurement requires better time resolution. Because the search strategy depends on unknown duration of the OT, and requirements for variability measurement contradict to those for search strategy, one needs to have a continuous set of frames with time exposure better than duration of the event which could be used for subsequent co-adding frames with the aim of increasing sensitivity.

Wide FOV versus sensitivity. The larger the FOV of a telescope, the larger is the probability to have in this FOV an error box of a GRB. On the other hand a more sensitive telescope has better chance to detect OT if the source of a burst is in the FOV of the telescope. In the case of searching, the probability of catch the OT is a function of the two above probabilities. Let us consider a detector with CCD matrix having fixed pixel size and number of pixels. The sensitivity S of the telescope equipped with that matrix is roughly proportional to l, $S \sim l$, where l is a filled size in degrees. (The sensitivity is defined as a detection limit with the same confidence level for the same exposure time.) The larger the FOV, the worse is the sensitivity. The cumulative distribution of OT versus their brightness may be written as $N(> S) \sim S^{-a}$, where N is a number of sources with brightness more than S. (In case of 3-dimensional Euclidean space and uniform distribution of sources it is $N(> S) \sim S^{-3/2}$.) Finally, the number of observed potential sources of OT is proportional to l^2 because of isotropic distribution of GRB. Combining these formulas one can obtain that the number of detected OT is $N \sim l^{(2-a)}$.

Strategy of prompt emission search depends on the parameter a. One can estimate the slope of $N(> S) \sim S^{-a}$ distribution by extrapolating already observed afterglow light curves backward to some standard moment of time after burst onset. The estimation gives $a = 0.7$. Of course this estimation is not fully correct due to possible bias and possible change in a power law index of OT light curve backward to the beginning of the burst. The parameter a could be estimated from theoretical predictions including cosmological nature of GRB, possible evolution of source intensity in cosmological reference frame, beaming optical emission, etc. In this case the a is varying from 0.5 to 1.5 depending on many uncertain suggestions. Because of $a < 2$ a telescope with wider FOV is more preferable.

All sky optical survey, which is widely discussed (e.g., Nemiroff & Rafert 1999; Paczynski 2001) may resolve the problem of GRB optical prompt emission and fast OT search while technological problems and limitations, including financial one, are evident. The most important factor is a large scanning time in comparison with short duration of the OT. To avoid some of the limitations and to increase the probability of synchronous coverage of the same part of the sky we propose to monitor by ground based optical system only "small" part of the sky, in particular the field of view of spaceborn X- and γ-ray telescopes. The data obtained by space lab and ground based observatory will be correlated later for joint search of transients. This approach has been already discussed (Beskin et al. 1999).

Taking into account the above requirements we have developed a low cost wide field camera ($15 \times 20°$) with relatively high time resolution (0.13–10 s) which will be able to monitor FOV of current and future X-ray telescopes, in particular Wide field X-ray Camera (WXC) of HETE-2. The main components of the optical camera are: (1) Main objective: focal length 180 mm, aperture diameter 150 mm; (2) Image intensifier: photocathode S25, quantum efficiency 0.1; input fiber optic window D=80 mm, output glass window, scaling factor

4.5:1; amplification coefficient 120; (3) Adapting objective: constructed from two commercial objectives AVENIR SE2509; (4) CCD camera: commercial TV-CCD camera equipped with SONY 2/3″IXL285 matrix, 1380 × 1024 pixels, variable exposure 1/7.5–10 s, readout noise 20 e^-/pixel.

To obtain wide FOV and to use the low cost commercial CCD matrix we use image intensifier for both image scaling and compensating light loss in adapting objective. The FOV of the camera is 20°, and the spatial resolution of the system is about 50 arcsec/pixel. The spatial resolution in fast observation is less important because the precise localization can be done later by observations of the afterglow with large telescopes. Because of large readout noise of TV-CCD the sensitivity of the camera is restricted by the noise at minimum exposure time and by sky background at maximum exposures. The modeled detection level of the system is about 12.5 mag at 0.13 s exposure and about 14 mag at 1 s for a dark night. The prototype of the camera (TT600 telescope of Kosmoten observatory) is now being used for current alerted observation of GRB afterglow.

The software includes frame comparator in video processor for ion and particle events elimination, storage system management, and a buffer for frame accumulation. Frame will be accumulated in different time windows and compared in real time. According to predefined criterion the system can generate alert in case of bright transient detection. This part of the system is similar to a usual trigger scheme of γ-ray burst detectors.

We estimate the rate of successful simultaneous observation of GRB errorbox with WXC of HETE-2 as 1.6 per year. More events will be investigated after correlation of weak bursts which occur in FOV of WXC but not sufficiently intense for source coordinates calculation. The same time-spatial correlation of events registered in our camera with HETE and time correlation with space born GRB detectors may help to resolve the problem of absence/presence of OT from short bursts and problem of possible GRB-orphans (GRBs which are not observed in γ-rays).

Acknowledgments.   This investigation is partially supported by U.S. Civilian Research and Development Foundation (CRDF).

References

Akerloff, C. et al. 1999, Nature, 398, 400

Barthelmy, S. D. et al. 1994, in Proceedings of the 2nd Huntsville Workshop, eds. G. Fishman, J. Brainerd, & K. Hurley (New York: AIP), 307, 643

Beloborodov, A. M. 2001, ApJ, 565, 808

Beskin, G. M. et al. 1999, A&AS, 138, 589

Guarnieri, A. et al. 1997, A&A, L13

Hurley, K. et al. 2002, ApJ, 567, 447

Mezaros, P. Ramirez-Ruiz, E. & Rees, M. J. 2001, ApJ, 554, 660

Nemiroff, R. J. & Rafert, J. B. 1999, PASP, 761, 886

Paczynski, B. 2001, astro-ph/0108522

Astronomical Data Analysis Software and Systems XII
ASP Conference Series, Vol. 295, 2003
H. E. Payne, R. I. Jedrzejewski, and R. N. Hook, eds.

An Interactive Java Plotting Package for Astronomy

A. Zhang, J. C. Good, G. B. Berriman

Infrared Processing and Analysis Center, California Institute of Technology, Pasadena, CA 91125

Abstract. This paper describes the architecture and functionality of a general purpose two dimensional plotting package for astronomy— QtPlot. It is a modification of an Open Source Java Plotting package, PtPlot, made available by the Ptolemy project at the University of California. QtPlot supports ASCII and XML format. It is in operation at the Infrared Science Archive (IRSA) of the California Institute of Technology, and supports mission services and a key astronomical data fusion toolkit—OASIS.

1. Introduction

The NASA/IPAC Infrared Science Archive (IRSA) has been developing a Java two dimensional plotting package for astronomy. The aim of the project was to develop at modest cost a general package that could be deployed as an applet through the IRSA web page. The package is based on PtPlot, an open source interactive plotting package released by the Ptolemy project at the University of California. This project studies modeling, simulation, and design of concurrent, real-time, embedded systems; see the Ptolemy II Ptplot page.[1] PtPlot is a Java application that supports ASCII, binary and basic eXtended Markup Language (XML) formats, and remote and local file access.

IRSA has extended and adapted PtPlot to provide a rich suite of user-controlled functions for modifying the appearance and attributes of plots, such as symbol, color, plot boundaries, data limits, plot annotations, etc. It supports interactive conversion between logarithmic and linear scales, as well as reversal of axes. This modified package, QtPlot, supports column delimited ASCII format tables (the so-called IPAC table format), but of greater importance is the fact that it supports XML structured for astronomical plot directives, underpinned by the eXtensible Data Format(XDF), a container for transporting scientific data. The XML support also supports plotting by reference to a path to a data file.

QtPlot has been deployed operationally as an applet at IRSA, where it supports interactive plotting of spectra from the Submillimeter Wave Astronomical Satellite (SWAS), and light curves from the American Association of Variable Star Observers (AAVSO). It has also been integrated into the On-Line Archive

---

[1]`http://Ptolemy.eecs.berkeley.edu/java/ptplot5.2/ptolemy/plot/doc/index.htm`

Science Information Service (OASIS), IRSA's primary data fusion toolkit, for general two dimensional plotting support (e.g., plotting two columns of a table retrieved from a database). It can access local files or remote files, through HTTP protocols, and can be directly called by a web application.

2.   Overview of the Functionality in QtPlot

The QtPlot package contains classes, applets, and applications for two dimensional graphical display of data. It can be used as an independent Java package, or it can be called by another Java package which manages passing arguments, controls input parameters, and handles opening or closing plots on the screen. Furthermore, QtPlot can graphically display data on web pages when deployed as a plug-in.

While the plot symbol and color can be changed by clicking on the plot legend, users generally interact with the tool largely through menu-driven control panels, which provide control over the plot appearance and attributes, such as plot labels, plotting ranges, plot symbol and so on. Two of these menu-driven features are of special interest: (1) control of the plot type: linear, logarithmic, or histogram; (2) enable overplotting of additional data, such as additional spectra or light curves.

3.   Data Format

Broadly speaking, QtPlot supports two formats: column delimited ASCII tables (IPAC table format), and XML. The IPAC table format is used throughout IRSA to return ASCII data to users and to allow users to upload data files to cross-compare them with IRSA's catalogs. Consequently, QtPlot naturally supports this format.

Of wider interest is XML support. QtPlot utilizes the XDF,[2] which supports transport of multiple n-dimensional tables and file attributes through references in the XML specification. The following is an example of the XML file that describes the display of the brown dwarf 2MASSI J0028394+150141 from Dr. Davy Kirkpatrick's Archive of L Dwarfs.[3]

```
<?xml version="1.0" encoding="ISO-8859-1" standalone="yes"?>
<PlotSet>
    <XYPlot name="2MASSI J0028394+150141">
      <axes>
         <title> 2MASSI J0028394+150141 (L4.5 V) </title>
         <xaxis>
            <scaling> linear </scaling>
            <min>     6300   </min>
            <max>     10200  </max>
```

---

[2]http://xml.gsfc.nasa.gov/XDF/XDF_home.html

[3]http://spider.ipac.caltech.edu/staff/davy/ARCHIVE/index_l_spec.html

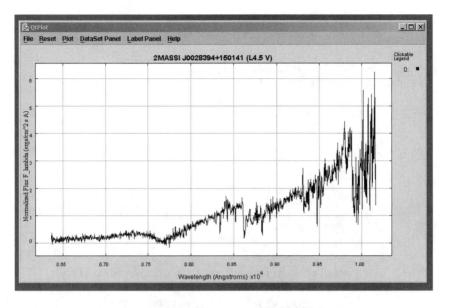

Figure 1.   Rendering of the Spectrum of 2MASSI J0028394+150141; the plot interprets the directives given in the XML.

```
        <label>    Wavelength (Angstroms) </label>
     </xaxis>
     <yaxis>
        <scaling> linear </scaling>
        <min>      -0.1    </min>
        <max>       4.5    </max>
        <label> Normalized Flux F_lambda (ergs/cm^2) s A)
        </label>
     </yaxis>
  </axes>
  <pointset name="spectrum">
     <source>
        <type>    XDF     </type>
        <table>    0028p1501_ascii </table>
        <xcolumn> wave    </xcolumn>
        <ycolumn> flux    </ycolumn>
     </source>
     <points>
        <color>  black    </color>
        <symbol> none     </symbol>
        <size>    1
     </points>
     <lines>
        <color>  black    </color>
        <style>  solid    </style>
```

```
            </lines>
        </pointset>
    </XYPlot>
    <XDF name="0028p1501\underline{ }ascii">
        <array name="data table">
            <axis axisId="columns" axisDatatype="real">
                <axisUnits><unitless/></axisUnits>
                <valueList size="2"/>
            </axis>
            <fieldAxis axisId="rows">
                <field name="wave" >
                    <units><unit>Angstroms</unit></units>
                    <dataFormat>
                        <fixed width="17" precision="11"/>
                    </dataFormat>
                </field>
                <field name="flux" >
                    <units><unit>ergs/cm^2) s A</unit></units>
                    <dataFormat>
                        <fixed width="11" precision="8">
                    </dataFormat>
                </field>
            </fieldAxis>

            <data><![CDATA[
                6361.90087890625      0.27137709
                        ....
        10158.09863281250     1.38749599
            ]]></data>
        </array>
    </XDF>
</PlotSet>
```

4. Conclusions and Future Work

This paper has presented an overview of QtPlot, a general astronomical plotting package that leverages the Open Source application QtPlot. The major upgrade that will be made in an upcoming release will be to support larger data files by swapping data disk rather than loading all the data into memory, as is currently done.

Acknowledgments. We are grateful to the Ptolemy project for distribution of the PtPlot package.

Astronomical Data Analysis Software and Systems XII
ASP Conference Series, Vol. 295, 2003
H. E. Payne, R. I. Jedrzejewski, and R. N. Hook, eds.

XAssist: A System for the Automation of X-ray Astrophysics Analysis

A. Ptak

Johns Hopkins University

R. Griffiths

Carnegie Mellon University

Abstract. XAssist is a NASA AISR-funded project for the automation of X-ray astrophysics, with emphasis on galaxies. It is nearing completion of its initially funded effort, and is working well for *Chandra* and *ROSAT* data. Initial support for *XMM-Newton* data is present as well. It is capable of data reprocessing, source detection, and preliminary spatial, temporal and spectral analysis for each source with sufficient counts. The bulk of the system is written in Python, which in turn drives underlying software (CIAO for *Chandra* data, etc.). Future work will include a GUI (mainly for beginners and status monitoring) and the exposure of at least some functionality as web services. The latter will help XAssist to eventually become part of the VO, making advanced queries possible, such as determining the X-ray fluxes of counterparts to HST or SDSS sources (including the use of unpublished X-ray data), and add the ability of "on-the-fly" X-ray processing. Pipelines are running on *ROSAT*, *Chandra* and now *XMM-Newton* observations of galaxies to demonstrate XAssist's capabilities, and the results are available online (in real time) at http://www.xassist.org. XAssist itself as well as various associated projects are available for download.

1. Introduction

We are currently in a renaissance for X-ray astronomy, with two major missions, *Chandra* and *XMM-Newton*, currently operating. These missions are producing large amounts of archival data, which is supplementing existing databases from missions such as *ROSAT* and *ASCA*. Historically, only X-ray "experts" usually attempted the analysis of X-ray data. This is because there were fundamental differences in the analysis of X-ray data compared with other bandpasses, most notably the fact that individual photons are detected as opposed to the accumulation of (only) spectra or images. Most modern X-ray detectors are imaging spectrometers so each observation results in a photon list from which images, spectra and light curves can be extracted. In general the numbers of photons are small so Poissonian rather than Gaussian statistical methods must be used. The spectral and spatial resolution of most detectors is moderate at best and forward-fitting convolution methods are needed to properly fit the data. All of these factors limit the accessibility of the X-ray data to non-experts. In addition each mission tends to have its own unique software package for the reduction and analysis of the data, and X-ray data often require reprocessing as the calibration improves. These latter two factors also limit the ability of experts to take advantage of all available data for a given project, particularly large-scale surveys.

We have developed a software package to address these concerns. XAssist is capable of performing data reduction and preliminary analysis for *ROSAT*, *Chandra* and *XMM-Newton* data. It is fully automatic making it well-suited for surveys, as well as for the reprocessing of existing data. Below we will discuss its capabilities and prospects for the future.

2. Capabilities

XAssist currently has the following capabilities:
- Downloads data
- Reprocesses data
- Creates exposure maps and detector masks (if possible)
- Detects sources (using built-in routine for *ROSAT* and *ASCA*, CIAO wavdetect for *Chandra*, etc.)
- Fits each source with "simple" (i.e., not including point-spread function) model to establish source extent and (Poisson-correct) significance (using the stand-alone python program ximgfit[1])
- Flags extended, confused and problematic sources
- Computes median (or mean) background level
- Excludes times of high background
- Extracts spectra, "postage stamp" images, and light curves of each source for more detailed analysis (a simple power-law model is fit to sources with more than 100 sources)
- Optionally performs chip-by-chip analysis (relevant just for *Chandra* right now)
- Analysis can be restricted to an energy band
- Large emphasis on detailed reporting
- Looks for correlations of X-ray sources with astronomy databases and provides links on the detailed source web reports to query Simbad (see below)

Note that in the case of *Chandra* analysis, most of the data reduction steps are based on the "threads" reported in the *Chandra* web site.[2] Most parameters controlling XAssist are read from IRAF/FTOOLS-style parameter file, and can be set on the command-line as well (allowing for the automated setup of XAssist for surveys). XAssist can be run (and configured) interactively (with a text-based interface).

---

[1] http://www.xassist.org/xassist/Download.jsp

[2] http://cxc.harvard.edu

3. Sample Output

Figure 1 shows images created as part of the report for the processing of the *Chandra* observation NGC 1569. Figure 2 shows the detailed report generated for a source. While there are admittedly "warts" that occur (as in any automated system), this example demonstrates that even in moderately crowded fields the system performs well and continues to the point of fitting a power-law spectrum model to the source spectrum. Obviously, this opens a powerful possibility for virtual observatories, namely that searches could be performed on high-level quantities such as spectral slope. Even though human inspection would of course still be necessary for science-grade results, an automated system such as this could cull samples and produce usable results for many of the sources, both of which would be particularly useful prior to observing proposal deadlines (especially if the data of interest had only recently become publically available and had not been published yet). Queries are also submitted to HEASARC to find correlations of X-ray sources with 2μass, USNO, FIRST, and other catalogs.

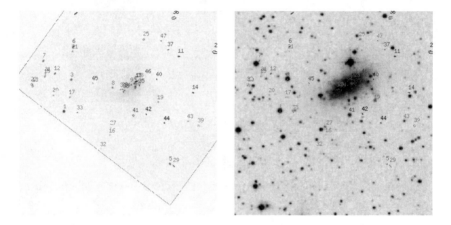

Figure 1. *Chandra* ACIS (left) and DSS (right) images of NGC 1569. Detected X-ray sources are marked in both images. The color code is: green = point source, red = problematic/questionable source, blue = extended source, magenta = asymmetric source (may be extended), cyan = estimated detector boundary.

4. Pipelines

To demonstrate XAssist's capabilities, pipelines[3] have been set up to run XAssist on *ROSAT* HRI and *Chandra* observations of RC3 galaxies. The *ROSAT* analysis is nearing completion, and crontab jobs are checking for the public release of *Chandra* observations that may containing RC3 galaxies in the FOV of

---

[3]http://www.xassist.org/xassist/Pipelines.jsp

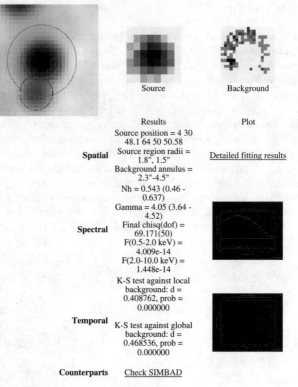

Figure 2.   Detailed web page report for a source in the *Chandra* observation of NGC 1569.

view, and these data sets are downloaded (using the script cda.py also available for download). *XMM-Newton* has recently been added as a supported mission, and we are in the process of establishing a pipeline for public *XMM* data. The pipeline products are searchable and work is in progress to allow users to request fields to be added to the processing lists.

5.   Current and Future Work

Tasks include: (*i*) finishing off details (especially for *ASCA* and *ROSAT* PSPC analysis), (*ii*) better installation and configuration support (including the creation of a GUI), (*iii*) web access to XAssist, and (*iv*) web services: limited status reporting is already available using SOAP and it will be possible to request full or partial processing of data via SOAP requests.

Astronomical Data Analysis Software and Systems XII
ASP Conference Series, Vol. 295, 2003
H. E. Payne, R. I. Jedrzejewski, and R. N. Hook, eds.

Solving for Polarization Leakage in Radio Interferometers Using Unpolarized Source

S. Bhatnagar,[1] R. V. Urvashi[2] and R. Nityananda[3]

National Center for Radio Astrophysics (NCRA), Pune, India 411007

Abstract. This paper presents an algorithm for solving antenna based polarization leakage in a radio interferometer using co-polar observations of unpolarized sources. If ignored, polarization leakage manifests itself as closure errors in parallel hand (co-polar) visibilities. Many working radio telescopes offer observational advantages for observations in non-polar mode (e.g., higher frequency resolution, lower integration time, etc.). Many observations are therefore done in non-polar mode and the computation of antenna based leakage gains in co-polar visibilities is scientifically useful for debugging and calibrating the instrument. Also, this is a useful option to use when one cannot or does not want to put in the additional measurement effort to determine the leakage term by means of cross-polar measurements. We also present results from test data taken with the Giant Meterwave Radio Telescope (GMRT) and discuss the degeneracy in the solutions and the equivalence of the leakage induced closure phase and the Pancharatnam phase of optics.

1. Introduction

Co-polar output of an interferometer, can be written as

$$\rho_{ij}^{pp} = \langle (g_i^p E_{i,o}^p + \alpha_i^q E_{i,o}^q + \epsilon_i)(g_j^p E_{j,o}^p + \alpha_j^q E_{j,o}^q + \epsilon_j)^\star \rangle \tag{1}$$

where p and q are two orthogonal polarization states (R and L or X and Y), g_i^p the antenna complex gain for the p-channel of antenna i, α_i^q the leakage of q-signal into the p-channel, $E_{i,o}^p$ the *ideal* response of the p-channel to the incident radiation, and ϵ_i the antenna based additive noise. For an unpolarized point source, $\langle E_{i,o}^q E_{j,o}^{p\star} \rangle = \langle E_{i,o}^q E_{j,o}^{p\star} \rangle = 0$ and $\langle E_{i,o}^p E_{j,o}^{p\star} \rangle = \langle E_{i,o}^q E_{j,o}^{q\star} \rangle = \rho_{ij,o}^{pp} = I/2$ where I is the total intensity. Writing $X_{ij}^{pp} = \rho_{ij}^{pp}/\rho_{ij,o}^{pp}$ we get

$$X_{ij}^{pp} = g_i^p g_j^{p\star} + \alpha_i^q \alpha_j^{q\star} + \epsilon_{ij} \tag{2}$$

---

[1]Now at the National Radio Astronomy Observatory (NRAO), Socorro, NM 87801, Email: sbhatnag@aoc.nrao.edu

[2]Birla Institute of Technology & Science (BITS), Pilani, India and now the department of Computer Science and Engineering, UCSD, CA 92093. Email: uraovenk@cs.ucsd.edu

[3]Email: rajaram@ncra.tifr.res.in

ϵ_{ij} is the independent baseline based noise. Usually this represents the noise in ρ_{ij}^{pp} after the correlation operation plus the antenna based noise. ϵ_{ij} therefore is a measure of the *true* closure errors in the system and is usually small. Assuming α_i^qs to be negligible, the usual Selfcal algorithm estimates g_i^ps such that $\sum_{\substack{i,j \\ i \neq j}} \left| X_{ij}^{pp} - g_i^p g_j^{p\star} \right|^2$ is minimized. However, leakage due to mechanical and/or electronic imperfections in the feed, cross talk, squint of *cross-polar* primary beam, off-axis primary beam polarization, etc., is hard to eliminate making α_i^qs potentially non-negligible.

In the presence of significant α_i^qs (compared to $\sqrt{\epsilon_{ij}}$), ignoring the second term in Equation 2 will be equivalent to a system with *apparent* increased closure noise ($\epsilon_{ij} + \alpha_i^q \alpha_i^{q\star}$ instead of just ϵ_{ij}). *Hence, polarization leakage manifests as increased closure errors.* This has also been pointed out by Rogers (1983) in the context of VLBA observations, and extensive study by Massi & Aaron (1997) for EVN shows that imaging quality is limited by these errors.

2.   Algorithm

When solving for only g_i^p using co-polar visibilities, the α_i^qs appear as increased closure noise and will result in non-optimal solutions. Hence, a simultaneous solution for g_i^p and α_i^q would be optimal. In the presence of significant polarization leakage, the correct estimator for the *true* closure noise is given by $S = \sum_{\substack{i,j \\ i \neq j}} \left| X_{ij}^{pp} - (g_i^p g_j^{p\star} + \alpha_i^q \alpha_j^{q\star}) \right|^2 w_{ij}^{pp}$ where w_{ij}^{pp} are the weights. Equating the partial derivatives $\partial S / \partial g_i^{p\star}$, $\partial S / \partial \alpha_i^{q\star}$ to zero, we get a set of non-linear equations for g_i^ps and α_i^qs which can be iteratively solved (Bhatnagar & Nityananda 2001).

3.   Solution Degeneracy, Simulations and the GMRT Experiment

Simulations demonstrate that with the use of the above algorithm, the χ^2 remains constant with increasing leakage, and that it solves for α_i^qs only if they are significant (i.e., distinguishable from $\sqrt{\epsilon_{ij}}$, Bhatnagar & Nityananda 2001). The decrease in χ^2, compared to that given by Selfcal, is due to the use of the correct estimator for the closure noise and not because of extra free parameters (the α_i^qs) in the problem. *The solutions for α_i^qs are therefore physically meaningful.*

However, an obvious degeneracy is rotation of all the g's by a common phase factor and the αs by an, in general different, phase factor, does not affect the left hand side of Equation 2. We also have the freedom to choose a suitable basis in polarization space (see Bhatnagar & Nityananda 2001 for details). We choose this basis in such a way that the sum of the absolute squares of all the leakage terms is minimized. Carrying out the maximization of $\sum |g_i|^2$ by the method of Lagrange multipliers, subject to a constant χ^2, we obtain the condition that $\sum \alpha_i^* g_i = 0$ (implying that the leakage coefficients be orthogonal to the gains) and can be incorporated by first choosing an overall phase for the α's so that $\sum \alpha_i^* g_i$ is real. Then, carry out a rotation in the $g - \alpha$ plane by an angle θ satisfying $\tan \theta = \sum \alpha_i^* g_i / (\sum (g_i g_i^* - \alpha_i \alpha_i^*))$. Results of such a

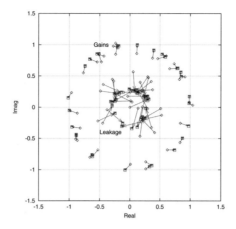

Figure 1. Simulations showing the decoupling of the solutions for g_i^ps and α_i^qs. Squares are the input test g_i^ps and α_i^qs on the complex plane while diamonds are the solutions. The arrows show the length and direction of correction due to the transformation.

transform on simulated data are shown in Figure 1. The absolute frame of reference in which α_i^qs are measured, also remain undetermined since the source is unpolarized. However this degeneracy is same as that in the phase of g_i^ps and is not important for correcting the data. We used GMRT L-band test data with circularly polarized feed on only one antenna (C03 in Figure 2) and linear feeds on the rest. In the mean linear basis of all the antennas, C03 appears as an antenna with $\alpha_i^q = \alpha_i^p \sim 1$ ($E_{C03}^R = E_{C03}^X e^{-\iota\delta} + E_{C03}^Y e^{\iota\delta}$; ideally $\delta = \pi/4$). The fractional leakage (α_i^q/g_i^p) for all antennas is plotted in the complex plane in Figure 2[Left]. Mean leakage of all the antennas define the reference frame in which the leakage of the nominally linear antennas is minimum. All but one nominally linearly polarized antennas are at the origin (minimal leakage); points corresponding to C03 are farthest from the center, grouped $\sim 180°$ apart.

4. Poincaré Sphere and the Pancharatnam Phase

A general elliptically polarized state can be written as a superposition of two states represented by the vector $[\cos\theta/2 \quad \sin\theta/2e^{\iota\phi}]$ in the basis defined by the left- and right-circular polarization states. Clearly, $\theta = \pi/2$ corresponds to linear polarization and $\theta \neq 0, \pi/2$ to elliptical polarization. The Poincaré sphere representation of the state of polarization maps the general elliptic state to the point (θ, ϕ) on the sphere. It can be shown that the closure phase between three coherent, non-identical, antennas (points I, J and K in Figure 2[Right]) is equal to half the solid angle IJK. This goes by the name Pancharatnam/Geometric/Berry's phase in optical literature (Pancharatnam, 1956). *The closure phase due to polarization mis-matches between phased antennas in a radio interferometer therefore naturally measures the Pancharatnam phase.*

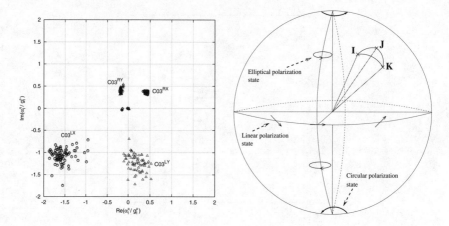

Figure 2.   [**Left**] Plot of α_i^q/g_i^p for all GMRT antennas. $C03^{LX}$ and $C03^{RX}$ (open circles) are from correlations of R- and L-channel of C03 with X-channel of other linear antennas. Similarly for $C03^{LY}$ and $C03^{RY}$ (triangles). One of the linearly polarized antennas is leakier than the others and L-channel of C03 is noisier than its R-channel. [**Right**] Poincaré sphere representation of polarization states. Closure phase between three coherent but non-identical antennas represented by the points I,J and K is equal to half the solid angle of IJK.

5.   Conclusions

The method described here measures the polarization leakage using the *co-polar* visibilities for an unpolarized calibrator. It is a useful tool for studying the polarization purity of the antennas of radio interferometers. Simultaneous solution of gain and leakage ensures that the method factorizes for leakage only if they are distinguishable from intrinsic *true* closure noise. The degeneracy between solutions of antenna based complex gains and leakage is broken by physically meaningful transform and the solutions can be used to remove leakage induced closure errors. Geometric interpretation of the results on the Poincaré sphere shows that the leakage induced closure phase is same as the Pancharatnam phase and the degeneracy in the solutions can be understood as a rigid rotation of the Poincaré sphere.

Acknowledgments.   We thank the GMRT staff, NCRA, BITS and NRAO for their support and co-operation.

References

Bhatnagar, S. & Nityananda, R. 2001, A&A, 375, 344-350

Massi, M. & Aaron, S. 1997, EVN Tech. Memo, N75

Pancharatnam, S. 1956, S. Proc. Indian Aad. Sci., A44, 247

Rogers, A. E. E. 1983, VLB Array Memo No. 253

Astronomical Data Analysis Software and Systems XII
ASP Conference Series, Vol. 295, 2003
H. E. Payne, R. I. Jedrzejewski, and R. N. Hook, eds.

PacketLib: A C++ Library for Scientific Satellite Telemetry Applications

A. Bulgarelli, F. Gianotti, M. Trifoglio

CNR/IASF sezione di Bologna - Via P. Gobetti 101, 40129 Bologna, Italy

Abstract.   PacketLib is a C++ open-source software library for writing applications which deal with satellite telemetry source packets, provided that the packets are compliant with the CCSDS Telemetry and Telecommand Standards. The library is being used within the Italian Space Agency (ASI) mission AGILE for simulation, graphical display, processing and decoding of the telemetry generated by the Test Equipment (TE) of two AGILE detectors. From an input stream of bytes, the library is able to recognize automatically the source packets (described by a simple configuration file), and provides a simple access to each packet field by means of an object oriented interface. In the same way the library writes source packets to output stream. Various types of input and output streams are abstracted by a software layer.

1.   Introduction

The equipment to support the test and calibration of scientific payload requires tailor-made software applications which are similar in overall design and functionality but are different in details. These applications must work with CCSDS satellite telemetry. The telemetry (TM) and telecommand (TC) packets are usually divided into two sections: (*i*) the Header section, which is the only mandatory part of a packet and contains the packet identifier, the packet length, and the Source Sequence Counter, and (*ii*) the Data Field section containing either the TM scientific and house-keeping data or the TC data. Although the CCSDS standard does not specify the Data Field internal structure, usually it contains an Header which precedes the data. In turn, the data are are grouped according to a logical sequence of bits which represent well defined information.

Based on these considerations, we have designed PacketLib, a C++ software library running on Unix platform which can be used as the basis for building applications able to handle the source packets, down to the level of the single logical structure contained in the data field.

The PacketLib[1] is aimed at providing a reusable software library for satellite telemetry production and processing and a rapid development for Test Equipment (TE), Electric Ground Support Equipment (EGSE) and Ground Segment

---

[1]`http://www.bo.iasf.cnr.it/~GSE`

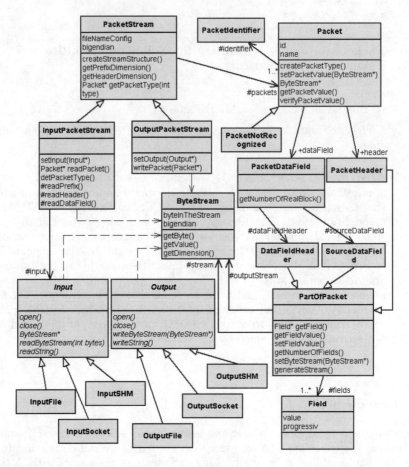

Figure 1.   The class diagram of PacketLib.

applications. It has been developed in the context of the Italian Space Agency (ASI) AGILE space mission (Tavani et al. 2001).

2.   The Architecture

PacketLib is structured into two main layers: the Telemetry Management layer, which interfaces the application, and the I/O Abstraction layer, which interfaces the Operating System. The former allows the application to address the various elements forming the packet data stream, without having to deal with the specific structure. The latter abstracts from the specific input and output mechanisms (e.g., sockets, files, and shared memories).

This approach allows a more rapid development of the user applications without having to deal with the kind of input and output sources, which could be changed at run time. Indeed the library could be used either to process or to generate a telemetry stream.

PacketLib abstracts the byte stream and all the details characterizing a given packet structure by means of the Object Model represented in the simplified UML class diagram shown in Figure 1.

In particular, for each kind of packet stream, the library requires one ASCII file containing the description of the overall stream, and a set of ASCII files containing all the parameters defining the various packets, one for each kind of packet identifier. At run time, PacketLib loads these files and builds the representation of the stream and the packets structures into memory.

3. An Example

The real functioning of the library can be easily understood with the following little coding example:

```
1.    InputPacketStream ips;
2.    char* parameters; //set the parameters of input
3.    Input *in = new InputSocket(parameters);
4.    in.open();
5.    ips.createStreamStructure("conf.stream");
6.    ips.setInput(in);
7.    Packet* p = ips.getPacket();
8.    cout << "The value of field 4 of header is " <<
         p->header->getFieldValue(4) << endl;
9.    cout << "The value of field 2 of source data field is " <<
         p->dataField->sourceDataField->getFieldValue(2) << endl;
```

Line 1 instantiates the object that represents the input byte stream, and line 5 loads the configuration files and creates into memory the byte stream structure and the packets structure (header, data field and fields). Lines 2, 3, and 4 create a telemetry input source and open it. To change the input source without modifying the rest of the code, it is only necessary to modify the line 3 by instantiating another type of input (e.g., InputFile instead of InputSocket), and opening it with the correct parameters. Line 6 links the input byte stream with the input source, and the remaining code extracts the required packet information from the input stream. In particular, line 7 reads a complete packet, whereas lines 8–9 print the value of the various fields.

Summarising, lines 2–4,6 provide the I/O Abstraction layer, while lines 1,5,7–9 are related to the Telemetry Management layer.

This example demonstrates that with a few lines of code it is possible to connect the application with an input byte stream and to obtain an object representing a packet with all the field value decoded. The library is able to manage either big-endian and little-endian format.

For a full comprehension of how the library works, it is necessary to understand how the input is processed. After having read the packet Header (which is of fixed length), the library knows the length of the subsequent Data Field. The actual structure of the Data Field is derived by its identifier which consists of one or more fields containing some predefined values. Typically, the APID field of CCSDS standard is used, but the library has not limitation, and allows identifiers which include others fields (e.g., in the AGILE case the Type/Subtype fields of the Data Field Header).

The identification of the various packets is performed by looking in the packets for one of the possible identifiers defined in the *.packet ASCII files. Identified packets are unpacked and the various fields are read into the packet structure defined in the *.packet files, where can be directly addressed as shown in lines 8–9. In the negative case, an object representing a generic not recognized packet is created, where the Data Field byte sequence is copied without any structure.

4.   Some PacketLib-Based Applications

Various PacketLib-based applications have been built in the AGILE framework: (*i*) a telemetry generator which is able to simulate the output of the Digital Front End (DFE) of Minicalorimeter, one of the instruments of the mission; (*ii*) the QPacketViewer which recognizes the packets of a telemetry stream and shows all the various fields; and (*iii*) the DISCoS ProcessorLib which extends the DISCoS system (Gianotti et al. 2001), in order to process the telemetry scientific data and convert them into FITS file.

The generator allowed us to write and test the processing software without the presence of the instrument's DFE. The QPacketViewer has been used for a preliminary analysis of the telemetry produced by the DFE TE. With these tools it has been possible to realize the analysis software (Quick Look or off-line analysis) in parallel with the building of the detectors, allowing, at the same time, a more accurate test of the overall software of the TE (either in functional and performance terms). This has enabled us to perform a more accurate analysis of all the possible errors into the telemetry data before using the processing software.

5.   Conclusions

We plan to extend the library in order to manage a generalized type of packet that will include all the possible AGILE packet type formats. In addition, the library flexibility will be improved by increasing the number of I/O communication channel types.

At the moment the library is used with success in the development of TE software for the AGILE space mission and it will be used for the AGILE Payload EGSE. It enables a rapid development of the TE and EGSE applications based on object oriented architecture.

References

Tavani, M. et al. 2001, Proceedings of the 5th Compton Symposium, AIP Conf. Proceedings, ed. M. McConnell, Vol. 510, 476

Gianotti, F. & Trifoglio, M. 2001, in ASP Conf. Ser., Vol. 238, Astronomical Data Analysis Software and Systems X, ed. F. R. Harnden, Jr., F. A. Primini, & H. E. Payne (San Francisco: ASP), 245

CCSDS, Packet Telemetry - CCSDS 102.0-B-5, November 2000

Astronomical Data Analysis Software and Systems XII
ASP Conference Series, Vol. 295, 2003
H. E. Payne, R. I. Jedrzejewski, and R. N. Hook, eds.

ChaRT: The Chandra Ray Tracer

Clayton Carter, Margarita Karovska, Diab Jerius, Kenny Glotfelty and Steve Beikman

Harvard-Smithsonian Center for Astrophysics, 60 Garden St., Cambridge, MA 02138

Abstract. In this paper we present the Chandra Ray Tracer (*ChaRT*), a distributed remote-computing application developed by the Chandra X-Ray Center (CXC) to simulate the High Resolution Mirror Assembly (HRMA) Point Spread Functions (PSFs). We will discuss the overall system architecture and the programmatic flow. This approach may be used as a prototype for other projects where either the software cannot be distributed and/or the system resources required to run the software would be prohibitive for the general user.

1. Introduction

Chandra produces sharper images than any other X-ray telescope to date and therefore provides an opportunity for high-angular and spectral resolution studies of X-ray sources. Crucial to these studies is the knowledge of the characteristics of the PSF. The blurring of the Chandra PSF is introduced by the HRMA PSF, the aspect, the limited size of detector pixels and detector effects. Simulating the HRMA PSF is the first and most important step in obtaining a good model of the Chandra PSF for a given observation.

Currently available PSF library files (Karovska et al. 2000) provide the general users with a grid of precomputed monochromatic HRMA PSFs. To calculate a HRMA PSF matching the location and spectrum of the observed source, users interpolate between model PSFs on a coarse spatial and energy grid using the *CIAO* tool mkpsf.[1] Model PSFs derived in this way suffer from a limiting precision which makes them unsuitable for very detailed analysis. To address this, the CXC has developed *ChaRT*, a soft- and hardware system designed to provide the general user community with access to the most precise and up to date HRMA PSF simulations available.

In the following, we describe the details of the *ChaRT* design and implementation, as well as the data products.

---

[1] *CIAO* is the Chandra Interactive Analysis of Observations data analysis system. *CIAO* is available at http://cxc.harvard.edu/ciao

2.   ChaRT System Design

The HRMA was designed to produce on-axis images with better than one arc-second resolution. However, the shape and size of the HRMA PSFs vary significantly with source location in the telescope field of view, as well as with the spectral energy distribution of the source. As such, in order to carry out spatial analysis of the *Chandra* data, each PSF must be simulated individually.

For calibration purposes, the *Chandra* Mission Support Team developed ray tracing code (*SAOsac*, Jerius et al. 2000) that can simulate the HRMA PSF using the official mirror model, and includes many of the details of the HRMA's physical construction. These include the stray light baffles and support structures as well as a detailed model of the reflective properties of the mirror surface. *SAOsac*, however, was designed for engineering support and analysis, and—as a result—is currently unsuitable for release to the general Chandra community (although work to change this is ongoing).

ChaRT is a soft- and hardware system designed to provide *Chandra* users with access to the *SAOsac* ray tracing routines and allow them to carry out HRMA PSF simulations. Using *ChaRT*'s user friendly web interface, the HRMA PSF can be simulated for point sources at multiple locations, each source characterized by either a monochromatic energy or an input spectrum. *ChaRT* verifies and submits the simulation parameters and notifies the user when their simulated PSFs are available for download via FTP. This is accomplished using middleware, developed at the CXC, that works in conjunction with some commonly available software components (Apache[2] and PBS,[3] for instance) on a distributed computer network located at the CXC.

2.1.   Goals and Implementation

In developing *ChaRT*, we sought to produce an application that was simple to use and configure, easy to maintain, lightweight and extensible. Our goal was to design this system as fault tolerant, scalable and resistant to abuse and attacks.

To that end, we created a set of Perl[4] CGI scripts which provide a simple interface for the user to enter source specifications for PSF simulations. These scripts were written to allow for flexible user input and data output, easily customized interfaces and simple configuration. After the scripts verify and translate the specifications, a series of jobs (representing one request) are submitted to a server for rendering. After the servers have finished rendering each source, the data are packaged into a gzipped tar archive and staged for FTP retrieval. The user is then notified via email that their request has been fulfilled and the working directory (unique to each user) is removed. (The FTP staging area is also automatically cleaned up on a regular basis.)

The rendering servers are located at the CXC and are self-managed by a *PBS* server which schedules and preempts the simulations based upon priorities and a complex set of interdependencies. The use of *PBS* automatically makes

---

[2]http://www.apache.org

[3]http://www.openpbs.org

[4]http://www.cpan.org

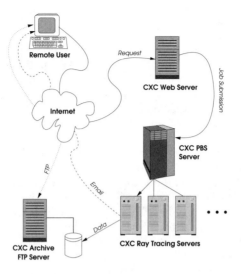

Figure 1.   The software and hardware architecture of *ChaRT*.

the ray tracing system a distributed system, but it also allows the network of rendering machines to be easily scaled to suit future needs.

We installed numerous checks and limits which are applied to everything from the users of the system to the actual simulation jobs. To keep the system responsive, upper bounds have been placed on the number of simultaneous users as well as the number of sources specifiable per simulation. To protect the system from being monopolized, we limit the number of requests a single user may run at once, as well as the maximum run time of each simulation. Additionally, *ChaRT* will be publicly accessible and we check all inputs to ensure no malicious commands are attempted. These limits and checks are easily configurable and will be adjusted in the future based on users requirements and usage.

2.2.   Software and Hardware Requirements

The *ChaRT* system is mostly comprised of Free Software components including Perl (and its CGI module), Bourne Shell, Apache and GNU `gzip` and `tar`. The freely available *PBS* batch system[5] is used to manage the rendering network and, of course, *SAOsac* is used to run the simulations.

While *ChaRT* could perform on a single machine, it is currently implemented such that the user interface (Perl scripts) are run along with Apache on a server dedicated to web tasks while *PBS* and the rendering jobs are run on a separate set of dedicated computers. (See Figure 1.)

---

[5]The license used by *PBS* is too restrictive for it be considered truly free software. It is still, however, freely available and redistributable.

3. Data Products

Our initial tests show that simulation runtimes average between 1 and 20 minutes, during which time no user interaction is required. When the simulation has completed, users will be notified by email that their data are ready for retrieval. This email includes a complete listing of the request (for user's archival purposes) as well as all information needed to retrieve the data from the CXC's public FTP server, CDA.[6]

As an auxiliary data product, we record a log of every request made of the system. With this, we will be able to monitor trends in the usage of *ChaRT* and tune the system to better suit the needs of our users.

When users retrieve their data, they receive a package in gzipped tar format. This package will contain a directory hierarchy which expands to one directory per source, each containing one FITS file for each simulation of that source. Each FITS file includes a list of rays which can later be projected to the detector planes using the *CIAO* tool psf_project_ray to obtain 2-D model HRMA PSF images. Furthermore, the *ChaRT* ray files can be input in the MARX simulator (Wise et al. 1997) to generate realistic Chandra PSFs which also include the instrumental effects.

4. Future Work

Currently, users are only able to specify point sources. In the future, we will make it possible for users to run simulations with more complicated source specifications, including the use of images as source definitions. We would also like to facilitate on-the-fly generation of spectra.

Additionally, we would like to adapt the *ChaRT* system design to similar applications which require either the use of remote software or substantial computing resources.

Acknowledgments. This project is supported in part by the Chandra X-ray Center under NASA contract NAS8-39073.

References

Jerius, D. et al. 1995, in ASP Conf. Ser., Vol. 77, Astronomical Data Analysis Software and Systems IV, ed. R. A. Shaw, H. E. Payne, & J. J. E. Hayes (San Francisco: ASP), 357

Karovska, M. et al. 2001, in ASP Conf. Ser., Vol. 238, Astronomical Data Analysis Software and Systems X, ed. F. R. Harnden, Jr., F. A. Primini, & H. E. Payne (San Francisco: ASP), 435

Wise, M. et al. 1997, in ASP Conf. Ser., Vol. 125, Astronomical Data Analysis Software and Systems VI, ed. G. Hunt & H. E. Payne (San Francisco: ASP), 477

---

[6]ftp://cda.cfa.harvard.edu

Astronomical Data Analysis Software and Systems XII
ASP Conference Series, Vol. 295, 2003
H. E. Payne, R. I. Jedrzejewski, and R. N. Hook, eds.

AIPS++ Reduction and Analysis of GBT Single-Dish Spectral Data

James Braatz, Joseph McMullin, Robert Garwood, Athol Kemball

National Radio Astronomy Observatory

Abstract. AIPS++ is composed of a suite of tools that are capable of both astronomy-specific and general purpose calculations and data processing. Mathematical analysis, data visualization, GUI development, database handling, and scripting are all integrated. A tool for analyzing single-dish data, DISH, is developed on this platform. DISH includes a number of modern features such as bulk processing of datasets and versatile GUI interaction. Recent improvements in the command line interface ease the learning curve and provide facile interaction with scan-based data. Here we give an example of the look and feel of the current command line interface in DISH.

Although its use is not limited to one telescope, DISH includes plug-in functions that relate specifically to calibration and processing of data from the Green Bank Telescope (GBT). The GBT offers versatile spectral line observing capabilities, all of which are handled by the DISH tool. Our example illustrates a simple reduction of total-power, position-switched data showing OH maser emission from an ultraluminous infrared galaxy.

1. Introduction

1.1. The GBT

The Green Bank Telescope,[1] located at the National Radio Astronomy Observatory (NRAO) in West Virginia, is a new 100-m diameter antenna with an unblocked aperture and an active surface. It is designed to operate at sky frequencies between 300 MHz and 100 GHz. The active surface provides remarkable aperture efficiencies, e.g., 50% – 60% at 22 GHz over all elevations, a figure that will continue to improve as commissioning proceeds. Considering the state of the art receivers and backends as well, the GBT offers a number of scientifically attractive features including full sky coverage, a clean beam at all frequencies, and a significant advance in sensitivity, especially at 3 mm – 2 cm wavelengths. First light on the GBT was on August 22, 2000; the commissioning program is continuing. Meanwhile, a growing number of spectral line projects are being assigned science time.

---

[1] http://www.gb.nrao.edu/GBT/GBT.html

1.2.   AIPS++

The Astronomical Information Processing System (AIPS++) is a software package designed and written by an international team of astronomers and computer scientists. AIPS++ is comprised of both general purpose and directed software tools that are tied together by a scripting language called Glish. While AIPS++ is intended to supercede classic AIPS for reduction of synthesis radio data, it also has the larger scope of addressing general data analysis problems. Both aperture synthesis and single-dish radio astronomical data are stored in a common format (the Measurement Set), making it possible to apply many common AIPS++ tools to either type of data.

The attractive general-purpose data analysis environment includes tools for line and image plotting and analysis, model fitting, GUI development, astronomical coordinate conversions, data table handling, and general scientific scripting.

AIPS++ is in the public domain. Complete documentation can be found at http://aips2.nrao.edu.

2.   DISH

DISH is the AIPS++ tool for reducing spectral line single-dish radio astronomical data. DISH uses a feature-rich plotter and a GUI that are described in the AIPS++ documentation available from the web page. For access to data in an online environment and to facilitate scripting, a more traditional command line interface has recently been developed for DISH. The CLI borrows much of its philosophy from familiar packages such as UNIPOPS and CLASS. The concept of a *globalscan* is used in DISH to simplify syntax. Most functions operate on the *globalscan* by default, including functions such as *show, scale, bias, baseline, gauss, hanning,* etc. The *globalscan* is in fact a Glish record that contains a complete description of a raw integration or reduced spectrum, including the data itself and a full header, flags, weights, and so on.

Part of the general philosophy of AIPS++ is to give the user complete access to the data records, making it possible to examine and modify data with great versatility. Glish itself offers a full suite of programming constructs and it includes array-based mathematical operations, so it is straightforward for the user to develop his own set of functions to complement the existing ones. Incorporating the CLI-based DISH functions into user-defined functions is also trivial, so even the occasional user can develop procedures to simplify repetitive processing techniques. For example, the user might write a simple procedure to inspect all scans in the opened data set, one-by-one, like so:

```
scanlist := d.lscans()
for (i in scanlist)
 d.plotc(i)
```

DISH can be used to produce publication-quality plots. The DISH plotter is built on the widely known PGPLOT package, and the full suite of capabilities (such as notation) are easily incorporated via the plotter tool.

3. Sample Data Reduction Session

The following example shows a sample data reduction session in DISH, presented to give the reader a sense of the look of the CLI. A complete Users' Manual and Reference Guide are available on the web in the AIPS++ documentation sections.

```
                              #   begins an AIPS++ session
                              #   and creates the DISH tool
                              #   referred to as "d".
                              #   d.show() hence calls the
                              #   dish function "show"

- d.import('/home/gbtdata/AGBT02B_28_02','ohmaser',
           startscan=23,stopscan=28)

                              # The import function converts
                              #  GBT FITS data to DISH format
- scans := [24,26,28]         #  define a glish vector of scans
- d.calib(scans)              #  calibrate the data
- d.plotc(24)                 #  inspect the scans; suppose
- d.plotc(26)                 #    we notice RFI in channels
- d.plotc(28)                 #    440-460 in all 3 scans
- d.flag(scans,channel=440:460)  # flag the bad data
- d.accum(scans)              #  add scans to the accumulator
- d.ave()                     #  average scans in accumulator
- d.show()                    #  plot result
- d.setregion()               #  define region for baseline
                              #    fitting using the cursor
- d.nfit(5)                   #  set polynomial order=5
- d.bshape()                  #  inspect the baseline fit
- d.baseline()                #  subtract the baseline fit
- d.show()                    #  plot result
- d.scale([0.5,1])            #  scale the data, different for
                              #    each polarization to correct
                              #    for a Tcal scaling problem
- d.show()                    #  plot result
- d.avgFeeds()                #  average polarizations
- d.show()                    #  plot result
- d.hanning()                 #  apply Hanning smoothing
- d.setYUnit('Jy')            #  Set units for purpose of plot
                              #    (does not change calibration)
- d.show()                    #  plot result
- d.gauss(1)                  #  fit a gaussian, result shown
                              #    below
Gauss:  1
Center: 3.58792e+04   Height: 5.41358e-02   Width: 1.25593e+02
Cerr: 1.05840e+00   Herr: 9.30979e-04   Werr: 2.49234e+00
```

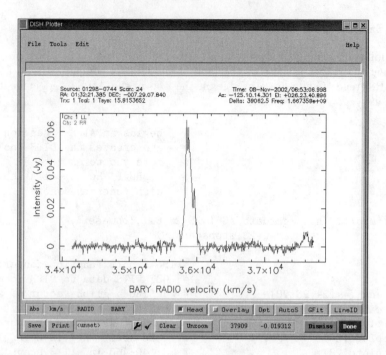

Figure 1.   The DISH plotter showing the result of the sample data
reduction script. The line reveals OH maser emission.

```
- d.fileout('my_saved_data')      #  open file for saving result
- d.save()                        #  save the result
```

Acknowledgments. The AIPS++ software is developed by an international consortium of astronomers and computer scientists.

The GBT is being developed and operated by the National Radio Astronomy Observatory in Green Bank, WV.

The National Radio Astronomy Observatory is a facility of the National
Science Foundation operated under cooperative agreement by Associated Universities, Inc.

Author Index

Subject Index

A LIST OF THE VOLUMES

Published
by

THE ASTRONOMICAL SOCIETY OF THE PACIFIC
(ASP)

An international, nonprofit, scientific and educational organization
founded in 1889

All book orders or inquiries concerning

THE ASTRONOMICAL SOCIETY OF THE PACIFIC
CONFERENCE SERIES
(ASP - CS)

and

INTERNATIONAL ASTRONOMICAL UNION VOLUMES
(IAU)

should be directed to the:

The Astronomical Society of the Pacific Conference Series
390 Ashton Avenue
San Francisco   CA   94112-1722   USA

Phone: 800-335-2624   (Within USA)
Phone: 415-337-2126
Fax: 415-337-5205

E-mail: service@astrosociety.org
Web Site: http://www.astrosociety.org

Complete lists of proceedings of past IAU Meetings are maintained at the
IAU Web site at the URL: http://www.iau.org/publicat.html

Volumes 32 - 189 in the IAU Symposia Series may be ordered from:

Kluwer Academic Publishers
P. O. Box 117
NL 3300 AA Dordrecht
The Netherlands

Kluwer@wKap.com

ASP CONFERENCE SERIES VOLUMES

Published by the Astronomical Society of the Pacific

PUBLISHED: 1988 (* asterisk means OUT OF STOCK)

Vol. CS -1   PROGRESS AND OPPORTUNITIES IN SOUTHERN HEMISPHERE
                 OPTICAL ASTRONOMY: CTIO 25TH Anniversary Symposium
                 eds. V. M. Blanco and M. M. Phillips
                 ISBN 0-937707-18-X

Vol. CS-2   PROCEEDINGS OF A WORKSHOP ON OPTICAL SURVEYS FOR QUASARS
                 eds. Patrick S. Osmer, Alain C. Porter, Richard F. Green, and Craig B. Foltz
                 ISBN 0-937707-19-8

Vol. CS-3   FIBER OPTICS IN ASTRONOMY
                 ed. Samuel C. Barden
                 ISBN 0-937707-20-1

Vol. CS-4   THE EXTRAGALACTIC DISTANCE SCALE:
                 Proceedings of the ASP 100th Anniversary Symposium
                 eds. Sidney van den Bergh and Christopher J. Pritchet
                 ISBN 0-937707-21-X

Vol. CS-5   THE MINNESOTA LECTURES ON CLUSTERS OF GALAXIES
                 AND LARGE-SCALE STRUCTURE
                 ed. John M. Dickey
                 ISBN 0-937707-22-8

PUBLISHED: 1989

Vol. CS-6 *   SYNTHESIS IMAGING IN RADIO ASTRONOMY: A Collection of Lectures
                 from the Third NRAO Synthesis Imaging Summer School
                 eds. Richard A. Perley, Frederic R. Schwab, and Alan H. Bridle
                 ISBN 0-937707-23-6

PUBLISHED: 1990

Vol. CS-7   PROPERTIES OF HOT LUMINOUS STARS: Boulder-Munich Workshop
                 ed. Catharine D. Garmany
                 ISBN 0-937707-24-4

Vol. CS-8 *   CCDs IN ASTRONOMY
                 ed. George H. Jacoby
                 ISBN 0-937707-25-2

Vol. CS-9   COOL STARS, STELLAR SYSTEMS, AND THE SUN: Sixth Cambridge Workshop
                 ed. George Wallerstein
                 ISBN 0-937707-27-9

Vol. CS-10 *   EVOLUTION OF THE UNIVERSE OF GALAXIES:
                 Edwin Hubble Centennial Symposium
                 ed. Richard G. Kron
                 ISBN 0-937707-28-7

Vol. CS-11   CONFRONTATION BETWEEN STELLAR PULSATION AND EVOLUTION
                 eds. Carla Cacciari and Gisella Clementini
                 ISBN 0-937707-30-9

Vol. CS-12   THE EVOLUTION OF THE INTERSTELLAR MEDIUM
                 ed. Leo Blitz
                 ISBN 0-937707-31-7

PUBLISHED: 1991

Vol. CS-13   THE FORMATION AND EVOLUTION OF STAR CLUSTERS
                 ed. Kenneth Janes
                 ISBN 0-937707-32-5

ASP CONFERENCE SERIES VOLUMES
Published by the Astronomical Society of the Pacific

PUBLISHED: 1991 (* asterisk means OUT OF STOCK)

Vol. CS-14   ASTROPHYSICS WITH INFRARED ARRAYS
ed. Richard Elston
ISBN 0-937707-33-3

Vol. CS-15   LARGE-SCALE STRUCTURES AND PECULIAR MOTIONS IN THE UNIVERSE
eds. David W. Latham and L. A. Nicolaci da Costa
ISBN 0-937707-34-1

Vol. CS-16   Proceedings of the 3rd Haystack Observatory Conference on ATOMS, IONS,
AND MOLECULES: NEW RESULTS IN SPECTRAL LINE ASTROPHYSICS
eds. Aubrey D. Haschick and Paul T. P. Ho
ISBN 0-937707-35-X

Vol. CS-17   LIGHT POLLUTION, RADIO INTERFERENCE, AND SPACE DEBRIS
ed. David L. Crawford
ISBN 0-937707-36-8

Vol. CS-18   THE INTERPRETATION OF MODERN SYNTHESIS OBSERVATIONS
OF SPIRAL GALAXIES
eds. Nebojsa Duric and Patrick C. Crane
ISBN 0-937707-37-6

Vol. CS-19   RADIO INTERFEROMETRY: THEORY, TECHNIQUES, AND APPLICATIONS,
IAU Colloquium 131
eds. T. J. Cornwell and R. A. Perley
ISBN 0-937707-38-4

Vol. CS-20   FRONTIERS OF STELLAR EVOLUTION:
50th Anniversary McDonald Observatory (1939-1989)
ed. David L. Lambert
ISBN 0-937707-39-2

Vol. CS-21   THE SPACE DISTRIBUTION OF QUASARS
ed . David Crampton
ISBN 0-937707-40-6

PUBLISHED: 1992

Vol. CS-22   NONISOTROPIC AND VARIABLE OUTFLOWS FROM STARS
eds. Laurent Drissen, Claus Leitherer, and Antonella Nota
ISBN 0-937707-41-4

Vol CS-23 *   ASTRONOMICAL CCD OBSERVING AND REDUCTION TECHNIQUES
ed. Steve B. Howell
ISBN 0-937707-42-4

Vol. CS-24   COSMOLOGY AND LARGE-SCALE STRUCTURE IN THE UNIVERSE
ed. Reinaldo R. de Carvalho
ISBN 0-937707-43-0

Vol. CS-25   ASTRONOMICAL DATA ANALYSIS, SOFTWARE AND SYSTEMS I - (ADASS I)
eds. Diana M. Worrall, Chris Biemesderfer, and Jeannette Barnes
ISBN 0-937707-44-9

Vol. CS-26   COOL STARS, STELLAR SYSTEMS, AND THE SUN:
Seventh Cambridge Workshop
eds. Mark S. Giampapa and Jay A. Bookbinder
ISBN 0-937707-45-7

Vol. CS-27   THE SOLAR CYCLE: Proceedings of the
National Solar Observatory/Sacramento Peak 12th Summer Workshop
ed. Karen L. Harvey
ISBN 0-937707-46-5

ASP CONFERENCE SERIES VOLUMES
Published by the Astronomical Society of the Pacific

PUBLISHED: 1992 (asterisk means OUT OF STOCK)

Vol. CS-28   AUTOMATED TELESCOPES FOR PHOTOMETRY AND IMAGING
eds. Saul J. Adelman, Robert J. Dukes, Jr., and Carol J. Adelman
ISBN 0-937707-47-3

Vol. CS-29   Viña del Mar Workshop on CATACLYSMIC VARIABLE STARS
ed. Nikolaus Vogt
ISBN 0-937707-48-1

Vol. CS-30   VARIABLE STARS AND GALAXIES
ed. Brian Warner
ISBN 0-937707-49-X

Vol. CS-31   RELATIONSHIPS BETWEEN ACTIVE GALACTIC NUCLEI
AND STARBURST GALAXIES
ed. Alexei V. Filippenko
ISBN 0-937707-50-3

Vol. CS-32   COMPLEMENTARY APPROACHES TO DOUBLE
AND MULTIPLE STAR RESEARCH, IAU Colloquium 135
eds. Harold A. McAlister and William I. Hartkopf
ISBN 0-937707-51-1

Vol. CS-33 *   RESEARCH AMATEUR ASTRONOMY
ed. Stephen J. Edberg
ISBN 0-937707-52-X

Vol. CS-34   ROBOTIC TELESCOPES IN THE 1990's
ed. Alexei V. Filippenko
ISBN 0-937707-53-8

PUBLISHED: 1993

Vol. CS-35 *   MASSIVE STARS: THEIR LIVES IN THE INTERSTELLAR MEDIUM
eds. Joseph P. Cassinelli and Edward B. Churchwell
ISBN 0-937707-54-6

Vol. CS-36   PLANETS AROUND PULSARS
ed. J. A. Phillips, S. E. Thorsett, and S. R. Kulkarni
ISBN 0-937707-55-4

Vol. CS-37   FIBER OPTICS IN ASTRONOMY II
ed. Peter M. Gray
ISBN 0-937707-56-2

Vol. CS-38   NEW FRONTIERS IN BINARY STAR RESEARCH: Pacific Rim Colloquium
eds. K. C. Leung and I.-S. Nha
ISBN 0-937707-57-0

Vol. CS-39   THE MINNESOTA LECTURES ON THE STRUCTURE
AND DYNAMICS OF THE MILKY WAY
ed. Roberta M. Humphreys
ISBN 0-937707-58-9

Vol. CS-40   INSIDE THE STARS, IAU Colloquium 137
eds. Werner W. Weiss and Annie Baglin
ISBN 0-937707-59-7

Vol. CS-41   ASTRONOMICAL INFRARED SPECTROSCOPY:
FUTURE OBSERVATIONAL DIRECTIONS
ed. Sun Kwok
ISBN 0-937707-60-0

ASP CONFERENCE SERIES VOLUMES
Published by the Astronomical Society of the Pacific

PUBLISHED: 1993 (* asterisk means OUT OF STOCK)

Vol. CS-42   GONG 1992: SEISMIC INVESTIGATION OF THE SUN AND STARS
ed. Timothy M. Brown
ISBN 0-937707-61-9

Vol. CS-43   SKY SURVEYS: PROTOSTARS TO PROTOGALAXIES
ed. B. T. Soifer
ISBN 0-937707-62-7

Vol. CS-44   PECULIAR VERSUS NORMAL PHENOMENA IN A-TYPE AND RELATED STARS,
IAU Colloquium 138
eds. M. M. Dworetsky, F. Castelli, and R. Faraggiana
ISBN 0-937707-63-5

Vol. CS-45   LUMINOUS HIGH-LATITUDE STARS
ed. Dimitar D. Sasselov
ISBN 0-937707-64-3

Vol. CS-46   THE MAGNETIC AND VELOCITY FIELDS OF SOLAR ACTIVE REGIONS,
IAU Colloquium 141
eds. Harold Zirin, Guoxiang Ai, and Haimin Wang
ISBN 0-937707-65-1

Vol. CS-47   THIRD DECENNIAL US-USSR CONFERENCE ON SETI --
Santa Cruz, California, USA
ed. G. Seth Shostak
ISBN 0-937707-66-X

Vol. CS-48   THE GLOBULAR CLUSTER-GALAXY CONNECTION
eds. Graeme H. Smith and Jean P. Brodie
ISBN 0-937707-67-8

Vol. CS-49   GALAXY EVOLUTION: THE MILKY WAY PERSPECTIVE
ed. Steven R. Majewski
ISBN 0-937707-68-6

Vol. CS-50   STRUCTURE AND DYNAMICS OF GLOBULAR CLUSTERS
eds. S. G. Djorgovski and G. Meylan
ISBN 0-937707-69-4

Vol. CS-51   OBSERVATIONAL COSMOLOGY
eds. Guido Chincarini, Angela Iovino, Tommaso Maccacaro, and Dario Maccagni
ISBN 0-937707-70-8

Vol. CS-52   ASTRONOMICAL DATA ANALYSIS SOFTWARE AND SYSTEMS II - (ADASS II)
eds. R. J. Hanisch, R. J. V. Brissenden, and Jeannette Barnes
ISBN 0-937707-71-6

Vol. CS-53   BLUE STRAGGLERS
ed. Rex A. Saffer
ISBN 0-937707-72-4

PUBLISHED: 1994

Vol. CS-54 *   THE FIRST STROMLO SYMPOSIUM: THE PHYSICS OF ACTIVE GALAXIES
eds. Geoffrey V. Bicknell, Michael A. Dopita, and Peter J. Quinn
ISBN 0-937707-73-2

Vol. CS-55   OPTICAL ASTRONOMY FROM THE EARTH AND MOON
eds. Diane M. Pyper and Ronald J. Angione
ISBN 0-937707-74-0

Vol. CS-56   INTERACTING BINARY STARS
ed. Allen W. Shafter
ISBN 0-937707-75-9

ASP CONFERENCE SERIES VOLUMES
Published by the Astronomical Society of the Pacific

ASP CONFERENCE SERIES VOLUMES
Published by the Astronomical Society of the Pacific

PUBLISHED: 1995 (* asterisk means OUT OF STOCK)

Vol. CS-71   TRIDIMENSIONAL OPTICAL SPECTROSCOPIC METHODS IN ASTROPHYSICS,
IAU Colloquium 149
eds. Georges Comte and Michel Marcelin
ISBN 0-937707-90-2

Vol. CS-72   MILLISECOND PULSARS: A DECADE OF SURPRISE
eds. A. S Fruchter, M. Tavani, and D. C. Backer
ISBN 0-937707-91-0

Vol. CS-73   AIRBORNE ASTRONOMY SYMPOSIUM ON THE GALACTIC ECOSYSTEM:
FROM GAS TO STARS TO DUST
eds. Michael R. Haas, Jacqueline A. Davidson, and Edwin F. Erickson
ISBN 0-937707-92-9

Vol. CS-74   PROGRESS IN THE SEARCH FOR EXTRATERRESTRIAL LIFE:
1993 Bioastronomy Symposium
ed. G. Seth Shostak
ISBN 0-937707-93-7

Vol. CS-75   MULTI-FEED SYSTEMS FOR RADIO TELESCOPES
eds. Darrel T. Emerson and John M. Payne
ISBN 0-937707-94-5

Vol. CS-76   GONG '94: HELIO- AND ASTERO-SEISMOLOGY FROM THE EARTH
AND SPACE
eds. Roger K. Ulrich, Edward J. Rhodes, Jr., and Werner Däppen
ISBN 0-937707-95-3

Vol. CS-77   ASTRONOMICAL DATA ANALYSIS SOFTWARE AND SYSTEMS IV - (ADASS IV)
eds. R. A. Shaw, H. E. Payne, and J. J. E. Hayes
ISBN 0-937707-96-1

Vol. CS-78   ASTROPHYSICAL APPLICATIONS OF POWERFUL NEW DATABASES:
Joint Discussion No. 16 of the 22nd General Assembly of the IAU
eds. S. J. Adelman and W. L. Wiese
ISBN 0-937707-97-X

Vol. CS-79 *   ROBOTIC TELESCOPES: CURRENT CAPABILITIES, PRESENT
DEVELOPMENTS, AND FUTURE PROSPECTS
FOR AUTOMATED ASTRONOMY
eds. Gregory W. Henry and Joel A. Eaton
ISBN 0-937707-98-8

Vol. CS-80 *   THE PHYSICS OF THE INTERSTELLAR MEDIUM
AND INTERGALACTIC MEDIUM
eds. A. Ferrara, C. F. McKee, C. Heiles, and P. R. Shapiro
ISBN 0-937707-99-6

Vol. CS-81   LABORATORY AND ASTRONOMICAL HIGH RESOLUTION SPECTRA
eds. A. J. Sauval, R. Blomme, and N. Grevesse
ISBN 1-886733-01-5

Vol. CS-82 *   VERY LONG BASELINE INTERFEROMETRY AND THE VLBA
eds. J. A. Zensus, P. J. Diamond, and P. J. Napier
ISBN 1-886733-02-3

Vol. CS-83 *   ASTROPHYSICAL APPLICATIONS OF STELLAR PULSATION,
IAU Colloquium 155
eds. R. S. Stobie and P. A. Whitelock
ISBN 1-886733-03-1

ATLAS   INFRARED ATLAS OF THE ARCTURUS SPECTRUM, 0.9 - 5.3 µm
eds. Kenneth Hinkle, Lloyd Wallace, and William Livingston
ISBN: 1-886733-04-X

PUBLISHED: 1995 (* asterisk means OUT OF STOCK)

Vol. CS-84   THE FUTURE UTILIZATION OF SCHMIDT TELESCOPES, IAU Colloquium 148
eds. Jessica Chapman, Russell Cannon, Sandra Harrison, and Bambang Hidayat
ISBN 1-886733-05-8

Vol. CS-85 *   CAPE WORKSHOP ON MAGNETIC CATACLYSMIC VARIABLES
eds. D. A. H. Buckley and B. Warner
ISBN 1-886733-06-6

Vol. CS-86   FRESH VIEWS OF ELLIPTICAL GALAXIES
eds. Alberto Buzzoni, Alvio Renzini, and Alfonso Serrano
ISBN 1-886733-07-4

PUBLISHED: 1996

Vol. CS-87   NEW OBSERVING MODES FOR THE NEXT CENTURY
eds. Todd Boroson, John Davies, and Ian Robson
ISBN 1-886733-08-2

Vol. CS-88 *   CLUSTERS, LENSING, AND THE FUTURE OF THE UNIVERSE
eds. Virginia Trimble and Andreas Reisenegger
ISBN 1-886733-09-0

Vol. CS-89   ASTRONOMY EDUCATION: CURRENT DEVELOPMENTS,
FUTURE COORDINATION
ed. John R. Percy
ISBN 1-886733-10-4

Vol. CS-90   THE ORIGINS, EVOLUTION, AND DESTINIES OF BINARY STARS
IN CLUSTERS
eds. E. F. Milone and J. -C. Mermilliod
ISBN 1-886733-11-2

Vol. CS-91   BARRED GALAXIES, IAU Colloquium 157
eds. R. Buta, D. A. Crocker, and B. G. Elmegreen
ISBN 1-886733-12-0

Vol. CS-92 *   FORMATION OF THE GALACTIC HALO .... INSIDE AND OUT
eds. Heather L. Morrison and Ata Sarajedini
ISBN 1-886733-13-9

Vol. CS-93   RADIO EMISSION FROM THE STARS AND THE SUN
eds. A. R. Taylor and J. M. Paredes
ISBN 1-886733-14-7

Vol. CS-94   MAPPING, MEASURING, AND MODELING THE UNIVERSE
eds. Peter Coles, Vicent J. Martinez, and Maria-Jesus Pons-Borderia
ISBN 1-886733-15-5

Vol. CS-95   SOLAR DRIVERS OF INTERPLANETARY AND TERRESTRIAL DISTURBANCES:
Proceedings of 16th International Workshop National Solar
Observatory/Sacramento Peak
eds. K. S. Balasubramaniam, Stephen L. Keil, and Raymond N. Smartt
ISBN 1-886733-16-3

Vol. CS-96   HYDROGEN-DEFICIENT STARS
eds. C. S. Jeffery and U. Heber
ISBN 1-886733-17-1

Vol. CS-97   POLARIMETRY OF THE INTERSTELLAR MEDIUM
eds. W. G. Roberge and D. C. B. Whittet
ISBN 1-886733-18-X

ASP CONFERENCE SERIES VOLUMES
Published by the Astronomical Society of the Pacific

PUBLISHED: 1996 (* asterisk means OUT OF STOCK)

Vol. CS-98   FROM STARS TO GALAXIES: THE IMPACT OF STELLAR PHYSICS
ON GALAXY EVOLUTION
eds. Claus Leitherer, Uta Fritze-von Alvensleben, and John Huchra
ISBN 1-886733-19-8

Vol. CS-99   COSMIC ABUNDANCES:
Proceedings of the 6th Annual October Astrophysics Conference
eds. Stephen S. Holt and George Sonneborn
ISBN 1-886733-20-1

Vol. CS-100   ENERGY TRANSPORT IN RADIO GALAXIES AND QUASARS
eds. P. E. Hardee, A. H. Bridle, and J. A. Zensus
ISBN 1-886733-21-X

Vol. CS-101   ASTRONOMICAL DATA ANALYSIS SOFTWARE AND SYSTEMS V – (ADASS V)
eds. George H. Jacoby and Jeannette Barnes
ISBN 1080-7926

Vol. CS-102   THE GALACTIC CENTER, 4th ESO/CTIO Workshop
ed. Roland Gredel
ISBN 1-886733-22-8

Vol. CS-103   THE PHYSICS OF LINERS IN VIEW OF RECENT OBSERVATIONS
eds. M. Eracleous, A. Koratkar, C. Leitherer, and L. Ho
ISBN 1-886733-23-6

Vol. CS-104   PHYSICS, CHEMISTRY, AND DYNAMICS OF INTERPLANETARY DUST,
IAU Colloquium 150
eds. Bo Å. S. Gustafson and Martha S. Hanner
ISBN 1-886733-24-4

Vol. CS-105   PULSARS: PROBLEMS AND PROGRESS, IAU Colloquium 160
ed. S. Johnston, M. A. Walker, and M. Bailes
ISBN 1-886733-25-2

Vol. CS-106   THE MINNESOTA LECTURES ON EXTRAGALACTIC NEUTRAL HYDROGEN
ed. Evan D. Skillman
ISBN 1-886733-26-0

Vol. CS-107   COMPLETING THE INVENTORY OF THE SOLAR SYSTEM:
A Symposium held in conjunction with the 106th Annual Meeting of the ASP
eds. Terrence W. Rettig and Joseph M. Hahn
ISBN 1-886733-27-9

Vol. CS-108   M.A.S.S. -- MODEL ATMOSPHERES AND SPECTRUM SYNTHESIS:
5th Vienna - Workshop
eds. Saul J. Adelman, Friedrich Kupka, and Werner W. Weiss
ISBN 1-886733-28-7

Vol. CS-109   COOL STARS, STELLAR SYSTEMS, AND THE SUN: Ninth Cambridge Workshop
eds. Roberto Pallavicini and Andrea K. Dupree
ISBN 1-886733-29-5

Vol. CS-110   BLAZAR CONTINUUM VARIABILITY
eds. H. R. Miller, J. R. Webb, and J. C. Noble
ISBN 1-886733-30-9

Vol. CS-111   MAGNETIC RECONNECTION IN THE SOLAR ATMOSPHERE:
Proceedings of a Yohkoh Conference
eds. R. D. Bentley and J. T. Mariska
ISBN 1-886733-31-7

ASP CONFERENCE SERIES VOLUMES
Published by the Astronomical Society of the Pacific

PUBLISHED: 1996 (* asterisk means OUT OF STOCK)

Vol. CS-112   THE HISTORY OF THE MILKY WAY AND ITS SATELLITE SYSTEM
eds. Andreas Burkert, Dieter H. Hartmann, and Steven R. Majewski
ISBN 1-886733-32-5

PUBLISHED: 1997

Vol. CS-113   EMISSION LINES IN ACTIVE GALAXIES: NEW METHODS AND TECHNIQUES,
IAU Colloquium 159
eds. B. M. Peterson, F.-Z. Cheng, and A. S. Wilson
ISBN 1-886733-33-3

Vol. CS-114   YOUNG GALAXIES AND QSO ABSORPTION-LINE SYSTEMS
eds. Sueli M. Viegas, Ruth Gruenwald, and Reinaldo R. de Carvalho
ISBN 1-886733-34-1

Vol. CS-115   GALACTIC CLUSTER COOLING FLOWS
ed. Noam Soker
ISBN 1-886733-35-X

Vol. CS-116   THE SECOND STROMLO SYMPOSIUM:
THE NATURE OF ELLIPTICAL GALAXIES
eds. M. Arnaboldi, G. S. Da Costa, and P. Saha
ISBN 1-886733-36-8

Vol. CS-117   DARK AND VISIBLE MATTER IN GALAXIES
eds. Massimo Persic and Paolo Salucci
ISBN-1-886733-37-6

Vol. CS-118   FIRST ADVANCES IN SOLAR PHYSICS EUROCONFERENCE:
ADVANCES IN THE PHYSICS OF SUNSPOTS
eds. B. Schmieder. J. C. del Toro Iniesta, and M. Vázquez
ISBN 1-886733-38-4

Vol. CS-119   PLANETS BEYOND THE SOLAR SYSTEM
AND THE NEXT GENERATION OF SPACE MISSIONS
ed. David R. Soderblom
ISBN 1-886733-39-2

Vol. CS-120   LUMINOUS BLUE VARIABLES: MASSIVE STARS IN TRANSITION
eds. Antonella Nota and Henny J. G. L. M. Lamers
ISBN 1-886733-40-6

Vol. CS-121   ACCRETION PHENOMENA AND RELATED OUTFLOWS, IAU Colloquium 163
eds. D. T. Wickramasinghe, G. V. Bicknell, and L. Ferrario
ISBN 1-886733-41-4

Vol. CS-122   FROM STARDUST TO PLANETESIMALS:
Symposium held as part of the 108th Annual Meeting of the ASP
eds. Yvonne J. Pendleton and A. G. G. M. Tielens
ISBN 1-886733-42-2

Vol. CS-123   THE 12th 'KINGSTON MEETING': COMPUTATIONAL ASTROPHYSICS
eds. David A. Clarke and Michael J. West
ISBN 1-886733-43-0

Vol. CS-124   DIFFUSE INFRARED RADIATION AND THE IRTS
eds. Haruyuki Okuda, Toshio Matsumoto, and Thomas Roellig
ISBN 1-886733-44-9

Vol. CS-125   ASTRONOMICAL DATA ANALYSIS SOFTWARE AND SYSTEMS VI
eds. Gareth Hunt and H. E. Payne
ISBN 1-886733-45-7

ASP CONFERENCE SERIES VOLUMES
Published by the Astronomical Society of the Pacific

PUBLISHED: 1997 (* asterisk means OUT OF STOCK)

Vol. CS-126   FROM QUANTUM FLUCTUATIONS TO COSMOLOGICAL STRUCTURES
eds. David Valls-Gabaud, Martin A. Hendry, Paolo Molaro, and Khalil Chamcham
ISBN 1-886733-46-5

Vol. CS-127   PROPER MOTIONS AND GALACTIC ASTRONOMY
ed. Roberta M. Humphreys
ISBN 1-886733-47-3

Vol. CS-128   MASS EJECTION FROM AGN (Active Galactic Nuclei)
eds. N. Arav, I. Shlosman, and R. J. Weymann
ISBN 1-886733-48-1

Vol. CS-129   THE GEORGE GAMOW SYMPOSIUM
eds. E. Harper, W. C. Parke, and G. D. Anderson
ISBN 1-886733-49-X

Vol. CS-130   THE THIRD PACIFIC RIM CONFERENCE ON
RECENT DEVELOPMENT ON BINARY STAR RESEARCH
eds. Kam-Ching Leung
ISBN 1-886733-50-3

PUBLISHED: 1998

Vol. CS-131   BOULDER-MUNICH II: PROPERTIES OF HOT, LUMINOUS STARS
ed. Ian D. Howarth
ISBN 1-886733-51-1

Vol. CS-132   STAR FORMATION WITH THE INFRARED SPACE OBSERVATORY (ISO)
eds. João L. Yun and René Liseau
ISBN 1-886733-52-X

Vol. CS-133   SCIENCE WITH THE NGST (Next Generation Space Telescope)
eds. Eric P. Smith and Anuradha Koratkar
ISBN 1-886733-53-8

Vol. CS-134   BROWN DWARFS AND EXTRASOLAR PLANETS
eds. Rafael Rebolo, Eduardo L. Martin, and Maria Rosa Zapatero Osorio
ISBN 1-886733-54-6

Vol. CS-135   A HALF CENTURY OF STELLAR PULSATION INTERPRETATIONS:
A TRIBUTE TO ARTHUR N. COX
eds. P. A. Bradley and J. A. Guzik
ISBN 1-886733-55-4

Vol. CS-136   GALACTIC HALOS: A UC SANTA CRUZ WORKSHOP
ed. Dennis Zaritsky
ISBN 1-886733-56-2

Vol. CS-137   WILD STARS IN THE OLD WEST: PROCEEDINGS OF THE 13th NORTH
AMERICAN WORKSHOP ON CATACLYSMIC VARIABLES
AND RELATED OBJECTS
eds. S. Howell, E. Kuulkers, and C. Woodward
ISBN 1-886733-57-0

Vol. CS-138   1997 PACIFIC RIM CONFERENCE ON STELLAR ASTROPHYSICS
eds. Kwing Lam Chan, K. S. Cheng, and H. P. Singh
ISBN 1-886733-58-9

Vol. CS-139   PRESERVING THE ASTRONOMICAL WINDOWS:
Proceedings of Joint Discussion No. 5 of the 23rd General Assembly of the IAU
eds. Syuzo Isobe and Tomohiro Hirayama
ISBN 1-886733-59-7

ASP CONFERENCE SERIES VOLUMES
Published by the Astronomical Society of the Pacific

PUBLISHED: 1998 (* asterisk means OUT OF STOCK)

Vol. CS-140 SYNOPTIC SOLAR PHYSICS --18th NSO/Sacramento Peak Summer Workshop
eds. K. S. Balasubramaniam, J. W. Harvey, and D. M. Rabin
ISBN 1-886733-60-0

Vol. CS-141 ASTROPHYSICS FROM ANTARCTICA:
A Symposium held as a part of the 109th Annual Meeting of the ASP
eds. Giles Novak and Randall H. Landsberg
ISBN 1-886733-61-9

Vol. CS-142 THE STELLAR INITIAL MASS FUNCTION: 38th Herstmonceux Conference
eds. Gerry Gilmore and Debbie Howell
ISBN 1-886733-62-7

Vol. CS-143 * THE SCIENTIFIC IMPACT OF THE GODDARD HIGH RESOLUTION
SPECTROGRAPH (GHRS)
eds. John C. Brandt, Thomas B. Ake III, and Carolyn Collins Petersen
ISBN 1-886733-63-5

Vol. CS-144 RADIO EMISSION FROM GALACTIC AND EXTRAGALACTIC COMPACT
SOURCES, IAU Colloquium 164
eds. J. Anton Zensus, G. B. Taylor, and J. M. Wrobel
ISBN 1-886733-64-3

Vol. CS-145 ASTRONOMICAL DATA ANALYSIS SOFTWARE AND SYSTEMS VII – (ADASS VII)
eds. Rudolf Albrecht, Richard N. Hook, and Howard A. Bushouse
ISBN 1-886733-65-1

Vol. CS-146 THE YOUNG UNIVERSE GALAXY FORMATION
AND EVOLUTION AT INTERMEDIATE AND HIGH REDSHIFT
eds. S. D'Odorico, A. Fontana, and E. Giallongo
ISBN 1-886733-66-X

Vol. CS-147 ABUNDANCE PROFILES: DIAGNOSTIC TOOLS FOR GALAXY HISTORY
eds. Daniel Friedli, Mike Edmunds, Carmelle Robert, and Laurent Drissen
ISBN 1-886733-67-8

Vol. CS-148 ORIGINS
eds. Charles E. Woodward, J. Michael Shull, and Harley A. Thronson, Jr.
ISBN 1-886733-68-6

Vol. CS-149 SOLAR SYSTEM FORMATION AND EVOLUTION
eds. D. Lazzaro, R. Vieira Martins, S. Ferraz-Mello, J. Fernández, and C. Beaugé
ISBN 1-886733-69-4

Vol. CS-150 NEW PERSPECTIVES ON SOLAR PROMINENCES, IAU Colloquium 167
eds. David Webb, David Rust, and Brigitte Schmieder
ISBN 1-886733-70-8

Vol. CS-151 COSMIC MICROWAVE BACKGROUND
AND LARGE SCALE STRUCTURES OF THE UNIVERSE
eds. Yong-Ik Byun and Kin-Wang Ng
ISBN 1-886733-71-6

Vol. CS-152 FIBER OPTICS IN ASTRONOMY III
eds. S. Arribas, E. Mediavilla, and F. Watson
ISBN 1-886733-72-4

Vol. CS-153 LIBRARY AND INFORMATION SERVICES IN ASTRONOMY III -- (LISA III)
eds. Uta Grothkopf, Heinz Andernach, Sarah Stevens-Rayburn,
and Monique Gomez
ISBN 1-886733-73-2

ASP CONFERENCE SERIES VOLUMES

Published by the Astronomical Society of the Pacific

ASP CONFERENCE SERIES VOLUMES

Published by the Astronomical Society of the Pacific

ASP CONFERENCE SERIES VOLUMES
Published by the Astronomical Society of the Pacific

PUBLISHED: 1999 (* asterisk means OUT OF STOCK)

Vol. CS-184   THIRD ADVANCES IN SOLAR PHYSICS EUROCONFERENCE:
MAGNETIC FIELDS AND OSCILLATIONS
eds. B. Schmieder, A. Hofmann, and J. Staude
ISBN 1-58381-010-2

Vol. CS-185   PRECISE STELLAR RADIAL VELOCITIES, IAU Colloquium 170
eds. J. B. Hearnshaw and C. D. Scarfe
ISBN 1-58381-011-0

Vol. CS-186   THE CENTRAL PARSECS OF THE GALAXY
eds. Heino Falcke, Angela Cotera, Wolfgang J. Duschl, Fulvio Melia,
and Marcia J. Rieke
ISBN 1-58381-012-9

Vol. CS-187   THE EVOLUTION OF GALAXIES ON COSMOLOGICAL TIMESCALES
eds. J. E. Beckman and T. J. Mahoney
ISBN 1-58381-013-7

Vol. CS-188   OPTICAL AND INFRARED SPECTROSCOPY OF CIRCUMSTELLAR MATTER
eds. Eike W. Guenther, Bringfried Stecklum, and Sylvio Klose
ISBN 1-58381-014-5

Vol. CS-189   CCD PRECISION PHOTOMETRY WORKSHOP
eds. Eric R. Craine, Roy A. Tucker, and Jeannette Barnes
ISBN 1-58381-015-3

Vol. CS-190   GAMMA-RAY BURSTS: THE FIRST THREE MINUTES
eds. Juri Poutanen and Roland Svensson
ISBN 1-58381-016-1

Vol. CS-191   PHOTOMETRIC REDSHIFTS AND HIGH REDSHIFT GALAXIES
eds. Ray J. Weymann, Lisa J. Storrie-Lombardi, Marcin Sawicki,
and Robert J. Brunner
ISBN 1-58381-017-X

Vol. CS-192   SPECTROPHOTOMETRIC DATING OF STARS AND GALAXIES
ed. I. Hubeny, S. R. Heap, and R. H. Cornett
ISBN 1-58381-018-8

Vol. CS-193   THE HY-REDSHIFT UNIVERSE:
GALAXY FORMATION AND EVOLUTION AT HIGH REDSHIFT
eds. Andrew J. Bunker and Wil J. M. van Breugel
ISBN 1-58381-019-6

Vol. CS-194   WORKING ON THE FRINGE:
OPTICAL AND IR INTERFEROMETRY FROM GROUND AND SPACE
eds. Stephen Unwin and Robert Stachnik
ISBN 1-58381-020-X

PUBLISHED: 2000

Vol. CS-195   IMAGING THE UNIVERSE IN THREE DIMENSIONS:
Astrophysics with Advanced Multi-Wavelength Imaging Devices
eds. W. van Breugel and J. Bland-Hawthorn
ISBN 1-58381-022-6

Vol. CS-196   THERMAL EMISSION SPECTROSCOPY AND ANALYSIS OF DUST,
DISKS, AND REGOLITHS
eds. Michael L. Sitko, Ann L. Sprague, and David K. Lynch
ISBN: 1-58381-023-4

Vol. CS-197 · XVth IAP MEETING DYNAMICS OF GALAXIES:
FROM THE EARLY UNIVERSE TO THE PRESENT
eds. F. Combes, G. A. Mamon, and V. Charmandaris
ISBN: 1-58381-24-2

ASP CONFERENCE SERIES VOLUMES
Published by the Astronomical Society of the Pacific

PUBLISHED: 2000 (* asterisk means OUT OF STOCK)

Vol. CS-211 MASSIVE STELLAR CLUSTERS
eds. Ariane Lançon and Christian M. Boily
ISBN: 1-58381-042-0

Vol. CS-212 FROM GIANT PLANETS TO COOL STARS
eds. Caitlin A. Griffith and Mark S. Marley
ISBN: 1-58381-041-2

Vol. CS-213 BIOASTRONOMY `99: A NEW ERA IN BIOASTRONOMY
eds. Guillermo A. Lemarchand and Karen J. Meech
ISBN: 1-58381-044-7

Vol. CS-214 THE Be PHENOMENON IN EARLY-TYPE STARS, IAU Colloquium 175
eds. Myron A. Smith, Huib F. Henrichs and Juan Fabregat
ISBN: 1-58381-045-5

Vol. CS-215 COSMIC EVOLUTION AND GALAXY FORMATION:
STRUCTURE, INTERACTIONS AND FEEDBACK
The 3rd Guillermo Haro Astrophysics Conference
eds. José Franco, Elena Terlevich, Omar López-Cruz, and Itziar Aretxaga
ISBN: 1-58381-046-3

Vol. CS-216 ASTRONOMICAL DATA ANALYSIS SOFTWARE AND SYSTEMS IX
eds. Nadine Manset, Christian Veillet, and Dennis Crabtree
ISBN: 1-58381-047-1   ISSN: 1080-7926

Vol. CS-217 IMAGING AT RADIO THROUGH SUBMILLIMETER WAVELENGTHS
eds. Jeffrey G. Mangum and Simon J. E. Radford
ISBN: 1-58381-049-8

Vol. CS-218 MAPPING THE HIDDEN UNIVERSE: THE UNIVERSE BEHIND THE MILKY WAY
THE UNIVERSE IN HI
eds. Renée C. Kraan-Korteweg, Patricia A. Henning, and Heinz Andernach
ISBN: 1-58381-050-1

Vol. CS-219 DISKS, PLANETESIMALS, AND PLANETS
eds. F. Garzón, C. Eiroa, D. de Winter, and T. J. Mahoney
ISBN: 1-58381-051-X

Vol. CS-220 AMATEUR - PROFESSIONAL PARTNERSHIPS IN ASTRONOMY:
The 111th Annual Meeting of the ASP
eds. John R. Percy and Joseph B. Wilson
ISBN: 1-58381-052-8

Vol. CS-221 STARS, GAS AND DUST IN GALAXIES: EXPLORING THE LINKS
eds. Danielle Alloin, Knut Olsen, and Gaspar Galaz
ISBN: 1-58381-053-6

PUBLISHED: 2001

Vol. CS-222 THE PHYSICS OF GALAXY FORMATION
eds. M. Umemura and H. Susa
ISBN: 1-58381-054-4

Vol. CS-223 COOL STARS, STELLAR SYSTEMS AND THE SUN:
Eleventh Cambridge Workshop
eds. Ramón J. García López, Rafael Rebolo, and María Zapatero Osorio
ISBN: 1-58381-056-0

Vol. CS-224 PROBING THE PHYSICS OF ACTIVE GALACTIC NUCLEI
BY MULTIWAVELENGTH MONITORING
eds. Bradley M. Peterson, Ronald S. Polidan, and Richard W. Pogge
ISBN: 1-58381-055-2

ASP CONFERENCE SERIES VOLUMES
Published by the Astronomical Society of the Pacific

PUBLISHED: 2001 (* asterisk means OUT OF STOCK)

Vol. CS-225   VIRTUAL OBSERVATORIES OF THE FUTURE
eds. Robert J. Brunner, S. George Djorgovski, and Alex S. Szalay
ISBN: 1-58381-057-9

Vol. CS-226   12th EUROPEAN CONFERENCE ON WHITE DWARFS
eds. J. L. Provencal, H. L. Shipman, J. MacDonald, and S. Goodchild
ISBN: 1-58381-058-7

Vol. CS-227   BLAZAR DEMOGRAPHICS AND PHYSICS
eds. Paolo Padovani and C. Megan Urry
ISBN: 1-58381-059-5

Vol. CS-228   DYNAMICS OF STAR CLUSTERS AND THE MILKY WAY
eds. S. Deiters, B. Fuchs, A. Just, R. Spurzem, and R. Wielen
ISBN: 1-58381-060-9

Vol. CS-229   EVOLUTION OF BINARY AND MULTIPLE STAR SYSTEMS
A Meeting in Celebration of Peter Eggleton's 60th Birthday
eds. Ph. Podsiadlowski, S. Rappaport, A. R. King, F. D'Antona, and L. Burderi
IBSN: 1-58381-061-7

Vol. CS-230   GALAXY DISKS AND DISK GALAXIES
eds. Jose G. Funes, S. J. and Enrico Maria Corsini
ISBN: 1-58381-063-3

Vol. CS-231   TETONS 4: GALACTIC STRUCTURE, STARS, AND
THE INTERSTELLAR MEDIUM
eds. Charles E. Woodward, Michael D. Bicay, and J. Michael Shull
ISBN: 1-58381-064-1

Vol. CS-232   THE NEW ERA OF WIDE FIELD ASTRONOMY
eds. Roger Clowes, Andrew Adamson, and Gordon Bromage
ISBN: 1-58381-065-X

Vol. CS-233   P CYGNI 2000: 400 YEARS OF PROGRESS
eds. Mart de Groot and Christiaan Sterken
ISBN: 1-58381-070-6

Vol. CS-234   X-RAY ASTRONOMY 2000
eds. R. Giacconi, S. Serio, and L. Stella
ISBN: 1-58381-071-4

Vol. CS-235   SCIENCE WITH THE ATACAMA LARGE MILLIMETER ARRAY (ALMA)
ed. Alwyn Wootten
ISBN: 1-58381-072-2

Vol. CS-236   ADVANCED SOLAR POLARIMETRY: THEORY, OBSERVATION, AND
INSTRUMENTATION, The 20th Sacramento Peak Summer Workshop
ed. M. Sigwarth
ISBN: 1-58381-073-0

Vol. CS-237   GRAVITATIONAL LENSING: RECENT PROGRESS AND FUTURE GOALS
eds. Tereasa G. Brainerd and Christopher S. Kochanek
ISBN: 1-58381-074-9

Vol. CS-238   ASTRONOMICAL DATA ANALYSIS SOFTWARE AND SYSTEMS X
eds. F. R. Harnden, Jr., Francis A. Primini, and Harry E. Payne
ISBN: 1-58381-075-7

Vol. CS-239   MICROLENSING 2000: A NEW ERA OF MICROLENSING ASTROPHYSICS
ed. John Menzies and Penny D. Sackett
ISBN: 1-58381-076-5

ASP CONFERENCE SERIES VOLUMES
Published by the Astronomical Society of the Pacific

PUBLISHED: 2001 (* asterisk means OUT OF STOCK)

Vol. CS-240   GAS AND GALAXY EVOLUTION,
A Conference in Honor of the 20th Anniversary of the VLA
eds. J. E. Hibbard, M. P. Rupen, and J. H. van Gorkom
ISBN: 1-58381-077-3

Vol. CS-241   CS-241 THE 7TH TAIPEI ASTROPHYSICS WORKSHOP ON
COSMIC RAYS IN THE UNIVERSE
ed. Chung-Ming Ko
ISBN: 1-58381-079-X

Vol. CS-242   ETA CARINAE AND OTHER MYSTERIOUS STARS:
THE HIDDEN OPPORTUNITIES OF EMISSION SPECTROSCOPY
eds. Theodore R. Gull, Sveneric Johannson, and Kris Davidson
ISBN: 1-58381-080-3

Vol. CS-243   FROM DARKNESS TO LIGHT:
ORIGIN AND EVOLUTION OF YOUNG STELLAR CLUSTERS
eds. Thierry Montmerle and Philippe André
ISBN: 1-58381-081-1

Vol. CS-244   YOUNG STARS NEAR EARTH: PROGRESS AND PROSPECTS
eds. Ray Jayawardhana and Thomas P. Greene
ISBN: 1-58381-082-X

Vol. CS-245   ASTROPHYSICAL AGES AND TIME SCALES
eds. Ted von Hippel, Chris Simpson, and Nadine Manset
ISBN: 1-58381-083-8

Vol. CS-246   SMALL TELESCOPE ASTRONOMY ON GLOBAL SCALES, IAU Colloquium 183
eds. Wen-Ping Chen, Claudia Lemme, and Bohdan Paczyński
ISBN: 1-58381-084-6

Vol. CS-247   SPECTROSCOPIC CHALLENGES OF PHOTOIONIZED PLASMAS
eds. Gary Ferland and Daniel Wolf Savin
ISBN: 1-58381-085-4

Vol. CS-248   MAGNETIC FIELDS ACROSS THE HERTZSPRUNG-RUSSELL DIAGRAM
eds. G. Mathys, S. K. Solanki, and D. T. Wickramasinghe
ISBN: 1-58381-088-9

Vol. CS-249   THE CENTRAL KILOPARSEC OF STARBURSTS AND AGN:
THE LA PALMA CONNECTION
eds. J. H. Knapen, J. E. Beckman, I. Shlosman, and T. J. Mahoney
ISBN: 1-58381-089-7

Vol. CS-250   PARTICLES AND FIELDS IN RADIO GALAXIES CONFERENCE
eds. Robert A. Laing and Katherine M. Blundell
ISBN: 1-58381-090-0

Vol. CS-251   NEW CENTURY OF X-RAY ASTRONOMY
eds. H. Inoue and H. Kunieda
ISBN: 1-58381-091-9

Vol. CS-252   HISTORICAL DEVELOPMENT OF MODERN COSMOLOGY
eds. Vicent J. Martínez, Virginia Trimble, and María Jesús Pons-Bordería
ISBN: 1-58381-092-7

PUBLISHED: 2002

Vol. CS-253   CHEMICAL ENRICHMENT OF INTRACLUSTER AND INTERGALACTIC MEDIUM
eds. Roberto Fusco-Femiano and Francesca Matteucci
ISBN: 1-58381-093-5

ASP CONFERENCE SERIES VOLUMES
Published by the Astronomical Society of the Pacific

PUBLISHED: 2002 (* asterisk means OUT OF STOCK)

Vol. CS-254   EXTRAGALACTIC GAS AT LOW REDSHIFT
eds. John S. Mulchaey and John T. Stocke
ISBN: 1-58381-094-3

Vol. CS-255   MASS OUTFLOW IN ACTIVE GALACTIC NUCLEI: NEW PERSPECTIVES
eds. D. M. Crenshaw, S. B. Kraemer, and I. M. George
ISBN: 1-58381-095-1

Vol. CS-256   OBSERVATIONAL ASPECTS OF PULSATING B AND A STARS
eds. Christiaan Sterken and Donald W. Kurtz
ISBN: 1-58381-096-X

Vol. CS-257   AMiBA 2001: HIGH-Z CLUSTERS, MISSING BARYONS, AND CMB
POLARIZATION
eds. Lin-Wen Chen, Chung-Pei Ma, Kin-Wang Ng, and Ue-Li Pen
ISBN: 1-58381-097-8

Vol. CS-258   ISSUES IN UNIFICATION OF ACTIVE GALACTIC NUCLEI
eds. Roberto Maiolino, Alessandro Marconi, and Neil Nagar
ISBN: 1-58381-098-6

Vol. CS-259   RADIAL AND NONRADIAL PULSATIONS AS PROBES OF STELLAR PHYSICS,
IAU Colloquium 185
eds. Conny Aerts, Timothy R. Bedding, and Jørgen Christensen-Dalsgaard
ISBN: 1-58381-099-4

Vol. CS-260   INTERACTING WINDS FROM MASSIVE STARS
eds. Anthony F. J. Moffat and Nicole St-Louis
ISBN: 1-58381-100-1

Vol. CS-261   THE PHYSICS OF CATACLYSMIC VARIABLES AND RELATED OBJECTS
eds. B. T. Gänsicke, K. Beuermann, and K. Reinsch
ISBN: 1-58381-101-X

Vol. CS-262   THE HIGH ENERGY UNIVERSE AT SHARP FOCUS: CHANDRA SCIENCE,
held in conjunction with the 113th Annual Meeting of the ASP
eds. Eric M. Schlegel and Saeqa Dil Vrtilek
ISBN: 1-58381-102-8

Vol. CS-263   STELLAR COLLISIONS, MERGERS AND THEIR CONSEQUENCES
ed. Michael M. Shara
ISBN: 1-58381-103-6

Vol. CS-264   CONTINUING THE CHALLENGE OF EUV ASTRONOMY:
CURRENT ANALYSIS AND PROSPECTS FOR THE FUTURE
eds. Steve B. Howell, Jean Dupuis, Daniel Golombek,
Frederick M. Walter, and Jennifer Cullison
ISBN: 1-58381-104-4

Vol. CS-265   ω CENTAURI, A UNIQUE WINDOW INTO ASTROPHYSICS
eds. Floor van Leeuwen, Joanne D. Hughes, and Giampaolo Piotto
ISBN: 1-58381-105-2

Vol. CS-266   ASTRONOMICAL SITE EVALUATION IN THE VISIBLE AND RADIO RANGE,
IAU Technical Workshop
eds. J. Vernin, Z. Benkhaldoun, and C. Muñoz-Tuñón
ISBN: 1-58381-106-0

Vol. CS-267   HOT STAR WORKSHOP III: THE EARLIEST STAGES OF MASSIVE STAR BIRTH
ed. Paul A. Crowther
ISBN: 1-58381-107-9

Vol. CS-268   TRACING COSMIC EVOLUTION WITH GALAXY CLUSTERS
eds. Stefano Borgani, Marino Mezzetti, and Riccardo Valdarnini
ISBN: 1-58381-108-7

ASP CONFERENCE SERIES VOLUMES
Published by the Astronomical Society of the Pacific

ASP CONFERENCE SERIES VOLUMES

Published by the Astronomical Society of the Pacific

A LISTING OF IAU VOLUMES MAY BE FOUND ON THE NEXT PAGE

INTERNATIONAL ASTRONOMICAL UNION (IAU) VOLUMES
Published by the Astronomical Society of the Pacific

PUBLISHED: 1999 (* asterisk means OUT OF STOCK)

Vol. No. 190   NEW VIEWS OF THE MAGELLANIC CLOUDS
eds. You-Hua Chu, Nicholas B. Suntzeff, James E. Hesser,
and David A. Bohlender
ISBN: 1-58381-021-8

Vol. No. 191   ASYMPTOTIC GIANT BRANCH STARS
eds. T. Le Bertre, A. Lèbre, and C. Waelkens
ISBN: 1-886733-90-2

Vol. No. 192   THE STELLAR CONTENT OF LOCAL GROUP GALAXIES
eds. Patricia Whitelock and Russell Cannon
ISBN: 1-886733-82-1

Vol. No. 193   WOLF-RAYET PHENOMENA IN MASSIVE STARS AND STARBURST GALAXIES
eds. Karel A. van der Hucht, Gloria Koenigsberger, and Philippe R. J. Eenens
ISBN: 1-58381-004-8

Vol. No. 194   ACTIVE GALACTIC NUCLEI AND RELATED PHENOMENA
eds. Yervant Terzian, Daniel Weedman, and Edward Khachikian
ISBN: 1-58381-008-0

PUBLISHED: 2000

Vol. XXIVA   TRANSACTIONS OF THE INTERNATIONAL ASTRONOMICAL UNION
REPORTS ON ASTRONOMY 1996-1999
ed. Johannes Andersen
ISBN: 1-58381-035-8

Vol. No. 195   HIGHLY ENERGETIC PHYSICAL PROCESSES AND MECHANISMS FOR
EMISSION FROM ASTROPHYSICAL PLASMAS
eds. P. C. H. Martens, S. Tsuruta, and M. A. Weber
ISBN: 1-58381-038-2

Vol. No. 197   ASTROCHEMISTRY: FROM MOLECULAR CLOUDS TO PLANETARY SYSTEMS
eds. Y. C. Minh and E. F. van Dishoeck
ISBN: 1-58381-034-X

Vol. No. 198   THE LIGHT ELEMENTS AND THEIR EVOLUTION
eds. L. da Silva, M. Spite, and J. R. de Medeiros
ISBN: 1-58381-048-X

PUBLISHED: 2001

IAU SPS   ASTRONOMY FOR DEVELOPING COUNTRIES
Special Session of the XXIV General Assembly of the IAU
ed. Alan H. Batten
ISBN: 1-58381-067-6

Vol. No. 196   PRESERVING THE ASTRONOMICAL SKY
eds. R. J. Cohen and W. T. Sullivan, III
ISBN: 1-58381-078-1

Vol. No. 200   THE FORMATION OF BINARY STARS
eds. Hans Zinnecker and Robert D. Mathieu
ISBN: 1-58381-068-4

Vol. No. 203   RECENT INSIGHTS INTO THE PHYSICS OF THE SUN AND HELIOSPHERE:
HIGHLIGHTS FROM SOHO AND OTHER SPACE MISSIONS
eds. Pål Brekke, Bernhard Fleck, and Joseph B. Gurman
ISBN: 1-58381-069-2

Vol. No. 204   THE EXTRAGALACTIC INFRARED BACKGROUND AND ITS COSMOLOGICAL
IMPLICATIONS
eds. Martin Harwit and Michael G. Hauser
ISBN: 1-58381-062-5

INTERNATIONAL ASTRONOMICAL UNION (IAU) VOLUMES
Published by the Astronomical Society of the Pacific

PUBLISHED: 2001 (* asterisk means OUT OF STOCK)

Vol. No. 205   GALAXIES AND THEIR CONSTITUENTS
AT THE HIGHEST ANGULAR RESOLUTIONS
eds. Richard T. Schilizzi, Stuart N. Vogel, Francesco Paresce, and Martin S. Elvis
ISBN: 1-58381-066-8

Vol. XXIVB   TRANSACTIONS OF THE INTERNATIONAL ASTRONOMICAL UNION
REPORTS ON ASTRONOMY
ed. Hans Rickman
ISBN: 1-58381-087-0

PUBLISHED: 2002

Vol. No. 12   HIGHLIGHTS OF ASTRONOMY
ed. Hans Rickman
ISBN: 1-58381-086-2

Vol. No. 199   THE UNIVERSE AT LOW RADIO FREQUENCIES
eds. A. Pramesh Rao, G. Swarup, and Gopal-Krishna
ISBN: 58381-121-4

Vol. No. 206   COSMIC MASERS: FROM PROTOSTARS TO BLACKHOLES
eds. Victor Migenes and Mark J. Reid
ISBN: 1-58381-112-5

Vol. No. 207   EXTRAGALACTIC STAR CLUSTERS
eds. Doug Geisler, Eva K. Grebel, and Dante Minniti
ISBN: 1-58381-115-X

PUBLISHED: 2003

Vol. XXVA   TRANSACTIONS OF THE INTERNATIONAL ASTRONOMICAL UNION
REPORTS ON ASTRONOMY 1999-2002
ed. Hans Rickman
ISBN: 1-58381-137-0

Vol. No. 208   ASTROPHYSICAL SUPERCOMPUTING USING PARTICLE SIMULATIONS
eds. Junichiro Makino and Piet Hut
ISBN: 1-58381-139-7

Vol. No. 211   BROWN DWARFS
ed. Eduardo Martín
ISBN: 1-58381-132-X

Vol. No. 212   A MASSIVE STAR ODYSSEY: FROM MAIN SEQUENCE TO SUPERNOVA
ed. Karel A. van der Hucht, Artemio Herrero and César Esteban
ISBN: 1-58381-133-8

Ordering information is available at the beginning of the listing